NATIONAL GEOGRAPHIC SOCIETY
Research Reports

NATIONAL GEOGRAPHIC SOCIETY

Research Reports

Abstracts and reviews
of research and exploration
authorized under grants from the
National Geographic Society
during the year

1969

Compiled and edited by Paul H. Oehser and John S. Lea
under the direction of the
Committee for Research and Exploration

NATIONAL GEOGRAPHIC SOCIETY
WASHINGTON, D. C.

*   *   *   *

Contents

EDITORS' NOTE

The following accounts published in *National Geographic Society Research Reports, 1967 Projects* and *1968 Projects,* pertain in part to projects that continued into 1969, and no further treatment of them is required in the present volume:

"The Regulation of Body Temperature by Bluefin Tuna," by Francis G. Carey, *1967 Projects,* pp. 21-27.

"The 'Acropolis' of Aphrodisias in Caria: Investigations of the Theater and the Prehistoric Mounds, 1968-1970," by Kenan T. Erim, *1968 Projects,* pp. 79-113.

"Behavior and Ecology of the Giant Sable," by Richard D. Estes and Runhild K. Estes, *1968 Projects,* pp. 115-129.

"Emergence of the Pliocene Epoch at Lothagam Hill, East Africa," by Vincent J. Maglio, *1968 Projects,* pp. 225-230.

"An Archeological Study of the Eskimo Thule Culture in the Northwest Hudson Bay Area," by Charles F. Merbs, *1968 Projects,* pp. 247-254.

"Mesozoic and Tertiary Vertebrates of Baja California, 1968-1971," by William J. Morris, *1968 Projects,* pp. 305-316.

"Excavation of Monte Alto, Escuintla, Guatemala," by Lee A. Parsons, *1968 Projects,* pp. 325-332.

"Development and Behavior of the White Gorilla," by Arthur J. Riopelle et al., *1968 Projects,* pp. 355-369.

"Biology and Ecology of Outer Reef Faces in the Western Caribbean and Bahama Islands," by Walter A. Starck, II, *1968 Projects,* pp. 411-416.

"Studies of the Avifauna of Some Rift Valley Lakes of Ethiopia," by Emil K. Urban, *1968 Projects,* pp. 425-435.

"Ecological Studies of the Monarch Butterfly," by Fred A. Urquhart, *1968 Projects,* pp. 437-443.

"Investigations of the Biology and Distribution of the Tropical Atlantic Deep-sea Fauna, 1967-1969," by Gilbert L. Voss, *1968 Projects,* pp. 445-452.

"Sensory Basis of Navigation in Homing Pigeons," by Charles Walcott, *1968 Projects,* pp. 453-466.

"Religious Symbolism in a New Guinea Tribe," by Wilson G. Wheatcroft, *1968 Projects,* pp. 493-502.

The Society has made two grants—nos. 648 (1967) and 795 (1969)—to Miss Theresa Goell in support of her archeological explorations at Samosata-on-the Euphrates, Turkey. Her report on the first phases of these excavations was published in National Geographic Society Research Reports, 1967 Projects, pp. 83-109 (1974). Report on the later phases of the work, under the 1969 grant, has been indefinitely delayed because of Miss Goell's illness. When completed, it will be published in a later volume.

Foreword

The National Geographic Society was founded in 1888 by a group composed largely of Washington scientists to increase and diffuse geographic knowledge and to promote research and exploration. The Society's activities toward achieving its second objective date from 1890, when the Society sponsored a geographic and geologic expedition to study the Mount St. Elias Range of Alaska. Since then it has made more than 1,800 grants in support of approximately 1,400 projects in research and exploration. The work has encompassed the broad scope of geography, including such scientific disciplines as geology, paleontology, astronomy, geophysics, oceanography, biology, anthropology, archeology, ethnology, and geographical exploration. The research program has increased as the Society has grown, until today the budget of the Society provides $1,500,000 annually in support of the program.

This is the tenth in a series of volumes that as projected will eventually contain abstracts and reviews of the results of all the research and exploration projects sponsored by the Society since it was established. These are being published volume by volume, as rapidly as the material can be assembled. The present volume contains 61 accounts covering work done under grants made during the year 1969. In some instances, when a continuing research program has been supported by grants over a number of years, and a breakdown of results by year is found impracticable, it has seemed best to include only one résumé for the entire project, with cross references to the main account inserted in other volumes as appropriate. Volumes now in print (1978) cover the following years: 1890-1954, 1955-1960, 1961-1962, 1963, 1964, 1965, 1966, 1967, 1968, 1969.

In presenting the résumés no attempt has been made to standardize the style and specific approach of the investigator, other than to confine each account to reasonable space limitations. In many cases fuller but scattered reports on the work have been, or will be, published elsewhere — in the technical scientific journals, occasionally in the *National Geographic,* or in book form. Published accounts emanating from the research projects are included in the literature references, which each author has been encouraged to supply.

The Committee for Research and Exploration takes this opportunity to thank all the grantees who have cooperated in this publication project. In the years ahead we shall be calling on many of them again in similar fashion, and we solicit their continued help.

Experience with the previous volumes of this series has convinced us that the presentation of research findings as given in these books is of real value to the scientific community. Scholars the world over find this record of the accumulating results of National Geographic Society research grants of real assistance in their own investigations and in the preparation of scientific publications. The general reader also gains new and important knowledge about the current state of research related to geography from each of these volumes.

MELVIN M. PAYNE
Chairman, Committee for
Research and Exploration
National Geographic Society

Excavation of a Late Roman Shipwreck
at Yassi Ada, Turkey

Principal Investigator: George F. Bass, University Museum of the University of Pennsylvania, Philadelphia, Pennsylvania.

Grant No. 768:   To continue excavation of a 4th-century Roman ship near Yassi Ada, Turkey, begun in 1967.

Between early June and the end of September 1969 an expedition of the University Museum of the University of Pennsylvania and the National Geographic Society continued and all but completed the excavation of a Late Roman shipwreck at Yassi Ada, Turkey.[1] The ship, whose excavation we began in 1967, was another of those sunk by Yassi Ada's reef and discovered by Peter Throckmorton in 1958.[2] It lay only 30 or 40 feet from the site of the 7th-century Byzantine wreck we had excavated between 1961 and 1964[3] and had come to rest on a slope 120 to 140 feet deep.

The diving staff consisted of George F. Bass, director; Frederick van Doorninck, Jr., in charge of the study of the hull, assisted by Peter Fries; David Leith and John N. Miller, physicians; Robert Henry, chief diver and object photographer; Sanford Low, administrative assistant; Fletcher Blanchard and John Owen, engineers, assisted by engineering students Warren Riess and Paul Dresser; Donald M. Rosencrantz, head of the photogrammetry program; John Gifford (coring) and Ludwig Beckman, geology students; Donald Frey, equipment maintenance; Jeremy Green, metal detecting; Ellen Ehrlich (dark-room chief), Donald Callender (machinery assistant),

---

[1] Additional financial support was provided by the Ford Foundation (which paid for transportation and living expenses of graduate archeology students Callender, Ehrlich, and Low), the Haas Community Funds, and the Old Dominion Foundation. The Office of Naval Research assisted with an equipment loan grant.

[2] For reports of the 1967 season, see Bass (1968a, 1968b, 1970a), Bass and Katzev (1968), and Bass and Rosencrantz (1968). For the discovery, see Throckmorton (1960, 1964).

[3] See Bass (1966, 1968c, 1970a, 1970b) and Bass and van Doorninck (1969).

Jeff Klein and William McClintock, archeology students; Claude Duthuit; Carl Semczak, conservator; and Eric J. Ryan, artist. Belkis Mutlu and Mustafa Kapkin both dived during their visits and assisted in many ways. The commissioners from the Turkish Department of Antiquities were Oğuz Alpözen and Yüksel Eğdemir.

The nondiving staff included Laurence T. Joline, in charge of the decompression chamber and the iron-replacement process[4]; Gündüz Gölönü, object artist; the always helpful wives — Ann Bass, Barbara Leith, B.J. van Doorninck, Yildiz Gölönü, and Nancy Fries — who shared the less glamorous but all important jobs of timekeeping for divers, object cleaning, typing, camp maintenance, and radio operating; and Mary Jane Cotton, assistant artist. Cynthia Jones, although unable to return to Yassi Ada in 1969, was most helpful in the organization of the expedition during the preceding months.

All the local logistics and hired boats were again in the capable hands of Mehmet Turguttekin, captain of the 65-foot trawler *Kardeşler* (which was, with its crew, used for setting up and breaking down the camp, barge, and work sites).

Our semipermanent camp on Yassi Ada (Flat Island) was re-established, with our four-man, double-lock recompression chamber again situated just opposite the diving barge; this year we added oxygen-breathing equipment to the chamber, with exhalation hoses leading outside to prevent oxygen buildup, and the resultant fire hazard, inside. The barge was anchored over the site, approximately 100 yards offshore.

The scaffolding of angle iron and pipe, used as both reference grid and physical support for divers working on the fragile hull, remained over the site from our previous season. The telephone booth was again lowered into place beside the wreck, and the submersible decompression chamber (SDC) was again anchored under water about halfway between the wreck site and Yassi Ada, where it was partially protected from wave action. This time, however, the large aluminum air lift on tracks, and our high-pressure water jet, were replaced by three extremely light and maneuverable air lifts of PVC irrigation pipe (ca. 6 inches in diameter), manufactured in Izmir and purchased locally.

We dived, twice a day in pairs, with either SCUBA or hookah (hose from compressor to regulator). When diving with hookah, each diver wore also an

---

[4] For the iron-replacement process, see Katzev and van Doorninck (1966) and Bass and van Doorninck (1969).

air tank with its own one-hose regulator, both for safety and for swimming to the SCD for decompression; the hookah hoses would not reach the SDC and were removed on the sea bed, along with their regulators, and hauled back up to the barge for the next team of divers.

As usual, the barge, the wreck site, the SDC, and the island were all linked together by a constant communications network of telephones and small transceivers, which proved instrumental in preventing a fatality. In our first diving accident since 1961, when L. T. Joline suffered the bends, Eric Ryan apparently had an air embolism. A veteran of all our campaigns since 1960, Ryan lost consciousness at a depth of 20 feet, while making a short decompression stop just before entering the SDC for longer decompression at 10 feet. Chief-diver Henry was able to raise Ryan into the SDC, telephone the island for help, and then lift Ryan into a boat directed to the emergency by a radio call to the barge. With Dr. Leith in the recompression chamber with the patient, and Joline in charge of outside operations and controls, Ryan was administered the latest U. S. Navy oxygen treatment. He responded and momentarily recovered, but a relapse, outside the chamber, could not be checked and has left possibly permanent numbness in both legs and one arm. Later in the summer we were called on to treat, successfully, a case of paralysis in a local diver; and, still later, a stricken sponge diver was brought to us for treatment but he did not recover (Dr. Miller reports that death was almost certainly due to a perforated ulcer rather than to his decompression sickness).

Following Ryan's accident the SDC was abandoned as being too isolated from the doctor, whose normal station was on the barge; we did not at that time in the season have a boat large enough to move the SDC and its 5-ton anchor to the actual diving site. Divers from that time decompressed in open water beneath the barge, using, for the first time, U. S. Navy diving tables with no added time for a safety margin; our safety margin was provided by breathing pure oxygen, brought to regulators at the 20- and 10-foot decompression stops by hoses attached to tanks on the barge deck. By the end of the summer we had logged nearly 1,800 individual dives, making a total of just under 3,600 for the two summers spent on the excavation; perhaps by coincidence, this is almost exactly the number of dives (3,533) required to excavate the Byzantine ship during four summers of work.

The removal of the cargo of amphoras, originally about 1,000 in number, was completed, and the hull remains below were carefully cleaned and mapped. Mapping was accomplished by an improved method of stereophotogrammetry, based on the methods we had devised in 1963 (Bass,

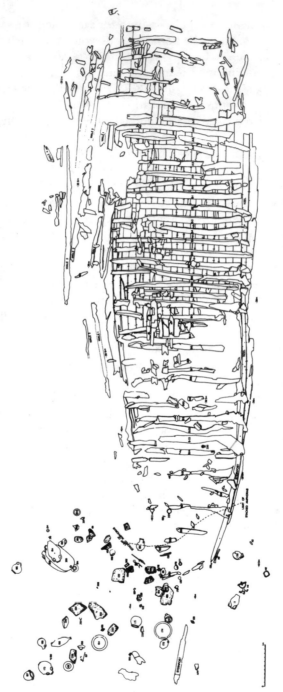

FIG. 1.   Plan of 4th-century Roman hull made by means of a Multiplex projector.

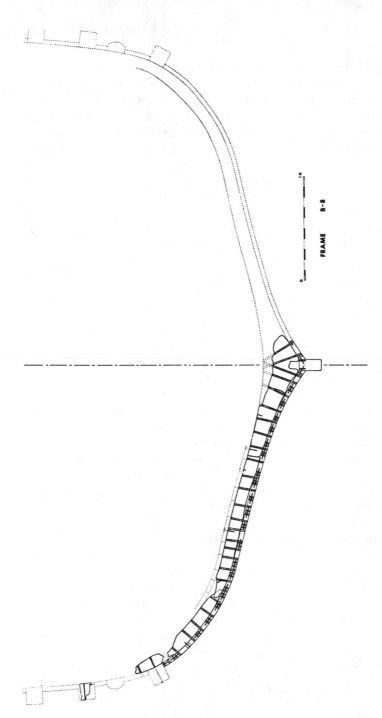

FRAME B-8

FIG. 2. Frame B-8, showing surviving portion of frame and outer shell of Roman shipwreck at Yassi Ada, Turkey.

1966, 1968c, 1970a). Our camera was a motorized Nikon F, housed in a special case with hemispherical port to prevent distortion in the pictures taken under water. These pictures were taken from predetermined points, a fixed distance apart, on a horizontal pipe floated about 12 feet above the wreck; the camera was slid along the bar while hanging from gimbals. The resultant negatives were printed as glass slides (diapositives) in the expedition dark room, and pairs of these diapositives were placed in a Multiplex lent by the U. S. Office of Naval Research; the Multiplex is an instrument designed to produce accurate topographic maps in the field from aerial photographs. Spikes driven into the wreck site, and carefully surveyed in three dimensions, were visible in the photographs as control points, allowing the adjustment of the Multiplex projectors for each stereo pair.

As the frames, or ribs, of the ancient ship were photographed and mapped *in situ,* they were removed, placed in a wire basket (also from our 1963 season), and carried to Yassi Ada by four divers who walked up the slope to the island. On land they were cleaned and, if broken, fitted together while placed on a grid painted over a level concrete floor. There, each wooden member was photographed and measured in detail. At the same time, on the sea bed, the treenails used for fastening these frames to the hull, as well as the smaller treenails that pinned tenons inside their mortises, were marked with white thumbtacks and photographed from the pipe.

The resultant plan, made by the Multiplex over a period of several months, shows the wreck as it never could have been seen by divers (fig. 1).

The ship had come to rest on her keel and port bilge and had worked so far down into a sea bed of loosely packed sand that substantial portions of the frames and outer shell on the port side had survived throughout most of the ship's length up to the fourth wale, which was probably set very near to or at deck level (fig. 2). Only the foremost 3 meters of the hull had disappeared entirely.

Preliminary reconstruction essays indicate that the ship's over-all length was in the neighborhood of 19 meters and that more or less equal contributions to this over-all length were made by sternpost, keel, and stem. The ship's maximum width occurred at or very near midships and was about 6.6 meters. The keel had a maximum width of about 12.2 centimeters and was 22 centimeters high. The outer hull planking had a thickness of 4.2 centimeters and the wales tended to be about 16 centimeters square in cross section. The frames, normally 12 centimeters wide and throughout most of their length 12.5 centimeters high, were set at regular intervals of about 24 centimeters from center to center. Frames with floors alternated with frames without floors. The inner lining, or ceiling, of the hull consisted of 3.8-centimeter planking.

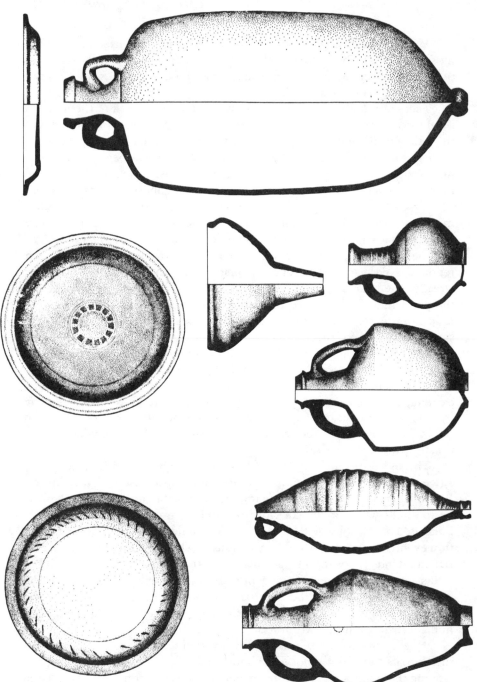

FIG. 3. Terracotta plate, funnel, storage jars, and jug from galley area of Roman shipwreck.

Mediterranean cypress *(Cupressus sempervirens)* was used throughout most of the hull. Only two exceptions have as yet been noted: the keel was of white oak, and large treenails used in fastening the frames to the outer hull planking were of live oak.

There is abundant evidence to show that the outer shell of the hull had been carried up at least as far as the second pair of wales girdling the sides of the hull before the frames were inserted, and it is quite likely that the outer shell was completed before the insertion of frames was begun. The outer hull strakes were edge-joined together with mortise-and-tenon joints. The normal interval from center to center between neighboring joints was about 25 centimeters throughout the outer shell. The mortises were 7-9 centimeters wide and 5.0-5.5 centimeters deep, and the tenons fit quite loosely within them, giving the shipwrights plenty of "play" while joining the strakes together. Once a strake had been properly fitted to the strake below, each tenon was permanently fastened in place by a pair of small treenails. As already noted, large wooden treenails were used in fastening the frames to the outer hull planking, but long iron spikes driven from the inside were used in fastening frames to the wales. There were no rabbets cut into the sides of the keel for the seating of the garboards, which were simply edge-joined to the keel in the same way that the other hull strakes were joined together. The extremities of the outer hull strakes, on the other hand, were seated in rabbets cut into the sides of the sternpost and stem. The planking extremities were fastened in place by iron nails; the wale extremities, by iron bolts. Iron bolts, normally set at 4- or 6-frame intervals, were also used in binding the spine of keel, sternpost, and stem to a keelson, which unfortunately did not survive.

The use of metal bolts and of loose-fitting tenons in relatively widely spaced joints is a constructional feature found also in some other known Greco-Roman hulls of the Roman imperial period but not in any Hellenistic period hulls where joints are close set, tenons are tight fitting, and metal bolts are conspicuous by their absence. These new trends in ship construction eventually led to the building of hulls in which the primary reliance on structural integrity was no longer placed on the edge-joined outer shell but rather on a strong skeletal framework of bolted members. As a result, the groundwork was laid for the eventual emergence of the skeleton or carvel system of hull construction, the most widely practiced method of wooden hull construction in the world today.

A galley or cookhouse was set down within the hull at the very stern of the ship, its forward wall located about 3 meters forward of the sternpost. Among the objects recovered from the galley were about two dozen large

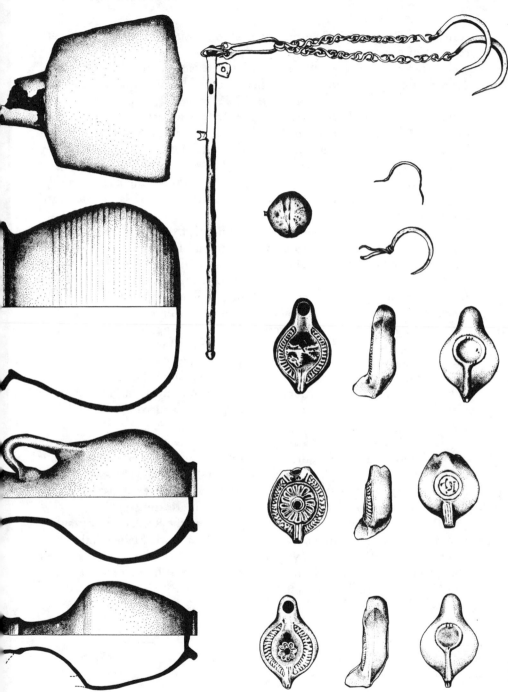

FIG. 4. Terracotta pitcher, jug, cooking pot, and lamps, with copper jug and bronze steelyard, found in galley area of Roman shipwreck.

stone slabs whose size, shape, and general composition suggest that they are remains of a stone hearth.

Terracotta objects in the galley included table wares, cooking wares, pantry wares, and lamps: two large plates, a smaller dish, one bowl, eleven pitchers, one cup, four cooking pots, one storage jar, three small storage amphoras, two very large amphoras (perhaps for water), a funnel, and four oil lamps. Of five glass vessels on board, only one — a yellow vase with ribbed body and flaring lip — was perfectly preserved. Metal objects in the galley included a copper jug, similar to one found on the later Byzantine ship, and two steelyards (one small and one medium size) for weighing cargo; a relatively heavy lead weight suggests the presence of a third, larger steelyard not yet located.

Although eight coins were found, all but one from the galley area, none was preserved well enough to give even a hint of its date. The shipwreck has been dated to the second half of the 4th century A.D., therefore, on the basis of the types of pottery, including the lamp signed KY, which was almost certainly made in a specific Athenian workshop at that time. The pieces of pottery for which parallels have so far been found were all common to the Aegean, although some of them, including the plates and some of the lamps, may actually have been manufactured in North Africa. Thus the ship may well have been only a local freighter whose commercial ventures did not take her far outside the Aegean, if at all. The actual route of her last voyage will be determined, it is hoped, after the identification of the three types of amphoras in the cargo; at present we have no idea of their place of origin.

In 1967, the remains of a ship of unknown date were found lying partly across the Roman wreck. Although the excavation of this later ship was not continued in 1969, a single silver coin of Philip III of Spain (1598-1621) was found in it by chance, dating the wreck (and the few pieces of glazed pottery we had found in 1967) to his reign or shortly thereafter.

This relatively recent wreck, so close to both the Roman and Byzantine wreck sites, led us to suspect possibly older hulls buried beneath the thick layers of sand. We searched a wide area, therefore, with both a core sampler and a metal detector, but the results were negative. A more intensive search would, we feel, still be warranted.

REFERENCES

BASS, GEORGE F.
   1966. Archaeology under water, 224 pp., illus. Frederick A. Praeger, New York and London.
   1968a. New tools for undersea archeology. Nat. Geogr. Mag., vol. 134, no. 3, pp. 402-423, illus.
   1968b. The Turkish Aegean: Proving ground for underwater archeology. Expedition, vol. 10, no. 3, pp. 3-10, illus.
   1968c. Underwater archeological expedition to Turkey. Nat. Geogr. Soc. Res. Rpts., 1963 Projects, pp. 21-34, illus.
   1970a. Archaeology under water, 175 pp., illus. Penguin Books, Baltimore, Maryland. (Revised ed. of Bass, 1966.)
   1970b. Underwater archeological expedition to Turkey, 1961-1962. Nat. Geogr. Soc. Res. Rpts., 1961-1962 Projects, pp. 11-20, illus.
BASS, GEORGE F., and KATZEV, MICHAEL L.
   1968. Tools for underwater archaeology. Archaeology, vol. 21, no. 3, pp. 165-173, illus.
BASS, GEORGE F., and ROSENCRANTZ, DONALD M.
   1968. A diversified program for the study of shallow water searching and mapping techniques. Report submitted to the Office of Naval Research: report no. AD 686 487, Clearinghouse (CFSTI), Springfield, Virginia.
BASS, GEORGE F., and VAN DOORNINCK, FREDERICK H.
   1969. Excavations of a Byzantine shipwreck at Yassi Ada, Turkey. Nat. Geogr. Soc. Res. Rpts., 1964 Projects, pp. 9-20, illus.
   1971. A fourth-century shipwreck at Yassi Ada. Amer. Journ. Archaeol., vol. 75, no. 1, pp. 27-37, illus.
KATZEV, MICHAEL L., and VAN DOORNINCK, FREDERICK H.
   1966. Replicas of iron tools from a Byzantine shipwreck. Studies in Conservation, vol. 11, no. 3, pp. 133-142, illus.
THROCKMORTON, PETER
   1960. Oldest shipwreck ever found. Nat. Geogr. Mag., vol. 117, no. 5, pp. 682-703, illus.
   1964. The lost ships: An adventure in undersea archaeology, 260 pp., illus. Little Brown & Co., Boston.

GEORGE F. BASS

FREDERICK H. VAN DOORNINCK, JR.

The Australian Fresh-water Fish Genus
Maccullochella

Principal Investigator: Tim M. Berra, Australian National University, Canberra, A.C.T., Australia.[1]

Grant No. 791:   In aid of a study of the evolution and biogeography of Australian fishes

Whether the Australian fresh-water percichyid fish genus *Maccullochella* contains one or two species has been argued in the ichthyological literature for more than a hundred years. Whitley (1937) provides a comprehensive review. This genus of large grouperlike fishes is known in Australia as cod. All fishermen and ichthyologists recognize the "Murray cod" as being a large, greenish, mottled fish, and some fishermen and scientists recognize a second form called "trout cod," which is smaller, gray, and speckled. Unfortunately, no one had been able to collect enough specimens of the rare trout cod until recently to make a meaningful comparison.

In 1967 I began corresponding with Dr. A. H. Weatherley, of the Zoology Department of the Australian National University in Canberra. During the next two years we set up a project to investigate various aspects of the evolution of Australia's depauperate fresh-water fish fauna. Upon receiving a Fulbright postdoctoral fellowship and a grant from the National Geographic Society to carry out research along these lines, I arrived in Canberra in August 1970 and spent the next 17 months working on the Murray cod–trout cod problem with Dr. Weatherley. I covered a total of 18,000 miles on 33 separate field trips along the length and breadth of Australia's largest river system, the Murray-Darling. This field work resulted in the collection of data from 53 trout cod and 156 Murray cod ranging in length from 31 to 1,235 millimeters.

The fishes were collected by gill netting, drum netting, and angling. The usual meristic and morphometric data were taken. In addition, the specimens were X-rayed to determine number and arrangement of the vertebrae, and immunoelectrophoresis of serum proteins was also carried out. The specimens were deposited in the Australian Museum in Sydney.

---

[1] Present affiliation: Department of Zoology, Ohio State University, Mansfield Campus, Mansfield, Ohio.

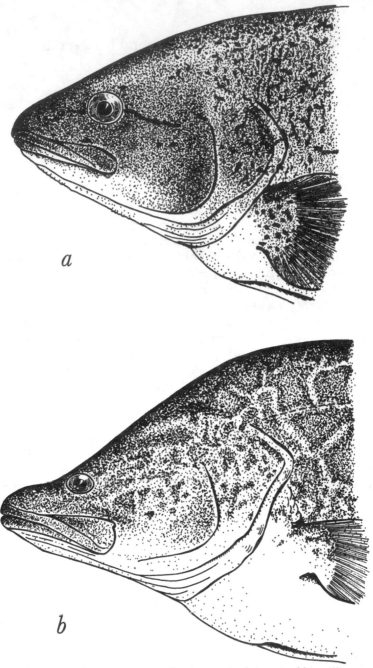

FIG. 1. Drawing of large trout cod (*a*), standard length 645 millimeters, and Murray cod (*b*), 640 millimeters. Note shape of head, jaws, length of snout, and pattern. Drawn by A. H. Weatherley.

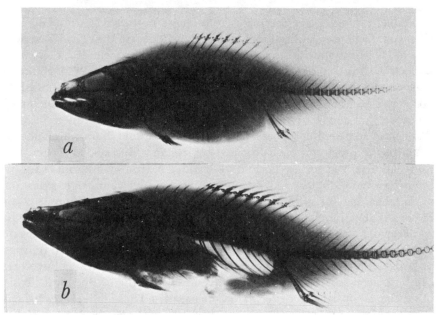

FIG. 2.   Radiograph of trout cod *(a)*, standard length 175 millimeters, and Murray cod *(b)*, standard length 210 millimeters. Note number of precaudal vertebrae and skull shape.

TABLE I. DIFFERENCES BETWEEN MURRAY COD AND TROUT COD.

Character	*Murray cod*	*Trout cod*
Dorsal and lateral background color	Green	Gray
Pattern	Mottled	Speckled
Jaws	Equal, or lower protruding	Upper overhangs lower
Snout length (percent of head length)	27.6 (32-24)	32.2 (37-25)
Precaudal vertebrae	15, no variation	14, no variation
Pyloric caeca	4, no variation	Usually 3, sometimes 4
Stripe through eye	Absent	Usually present
Head slope	Concave	Straight
Largest size reported	250 pounds	35 pounds

Table 1 summarizes the major differences between Murray cod and trout cod. Detailed results of this study can be found in Berra and Weatherley (1971). Illustrations of trout cod from all known localities are given in Berra (1974) and color illustrations can be found in Berra (1975). Figure 1, drawn by Dr. Weatherley, shows some of the obvious head differences. Figure 2 is a radiograph of the two forms showing the different number of precaudal and caudal vertebrae and indicating that the differences in head shape have an osteological basis. Figure 3 is a dark field illumination photograph of the precipitin bands formed by reacting Murray-cod serum (top well) and trout-cod serum (bottom well) with anti-trout-cod serum raised by injecting albino rabbits with homologous trout-cod serum. An explanation of the technique can be found in Berra and Weatherley. Slight differences can be seen in the branching pattern of the bands to the left of the center holes.

Previous hypotheses were that the two forms were different sexes or that one was the juvenile stage of the other. I examined males and females of both forms and was able to collect very small specimens (64 millimeters) of Murray cod and trout cod. These juveniles were identifiable on the basis of the characters in table 1 even at the smallest size. These differences led me to conclude that there are two distinct species in the genus *Maccullochella*.

In the recent literature (Whitley, 1964; Lake, 1967a, 1971) the Murray cod has been referred to as *M. macquariensis* (Cuvier and Valenciennes, 1829) and the trout cod as *M. mitchelli* (Castelnau, 1873). This is incorrect. The type specimen of *macquariensis* was obtained from the Muséum National d'Histoire Naturelle, Paris, and it proved to be a trout cod. Henceforth this name must be applied only to that species. The first description and, therefore, the correct name, of the Murray cod is *M. peeli* (Mitchell, 1838).

The Murray cod has been and currently is widely distributed throughout the inland rivers of eastern Australia: Murray, Darling, Lachlan, and Murrumbidgee Rivers and their tributaries. Museum data indicate that trout cod formerly had much the same distribution. The only localities where trout cod were collected for this study were Seven Creeks, a small tributary of the Goulburn River in Victoria, and Lake Sambell, an artificial lake in Beechworth, Victoria (fig. 4). Trout cod still exist in the Murray-Darling river system, but they are so few as to be virtually undetectable today. *M. macquariensis* is definitely a rare species. It is hoped that the government of Victoria will recognize the chance to preserve it by protecting its two known habitats and initiating a breeding program, especially in Lake Sambell, which has a population of large individuals. If trout cod could be bred as Murray cod have been (Lake, 1967b, c), perhaps they could be distributed to more lakes, thereby decreasing the chance that a catastrophe could destroy the only two known populations of this rare species.

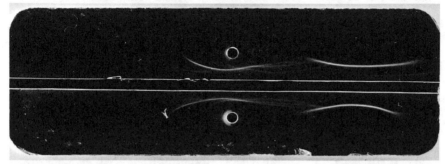

FIG. 3.   Murray-cod serum in well at top and trout-cod serum at bottom. The anti-serum is homologous with the trout-cod serum. The anode is on the left.

FIG. 4.   Lake Sambell, a 42-acre artificial lake in Beechworth, Victoria.

REFERENCES

BERRA, TIM M.

1974. The trout cod *(Maccullochella macquariensis)*, a rare freshwater fish from eastern Australia. Biol. Conserv., vol. 6, pp. 53-56.

1975. Two cod species in Murray-Darling system. Australian Fisheries, vol. 34, no. 3, pp. 8-10.

BERRA, TIM M., and WEATHERLEY, A. H.

1972. A systematic study of the Australian freshwater serranid fish genus *Maccullochella*. Copeia, 1972, no. 1, pp. 53-64.

LAKE, J. S.

1967a. Freshwater fish of the Murray-Darling river system. New South Wales State Fisheries Res. Bull. 7, 48 pp.

1967b. Rearing experiments with five species of Australian freshwater fishes, I: Inducement to spawning. Australian Journ. Freshwater Res., vol. 19, pp. 137-153.

1967c. *Idem*, II: Morphogenesis and ontogeny. *Ibid.*, vol. 18, pp. 155-173.

1971. Freshwater fishes and rivers of Australia, 61 pp. Nelson, Melbourne.

WHITLEY, G. P.

1937. Further ichthyological miscellanea. Mem. Queensland Mus., vol. 11, no. 2, pp. 113-148.

1964. Native freshwater fishes of Australia, 127 pp. Jacaranda Press, Brisbane.

TIM M. BERRA

A Cultural-ecological Analysis of Karnali Zone
in the Western Nepal Himalaya

Principal Investigator: Barry C. Bishop, National Geographic Society, Washington, D. C.

Grant Nos. 689, 690,   For a cultural-ecological analysis of the Karnali Zone in
712, 762, 763, 925.   western Nepal, with emphasis on the movements of people, animals, and goods, seasonality, and recent change.

From October 1968 through May 1970, assisted by my wife, I conducted a geographical research project on Karnali Zone in far western Nepal under grants from the National Geographic Society and the National Science Foundation. Structured as a cultural-ecological analysis, the project sought to identify, describe, and analyze the hierarchy of economic systems existing in the study area, the dynamics of these systems, including their interaction through the movement of people, animals, and goods, and their roles in the infrastructure of the larger developing economy of Nepal.

The study examined one Nepalese calendar year, 2026 BS (A.D. mid-April 1969 to mid-April 1970). Potentially quantifiable data were collected at the district, panchayat, village, and individual household levels; these data included several dozen cultural and physical variables significant in the dynamics of the systems. Also, data from two existing Nepal Government sources, the Revenue Office tax records, dating back 140 years, and the more recent Land Reform records, were obtained and synthesized. Four weather stations were established at appropriate locations (Jumla, Dillikot, Bumra, and Gum; see figs. 1 and 2) and continuous temperature records, as well as monthly rainfall records, were obtained for 2026 BS. Soil samples were collected and evapo-transpiration rates were derived.

A significant aspect of the research was a detailed study of the flow of people, animals, and goods into and through Jumla, the headquarters of Karnali Zone, made possible by a USAID/Nepal contract. This study sought to measure the quantities and values of goods being transferred, as well as their origin and destination. People and animals were enumerated and their home village, their destination, the route followed, the time taken, and the

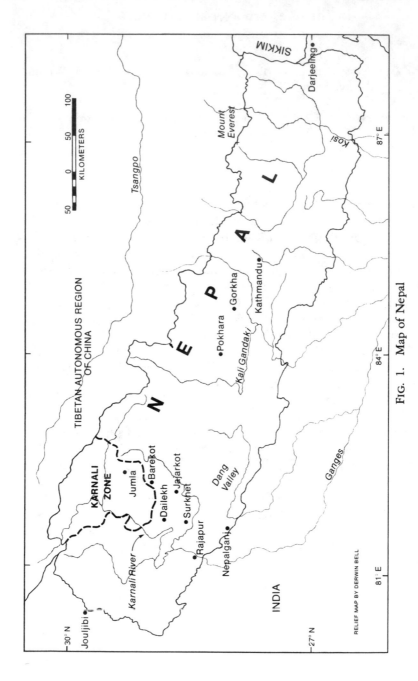

FIG. 1.   Map of Nepal

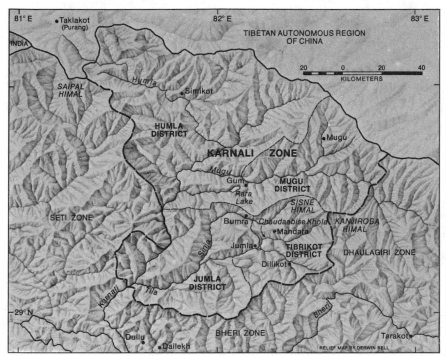

FIG. 2.   Nepal, showing Karnali Zone.

purpose of the trip determined. These studies were carried out under the aegis of the Research Council of Tribhuvan University, in Kathmandu, with which I was affiliated as a Research Associate, and they were coordinated among appropriate departments of His Majesty's Government. This report presents a brief description of Karnali Zone, a simplified model of the zone's economic systems, and a discussion of the constraining forces on the system. A complete report, my Ph.D. dissertation in the University of Chicago Department of Geography, is being published as a monograph in the Geographic Research Series, University of Chicago Press.

Karnali Zone, The Physical Environment

Mountainous, remote, and isolated, Karnali (see fig. 1) is the largest of Nepal's 14 zones, with an area of approximately 13,000 square kilometers.

It is bounded on the north by China, on the west by Seti Zone, on the south by Bheri Zone, and on the east by Dhaulagiri Zone. These boundaries follow either interfluves or rivers.

As in the middle-hill and Himalayan zones across the entire breadth of Nepal, the topography of the area produces a great complexity and diversity in both the physical and cultural landscapes. The Himalayas in this portion of western Nepal trend generally east-west in a succession of ranges, or *lekhs,* that vary in average height between 4,200 and 5,800 meters, an average that decreases from the international crestline southward. The highest mountains are found not along the international boundary with Tibet, but in three massifs farther south — Saipal in the northwest, Sisne in the northeast, and Kanjiroba in the east — which rise to over 7,000, 6,400, and 6,700 meters, respectively. The area does not generally exhibit the extremely jagged and confining relief found in the central and eastern Nepal Himalaya. Instead, the landforms are relatively less rugged, the country is more open, and the horizontal component of the landscape is as apparent as the vertical.

The country, which opens to the east and the south, is drained by the three major tributaries of the Karnali River — the Humla, Mugu, and Tila — and three secondary tributaries (see fig. 2): This drainage system, which has a dendritic pattern and is superimposed on the terrain, predates the Alpine Orogeny that produced the Himalayas. One striking landform in the area is Rara Lake, the nation's largest, perched at approximately 3,000 meters in Mugu District. It has survived the mountain-building although its drainage has changed from east to west in the process.

In many of the rivers, as well as in Rara Lake, fish are plentiful, but this resource is exploited by only a very small percentage of the population. In addition, the river system offers considerable hydroelectric potential.

The climate of the area is Alpine or Nival along the northern border and high in the massifs themselves, Temperate in the central and southern regions, and Subtropical in the extreme southwest. Indian monsoonal controls create a three-season pattern: a cold-dry period from October through March; a warm-dry period from April through June; and a cool-wet period, the monsoon season, from July through September.

Great local variations in temperature and precipitation occur from valley to valley, as well as with elevation. The east-west trending Tila and Mugu Karnali rivers lie in rain shadows produced by the adjacent high *lekhs* to the south. High catchment areas have cooler temperatures and tend to generate greater rainfall. For example, within a 40-kilometer radius of Jumla average monthly temperature values vary from 2° to 8° C. in winter and from 14° to

23° C. during the pre-monsoon warm season. Yearly rainfall will vary from 700 to 1,200 millimeters, approximately 75 percent of which falls during the monsoon. At this time rivers flood, landslides are common along many lowland trails, and bridges are washed away. During the winter months the mountains cause some orographic precipitation. Snow blocks the passes across the *lekhs* for a few days to many weeks, making travel by the high trails dangerous and difficult, if not impossible.

The bedrock of the area is composed of meta-sediments and gneisses of Precambrian, Eocambrian, and Paleozoic age, as well as some granites associated with the Himalayan Orogeny. Mineral resources include both copper and limestone, the latter in sufficient quantities for exploitation. *Silagit,* a black, sticky, hydrocarbon similar to tar, found in some areas of Mugu District, is collected, processed, and sold in the Terai for use in the Indian drug industry. The zone's soils, which reflect both its geomorphology and its climate, are generally thin, rocky, acidic, and of poorly developed profile. Those found in flood plains and alluvial terraces are of greater fertility than those on upland slopes. Soil quality varies greatly within a small area.

Wild vegetation reflects not only climate, elevation, soils, drainage, aspect (compass orientation) and angle of slope, but also the severe altering impact of man. Again, great variety is found. In much of the zone between 2,000 and 3,000 meters grows a Temperate coniferous forest of pine, spruce, and fir *(Pinus excelsa, Picea smithiana, Abies pindrow)* with broadleafed horsechestnut, walnut, and maple occupying the more moist watercourses and gullies. For 1,000 meters above this grows a Temperate mixed oak and conifer forest of *Quercus semicarpifolia* and *Abies spectabilis,* above which is Subalpine white birch, *Betula utilis.* Timberline varies between 3,700 and 4,000, above which is found moist Alpine scrub, principally juniper and rhododendron, or an arid Alpine steppe of *Caragana, Artemisia,* and *Lonicera.* In contrast is the hot, low, arid valley of the main Karnali, where xerophytic species such as *Dalbergia sissoo* and *Acacia catechu* grow in a thin belt along the river. Above this belt treeless windparched slopes with "cactus forests" of *Euphorbia royleana* rise for as much as 1,000 meters to a point where villages occur on the edge of *Pinus roxburghi* and oak forests. Banana, orange, fig, and mango grow around these villages, while in higher, cooler, and more humid regions apple and peach thrive near the settlements. Although extensive conifer forests are found in Humla District, their remote location and the difficulty of transportation deter the development of lumbering. As a rule, deodar cedar is now found only at the sites of shrines. Herbs and grasses present similar patterns.

For centuries man has exploited the wild flora. Several dozen species are collected not only for wood-fuel and building material but also for dye, oil, fiber, soap, and other uses. Of particular importance as "cash crops" are several species of medicinal herbs found on the *lekhs,* and *charas* (hashish). The latter is usually collected from the wild, but in some locations it is planted as a crop.

A number of mammal species still exist in the forests: wild boar, bear, musk deer, porcupine, lesser panda, some leopard, as well as monkey. In more isolated Humla such mammals as wild sheep and goats are also prevalent. Despite recent laws prohibiting the hunting of musk deer, poaching with the aid of dogs is common in certain areas and the species probably faces extinction here in the near future.

The People and Their Social Structure

Karnali Zone has a population of approximately 186,000. Its population density is only 14 per square kilometer, a statistic that obscures reality, for only about 1.1 percent of the area, comprising the flood plains of the major rivers and the alluvial fans of secondary and tertiary drainages, plus adjacent upland slopes, is used for agriculture, the principal livelihood of the region. The population is, therefore, superimposed upon the dendritic drainage pattern of the area and its density is in direct relationship to the scale of the drainage — primary, secondary, tertiary. It is, then, much more pertinent to think of a staggeringly high population density of 1,240 per square kilometer, this being the ratio of people to the area of tilled land.

This population lives in over 700 small, loosely to tightly clustered villages of from 20 to more than 100 households located in elevations varying from 1,100 meters along the Karnali River in southwest Jumla District to more than 3,800 meters in upper Mugu and Humla Districts, the average elevation being about 2,400 meters. Village sites are determined not only by the location of farmlands but also by slope orientation vis-à-vis the sun, by the angle of slope, and by the proximity to water and wood-fuel. Normally they are found at breaks in slope, in valley bottoms, on alluvial fans of tributary drainage, and up to 1,000 to 1,300 meters above primary river courses.

The ethnic composition and distribution of the population differ strikingly from other mountainous zones farther east in Nepal. Older indigenous tribal groups, such as Magars and Gurungs, usually found at middle elevations in the hill-mountain belt, are totally absent in Karnali Zone. Instead, there is a direct contact between Hindus of Indian origin and Buddhists of Tibetan origin. The Hindu Brahmins, Chhetris, and Thakuris, as well as associated occupational castes, comprise 93 percent of the population and occupy all but the highest parts of the zone. The minority Bhotias (4 percent) have their permanent habitations in the upper reaches of Mugu and Humla, as well as in a few isolated niches high in tertiary valleys farther south.

Over the past few centuries distinctive acculturation has resulted from the contact of these two ethnic groups. To some extent many Hindus have adopted a few aspects of the Bhotias' material culture, such as types of jewelry, dress, shoes, and cooking implements and techniques. The cultural dominance of the Hindu majority, however, has steadily increased in that same period, and to varying degrees the Bhotias have adopted many basic aspects of Hindu culture such as caste, clan names and structure, and gods. Nevertheless, elements of an older indigenous animism are still present in the *Masta* shrines at which many of the population, both Hindu and Bhotia, worship. It is also of note that over past centuries Nepali, now the national language, originated and developed in this region and spread eastward, primarily by conquest.

Many other vestiges of the area's past are still discernible today in the social structure, primarily because of the area's remote and isolated location. Compared with central and eastern Nepal, the far western Nepal Himalaya have been little affected by change. The region has a long history of petty kingdoms, and today a considerable degree of insularism remains, as manifested by the general orthodoxy and traditionalism of the population. Not surprisingly, too, vestiges of recent feudalism can still be found.

One important aspect of the culture is the practice, to varying degrees, of the jajmani system. This social-religious-economic structure was probably introduced into the area with the great in-migrations of Hindus from India (primarily Rajasthan) that followed the Muslim invasions. In its original form on the plains of northern India, the jajmani system was a successful means of creating a totally self-sufficient community. The wide range of occupational castes, as well as Brahmin priests, served a number of landlords, or *jajman*. In return for these services the landlords provided food, housing, and other material needs.

This complex mechanism underwent many modifications introduced into the hills and mountains of western Nepal. Currently it is breaking down at an increasingly rapid rate as a result of such factors as the monitization of the economy, the increasing availability of consumer, or ready-made, goods, and the acquisition of their own lands by the occupational castes. Certain aspects that remain, however, are important to Karnali Zone's economy, particularly those with respect to location and function of the blacksmith, the leather worker, the tailor, as well as the Brahmin priest.

The Economy

Livelihood Practices. In examining the peasant subsistence-economic system of the Karnali Zone, it seems best to consider man within the context of the total ecological framework. Within this framework, all communities, including man, occupy natural zones and/or niches, and all interact in delicate symbiosis. But it should be constantly borne in mind that man is the dominant species present; in pursuit of his livelihood he not only exploits but also greatly alters the landscape.

Since the livelihood pursuits of the people are fitted to the heterogeneous environment, they are extremely complex and varied. The principal livelihood pursuit is agriculture, but by itself it is not sufficient for even subsistence living. Therefore, the economy is composed of a combination of agriculture, animal husbandry, trade, and, to a lesser degree, home industry. These components interact among themselves. Their presence, and their importance, vary among households in a single village, among villages in a valley, as well as from valley to valley, and from area to area within the zone. The result is a hierarchy of economic systems that differs temporally as well as spatially.

Movements and the Labor Force. It is the temporal diversity within this hierarchy of economic systems that allows all of its components to be articulated or tied together by the movements of people, animals, and goods. Conversely, these movements, which are considerable, show varying periodicity and extent, or scale, for they reflect the peasant's adjustment to climatic variations and seasonality. These movements, furthermore, constitute labor responses to various needs or requirements of the peasant household, for it is only by his generally frequent movements that the peasant can supply the needs of his family and bring his standard of living to a subsistence level.

During the yearly cycle, the labor force of Karnali Zone is allocated in the following ways: From April through October the people are primarily required in their home villages for work in the fields. But during this time many also must be involved in movements of varying duration and extent. This is the time that food grains are exchanged for Tibetan salt and wool at border markets either in Tibet itself or in upper Mugu and Humla. It is the time for animals to be taken to the high pastures on the *lekhs* and shepherded. In some locations medicinal herbs are gathered. During this agricultural period, however, there are times when considerable buying and selling of food grains must be undertaken among the various valleys, or between high and low elevations, in order to meet immediate subsistence-level food requirements. These activities have to be coordinated with the agricultural labor demands, particularly during those labor-intensive periods of planting, transplanting, and harvest. In these short periods not only is the total family labor force required in the fields, but often also exchange, *jajmani,* and hired labor as well. All these demands on the family labor force impose a serious time bind on most households, one in which they are continually having to "rob Ram to pay Ratna." This time bind is even more serious in those areas where a winter-summer crop sequence is followed in *khet* (irrigated fields): for example, at those locations where a barley-rice sequence is followed, the optimum number of growing days can be allowed for neither crop.

During the nonagricultural season from November through March, a great out-migration to the south takes place. It is the time for the annual trading trip to the Terai and to India. Many families living at very high elevations (2,700 to 3,700 meters) take their animals to lower areas not only within the zone, but south to the hills or valleys of the Bheri Zone. Moreover, many young people from poorer households seek work to the west, in the hills of Kumaon in India. There, principally in the Naini Tal and Almora areas, they work as laborers in the construction and lumber industries in order to make enough money to buy their yearly needs in such consumer goods as ready-made cotton cloth, cooking utensils, and iron implements. While most return to their homes in the spring, some remain for a year or more.

Agriculture. The primary means of livelihood in all of Karnali Zone except upper Mugu District, where soils are too infertile and the climate too severe, is agriculture. Rice, maize, millet, barley, wheat, buckwheat, and potatoes are the chief crops. But more than a dozen other crops such as soybeans, beans, mustard, grain amaranth, coriander, and several types of "dry rice" are also grown. Cotton is grown in the lower reaches of the Mugu Karnali, but only in amounts sufficient for local consumption. Oats are grown in some upland areas solely as an exchange crop for Tibetan salt. Usually every house has a kitchen garden, a very small plot in which beans, squash, onions, peppers, garlic, tobacco, tomato, and eggplant are grown for home consumption.

The average household's land holding is extremely small; whereas a few large extended families of high caste may have 4.5 hectares or more, the average occupational caste household has only 0.25 hectare. The average holding per capita in Karnali Zone is less than 0.1 hectare (1,000 square meters).

The highest paddy culture in the world is found in Karnali Zone. Wet rice was introduced more than five centuries ago from Kashmir in the Tila and Sinja Valleys. Since it is the preferred crop, the population is constantly attempting to extend its cultivation despite the many restrictions imposed by the rugged habitat. While it is found today at elevations as high as 2,700 meters, it is primarily confined to the major valleys and adjacent alluvial fans of secondary drainage. Here extensive systems of irrigation have been developed. On the other hand, dry farming has also been pushed to marginal elevations of more than 3,700 meters. Extensive terracing, for both wet and dry farming, is required throughout the area. Fields have been carved from extremely steep hillsides; some have an angle of slope of more than 40 degrees.

A major deterrent to efficient farming is the steadily increasing land fragmentation that results from the extended family structure. Today it is common to find a peasant's holdings made up of 40 to 50 or more discontinuous plots, widely dispersed from next to his home to a distance of several hours, or even days, of travel. Because of the time-distance factor that these dispersed locations present, the amount of time invested in a field is inversely proportional to its distance from the farmstead. This is reflected in both the type of crop grown and the yields of that crop.

Intricate inter-cropping, the growing of two to four crops in a single field simultaneously, is practiced. At lower elevations, usually on irrigated land, a sequence of two crops such as rice and barley or maize and barley is grown in a single field. These are summer-winter crop combinations. Moreover, complex crop rotations (i.e., the alternation of crops planted in a given field from year to year) are followed. While irrigated fields are rarely left fallow for a year in order to rejuvenate their fertility, this practice is not uncommon for less-fertile upland fields.

At the same time, agricultural technology is extremely backward. While approximately a dozen different hand tools of iron are used for various planting, cultivating, weeding, and harvesting procedures, the wood-tipped plow is used almost universally. Only in a few random instances in the lower Tila and lower Sinja valleys is an iron-tipped plow to be found. A farmer may break five or six wood tips of oak in a day's plowing because of the rocky soil, yet while he is aware of the iron-tipped plow and knows that an iron tip costs only a few rupees, he is loath to change, primarily because of tradition. He believes that it is easier for his oxen to pull a wood-tipped plow and so has no incentive to change his technique.

Animal Husbandry. A variety of domestic animals are kept by the people of Karnali Zone: buffalo, yaks and cross-breeds (the product of yak and cow), sheep and goats, horses, and pigs. These are used for such varied purposes as fertilizer, transportation, plowing, milk and ghee, meat, hides and hair, and for sale.

The presence of yaks and cross-breeds coincides with the location of the Bhotia minority. These animals, found in northern Mugu and Humla, as well as in a few scattered, high enclaves farther south, provide transportation, fertilizer, milk, and hair. Yak tails are used as a trade item.

Cattle, the most important animals for the Hindu majority, are principally used to supply fertilizer for the fields. However, they furnish only about 50 percent of what the farmer perceives to be his minimum requirements. Because of its scarcity, manure is mixed with pine needles and leaves at a ratio that varies from 1:1 to 1:3. Moreover, many fields are fertilized only every other year and some fields never receive fertilizer. There is a definite correlation between the amount of fertilizer used on a specific field and the distance of that field from the farmstead. Therefore, a distance decay factor is present in the use of fertilizer as well as other agricultural techniques already discussed. The amount of fertilizer used decreases with the distance of the field from the farmstead. Oxen are used for plowing, while cows provide milk for home consumption, but their yield is extremely low, averaging less than 0.25 kilogram per day during the winter and 1 kilogram during the summer months.

Water buffalo are kept for milk and for the production of *ghee* (clarified butter). However, as with milch cows, yields are low: during winter the average milch buffalo gives approximately 1 or 2 kilograms of milk per day and during summer around 4-5 kilograms per day, with the maximum seldom above 6 kilograms per day. The production of milk and *ghee* is therefore generally sufficient for home consumption and occasional local sale.

Although buffalo are found throughout the zone at low and middle elevations up to 3,000 meters, their greatest concentration is in the climatically more suited southwest. There, a surplus of *ghee* is produced that is used as a trade commodity. This is a reflection of both the greater number of animals kept and of greater yields.

In the middle and high regions of the zone, where trading is the most

important of the triad of livelihood pursuits, sheep and goats are found in
large numbers, some families owning as many as 200-300. They are used
principally as transport animals. One animal can carry an 11-kilogram load.
Secondary uses include fertilizer, wool or hair, meat, and for sale.

Horses are raised by only the more affluent and/or the more nomadic
households. While used for riding, they are primarily raised for sale, either
within the region or the Terai (i.e., Jouljibi and the Dang Valley). Hair from
the mane and tail is an important trade item locally, for it is used to make
rope. In Karnali Zone there are few donkeys and only about a dozen mules.

Pigs are relatively unimportant and are kept by only a few occupational
caste families for meat.

The number of animals kept by a household varies greatly. Those families whose principal livelihood pursuit is trade keep as many sheep and
goats as possible. The majority of occupational caste families keep no livestock. With the principally agrarian Hindu majority the number depends on
the size of both the farm and the family. All peasant farmers would like to
keep more livestock, especially cattle and buffalo, for fertilizer and milk.
But winter food is scarce; this scarcity prevents the population from keeping more livestock. Fodder crops are not grown because all fields must be
planted in crops for human consumption. Animals are grazed or fed on wild
grasses and, during brief periods, are allowed to graze on the stubble of
harvested fields.

The complexity of pastoral regimes followed in the zone reflects not
only the diversity of the region's climate, vegetation, and topography but
also the type of animal involved and its uses to man. Each species occupies
its own ecological niche, which varies according to the season.

While a detailed discussion of the pastoral cycles practiced cannot be
included here, one principle is particularly significant to the articulation of
the entire regional economy: the distances that animals are taken in search
of food during the rhythmical seasonal pastoral cycles are usually directly
proportional to the severity of the environment at the site of the home
village.

All villages have on the *lekhs* at least one and usually a number of summer grazing grounds, or *patans,* that may vary in distance from one day to
several days away. During winter, cattle are usually kept sheltered in the
farmstead and fed on grasses cut during the summer. Other livestock are
taken to lower elevations, often as far south as the Jajarkot, Dailekh, and
Surkhet areas. In a few cases such as the Bhotia enclave at Mandhara, the
entire village follows a seminomadic yearly cycle.

Home Industry. As in peasant subsistence economies everywhere, home industry is essential for most of the households in Karnali Zone, but it is relatively undeveloped and crude and lacks any great diversity. The principal items produced are wool and cotton cloth, woolen knit goods such as sweaters and mufflers, and wool or hair rugs and blankets. In addition, bamboo products such as baskets, winnowers, and "umbrellas" are made. Within a household the types of items produced, as well as the volume of production, reflect not only the level of the household's economy but also its location and ethnic composition as well.

The less viable the agricultural component of a family's economy, the more important is home industry. It is relatively unimportant to those Hindu households that produce an agricultural surplus, for they have purchasing power to obtain these items, but the majority of families must produce some articles each year for their own needs, and for many households in the zone, primarily among the Bhotias and those engaged chiefly in animal husbandry, the production of such items for sale or trade is important if they are to make ends meet. Within the family the men do much of the spinning and weaving as well as all the knitting. Among the Bhotias, aprons and leather-soled boots, or *lam,* are also important home products. The latter are sold to their Hindu neighbors, among whom they are in great demand during winter. The production of these items is mainly a spare-time and winter activity for most of the family. Only old people, who can no longer perform hard physical labor, can work full time on home industry during the agricultural season.

Trade and Marketing. During the year a diversity of rhythmical trading activities is pursued both within Karnali Zone and with surrounding regions. These, interwoven with the other components of the economy, are keyed to the supply and demand of food grains, to the seasonal and locational availability of goods in general, and to travel conditions. Thus they exhibit multidimensional time-space patterns.

The supply and demand of food grains are singularly important. In order to understand how the economy is articulated by the movement of people, animals and goods in general, and by trading activities in particular, one must keep in mind that there are not only entire areas producing an agricultural surplus but also generally some households within deficit agricultural areas that do so as well.

Households that produce a food deficit experience their food shortage during the spring months (March through May), before winter crops of barley and wheat are harvested, and during the last part of the monsoon

(September and October), before summer crops are harvested. These households seek in various ways to alleviate their food problem. Many borrow grain in spring against a payment of summer labor or cash, or they obtain grain in fall, after harvest, in return for recent summer labor, or for cash. Trading is for others the most important method for obtaining food grains. In summer, as soon as the mountain trails are free of snow, members of many households, or groups of households, take grains (rice, barley, wheat, oats) to upper Humla and Mugu, or to markets just across the international boundary in Tibet, where they exchange them for salt at 1:2 to 1:8 ratios (i.e., one unit of grain for 2 to 8 units of salt). Some of the salt is retained for their own needs, and the rest is transported to the central or southern parts of the zone, where it is again exchanged for grain at similar ratios. In this way the trade is perpetuated and the family's food requirements are met.

It appears that this Tibetan salt–Nepalese grain exchange triggers subsequent trading activities within the zone and with areas immediately to the south, in upper Bheri Zone. Within these regions, food grains are a principal medium of exchange, and only in recent years has a transition from an economy totally based on exchange to a cash economy begun. But the lack of specialization in livelihood pursuits, as well as the absence of any marketing structure, continues to retard the monetization of the economy. Indeed, the exchange of grains, as well as other foods and basic commodities, is essential to the economy's operation. Thus, during spring, summer, and fall a variety of items is traded. Some people from Dolpo come to Tibrikot District with salt and woolen handlooms which they exchange for grain or cash. With the cash they may buy sheep and goats in Tibrikot or in eastern Jumla. It should be noted, however, that most trade movement from Dolpo follows the Bheri River to the south and does not interact with Karnali Zone. From Jajarkot District, principally the Barekot area, come grains, peanuts, bamboo products, some iron and iron implements, wooden vessels, as well as cattle and buffalo. During late fall and early winter, vegetables and oranges from Dailekh District are brought as far as Jumla bazaar.

Each winter members of almost every family make a trading trip to the Terai, usually to Nepalganj or Rajapur. They leave in November or early December after the harvest and return in March or April. The principal purpose of this annual trip is to obtain certain food stuffs and consumer goods needed during the coming year. Since grains cannot be used as an exchange item in the Terai "bread basket," medicinal herbs, hashish, *silagit,* handloomed goods and knitted items, and, when possible, cash are carried south. Those peasants who have no purchasing power will work in India for 3 to 4 months and with the rupees they are able to save will purchase their needs en route home. The principal items obtained on this annual trip are cotton cloth, tea, sugar, spices, copper and aluminum utensils, and ready-made iron implements or raw iron.

The few horse traders of the zone take their animals either to Jouljibi or to the Dang Valley for sale. From southwestern Jumla District, *ghee* is taken to Rajapur or Nepalganj.

The purchase of luxury items is insignificant. The vast majority of the peasants carry their own purchases home and therefore attention is paid to weight. An average load is 37 kilograms.

Two areas of Karnali Zone are noted for their trading activities. Many Bhotias from upper Mugu District concentrate on trade (in conjunction with animal husbandry) primarily because they live in an area unsuited for agriculture. But Thakuris and Chhetris from the lower Sinja Valley are the most far-ranging and diversified traders in the zone, although they have relatively good agricultural lands. For them trading is a tradition inherited from a period of 400 to 500 years ago when Had Sinja was the summer capital of the Malla Kingdom. It was, as the word *Had* implies, a market center.

Today no market system of any kind exists in Karnali Zone. Its remote situation prevents it from having a periodic or shifting system such as that which exists in the eastern Nepal Himalaya, where there is relatively easy access to Darjeeling District in West Bengal and where a greater variety of foods and goods is produced in a small area. For the same reason Karnali Zone has not developed any hierarchy of permanent markets, and its households must therefore make annual trading trips to the Terai.

Jumla and Its Bazaar. The only truly central place in all of Karnali Zone is Jumla, the zonal capital. Its situation in the upper Tila Valley was most conducive to the growth of a relatively large town or, in actual fact, a complex of towns. This growth began during the Malla regime and experienced a later impetus during the Rana regime. It then served as the capital and administrative center of old Jumla District, an extensive area composed of 18 *daras,* or subdivisions, that correspond generally to present-day Karnali Zone and, in addition, to much of Dolpo District as far east as Tarakot. It was the headquarters of the Bara Hakim, the Rana's representative from Kathmandu, as well as being the site of a military garrison, a revenue office, and a court. Because of its remote location, considerable *de facto* autonomy must have been held by the Rana's representative as well as by key landlords or headmen in the area. This was undoubtedly a period of considerable exploitation of the general population.

Between 80 and 100 years ago several Newars, who had previously served in the area as civil servants, opened shops in Jumla, thus forming the nucleus of a permanent bazaar. Their clientele was the civil servants and the military posted there. Seeing the success of the Newars, a number of landed Brahmans, Chhetris, and Thakuris also opened shops. This resulted in a division of the limited market and forced the Newars, who previously did not farm, to buy land in order to make ends meet.

Today there are 30 shops comprising both the old and new bazaars that collectively stock over 200 different items for sale primarily to the government servants. The indigenous population has been slow to use the bazaar, principally because of the cost of the goods. Transfer costs for one *maund* (a porter load of 37 kilograms) from Nepalganj to Jumla is 100 rupees, NC. These costs are reflected in the retail prices, which average 2 to 3 times that of Kathmandu and 3 to 4 times that of Nepalganj. The peasants of the area lack cash for such purchases. They find it more economical to continue their annual winter trade trips south to the Terai.

Viewed at a larger zonal or regional scale, Jumla does not function as a market center. In Karnali Zone the major trails are, as one would suspect, the major trade routes. These tend to conform to, or follow, the dendritic drainage pattern of the upper Karnali River, which trends generally west or southwest. Relatively few major trails cross from one drainage basin to another; therefore, Jumla with its site on the upper Tila River has a natural hinterland of only about 20 percent of the zone — the extreme eastern part of Jumla District itself, most of Tibrikot District, and, during summer only, parts of Mugu District.

Four major trails lead into Jumla: one from eastern Tibrikot District down the Tila River; one down the Chaudhabise Khola and entering the Tila a half-hour's walk east of Jumla at Dansangu; one entering Jumla from the north over the Dore Lekh; and one down the Tila River, entering Jumla from the west. In 2026 BS approximately 20,000 people passed into or through Jumla over these trails. The great majority of them lived within a day's march of the zonal capital. Only a small percentage of the remainder had Jumla as their destination, but trade or commerce was not their objective; they were traveling to Jumla for government or administrative reasons, primarily for court cases. The majority of those people, living more than a day's march from Jumla, passed only through the zonal headquarters en route to the Terai. This is reflected by the fact that trail traffic through Jumla is heaviest in November and December, when people go south on their annual trade trip, and in March and April, when they return.

It should also be mentioned that until about ten years ago the Chandannath and Bhairabnath temples in Jumla drew both Indian and Nepalese pilgrims off the main Karnali River route to Manasarowar and Mount Kailash in Tibet. Today, such pilgrim traffic through Jumla has stopped as a result of border restrictions by the Chinese.

Simplified Model of the Subsistence Economic System

The preceding brief explanatory description, while by no means complete, touches upon the salient features of both the physical and cultural landscapes of Karnali Zone. It is focused upon the components of the peasant's subsistence economic system, which for more than a hundred years, the Rana period of 1846 to 1951, while necessarily being an open system, operated in a relatively steady state and was little affected by external forces, primarily because of its remote location and the difficulty of communication with the central government in Kathmandu. During the past 20 years, however, there has been a steady increase in external social and political influences, of which the following are but a few:

1. The end of isolationism, following King Tribhuvan's overthrow of the Rana regime in 1951.
2. The ever-decreasing amount of trade, or movement of people, animals, and goods between Nepal and Tibet since 1959, when the Dalai Lama escaped from Lhasa to India.
3. The 1962 reorganization of the internal administrative divisions of Nepal "on the basis of uniformity of area and population." These consist of 14 first-order zones, 75 second-order development districts, and some 3,800 village and town councils, or panchayats. This scheme was an attempt systematically to delimit zones and districts in order to reduce internal communication and transportation barriers and to promote economic self-sufficiency. Karnali Zone, with its 4 districts, was formed by this reorganization. Humla and Mugu districts each have 20 village panchayats. Jumla District has 49, and Tibrikot District, which between 1962 and 1966 lost much of its territory to the Dolpo District of Dhaulariri Zone, had only 5 panchayats until April 1970 when these 5 were expanded to 20.
4. Attempts in the last few years to carry out measures of the Land Reform Act of 1957.
5. The advent of the transistor radio, both panchayat and privately owned, has resulted in an increasing awareness of the "outside world."

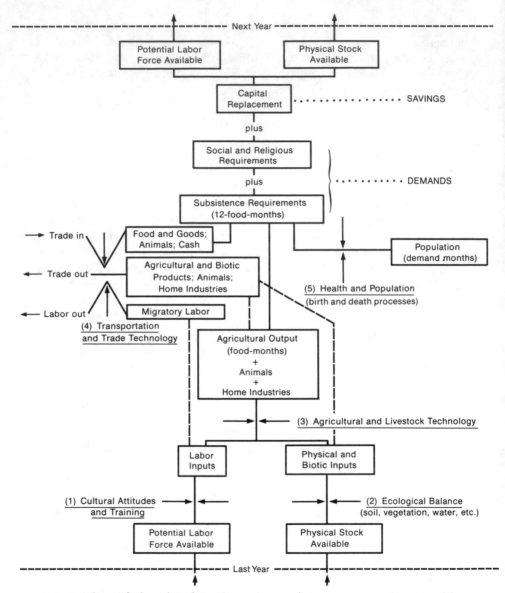

FIG. 3.   Simplified model of the Karnali Zone subsistence economic system. Note:
Constraints on the system are numbered and underlined, their pressure points are
indicated by double arrows.

6. In the past 10-15 years a variety of facilities has been established in Karnali Zone, including primary, middle, and high schools; and at Jumla a telecommunication station, an 800-meter STOL airfield, a "fifteen bed" hospital, an agricultural station, and a cottage industry training program.

It should be noted that the northern border areas of Nepal, including Karnali Zone, are the first areas affected negatively by external forces and the last helped by the central government. Only since 1965 has His Majesty's Government shown *particular* interest in promoting the economic and social development of Karnali Zone. The external and sociopolitical forces mentioned have destroyed the steady-state condition. The rapid changes that have and are taking place are creating an unstable system. It is this currently unstable economy that is under examination here.

Analysis of and development planning for Karnali Zone's economy are difficult because of its multidimensional character, which exhibits great inherent complexity of processes in relation to scale, place, and time.

On the basis of the field research conducted during this study, it has been possible to construct a simplified model of the Karnali Zone subsistence economic system as an aid to economic analysis. This simplified model (see fig. 3), which might well be applied to other regions of Nepal for purposes of analysis and planning, since no area is completely unique, serves to eliminate the mass of peripheral information that often obscures the key issues and it permits one to focus on the essential components and processes of the system and to identify the pressure points at which these processes are impended by constraining forces.

As the model indicates, five major forces restrict the present dynamics of Karnali Zone's economy and impede its growth and development: 1, cultural attitudes and training; 2, the ecological balance; 3, agricultural and livestock technology; 4, transportation and trade technology; 5, health and population. To have a sound understanding of these constrictive pressure points, an amplification and discussion of each is appropriate.

1. Cultural Attitudes and Training

A variety of beliefs, practices, and attitudes, exhibited primarily by the Pahari (or hill Hindu) majority, but to a lesser extent by the Bhotia Buddhist minority, consorts to constrain the livelihood system of Karnali Zone. Interwoven in the sociopolitical fabric of the region, all are manifestations of extreme orthodoxy and traditionalism. Two important factors contributing to this conservatism are the remote and isolated location of the region and the political history of both the region and the nation. Although some of these parochial beliefs and attitudes are beginning to break down — primarily because of the advent of the government's educational program, the panchayat system, and the transistor radio — they continue to be serious deterrents to development and among the most difficult to overcome.

Historically, the region has suffered a series of in-migrations and conquests; petty hill kingdoms have risen and fallen, until, around the 12th century, the Paharis predominated. They occupied the better agricultural lands in the valley bottoms and adjacent slopes, pushing or confining the Bhotias to higher, agriculturally unproductive terrain along the northern border and into isolated enclaves farther south. An exploitive feudal system was imposed in the region, many vestiges of which, such as jajmani practices, are still present. The rugged, and in many respects unhospitable, physical landscape has contributed to an insular cultural landscape characterized by the complex symbioses discussed earlier.

The fact that Prithvi Narayan Shah united the many Himalayan hill kingdoms, including the Karnali Zone region, into the nation-state of Nepal at the end of the 18th century, has had little effect on the actual way of life in this remote region. Moreover, the 105-year period of Rana repression and isolation, which ended only in 1951, further contributed to the insularism of the region.

All these factors helped to produce a relatively backward population which was, and still is, suspicious and distrustful of outsiders and of "foreign influences." Typical of the many local aphorisms coined during the Rana regime and still current is "a visit from a government official means certain death."

It is not surprising, then, that until recently most of the population either had no concept of nation-state or were reluctant to think in terms of Nepal as a whole. Even today one meets an occasional traveler on the trail who, when asked where he is from and where he is going, replies that he is from *"malaria,"* meaning the Terai, or that he is on his way to "Nepal," meaning the Kathmandu Valley.

Since 1951, when Rana isolationism ended and Nepal opened her doors to the outside world, thus entering the 20th century, the government has been struggling to build a politically, socially, and economically viable nation. The decade of the 1950's was one of general chaos and confusion for the Jumla region as well as for the country as a whole, even though the more remote hill regions of Nepal were the last to receive the attention of the central government. A valid comparison may be drawn between these hill regions and those of Appalachia. For all practical purposes, only since 1963 has His Majesty's Government undertaken programs to develop the economic and social well-being of Karnali Zone. These have been integrated with the institution of a party-less democracy. King Mahendra's purpose in creating the new panchayat system was "democratization of government by decentralizing the administration and by bringing the mass of the people into participation in economic development and public affairs." But these programs, as well as the panchayat system itself, have enjoyed only limited success in Karnali Zone, principally because of the cultural constraints noted above.

Prior to the establishment of the panchayat governmental system, local village government was of the traditional head-man or the village-elders-council types in which these positions were generally held by men from affluent and influential families. In Pahari areas, these were usually of high caste and were key men in the local social and economic framework of the communities. Because such families produced an agricultural or trading surplus, they were less constricted by the common household-labor bind. This, in turn, permitted them to give their male children traditional education, either by Brahman tutors or in Brahminical schools (in Jumla, in the Terai, or in India). It was only natural that members of this same small, "educated" elite group were elected to the village panchayats.

On the other hand, the vast majority of the population were, and still are, uneducated and politically unsophisticated. While they now increasingly aspire to a better way of life, they are conditioned to a subservient role. Although the government's efforts in education are beginning to break down this condition, the majority still suffer from what can be termed the "vested interest syndrome," a common attitude of frustrated acceptance of a second-class role, manifested by general apathy and lack of initiative. Despite efforts in land reform, as well as the potential of the panchayat system, very few examples can be cited where the wide gap between the small power-elite minority and the vast, less-affluent majority has been narrowed.

In general, the civil servants posted in Karnali Zone are confronted by a local population not only suspicious but steeped in traditional parochial attitudes. They are usually unhappy in their isolated, primitive field setting and miss the amenities of the Kathmandu Valley. Moreover, they feel that they have been ostracized from the main stream of civil service and that their chances for advancement in government are thus seriously jeopardized. The resulting state of mind in turn affects their ability to develop good rapport with the local leaders and the population as a whole.

To the factionalism among the local population and their distrust of governmental officials, factors that generally deter cooperation at all levels — village, panchayat, district, and zone — must be added a number of additional roadblocks caused by the dearth of education and training. One is the almost total lack of managerial skills. Another is lack of any large-scale coordinated home industry.

Finally, the extended family system contributes to the seemingly insurmountable problem of ever-increasing land fragmentation. If a family splits upon the death of the father, each individual plot is divided among his sons, so that over a period of time the size of family holdings decreases while the number of plots increases. Although the people recognize this to be a paramount problem, they are fatalistic, for they perceive no way within their own social system that such fragmentation can be stopped.

2. ECOLOGICAL BALANCE

The relation of man to the biota of his habitat has been discussed earlier. The conclusion might be drawn that this peasant subsistence society lives in harmony with its environment. Nothing is farther from the truth. Throughout most of the zone and principally below 3,800 meters, man, the dominant species in the ecosystem, destructively exploits and alters the other components of the system, creating an ecological imbalance. Thus, while seemingly less acute than in other parts of Nepal, deforestation, burning, and overgrazing are increasing at an alarming rate. It is the rule, not the exception, that in most of central and southern Karnali Zone the collection of a load of firewood requires a one-day round trip from the farmstead. A generation ago (18 to 20 years), such a trip would have required only an hour or two. Projecting this rate of deforestation, the wood supply for many villages soon will be more than a day away, and the villagers will not be able to afford the increased time required for obtaining wood. They will then be forced to burn dung as is now done in the lower regions of Nepal. But the average family's animals produce only 50 percent of the fertilizer they believe is needed for their fields. Thus a negative chain reaction will have been set in motion.

Although the people are well aware that their wood-fuel supply is becoming increasingly scarce, they have no appreciation of the immediate need for the initiation of sustained-yield forestry. Only in Phoi Panchayat in Jumla District has an attempt been made at tree farming. This was started by a representative of the Farmer's Organization to the National Panchayat.

The practice each spring of burning off the grasses on the grazing slopes, most of which are forested, further contributes to deforestation. And finally, many of the *patans* are overgrazed. The combination of deforestation, burning, and overgrazing leads to soil erosion and the eventual lowering of the water table. Unfortunately, the people are unable to connect this cause-and-effect. Thus, if drastic measures are not immediately taken, much of lower Karnali Zone will be so altered that any sort of productive agriculture will be impossible. Similar destructive practices over past centuries in the Zagros and Elbruz Mountains of Iran have resulted in arid landscapes.

The alteration of the forest ecology of the Zone is having many other results detrimental to the economy. Medicinal herbs, as well as other wild species of vegetation, are becoming increasingly scarce and face possible extinction. Despite government laws prohibiting the killing of musk deer, this species faces extinction by poachers because of the high price the musk gland brings for aphrodisiacs and perfumes. Conversely, gun-restriction measures imposed on the population by the central government since 1960 have caused an increase in the number of monkeys, Himalayan blue bear, wild boar, and porcupine. These four species constitute an increasing pest problem. In the higher and more isolated agricultural areas of the zone, these uncontrolled pests now consume an estimated 25 percent of the potential food grain yield.

3. AGRICULTURAL AND LIVESTOCK TECHNOLOGY

A major constraint on the agriculturally based economy of Karnali Zone is the primitive state of both the agricultural and animal technology. With few exceptions, the wood-tipped plow, and about a dozen iron-tipped digging tools, constitute the farmer's inventory of field equipment. The fields themselves—numerous, small, fragmented and dispersed terraced plots on steep slopes—do not lend themselves to more efficient plowing, weeding, and harvesting methods. In many areas fields have been extended to peripheral uplands ill-suited for agriculture. In addition the farmer continues to extend the preferred crop, rice, with increasingly marginal returns.

The recent introduction of improved seeds (wheat and rice) has been sporadic and quite limited. Where introduced, these seeds have had varying but sometimes spectacular success. A tenfold increase in wheat yield was obtained in 1970 at a test plot in the upper Tila Valley. There exists a critical need for widespread and systematic distribution of these improved seeds. Those chosen should not only give increased yields but also should have shorter growing seasons in order to obviate the time bind that has been noted earlier. Development and introduction of improved maize varieties are of particular importance.

Every farmstead has its kitchen garden producing strictly for home consumption. Although the region is climatically well-suited for developed horticulture, this is totally lacking today, its development hampered by the absence of transfer and marketing systems. Nevertheless, the variety of kitchen garden crops could be immediately enlarged, particularly with respect to green and yellow vegetables.

In the valley bottoms of the major rivers, where well-developed irrigation canal systems have been used for many centuries and where water is still in good supply, there appears to be a tendency for the farmer to over-irrigate.

Only in 1969 were government efforts begun to improve the animal technology of the area. Until then, the local farmer had made no attempt at controlled breeding or the improvement of grasses.

The present animal population of the region supplies insufficient fertilizer for the fields. Moreover, the fertilizing methods used today are crude at best. While a few farmers recently attempted to use compost pits, recognizing the advantage of this technique, they were forced to stop the practice because of the ever-present time-labor bind problem. During the short, critical spring harvest-planting period, the farmers found that they had insufficient time and labor to move great amounts of fertilizer from the farmsteads' compost pits to their widely dispersed fields.

Finally, government efforts in agricultural experiment stations and in farm extension services have been confined to the area immediately around Jumla. Even in this small area, they have been generally ineffectual. If the region is to enjoy agricultural development, concerted efforts must be made throughout the region to convince the tradition-bound farmer that it is in his interest to adopt new techniques. The programs can be successful only if extensive "show and tell" programs are carried out, with the emphasis on the "show." Demonstrations over a long period of time are required before the farmer will change and innovate. The experiment in hill agriculture at Ampipal, north of Gorkha, showed that only after 10 years was there a residual effect.

Much of the region is ideally suited for arboriculture. One bright note in the agricultural scene has been the government's program in 1969 and 1970 to plant some 200,000 apple seedlings, as well as some improved walnut seedlings, in the region. The survival rate has varied from 5 to 95 percent, depending on the care given them. When proper transfer and market facilities are provided, a viable apple industry should result. In addition, crocus for saffron has been introduced recently on an experimental basis near Jumla.

4. TRANSPORTATION AND TRADE TECHNOLOGY

The absence of a well-organized marketing system within Karnali Zone (explained on p. 33) hinders development of a viable economy. The Zone's remote location and the mountainous character of its landscape, cited as contributing factors in this absence, are also major factors that contribute to the backward state of its transportation and trade technology. At present, travel throughout the region is limited to the topographically controlled network of trails. Moreover, the closest motorable road-head is at Nepalganj, 240 kilometers to the south in Bheri Zone on the Indian border. Not until the east-west highway, now under construction across the Terai, is completed will western Nepal have any internal road connections with the east. All traffic must now transit northern India.

Within the zone itself, climatic factors impose seasonal restrictions on the movement of people, animals, and goods. During winter (December through April), deep snows on the high passes and forested slopes make travel difficult and often impossible. During the monsoon (July through September), floods and landslides restrict and sometimes prevent summer travel. Often key bridges are washed away. When this happens, large areas of the Zone are often cut off and isolated for weeks, or even months. This is particularly true for Humla District, north of the Mugu Karnali, and for that part of Jumla District lying west of the Karnali River. On August 6, 1969, for example, all bridges across the upper reaches of the Mugu Karnali were washed away, thus cutting off Humla District from the south for many weeks. While bos'n's chairs were soon erected to permit people to cross the swollen river, the important movement of sheep and goats needed for transport of grains, salt, and wool during the summer season was almost totally curtailed.

Horses and mules, commonly employed as a more efficient means of transportation in other roadless parts of Nepal, are not used in Karnali Zone. A decade ago, an attempt by Jumla merchants to establish a mule train failed because of the inability of the shopkeepers to work among themselves in this cooperative endeavor. More recent attempts to transfer consumer goods from Nepalganj to Jumla by STOL aircraft have failed because dependable service could not be maintained.

Over the past ten years Chinese restrictions on the traditional trade with Tibet have seriously affected the food-grain for salt-and-wool exchange in the entire central and northern parts of the zone. Exchange of grain for Tibetan consumer goods, in much demand by the Bhotias, has been completely stopped. Therefore, those Bhotias who depend almost entirely on trade for their livelihood have been seriously hurt. Now many Bhotia traders from Mugu District sell medicinal herbs in Nepalganj and then, with the cash obtained from this sale, travel some 1,100 kilometers across northern India to Kalimpong in Darjeeling District of West Bengal in order to buy such items as Tibetan brick tea, snuff, leather boots, and *bakus* (the traditional Tibetan garment), as well as Chinese sweatshirts and corduroy cloth.

5. HEALTH AND POPULATION

Health and demographic problems in Karnali Zone further constrain its economic system. Dietary deficiencies and a broad spectrum of illnesses, similar to those in other areas of the country, combine to lower the people's general level of health. The basis of the diet is rice and lentils, or *chappatis,* and in some areas potatoes or maize. Meat (sheep and goats) and poultry are infrequently used. Caste taboos limit the diet of many families. This results in a significant protein deficiency.

In order to offset the bland nature of the diet, the people consume large quantities of *khorsani* (chili peppers) and other spices. In turn, this produces a high prevalence of digestive problems. Because all Tibetan salt, as well as most Indian salt, is uniodized, goiter is one of the primary health problems in the area. Almost 90 percent of the population suffers from an iodine deficiency. Moreover, there are indications that this deficiency contributes to the striking number of deaf mutes and cretins found in the region. The spectrum of illnesses include worms, dysentery, malnutrition, low-order infections, and upper-respiratory ailments, as well as tuberculosis and some malaria. Two problems are of particular note: the population is particularly susceptible to communicable diseases like measles and whooping cough, and there is a high frequency of occupational injuries such as broken bones, cutting-tool wounds, and burns. Because of improper or delayed treatment (or no treatment at all) the injured commonly are crippled and often die.

These health problems have a debilitating effect on the people, thus seriously sapping their work potential. Moreover, the region in 1970 was almost totally without medical services. Although a 15-bed hospital had been built in Jumla a few years earlier, it was by then already in serious disrepair. Only one doctor, often absent from the region, served this largest of the nation's zones, and a critical shortage of medicines at Jumla and at district dispensaries in Humla and Mugu, as well as a lack of trained assistants, further restricted medical services.

The people are anxious to have medical help. They received the government's initial efforts in this area with enthusiasm, but many soon became disillusioned. They often found that after making a long journey from their home to the district dispensary or to the zonal hospital the compounder or the doctor was unavailable or that medicine was nonexistent. Because of this, they are now not taking advantage of even the minimal medical help available. Moreover, they feel their work schedule will not permit them to take the time. Finally, many believe that medical attention will be too costly. On the other hand, the doctor becomes increasingly frustrated because of the overwhelming problems with which he is confronted.

The demographic picture in the region is even more serious. Population trends are similar to those of much of the rest of the country. It can be assumed that the birth rate is approximately 55 per 1,000 and holding steady, while the death rate is 27 per 1,000 and dropping. The annual population increase is therefore 2.7 percent. If this increase continues the population will double in the next 26 years.

Today serious pressures are already being felt, for the region is ill-suited to support even the present population of 186,000. Yet prospects for controlling the increase are not good. The average peasant family requires a large family labor force, and if they are to achieve an ideal size of four or five children who survive beyond the age of five, the wife or wives must have many pregnancies as insurance against the high rate of infant and child mortality. Although the people are not restrained by religious taboos, they are unwilling or reluctant to adopt contraceptive practices because of the family labor requirements. Only after infant and child mortality rates have been drastically lowered by health education, care by midwives, and by formal medical attention, will birth-control programs be successful.

Conclusions

In the above research I employed a design that differs from the traditional broad-scale gross treatment of the economic geographer, from the specific topic orientation of the physical geographer, and from the classical village study of the anthropologist. Rather, I examined Karnali Zone within a holistic geoecological framework that involved a spectrum of cultural and physical variables operating in a multidimensional time-space matrix at several levels (regional, village, and household) and scales.

A traditional peasant subsistence-economic system was identified that had developed historically and had continued to operate successfully in an extreme environment by carefully orchestrated seasonal scheduling that was articulated by the regulated movements of peoples, animals, and goods. However, a variety of change-effecting forces, increasingly felt in the past three decades, has intensified the five constraints on the system mentioned above (cultural attitudes and training, ecological balance, agricultural and livestock technology, transportation and trade technology, and health and population), destroying the steady state that had existed for at least a hundred years. These forces at present are accelerating at a rate exceeding that at which the people can adapt. At the moment, therefore, the system is becoming maladaptive since there are no buffers or backups and the land resources are limited. The catalyst precipitating this disruption is the population growth, which between 1940 and 1970 has burgeoned from approximately 85,000 to 186,000. Human impact on the wild biota has paralleled this population explosion.

As His Majesty's Government of Nepal addresses itself to the country's development needs, it must concentrate on alleviating through coordinated schemes these five major deterrents to the development. If development is to proceed in an ecologically balanced manner that will sustain and preserve both the physical and cultural landscapes of the country, it must, because of the country's great natural diversity, follow a plan on regional lines that is well-conceived, well-implemented, and well-enforced. Such a plan must ultimately accomplish the increase of agricultural productivity, the internal redistribution of surpluses, the better use of the environment and its existing resources, the preservation and fuller use of its natural flora and fauna, and the control of future population growth.

But these goals cannot be realized solely by applying economic-growth models from developed western nations of high technology. They can result only from the application of appropriate models that fit Nepal.

Since completion of the field work, my wife or I revisited Karnali Zone every two years (in 1972, 1974, and 1976) in order to assess the efforts being made by the government to achieve a total, balanced ecological solution which will achieve stabilization of the hierarchy of systems here identified, described, and analyzed.

At the moment, it is premature to evaluate the success of these efforts.

REFERENCES

AMATYA, SOORYA L.
1968. Agricultural crops and their distribution in Nepal. The Himalayan Review, Nepal Geogr. Soc., 21st Int. Geogr. Congr., Spec. Issue, 1968, pp. 21-41.

BERREMAN, GERALD D.
1972. Hindus of the Himalayas: Ethnography and change, ed. 2, 440 pp., illus. University of California Press, Berkeley.

BHATT, DIBYA DEO
1970. National history and economic botany of Nepal, 160 pp., illus. HMG Nepal, Dept. Inf., Min. Inf. & Broadcasting, Kathmandu.

BISHOP, BARRY C.
1972. The rooftop of the world. Pp. 130-136 *in* "Marvels and Mysteries of the World Around Us." Reader's Digest, Pleasantville, New York.

BISHOP, BARRY C., and BISHOP, LILA
1971. Karnali, roadless world of western Nepal. Nat. Geogr. Mag., vol. 140, pp. 656-689, illus.

BISTA, DOR BAHADUR
1972. People of Nepal, 210 pp., illus. Ratna Pustak Bhandus (publ.), Kathmandu.

CAPLAN, A. PATRICIA
1972. Priests and cobblers, 103 pp., illus. Chandler Publishing Co., San Francisco.

COOL, JOHN C.
[1967.] The far western hills (some longer term considerations), 32 pp., unpublished. A Report to HMG Nepal, February 1967.

FISHER, JAMES F.
[1972]. Trans-Himalayan traders: Economy, society, and culture in northwest Nepal, 209 pp., illus. Ph.D. dissertation, University of Chicago, December 1972.

FÜRER-HAIMENDORF, CHRISTOPH VON
1975. Himalayan traders (life in highland Nepal), 316 pp., illus. John Murray, London.

GANSSER, AUGUSTO
1964. Geology of the Himalayas, 289 pp., illus. John Wiley & Son, Ltd.–Interscience Publishers, London.

GOLDSTEIN, MELVIN C.
[1975]. A report on Limi Panchayat, Humla District, Karnali Zone, 21 pp., unpublished. Case Western Reserve University, Department of Anthropology.

HAFFNER, WILLIBALD
1965. Nepal Himalaya. Erdkunde, vol. 19, no. 2, pp. 89-111, illus.

HAGEN, TONI
1971. Nepal, 3d ed., 180 pp., illus. Kummerly & Frey, Berne.

JHINA, PADAM SINGH
1962. Agriculture in the hill regions of north India, 122 pp., illus. India, Ministry of Food and Agriculture, New Delhi.

McDougal, Charles
    1968. Village and household economy in far western Nepal, 126 pp.   Trib-
        huvan University, Kirtipur, Nepal.
Messerschmidt, Donald A.
    1976. Ecological change and adaptation among the Gurungs of the Nepal Him-
        alaya.   Human Ecology, vol. 4, no. 2, pp. 167-185, illus.
Nepal, HMG Central Bureau of Statistics
    1962. National sample census of agriculture: Yield data for principal crops.
        His Majesty's Government Press, Kathmandu.
Nepal, HMG Ministry of Food and Agriculture
    1972. Agricultural statistics of Nepal.   Report of the Economic Analysis and
        Planning Division, July 1972, Kathmandu.
Ohta, Yoshihide, and Akifa, Chikara, editors
    1973. Geology of the Nepal Himalayas, 292 pp., illus.   Saiko Publishing Co.,
        Ltd., Tokyo (for Himalayan Committee of Hokkaido University, Sap-
        poro, Japan).
Okada, Ferdinand E.
    1970. Preliminary report on regional development areas in Nepal, 125 pp.
        HMG National Planning Commission, Regional Planning Series no. 2,
        Kathmandu.
Pant, S. D.
    1935. The social economy of the Himalayans, 264 pp., illus.   George Allen &
        Unwin, Ltd., London.
Regmi, Mahesh C.
    1963-68. Land tenure and taxation in Nepal, 4 vols.   University of California,
        Institute of International Studies, Research Series no. 8, Berkeley.
Schweinfurth, Ulrich
    1957. Die horizontale und vertikale Verbreitung der Vegetation im Himalaya.
        Bonnes geographische Abhandlungen, vol. 20, 373 pp.
Shresta, Bhim Prashad, editor
    1971. [Karnali Zone (one piece of study)], 123 pp.   Association of Social
        Studies, privately published (BS 2028). (Original in Nepali.)
Stainton, J. D. A.
    1972. Forests of Nepal, 181 pp., illus.   John Murray, London.
Tucci, Guiseppe
    1962. Nepal: The discovery of the Malla, 96 pp., illus.   E. P. Dutton & Co.,
        Inc., New York.
Uhlig, Harald
    1969. Hill tribes and rice farmers in the Himalayas and south-east Asia.   Inst.
        British Geogr., Trans. Pap., publ. 47, pp. 1-23.
Worth, Robert M., and Shah, Narayan K.
    1969. Nepal health survey 1965-1966, 158 pp.   University of Hawaii Press,
        Honolulu.

Barry C. Bishop

Studies of the Horse Flies of Thailand
(Diptera: Tabanidae)

Principal Investigator: John J. S. Burton, Cornell University, Ithaca, New York.[1]

Grant No. 749:   For field research on the taxonomy of the flies of the family Tabanidae in Thailand.

The insect fauna of the Oriental Region is probably the least known of that of any zoogeographic area. The humid tropical climate and diversity of physical features (including island archipelagoes) have been highly favorable for speciation, and this is clearly reflected in the insects. Until recently Thailand in particular has received less than its fair share of attention by entomologists, and taxonomic works on its fauna characteristically include a high proportion of new species.

It was decided to undertake taxonomic studies of Thailand's horse-fly fauna, based on my earlier knowledge of the country from service in the U. S. Peace Corps. Grants by the National Geographic Society and by Geigy Agricultural Chemicals Division of Ciba-Geigy Corporation funded a 6-month collecting trip. A Ph.D. thesis was written on the material (Burton, 1974). Included in it are full accounts of 80 species, including 32 described as new from Thailand and Laos. Based on examinations of historical material, lectotypes were designated for eight nominal species and many synonymic changes were made. The more important previous collections of Indochinese Tabanidae were discussed.

The entire collection of the genus *Haematopota* made by my employees and me during tenure of the grant, which came to nearly 9,000 specimens, was turned over to Dr. Alan Stone, at the U. S. National Museum of Natural History, for a monographic revision of the Oriental members of the genus (Stone and Philip, 1974). Many of these specimens have been made holotypes and paratypes of new species by these authors.

The present report is a summary of topics that may be of more than strictly taxonomic interest.

---

[1] Present affiliation: University of California ICMR, Institute for Medical Research, Kuala Lumpur, Malaysia.

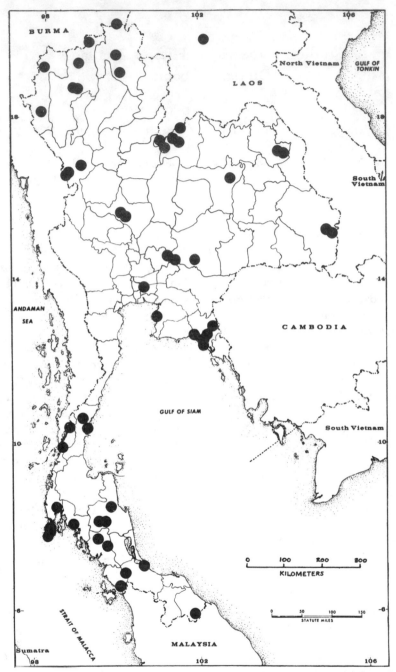

FIG. 1.   Localities visited for collecting purposes, 1969 only. (Base map from Smith et al., 1968.)

Zoogeography

Thailand lies entirely within the Oriental Region but is divided between the Indochinese and Malayan Subregions. Zoogeographers differ as to where the dividing line should be drawn. Wallace (1876) drew his line diagonally across the peninsula from the upper limit of the Bight of Bangkok at the east end downward to about lat. 12°N. at the west end, below Mergui, Burma. Kloss (1929) simply chose the narrowest point on the Isthmus of Kra (about lat. 10°N.) to draw his line directly across. Usinger (1963) drew his line all the way across the entire Indochinese peninsula, crossing Thailand at about lat. 14°N., near the latitude of Bangkok. In terms of present physiography, none of these is marked by any particular barriers to dispersal. For most animal groups there may still be insufficient evidence to make generalizations, and of course there may be little agreement among groups. For butterflies, Corbet and Pendlebury (1956) discovered the greatest differences in the fauna on either side of a line cutting the peninsula diagonally just above lat. 6°N., crossing the present border of Thailand and West Malaysia in a roughly perpendicular manner. They concluded that this is a largely climatic barrier but postulated that the Malay Peninsula was indeed once cut off from the mainland by the sea. They noted that "the presence of a strong Burmese element among the Malayan butterflies, which is absent from the Sumatran fauna, indicates that the final union between Malaya and continental Asia took place after the final separation of Malaya and Sumatra."

It is not yet time to make more than the most preliminary suggestions about how tabanids fit these lines. Specimens were collected at many sites within Thailand, including the southern provinces, but the upper provinces of the Isthmus of Kra have yet to receive attention. At this writing (1975) the southern material obtained (from Tha Sae District of Chumphon Province southward) has not yet been fully analyzed, but it has been searched for members of species that were found also above the Isthmus (northward from Ratchaburi), and these were included in the thesis account. Given the artificial gap in the collecting record, only an estimated one-fourth of the species of Tabanini known to occur above the gap are also known to occur below it. Species that appear to be strictly coastal breeders (e.g., around the Bight of Bangkok and eastward down the Chanthaburi coast) seem to me to be extensions of the Malayan fauna, and as such these were not included in the thesis account. It is tentatively suggested from examination of this group that the Indochinese faunistic element is weak below Chumphon, and so the demarcation may be drawn at or above this latitude; and that the coastline of the Gulf of Thailand provides the conditions for Malayan elements to extend northward and eastward, coexisting there with Indochinese elements.

In compensation for omitting the Malayan fauna, the related Indochinese Tabanini of the neighboring areas of Laos and Cambodia were accounted. There are no noteworthy barriers to dispersal between these countries and Thailand, but the Laotian highlands assume a different character. In Thailand, altitude did not seem to have an appreciable effect on species composition until at or above 350 meters. The northern highlands fauna probably bears a substantial relationship to that found farther west and north, though Burma and southern China are not well collected, and so this cannot now be substantiated. Some of the species, both common and relatively uncommon, are widespread in the Oriental Region and their distribution embraces all of Thailand. Much more often the fauna appears to be quite precinctive, though this may in part reflect the status of collecting. As expected in the humid tropics, Thailand's fauna is very rich in species.

Notes on Collecting

Collecting sites were chosen to sample the widest range of geographic and ecological conditions feasible in 6 months (fig. 1). My own collecting produced an extensive sampling, and four assistants were hired in order to obtain an intensive sampling also. One of these was the elephant keeper at the Chiang Mai zoological garden at Huai Kaeo; another was a farmer at Loei; the third was a youth from Bang Phra (Chon Buri Province) who often traveled with me. Of all the localities collected, Huai Kaeo (Chiang Mai) was outstanding. It was situated at the base of Doi Suthep (mountain) just northwest of the city, was easily accessible, and contained both the zoological garden and a commercial dairy farm. Higher-altitude species are attracted to the animals from the mountain; plains species are attracted from the valley; and the ecotone, in which the site is located, can probably be said to have its own characteristic species. A large fraction of the total number of Thailand Tabanini known from above Bangkok have been collected there. The fourth assistant was a farmer in the Canton of Tha Chamuang (Songkhla Province, Rattaphum District) in the far south. Owing to the locality, his collection played a minor part in the thesis study, but he was retained for an entire year, and his material is a valuable asset for further research projects.

A few of the localities selected for sampling had special characteristics. These were chosen to detect the existence of any species that through their developmental cycle might be restricted to such sites. This appeared to be

FIG. 2.   Hot-springs basin at the Fang Agricultural Experiment Station (Chiang Mai Province), type locality of *Tabanus thermarum*. Malaise trap set in background.

FIG. 3.   Malaise trap set over small stream on the outskirts of Mae Hong Son, a
paratype locality of the crepuscular species *Tabanus jeanae.*

the case at a hot-springs basin west of Fang in the far north, the only locality
where *Tabanus thermarum* was found (fig. 2).

During the study the great majority of specimens were collected with
a hand net while they were in the act of attacking domestic livestock. The
method was highly successful, though a dearth of males resulted. The net
used was a short-handled collapsible aerial net made by BioQuip Products
Co., Santa Monica, California. This has the advantage that it can be carried
at all times, and the lack of a long handle probably helps to reduce the disturbance felt by livestock during collecting activities.

Visual collecting from vegetation worked well for finding specimens at
rest on tree trunks (usually in proximity to tethered animals), but this generally produced only common and widespread species (*T. rubidus* Wiedemann, *T. brunnipennis* Ricardo, etc.), as others used more concealed resting
sites before and after feeding. Sweeping vegetation seemed relatively unproductive. In North America a collector using himself as moving bait can
apparently improve his catch (at least of *Chrysops*) by wearing a dark shirt. I

FIG. 4. *Tabanus geographicus,* from Huai Kaeo near Chiang Mai. Photo by H. Lyon.

purposely wore dark shirts most of the time in Thailand, but this procedure did not seem to increase the very low number of specimens collected attacking man, and it intensified the discomfort of the sun's rays. Because of a "crepuscular phenomenon" (see below), a collecting day commonly involved traveling in the morning, extensive local scouting and collecting in the afternoon, and stationary collecting from an animal in the hour(s) before nightfall. Specimens were usually pinned the same night. For prospective tabanid collectors in this part of the world with only a short time to spend, my advice is to find a docile animal tethered in an area with some ecological diversity, and collect from it especially during the final hour before darkness.

Some trapping was also done. A Malaise trap provided by the Bernice P. Bishop Museum was used on a number of occasions (fig. 3). This was essentially a 2-dimensional (single-baffle) model (Gressitt and Gressitt, 1962). The effectiveness of an unbaited Malaise trap depends on proper site selection, and a spot in which the vegetation and other landmarks form a natural flyway is usually required. For several reasons good sites were not readily found, and catches were relatively low. It was found that fewer tabanids escaped the trap if it was hung with the upper (suspension) line slanting and the higher end unshaded. Dry ice (CO_2) used as bait in connection with the trap was tried, but I could not transport it from Bangkok in sufficient quantity by public transportation. Dr. Paul Catts provided a white-skirted canopy trap, which was used several times but not given a fair trial, again because of logistics. Another device tried was a small portable plastic trap (Steiner, 1957), provided by the U. S. Department of Agriculture. This is baited with chemical lures and is used in the control of fruit flies (Tephritidae) in the U.S.A. Only a single tabanid was caught in it in Thailand and under circumstances that suggest that this catch may possibly have been a practical joke. The trap did provide, however, some specimens for the study of Hardy (1973).

The greatest threat to insect collections in Southeast Asia is ants, and it is absolutely necessary to have specimens protected at all times. For this I used paradichlorobenzene (PDB) granules, placed in plastic bags along with the specimen boxes. PDB is a toxic fumigant that not only repels but also kills pests. Unfortunately I learned all too late during the 1969 trip that the fumes also adversely affect the chemistry of photographic film emulsions, and consequently my color slides had a rather strong magenta tint. This hazard is noted in a Kodak manual (1965) as follows: "Whilst compounds of formaldehyde seem to represent the greatest danger [to the stability of colour film dyes], other chemicals, such as paradichlorobenzene (often contained in insect and moth repellent), are also harmful." Others are warned to choose a suitable alternative if their cameras are to be kept in proximity with the fumigant.

Daily Flight Activity

It was quickly found that there was a tremendous hourly difference in the daily activity period of Tabanidae. Although this observation was not quantified by making hourly biting rate counts, it was very clear that there was an enormous rise in attack activity during the final hour before darkness, which in Thailand was at approximately 1800-1900 hours or slightly after. A given locality could be collected all day with very meager results; then in the final hour the air often appeared to come alive with flies. This activity seemed to cease at the point when I could no longer see to collect. The reasons for this crepuscular phenomenon deserve further study. It appeared to be less

FIG. 5. Water buffalo *(Bubalus bubalis)* about which most of the Tha Chamuang (Songkhla Province) specimens were collected. Assistant Aree Wanchitnai checks underside for flies. Note short-handled collapsible net.

pronounced in far northern Thailand. Some species were found to be restricted to the final hour, while others were active through the day, but in some cases their activity intensified during the last hour. The several most widespread, common species also seemed to be active daytime biters, and this lack of activity restriction may at least in part have been responsible for their original success in dispersal.

Some species were found to be attracted to lights at night. The individuals thus collected are believed to have been resting on vegetation nearby when darkness fell; then eventually they flew to the illumination. I do not at present consider these as truly nocturnal, since if the light was not observable from the resting place they would probably not have taken purposeful flight.

However, while doing research on lachrymophagous moths at the Huai Kaeo (Chiang Mai) locality subsequent to my studies there, Bänziger

(1975) collected 5 specimens of *Tabanus* at 2200 hours from an elephant. He considered these flies to be actively on the attack and not simply attracted by his flashlight (personal communication), therefore apparently truly nocturnal. They belong to a species that, when I received Bänziger's specimens, I had already named in manuscript as *Tabanus geographicus,* in appreciation of the field research support of the National Geographic Society (fig. 4).

I have not had a chance to observe copulation in Tabanidae. One afternoon in Loei, an assistant observed and collected three mating pairs (two different species of *Tabanus* and one of *Chrysops*). One pair was collected just before a rainstorm at 1430 hours from the eaves of a house; the other two were taken just after the rainstorm at about 1530 hours from vegetation, and the atmospheric conditions might have influenced mating.

Seasonal Distribution

Tabanid flies are present throughout the year in Thailand, but the individual species may have distinct seasons. The major climatic dichotomy is between wet and dry seasons, each of which may be said to last about 6 months over most of the country. My collecting trip was scheduled to cover the latter part of the dry season and the early part of the rainy season. This seemed to work well in terms of species recovery but left open the question of the total seasonal ranges. As noted above, a deep southern locality was well sampled for a full year with very good results, and such sampling should be done in other localities. The changing season did appear to have an effect on the life cycles of various species. At the upper latitudes it is likely that the season of relatively cooler weather significantly reduces tabanid populations. Years later I returned to the excellent Huai Kaeo (Chiang Mai) locality in late December and saw almost no specimens.

Host Relationships

Host orientation data were duly recorded for most specimens collected. The majority of specimens were taken while attacking water buffalo (fig. 5). Collections from cattle and elephants were also important, and collections from horses were made in some localities. Some were taken attacking man, serow *(Capricornis)*, deer, and goat. Hogs were often checked and no attacks were observed firsthand, but I have seen photographic proof (furnished by G. R. Ballmer, formerly of the U. S. Peace Corps in Thailand) of

FIG. 6. Elephant using part of a coconut palm frond as a fly switch, Tha Sae District (Chumphon Province).

one attack. Man is not frequently attacked, at least when there is an alternative available; many times I have stood unmolested next to water buffalo that were "swarming" with tabanids. Movement, however, including that of motor vehicles and man, does attract at least some *Haematopota* and *Chrysops*.

No true host specificity was identified. In some cases, the specimens of a given species may all have been collected from a single host, but this is believed to be a circumstantial phenomenon where no alternative was available. For example, hill-forest tabanids are not likely to be collected attacking water buffalo since these animals are not usually used for hill-forest work; on the other hand, lowland-plains tabanids in many localities may have only water buffalo as a large-mammal blood source. A proper study of host preference would involve making a variety of animals available at the same site. The Huai Kaeo (Chiang Mai) locality could be a good place for such a study (though the elephant has since been removed). My impression thus far is that tabanids are not noticeably selective among large mammals.

Many people have expressed surprise to me upon learning that elephants should be such a satisfactory source of tabanid blood meals. In fact, elephants were observed being bitten all around the head and body, and even relatively small species seemed to have no difficulty in penetrating the skin. Accounts of the suffering of elephants due to biting flies have appeared in the literature, and one author (Hallett, 1890) commented on the elephants' use of palm leaves as tools to switch at flies. The photograph (fig. 6) shows this phenomenon, and I have seen it also in Malaysia.

The three major genera *(Tabanus, Haematopota,* and *Chrysops)* each tended to have preferred sites for attacking the bodies of animals. Although there does not seem to be any case to be made for competitive displacement, it appeared to me that on occasions when members of all three genera were found on an animal simultaneously (as at Loei) the distinction seemed more pronounced. *Tabanus* most often attacks the underside of an animal, though frequently it bites elsewhere as well. *Haematopota* prefers the back and head. *Chrysops* prefers the legs, especially the inside and rear-facing parts of the upper front legs.

Relative abundance of these genera in Thailand is greatly different from that in North America. In Indochina, *Chrysops* forms a very minor part of the tabanid fauna, while *Haematopota* is second only to *Tabanus.*

Muscid Haematophagy Associated with Tabanidae

Haematophagy is not restricted to those species of Diptera that themselves possess the ability to pierce for a fresh supply of blood. On several continents nonbiting muscid flies have been reported to benefit from the wound made by tabanids, sometimes even dislodging the tabanids in their haste to obtain a blood meal. The potential for disease transmission to animals by these secondary feeders is clear.

The photographs (figs. 7, 8) show a sequence of muscids attempting to take advantage of the presence of a feeding tabanid on an ox in Thailand. Three or more species of muscids may be distinguished, and both sexes are represented (as, unlike the tabanids, the muscids do not have a sexually differentiated diet). The black pair at the upper right of figure 7 has apparently lost place seconds later to the other arrivals (fig. 8). The fly in front of the left eye of the tabanid in figure 8 is upended in its quest to get to the base of the wound. A. C. Pont of the British Museum (Natural History) indicated that this and adjacent specimens appear to be *Musca* sp., probably *sorbens* Wiedemann, while the specimen below the wing costa of the tabanid is apparently a *Morellia.*

FIGS. 7, 8. Sequential photographs of a tabanid, *Tabanus hypomacros* Surcouf, biting an ox, as the muscids move in to share the blood. Pak Chong District (Nakhon Ratchasima Province). Photos by G. R. Ballmer.

Garcia and Radovsky (1962) have provided interesting observations on the orientation of muscids to tabanids for the purpose of blood feeding and have noted that "attraction to biting flies of flies unable themselves to pierce skin is a logical step in the evolution of obligatory haematophagy, since the former can provide the secondary blood-feeders with a dependable source of fresh blood." Likewise, Greenberg (1973) spoke in terms of "evolution of the primary haematophage" in some higher Diptera through development of prestomal teeth. Downes (1971), in discussing the direction of evolution in Diptera, has argued that possession of the equipment for penetrating skin and sucking blood should be regarded as the primitive ("plesiotypic") condition and not the derivative condition in the order. Haematophagy in muscoid groups (which do not possess mandibulate biting mouthparts) is regarded as a subsequent development, since the ancestral stock once possessed (in Brachycera) and then lost the ability to procure blood independently. Haematophagy in such groups in general has apparently most often tended to remain at the facultative level, thus incurring less risk.

Note on Economic Considerations

It was not the purpose of the Thailand study to undertake economic work, but I submit a few random observations. The importance of the Tabanidae to local livestock is probably badly underestimated. This may be in part because most of the biting activity usually occurs at a time when it is likely to go unobserved. The concentration of this activity during the final hour before darkness suggests that the problem might be alleviated by protecting the livestock, if feasible, through the mechanical exclusion of flies during this time. I have seen individual water buffalo escape the brunt of the evening onslaught of flies simply by lying down while those nearby remained standing with venters exposed. I recall one case in which a buffalo was even fairly successful at avoiding being bitten under the chin by placing it on the ground too.

Dairy organizations in particular would be advised to be vigilant about the economic threat posed by tabanids. The Thai-Danish Dairy at Muak Lek (Sara Buri Province) and the Northeast Agricultural Center (Khon Kaen Province), had, at the time of my visit, accomplished protection for their cattle apparently through chemical means. By contrast, the cattle at the Thai-German Dairy at Huai Kaeo (Chiang Mai Province) were under attack.

REFERENCES

BÄNZIGER, H.
1975. Skin-piercing blood-sucking moths, 1: Ecological and ethological notes on *Calpe eustrigata* (Lepid., Noctuidae). Acta Tropica, vol. 32, no. 2, pp. 125-144.

BURTON, JOHN J. S.
1974. Tabanini of Thailand above Isthmus of Kra, vii + 422 pp. Ph.D. thesis, Cornell University.

CORBET, A. S., and PENDLEBURY, H. M.
1956. The butterflies of the Malay Peninsula, ed. 2, xi + 537 pp., illus. Oliver & Boyd, Edinburgh and London.

DOWNES, JOHN A.
1971. The ecology of blood-sucking Diptera: An evolutionary perspective. Pp. 232-258 *in* "Ecology and Physiology of Parasites, a Symposium Held at University of Toronto 19 and 20 February 1970," A. M. Fallis, ed. University of Toronto Press.

GARCIA, RICHARD, and RADOVSKY, FRANK J.
1962. Haematophagy by two non-biting muscid flies and its relationship to tabanid feeding. Can. Ent., vol. 94, no. 10, pp. 1110-1116.

GREENBERG, BERNARD
1973. Flies and disease, vol. 2: Biology and disease transmission, xi + 447 pp. Princeton University Press.

GRESSITT, J. LINSLEY, and GRESSITT, M. K.
1962. An improved Malaise trap. Pacific Ins., vol. 4, no. 1, pp. 87-90.

HALLETT, H. S.
1890. A thousand miles on an elephant in the Shan States, xxxvi + 484 pp., illus. Wm. Blackwood & Sons, Edinburgh and London.

HARDY, D. ELMO
1973. The fruit flies (Tephritidae Diptera) of Thailand and bordering countries. Pacific Ins. Monogr., vol. 31, 353 pp., illus.

KLOSS, C. BODEN
1929. The zoo-geographical boundaries between Asia and Australia and some Oriental sub-regions. Bull. Raffles Mus., vol. 2, pp. 1-10.

KODAK LTD.
1965. Data book of applied photography, vol. 1. London.

SMITH, HARVEY H., et al.
1968. Area handbook for Thailand. DA Pam 550-53, xvi + 558 pp. U. S. Government Printing Office, Washington, D. C.

STEINER, LOREN F.
1957. Low-cost plastic fruit fly trap. Journ. Econ. Ent., vol. 50, no. 4, pp. 508-509.

STONE, ALAN, and PHILIP, CORNELIUS B.
1974. The Oriental species of the tribe Haematopotini (Diptera, Tabanidae). U. S. Dept. Agr. Techn. Bull. 1489, 240 pp.

USINGER, R. L.
  1963. Animal distribution patterns in the tropical Pacific. Pp. 255-261 *in* "Pacific Basin Biogeography, a Symposium," J. L. Gressitt, ed. Bishop Museum Press, Honolulu.
WALLACE, ALFRED RUSSEL
  1876. The geographical distribution of animals, vol. 1, xxiii + 503 pp., illus. Harper & Brothers, New York.

JOHN J. S. BURTON

Reproduction Dynamics and Behavior of the
Torrent Duck

Principal Investigator: Marvin C. Cecil, Naples Community Hospital, Naples, Florida.

Grant Nos. 785, 829:   For study of the reproduction behavior and dynamics of the torrent duck.

The Patagonian region high in the Cordillera of El Bolsón, Río Negro Province, Argentina, with its incredible vastness and remoteness, was the principal area for 30 months of research on the Chilean torrent duck (*Merganetta armata armata*) beginning in April 1968. Few biologists have seriously attempted to study this extraordinary bird, because of the difficulty of reaching its habitat and the minimal numbers that could be found to research.

The present study, principal objective of which was to investigate the behavior and incubation style of the torrent duck, was a continuation of two previous exploratory expeditions: April 28-May 11, 1968, with preliminary research in Argentina (Navas and Olrog), Buenos Aires, and El Bolsón; and August 25-September 21, 1968 (Florida Atlantic University grant 1234), research in Argentina (Navas and Olrog), Buenos Aires, and El Bolsón; and August 25 - September 21, 1968 (Florida Atlantic University grant 1234), an expedition to El Bolsón, Provinces of Río Negro and Chubut, with the primary objective of locating nesting torrent-duck populations and collecting viable eggs of *Merganetta* for transport to the United States. The role of the National Geographic Society in the project began with substantial support in July and September 1969.

The uniqueness of the torrent duck, its obvious rarity, and its inaccessibility all contribute to the desirability of base-line natural-history research on the species. My research of the bird during April and September 1968, although limited, yielded a great deal of tantalizing but suspect information. Just to locate an area where a concentrated population could be studied was a time-consuming and laborious task, for this small, elongated duck is found only in the torrential streams of the South American Andes, at varying altitudes, from the Cordilleras of northwestern Venezuela to Tierra del Fuego. There the ducks live a highly specialized existence beside rushing

FIG. 1. Typical stream habitat of the torrent duck.

streams which may flow at a rate of 6 to 10 feet per second and include falls, rapids, overhanging trees (in Argentina), large boulders, and rocks (see figs. 1 and 2).

Adult Chilean torrent ducks are teal-bodied in size with long-tailed stiff rectrices used for underwater and surface maneuvering. Both male and female possess a bright red bill, and the female breast is a reddish brown below and gray above. The male head pattern is a black ocular stripe, which extends down from the eyes and blends with a black throat and neck. The body is vermiculated in black and white. It has been suggested that the carpal spur on the wings of both female and male might be an integumentary structure used for defense and rock clinging. This brings to mind the possibility of an evolutionary adaptation now used primarily by the female for entering and leaving the nest cavity.

In and around El Bolsón, *Merganetta a. armata* inhabits at least four torrential streams: Río El Ternero, Río Los Repollos, Río Quemquemtreu, and Río Azul. It has also been observed on two streams north of El Bolsón, the Río Los Villegas and the Río Foyel. The four torrential streams are interconnecting, spreading over some 94 kilometers and providing generally similar ecological habitats. Water-temperature gradients of the rivers during September through January ranged from 3° to 6° C. Average altimeter readings were 750 to 875 meters above sea level with a relative humidity of 40 to 60 percent. Air temperatures average +2° C. in the morning and +18° in the late afternoon.

I returned to Argentina in July 1969 with electronic microclimatic indicator units designed by Atkins Technical, Inc., Gainesville, Florida, which would be used to monitor egg temperature and humidity of the nesting torrent duck. In addition, a portable egg carrier (ECU incubator) designed by the Petersime Incubator Co. of Gettysburg, Ohio, was taken along to collect torrent-duck eggs and transport them back to Florida for the specific purpose of rearing the birds in captivity. Viable eggs are more easily transported and do not require the three weeks' quarantine imposed upon live birds entering the United States, and the hatchlings stand a much better chance of adapting than do adult torrent ducks.

El Bolsón is located some 120 kilometers south of San Carlos de Bariloche. Inclement weather and road washouts can make the mountain road from Bariloche to El Bolsón treacherous in early spring. The one-way trip usually takes 4½ hours. The base camp for our research was located where we had previously found a small population of *Merganetta,* on the Río El Ternero, 36 kilometers north-northwest of El Bolsón. However, I

FIG. 2. Torrent duck perched beside waterfall (top) and in stream (bottom), show-ing stiffened tail.

encountered very severe weather and an exceptionally bad winter. Apparently, a few days prior to my arrival the torrent ducks had dispersed, owing to heavy flooding, and they did not return to a suitable nesting habitat until the middle of September. Upon mist-netting several *Merganetta*, I determined that the reproductive cycle would not commence until the last of October. Ironically, my assumption was correct, since I received word from an associate and friend, Señor Andor Kovacs, of El Bolsón, the premier Andean taxidermist of Argentina, that he had located two nest sites. Meanwhile, however, on October 3 I had returned to the United States and did not arrive back in El Bolsón until November 7.

By searching the canyons of the Río El Ternero, torrent-duck nest sites could be located in coihue trees *(Nothofagus dombeyi)* rising at varying angles from 3 to 22 feet from the shoreline of the raging torrents. The telltale sign of a suspected nest involved several pieces of down clinging to the bark outside the entrance hole of a cavity in the coihue. Handmade nylon-rope ladders were used to investigate the nesting cavities.

The sexual behavior and display of *Merganetta a. armata* have been accurately described by Johnsgard (1966) and Moffett (1970). It is very clear to me that the torrent duck's specialization, as far as perpetuating the species, is certainly unique. Its survival depends on those highly oxygenated, swiftly flowing rivers which produce stone-fly *(Rheophila)* nymphs, the bird's major food supply. Its highly refined feeding behavior involves upper and lower mandibles that are pliable and can take the tremendous pounding of the torrents and rocks. While feeding, the ducks submerge from 7 to 10 seconds, moving upstream and usually emerging behind a rock where there is a reverse eddy, obviously so as not to be swept downstream. To be able to maneuver under these conditions requires long, stiffened tails for stabilization and movement (see fig. 2, bottom).

Unpredictable weather in the high Andes places a tremendous burden on the reproduction cycle of the torrent duck. Heavy snow, rain, and flooding often disturb initial nesting efforts of the female. I can report that females have laid a completed clutch of eggs but, because of inclement weather, were unable actually to start incubation. The eggs are kept viable for a week and perhaps longer (until the weather clears) as the female visits the nest site (covered with heavy down, see fig. 3) and by hovering over the nest, for short periods of time, introduces enough calories into the eggs (pre-thermic incubation) to keep them zoetic.

Nest-site selection by the torrent duck along the rivers is limited to the coihue tree and (in two cases) mud banks. Territorial density by a pair usually exceeded 1 per square kilometer. During the period of this research 14 nests were located on the 4 rivers named, and of these nest sites 2 were reused during two consecutive nesting seasons.

Two nests were monitored on the Río Los Repollos with the Atkins electronic microclimatic units; power was supplied by batteries (24 volts DC) and a portable Honda generator (110 volts, 50 cycles). The temperature indicator and recording units as well as a portable thermistor psychometer with cable to the nests were the principal components of the equipment used. Five colored thermistor probes were inserted into the nest cavity, i.e., 1 probe was sealed into the air cell of a fertile egg by porcelain

FIG. 3.   Nest in hole in coihue tree, with eggs surrounded by down.

cement, 1 probe was placed immediately under the eggs, and 1 probe each in the upper and lower cavity of the nest; the psychometer, or dewpoint, probe was placed as near the eggs as possible, but not too close, as the probe produces heat that would affect the over-all air temperature.

Difficulty at nest site (B), that could only be attributed to a malfunction in the main cable to the nest, was immediately apparent and this attempt had to be abandoned.

Nest site (A) was operational on November 12, 1969, after a correction of a minor problem involving the automatic sequencing system of the temperature unit. This nest was in a dead coihue, which had the root system washed out so that what was left of the main trunk of the tree angled out over the river at 30°. The nest, located at the splintered top of the tree, had two entrances; the main entrance was 4 inches in diameter. The clutch consisted of 4 creamy-tan eggs lying in the bottom of the cavity and covered with heavy down. By candling the eggs it was determined that incubation had commenced. The monitoring period was uneventful except for vandalism of the main unit in which the temperature indicator dial was knocked out by a thrown rock. Fortunately, I was able to replace it with a temporary dial.

Data from the nest site (A) are still being evaluated. However, it can be confirmed that the highest incubation temperature of the probe egg was 97.5° F. Relative humidity in the nest cavity averaged 40-50 percent. The low temperature of the nest cannot be confirmed at this time, because the female had entered the nest dripping with moisture which fell on the probe egg and caused the temperature to drop drastically. Study of the recording paper can determine this temperature at a later date.

The average clutch size of the 14 nests was 3 eggs per nest, and the incubation period was determined to be 42-45 days. It is probable that a high mortality in 5-7-day-old ducklings occurs as they leave the nest, for they must jump out of the nest cavity into a raging torrent and can be swept downstream and lost. Upon hatching the ducklings have a week's food supply, as the egg-yolk absorption rate is 5 to 7 days.

On December 9, 1969, 16 viable eggs were collected from nests on the Ríos El Ternero, Quemquemtreu, and Repollos and transported in the same manner from El Bolsón, to Naples, and thence to the Bronx Zoo in New York City. Of these 3 ducklings hatched out enroute to New York.

Word from Joseph Bell, chairman and curator of the Department of Ornithology, New York Zoological Society, indicates that in July 1976 there were "three of these birds left in the collection. They are in fact two males and one female. The pair are kept together in one of our aviaries and have shown every indication that they might breed, going through all of the courtship displays that have been recorded for the species, but unfortunately eggs have never been laid. They are certainly old enough to breed and we have not given up hope that they might do so in the future."

REFERENCES

CONOVER, H. BOARDMAN
    1943. A study of the torrent ducks.   Field Mus. Nat. Hist., Zool. Ser., vol. 24,
        no. 31, pp. 345-356.
DELACOUR, JEAN THÉODORE
    1956. Torrent ducks.   Pp. 208-225 *in* "The Waterfowl of the World," vol. 2.
        Country Life, London.
JOHNSGARD, PAUL A.
    1966. The biology and relationships of the torrent duck.   Wildfowl Trust, 17th
        Annual Report, pp. 66-76.
KENDEIGH, S. CHARLES
    1963. New ways of measuring the incubation period of birds.   Auk, vol. 80,
        no. 4, pp. 453-461.
MOFFETT, GEORGE M., JR.
    1970. A study of nesting torrent ducks in the Andes.   Living Bird, vol. 9, pp.
        5-27.
PHILLIPS, JOHN CHARLES
    1926. Chilean torrent duck.   Pp. 211-224 *in* "A Natural History of the Ducks,"
        vol. 4. Houghton Mifflin Co., Boston.
WELLER, MILTON W.
    1968. Notes on some Argentine anatids.   Wilson Bull., vol. 80, no. 2, pp. 189-
        212.

MARVIN C. CECIL

Satellite Tracking of Elk, Jackson Hole, Wyoming

Principal Investigators: Frank C. Craighead, Jr., Atmospheric Sciences Research Center, State University of New York at Albany, and Environmental Research Institute, Moose, Wyoming; John J. Craighead, Montana Cooperative Wildlife Research Unit, Missoula, Montana; Charles E. Cote, Goddard Space Flight Center, Greenbelt, Maryland; and Helmut K. Buechner, Smithsonian Institution, Washington, D. C.[1]

Grant No. 803: For evaluation of a combined ground-satellite telemetry system for wildlife research and elk satellite-tracking feasibility experiment.

A free-roaming female elk was tracked and monitored by satellite in its natural environment for 29 days during April 1970. Information derived from the experiment served to demonstrate the feasibility of locating and tracking wild animals with simultaneous monitoring of physiological and environmental parameters.

This project was a joint endeavor between the Smithsonian Institution and the National Aeronautics and Space Administration, conducted in collaboration with the Montana Cooperative Wildlife Research Unit, the Environmental Research Institute, the State University of New York at Albany, and the National Geographic Society. Pretesting was conducted at the National Bison Range, Moiese, Montana, in cooperation with the U. S. Bureau of Sports Fisheries and Wildlife. The experiment was carried out at the National Elk Refuge, Jackson Hole, Wyoming, in cooperation with the U. S. Bureau of Sports Fisheries and Wildlife, the Wyoming Game and Fish Commission, the U. S. Forest Service, and the National Park Service.

The Interrogation Recording Location System (IRLS; see Cressy and Hogan, 1965, and Cote, 1969, 1970) is an experimental system aboard the Nimbus 3 and 4 meteorological satellites to test the feasibility of locating and collecting data from remote instrumented platforms deployed on the

---

[1] Dr. Buechner died on October 7, 1975.

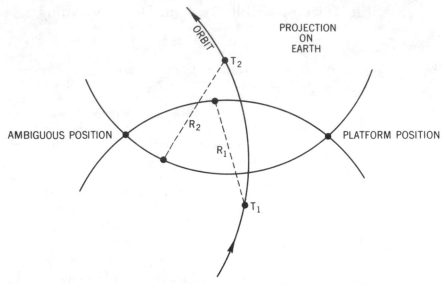

FIG. 1. Short-range distances (R) from the satellite to the platform generate spheres in space with the satellite at the center. Where two such spheres intersect the earth, intersecting circles are formed on the earth's surface. The animal is located at one of the two points of intersection of the circles, the ambiguity being resolved by prior information of the animal's last position.

surface of the earth. The IRLS system consists of the satellite, instrument platforms, and a central ground acquisition and command station (located in Fairbanks, Alaska). Each platform is equipped with a transmitter, receiver, and data encoder, which are activated upon receiving a discrete 16-bit address code from the satellite. In operation the addresses of electronic platforms and anticipated times of platform overpass are programmed into the satellite on an orbit-by-orbit basis from the command station. As time elapses into the orbit, interrogations of platforms are executed at the pre-programmed times. During each interrogation the short-range distance from the satellite to the platform is measured by the satellite; simultaneously, the platform transmits encoded sensor data to the satellite. The range information, time of ranging, and sensor data are stored in the satellite for readout at the end of the orbit (107 minutes later). A minimum of two interrogations is required per platform to determine its position. Through computer modeling, the locus of each range measurement forms a circular sphere in

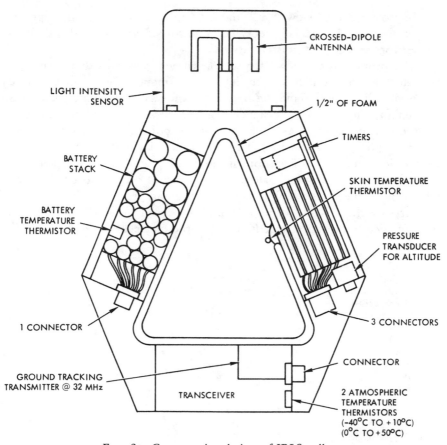

CROSSED-DIPOLE ANTENNA

LIGHT INTENSITY SENSOR

1/2" OF FOAM

TIMERS

BATTERY STACK

SKIN TEMPERATURE THERMISTOR

BATTERY TEMPERATURE THERMISTOR

PRESSURE TRANSDUCER FOR ALTITUDE

1 CONNECTOR

3 CONNECTORS

CONNECTOR

GROUND TRACKING TRANSMITTER @ 32 MHz

TRANSCEIVER

2 ATMOSPHERIC TEMPERATURE THERMISTORS ($-40°C$ TO $+10°C$) ($0°C$ TO $+50°C$)

FIG. 2.   Cross-sectional view of IRLS collar.

space with the satellite situated at its center. Each ranging sphere in turn intersects the surface of the earth (a third sphere) to project intersecting circles (fig. 1). The platform must necessarily be located at one of the two intersections; the ambiguity is resolved through prior knowledge of the platform's position. The accuracy of locations increases with increasing distance between the satellite's orbital plane (ground track) and the platform. Data from passes nearly overhead translate into large errors in location in the geometrical calculations for position. The Nimbus III satellite was launched into a polar sun-synchronous orbit with Equator crossings at local high noon and midnight, around the globe.

In cross-sectional view (fig. 2) the IRLS collar is triangular in shape for conformance to the animal's neck. The interior sides were lined with foam rubber for protection against abrasions.

The prime power source for the instrument was provided by nickel-cadmium batteries contained in the left compartment of the collar. To insure a minimum lifetime of 6 months operation, an electromechanical timer was utilized to eliminate battery standby power during the 12-hour intervals between orbital overpasses. Solar cells were mounted to the sides of the collar to provide continuous charging during daylight hours. The IRLS electronic equipment utilized for this application was initially designed for operation on high-altitude balloons; and only through the coordinated efforts of engineers and biologists in government, private institutions, and industry was the successful completion of the design possible. The detailed performance and physical specifications of the collar are listed below:

Transmitter (FM)		
Power	15	watts
Frequency	466.0 MHz	
Band width	100	KHz
Receiver (FM)		
Sensitivity	-114	DBM
Frequency	401.5 MHz	
Band width	100	KHz
Antenna	Crossed dipole; 2 DB gain; right circular	
Sensors	10 (1% accuracy)	
Batteries	Nickel cadmium (20)	
Solar panels	Cadmium sulphide (710 cm²)	
Weight (kg)		
Antenna	.477	
Antenna cover	.350	
Electronics	1.058	
Electronics housing + solar cell cover	1.149	
Batteries	2.097	
Battery housing + solar cell cover	1.149	
Transmitter/receiver	1.149	
RF housing	.649	
Collar materials	1.571	
Ground-tracking transmitter	.717	
Cable + connectors	.908	

Total   11.274

The Craighead-Varney ground-tracking 32-MHz transmitter (Craighead and Craighead, 1963, 1965a; Varney, 1971) was installed in the lower compartment of the collar. A separate set of batteries and the antenna for this system were located at the top of the collar. Installation of the collar on the elk was accomplished by separating the instrument into two parts. It took 10 minutes to make the electronic connections and fasten the two parts of the collar on the animal.

The design specifications of the IRLS system permit multiple sensory functions to be monitored by the platform (collar) for transmission and storage aboard the satellite. In normal operation, data are available to experimenters or users within 1 to 2 hours of the overpass. Data formats of various lengths are available to meet specific requirements. The standard format consists of 22 data words encoded to ± 1 percent accuracy (7 bits). Up to 30 such frames may be collected with each interrogation. The elk experiment required 10 channels to provide internal telemetry for the instrument and monitoring of external sensors. The data format selected for the experiment is as follows:

Date of Run		Mo.	Day	Yr.
		4	28	70
Orbit Number	5082			
Platform ID	105452	Elk		
Command Time	Hr.	Min.	Sec.	
	07	54	10.6	
Frame	1			

Channel and Data Received

2 Unused	1 Unused
4 Altimeter	3 Unused
6 +12 volt battery	5 Receiver signal
8 Battery temperature	7 Skin temperature
10 −40 to +10° C ambient	9 0 to +50° C ambient
12 Timer	11 +4.8-volt battery
14-28 Unused	13-27 Unused

Computed Platform Location and Time

Lat.	Long.	Day	Hr.	Min.	Sec.
43.492 N.	110.721 W.	118	07	54	11.0

One such frame of data was collected during each interrogation of the instrument collar. Interrogations were programmed on each overpass for up to five samples for each sensor at intervals of 1.5 minutes. Temperature readings were obtained through thermistors mounted in the appropriate locations. The light-intensity sensor consisted of a standard photodiode mounted at the base of the antenna. A pressure transducer consisting of a bellows, acting on a potentiometer, and a vacuum reference was installed to

FIG. 3.   Elk with IRLS collar.

measure altitude. The transducer bellows mechanism failed, and was in-
operative throughout the experiment. Readings of external skin temperature were obtained by a thermistor mounted on a tension arm attached on
the inside surface of the collar. The tension was calibrated to enable skin
contact under normal activity conditions. Battery voltages were monitored
directly, and the received signal strength was obtained at the output of the
first intermediate-frequency stage. The electromechanical timer settings
were translated into a linear voltage scale to enable orbit-by-orbit monitoring of the instrument's "on" window. Overlapping scales on two thermistors
(−40 to +10° C., 0 to +50° C.), located at the bottom of the collar to prevent
solar heating and to preclude thermal conductance from the battery power
source, provided a range in ambient temperature from −45 to + 50° C.

A unique feature of the elk collar, which provided a 6-month battery
lifetime, despite the high power requirement of the IRLS equipment (150

milliwatts continuous standby), was the low-power electromechanical timer-control unit. The timer served to eliminate standby power by completely unloading the battery during the 12-hour intervals between orbital over-passes. During each overpass a 10-minute "power-on" period was initiated precisely as the satellite came into radio view. Orbital overpasses vary in absolute time from day to day, and the timer provided perfect synchronization with each orbit. Conceptually, the timer represented an electro-mechanical model of the physical conditions of the Nimbus orbit. In operation, two separate timers were used: a 24-hour earth rotation clock and a 107.417-minute orbital period clock. Contact points on the respective timers were engaged at 12-hour intervals coincident with each satellite overpass. Since the best low-power timers available could not maintain needed accuracy for 6 months, a periodic adjustment was required to maintain synchronization. This was accomplished by using the interrogation link to transmit a special coded sequence of binary bits whenever adjustment was required. The timer setting was monitored at each interrogation.

A mockup fiberglass collar (11.3 kilograms) to accommodate the IRLS electronic equipment was developed during the summer and fall 1969. The model was tested for 90 days on a semitame female elk in a large corral at the National Bison Range, Moiese, Montana. The elk experienced no apparent discomfort, nor did the collar interfere with her daily activities. When lowering and raising the head during feeding the collar slid slowly back and forth on the elk's neck. No skin abrasions or excessive removal of hair resulted from the rubbing.

Meanwhile, the IRLS transponder and Craighead-Varney transmitter were packaged into a metal collar (11.3 kilograms) of the same configuration. Following the favorable results with the mockup collar, the IRLS instrument collar was placed on the same elk on January 20, 1970. Ten minutes after the elk recovered from the immobilizing drug (M-99, etorphine) the instrument package was successfully interrogated by the Nimbus III satellite. Over the next 12 days, interrogations were obtained on 16 orbits.

Having tested the system on an elk under controlled conditions, preparations were made for testing it on a free-roaming elk at the National Elk Refuge, Jackson, Wyoming. On February 5 two wild female elk were immobilized and fitted with mockup collars to condition them to accept the electronic collar. They were members of a herd of about 10,000 elk that are fed on the Refuge during the winter.

On the morning of April 1, 1970, one of the two females wearing mockup collars was instrumented with the IRLS collar (fig. 3). A veterinarian was on hand to ascertain the health of this elk. Her body temperature was

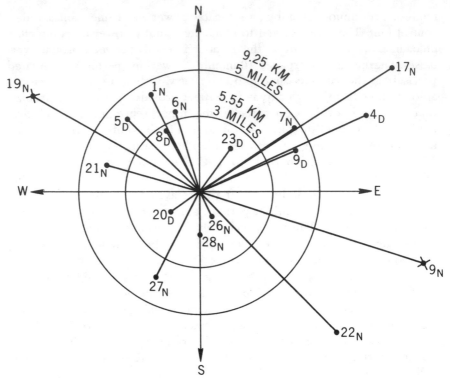

FIG. 4. Resolution of positions determined by satellite. Numbers indicate day of month; subscripts indicate daytime (D) and nighttime (N). Origin represents zero error in distance; compass directions indicate direction of error from position observed on the ground.

normal (38.5° C.) and she appeared to be in good condition. The drug was administered by a projectile syringe fired from a gun. During the 27 minutes the elk remained immobile, engineers connected the electronic components of the 2-piece collar. Immediately thereafter the elk received 12 milligrams of an etorphine antagonist (M-285, diprenorphine). Within 3 minutes she arose, looked around briefly at the observers, and then lowered her head to nibble hay, after which she slowly ran off to join the herd about 200 meters away. She immediately encountered another female. Both stood on their hind legs and struck with their forelegs, a behavior pattern which seems to establish dominance-subdominance relationships between individuals within the herd. The animal's behavior indicated a return to normal almost immediately after recovering from the drug.

On April 8 Nimbus IV was launched in an orbit slightly lower than Nimbus III, and for 5 days the two satellites were orbiting together, one below the other. Under these conditions the window of the IRLS collar on the elk opened when Nimbus IV was overhead, and this instrument was the first to be interrogated by the new satellite. Good interrogations were obtained on three orbits prior to returning to Nimbus III for further monitoring of the instrumented elk.

During the period of operation, 20 locations were obtained by satellite. On 5 orbits only one frame of data was received, precluding a location computation.

Ground sightings of the elk and radio fixes by field observers within the Refuge were used to determine the accuracy of the satellite locations. Since observations were made during daytime only, the resolution of nighttime interrogations could not be ascertained. Also, the fact that daytime observations could not coincide exactly in time with satellite overpasses imparts some degree of uncertainty to the references. Through interpolation of observed positions and radio fixes a set of reference points was derived (Craighead et al., 1972).

The distance and direction of the satellite position with respect to the corresponding reference position (shown as origin) are plotted in figure 4. The points on the plot indicated by x's denote locations obtained on near overhead passes, where large errors were expected; three additional points obtained under these conditions yielded errors beyond the scale of the plot. Excluding the latter three points, the mean errors were: latitude 4.8 and longitude 6.2 kilometers. The location distributions shown in the figure fall into the following categories: < 5 kilometers, 5 points; 5 to 9 kilometers, 7 points; > 9 kilometers, 5 points; and 3 points off scale.

The accuracy of locations can be improved by using low profile, omnidirectional, circularly polarized antennas. The particular antenna utilized for the elk experiment afforded coverage above 45° with respect to the horizontal. The most accurate locations are made when the satellite is between 10° and 50° above horizontal. This fact was evident in the large east-west errors (longitude), which are typically less than the north-south errors (latitude). The requirement for small-aperture antennas having moderate gain, circular polarization and lightweight characteristics present many problems to antenna designers. Progress is being made, and will continue as animal tracking grows in importance.

Five internal and five external sensory points were to be monitored with each interrogation, the format of each frame being that shown on page 77. From April 1 to 29, 86 measurements were obtained from each sensor,

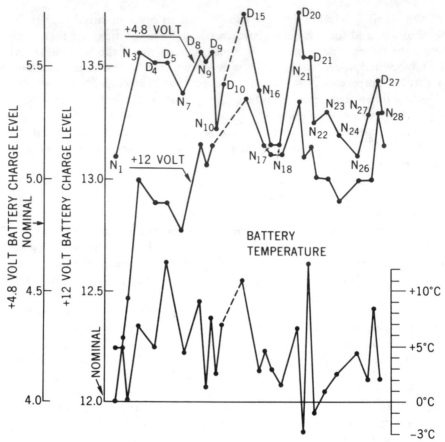

FIG. 5.   Battery voltages and temperature monitored by satellite. Letters indicate
daytime (D) and nighttime (N); subscripts indicate day in April. Dotted line shows
5-day interruption at launching of Nimbus IV.

except the altimeter. The day and night distribution was 33 and 53, respectively. Clearly, the night passes yielded more data; this was attributed to
improved antenna orientation and stability while the animal was at rest.

Trends observed in various sensors during April are plotted in figures
5 and 6. The values plotted were selected from one representative data
frame from each sequence of interrogations.

The steady increase in voltage levels during the first 3 days of the experiment showed that the solar panels functioned well in charging the bat-

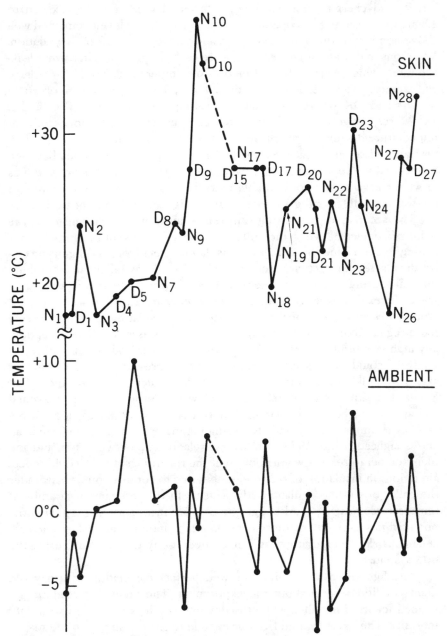

FIG. 6.   Ambient and skin temperatures monitored by satellite. Letters, subscripts, and dotted line same as figure 5.

teries. Had charging not occurred, sufficient battery capacity existed to enable the instrument to operate for 6 months. Charge levels remained well above nominal throughout the period, and showed no signs of degradation. Variations in day and night readings were caused by changes in battery leakage rates, which were a direct function of temperature. Trends in voltage and temperature were almost identical. The highest voltages were obtained on D_{15} and D_{20} where temperature readings were high ($\pm$ 11° C. and $\pm$ 12° C., respectively). The battery temperature remained above ambient temperature during interrogations (as a result of heating effects of the battery under load and heat from the animal's body), but the trends between battery and ambient temperatures were identical (figs. 5, 6). Previous studies in winter have shown considerable increase in battery temperature due to the warming effect of the animal's body (Craighead and Craighead, 1965b).

The accuracy of measuring skin temperature with a thermistor at the point of contact between the collar and the animal's skin requires further testing to determine the changes in insulating effect from sliding of the collar during feeding activity. Individual skin readings taken at 1.5-minute intervals during interrogation sequences suggest that the animal was at rest when the readings were constant and active when the readings were variable. Apparently movement of the collar altered its insulating effect, producing more regular temperature readings when the elk was at rest. The exceptionally high skin temperature (37.5° C.), which was near body temperature, on April 10 could have resulted from continued pressure of the thermistor against the elk's neck as the animal lay with its neck resting on the collar. Similarly, a skin temperature of 35.9° C. was recorded from an awakened and alert black bear in its winter den as it lay on a thermistor located between the animal's body and the insulating material of its bed (Craighead and Craighead, 1966, 1974). An inverse relationship between skin and ambient temperatures, shown in about half the recordings (fig. 6), could reflect alterations in insulation of the integument due to compaction of hair under the collar or thermoregulatory adjustments in the integument at ambient temperatures near 0° C. Although the data are inconclusive, they show the potentialities for studying thermoregulation by monitoring surface and subcutaneous skin temperature, as well as deep body temperature, using the IRLS system.

The light-intensity readings showed perfect correlation with day and night conditions throughout the experiment. The nighttime readings remained identical in value, while the daytime readings fluctuated with light intensity. The values varied from bright sun to shaded sun, with the majority in the brighter area. No readings were obtained under forest canopy, but results indicate the feasibility of determining whether an animal is in open or timbered situations.

Except for the longer movements, the locations obtained with the IRLS system were too inaccurate for determining the local minimum movements of the elk within the refuge. For long-range migrations satellite locations of the elk's position could have yielded useful new information.

Contact between the elk and the satellite was lost on May 1 when the collar inverted. Communication was impossible with the antenna pointing groundward. Until June 10 the elk was located by the ground-tracking system. When the elk moved far or rapidly it was relocated by air, using a Cessna 150 with a small loop antenna attached to the wing strut. Under favorable conditions the signal was received in the airplane from a distance of up to 40 kilometers at altitudes above ground level of 300 to 1,000 meters, the strength of the signals improving with altitude. On May 15, when the elk had moved to the northern portion of the refuge, she was approached, by using the directional receiver, and was observed to feed and run well with a band of 15 elk. The instrumented elk appeared in better physical condition than most of the other elk. Two days later she left the refuge, moved north along the east side of Blacktail Butte, and arrived on the following day in the area of Signal Mountain, 28 airline kilometers from her last position on the refuge. After remaining here and in the area of Uhl Hill and lower Spread Creek for 5 days the elk began moving up Spread Creek on May 25, traveling southward into the Gros Ventre drainage to Slate Creek. There she joined a group of about 300 elk that annually calve in the area. When observed closely on June 8 she appeared to be in good physical condition. Most of the winter coat remained, and no abrasions or sores that might have been caused by the collar were observed. The elk was last located by ground-tracking radio on June 10. The next contact was on July 28 in Cottonwood Creek about 20 kilometers east of Slate Creek. On November 14 the instrumented elk was inadvertently shot 8 kilometers from Cottonwood Creek by a hunter when the elk's head and shoulders were hidden in trees. This was immediately prior to her expected safe return to the National Elk Refuge. An autopsy of the animal showed that she was in good physical condition and pregnant; her kidney fat index was 175 (Riney, 1955) and the femur marrow was white and did not compress (Greer, 1968); the left ovary contained a corpus luteum 13 millimeters in diameter; the embryo was in the thread stage with membranes approximately 18 inches long.

The circuitous route taken by the elk to reach its summer range, covering about 65 kilometers, rather than traveling directly up the Gros Ventre

River Valley for a distance of about 20 kilometers, was unanticipated. The route taken also involved crossing a high divide that was still snowbound. These observations indicate that the detailed movements involved in an elk migration can be studied with a combination of ground and satellite-tracking equipment. Such information is valuable in the management of elk populations.

Summary

Free-living animals can be tracked and monitored by satellite in natural environments, as indicated by the present feasibility study with the IRLS system. Satellite interrogations of an instrument collar on an elk at the National Elk Refuge were made over a period of 30 days, with a mean error of 4.8 kilometers for latitude and 6.2 kilometers for longitude. Improvement of the resolution of locations to within 1 kilometer requires the development of low profile, omnidirectional, circularly polarized antennas.

Sensory data from the instrument showed the solar cells functioning so effectively that the number of batteries could have been reduced substantially to conserve weight. The data on skin temperature require verification by future experiments. They do, however, demonstrate the potential for monitoring physiological and environmental parameters with the 28 channels of the IRLS system.

The prototype instrument collar has weight limitations. Information derived from the experiment provided a basis for calculating a potential reduction in weight by at least 50 percent. A 5-kilogram instrument collar will make the IRLS system available for a wider variety of animals. Microminiaturization could reduce the weight of the IRLS package still further. However, IRLS is a highly regimented 2-way system, and weight reduction has a limit. Weight limitations lie between 5 to 10 percent of the animal's body weight. There is, therefore, a need to develop satellite systems with instrument packages useful for birds and other small animals. The dopplershift system has been proposed (Balmino et al., 1968; Buechner and Maxwell, 1968) to bring the weight of the instrument on the animal to 50 grams or less (Varney and Pope, 1974; Craighead, 1976; Craighead and Dunstan, 1977).

Satellite tracking and data-collection systems provide powerful new tools for studying biological phenomena, such as animal migration, and for obtaining information useful in the management of ecosystems and wildlife and fisheries resources. Additional cooperative research projects among biologists and engineers could advance this new technology to a widely applicable and economical system over the next decade.

Acknowledgments

We thank biologists Harry V. Reynolds, 3d, and Vincent Yanonne and graduate student Steven M. Gilbert of Montana State University for assistance, especially in making field observations.

The idea of tracking animals by satellite, proposed several years ago, has been encouraged by Sidney R. Galler, former Assistant Secretary (Science), Smithsonian Institution, and also by George J. Jacobs, Chief, Physical Biology, National Aeronautics and Space Administration, both of whom we thank for their help and inspiration. Joel R. Varney, Research Associate, Montana Cooperative Wildlife Research Unit, University of Montana, played an important role in testing and applying the electronics systems throughout the study. James C. Maxwell, Staff Engineer, Ecology Program, Office of Environmental Sciences, Smithsonian Institution, also aided in the pretesting of the IRLS collar. Radiation, Inc., of Melbourne, Florida, conformed the IRLS instrument in the collar for the elk. Previous research under NSF (G-17502) and AEC AT(45-1)-1929 made possible the use of the ground radiotracking system. This study was supported by a grant (NASW-1983) to the Smithsonian Institution by the National Aeronautics and Space Administration and by National Geographic Society grant no. 803 (made in 1969).

REFERENCES

BALMINO, G.; CRISWELL, S. J.; FERNALD, E. H.; JENTSCH, E. H.; LATIMER, J.; and MAXWELL, J. C.
    1968. Animal tracking from satellites. Smithsonian Astrophysical Observatory, Spec. Rpt. 289, 40 pp.
BUECHNER, HELMUT K., and MAXWELL, J. C.
    1968. Proposal for an experiment to track animals from artificial satellites. Smithsonian Astrophysical Observatory, Publ. 140-9-68.
COTE, C. E.
    1969. The interrogation, recording and location system experiment. Goddard Space Flight Center, Publ. X-733-69-336, 22 pp.
    1970. The interrogation, recording and location system experiment. Geoscience Elec. Symp., Trans. IEEE, Spec. Issue, 5 pp.
CRAIGHEAD, FRANK C., JR.
    1976. Development of an ultra-high-frequency radiolocator system for studying birds, 17 pp. (unpublished). Progress Report to National Geographic Society Committee for Research and Exploration.

CRAIGHEAD, FRANK C., JR., and CRAIGHEAD, JOHN J.
1963. Progress in biotelemetry studies of grizzly bears. Proc. 18th Ann. Instrum. Soc. Amer. Conf., Biotelemetry Session, Chicago.
1965a. Tracking grizzly bears. BioScience, vol. 15, no. 2, pp. 88-92.
1965b. Yellowstone field research expedition V. State Univ. of New York at Albany, Publ. 31, ASRC, 8 pp.
1966. Radiotelemetry of large western mammals. Prog. Rpt. 1965-66, AEC Contract No. AT (45-1)-1929, 67 pp.
1974. Radiotelemetry research on large western mammals in Yellowstone National Park, Wyoming, 1967. Nat. Geogr. Soc. Res. Rpts., 1967 Projects, pp. 35-51, illus.
CRAIGHEAD, F. C., JR.; CRAIGHEAD, J. J.; COTE, C. E.; and BUECHNER, H. K.
1972. Satellite and ground radiotracking of elk. Pp. 99-117 *in* "Animal Orientation and Navigation," NASA Scientific and Technical Office, Washington.
CRAIGHEAD, F. C., JR., and DUNSTAN, THOMAS C.
1977. Progress toward tracking migrating raptors by satellite. Raptor Research (in press).
CRESSEY, J. R., and HOGAN, G. D.
1965. The interrogation, recording and location system experiment. Proc. Nat. Telemetering Conf. Sec. 6, 6 pp.
GREER, K. R.
1968. A compression method indicates fat content of elk (wapiti) femur marrows. Journ. Wildl. Man., vol. 32, no. 4, pp. 747-751.
RINEY, T.
1955. Evaluating condition of free-ranging red deer *(Cervus elaphus)*, with special references to New Zealand. Journ. Sci. Techn., Sec. B, vol. 36, no. 4, pp. 429-464.
VARNEY, JOEL R.
1971. A tracking and telemetry system for wildlife research. IEEE National Telemetry Conference Record 71 C 10-NTC, pp. 247-252.
VARNEY, JOEL R., and POPE, ROGER L.
1974. Final report, Nimbus-F/RAMS DCP transmitter micro-miniaturization feasibility study. Philco-Ford Corporation, Western Development Laboratories Division, Palo Alto, Calif.

FRANK C. CRAIGHEAD, JR.
JOHN J. CRAIGHEAD
CHARLES E. COTE
HELMUT K. BUECHNER

Ecological Studies in Southwest Florida

Principal Investigator: Frank C. Craighead, Sr., Estero, Florida.

Grant Nos. 802, 823 [1]:   For continuing study of the ecology of the Everglades.

This report discusses changes occurring in several of south Florida environments, particularly southwest Florida, as a result of man's impact. It emphasizes practical aspects that may be helpful in attempting restoration in some areas and avoiding future serious damage in others. These studies were made possible largely through the support of the National Geographic Society.

The Original Ecosystem

The original pattern of the south Florida landscape (fig. 1), as it existed before modification by man, was a well-balanced interdependent series of ecosystems formed on a nearly level terrain by ample rainfall (55 to 60 inches annually), by a slowly rising sea, and to some extent by hurricanes. Low coastal ridges on the east, sand dunes on the west, and a mangrove forest abutting the sea completely around the tip shaped the pattern of inland wetlands spotted with slightly higher elevations, often deposits of eolian sand. Over 5,000 years ago, the sea was some 12 feet (4 meters) lower than its present elevation, and the coastal shoreline much farther seaward, approximately at Man O War Key in Florida Bay and even farther west on the continental shelf of the west coast. Gradually, the rising sea pushed the mangrove belt inland. At the same time there formed on its inner, or landward, edge a slight embankment. This feature, named Buttonwood Embankment, impounded an inland freshwater marsh completely around the tip of Florida. This levee-like structure follows inland along the banks of the numerous estuaries that transverse the mangrove zone and the small creeks of the freshwater marshes. The sources of the estuaries lie in the numerous fingerlike creeks in the freshwater zone, its origin being in most

---

[1] Grant no. 823 provided illustrations for the author's book *The Trees of South Florida.*

FIG. 1. Outline map of south Florida, showing major features of the area.

cases a gator hole. The mouth of each estuary was partially blocked by sand bars or oyster bars, leaving only a narrow, tortuous channel. These bars effectively slowed down tidal intrusion and controlled rapid runoff of the ample rainfall (Craighead, 1964).

These geomorphic forces that were responsible for shaping the major features of the landscape are still active and cannot be ignored by man. Already the original landscape has been much battered or even destroyed by drainage, fires, and bulldozers at the expense of very desirable features. These forces must be respected if man is to invade South Florida success-fully and retain those amenities that have made life so worthwhile in this remarkable country.

Saline Mangrove Belt

The saline mangrove belt as an ecosystem has been defined (Craighead, 1971) as that portion of the mangrove forests between the coast and the Buttonwood Embankment along its landward edge. Its great mass of tough erosion-resistant peat serves as a most effective plug that formerly held an extensive freshwater marsh completely around the tip of the peninsula.

Much has been written about the value of the mangroves as a source of nutrients and a nursery ground for aquatic life, largely based on a study on red mangrove by Heald (1971). This was later amply verified by Carter et al. (1973) as well as for other coastal environments. Prior to this, however, studies of the brackish and freshwater coastal marshes and swamps of Georgia and the Carolinas showed these wetlands to be highly productive, better than many farmlands (Odum, 1961).

Although much of the mangrove belt has already been dredged and filled outside of the Everglades National Park (ENP), stricter regulations are gradually being enforced and much that remains, it is hoped, may be saved.

Buttonwood Embankment

The Buttonwood Embankment extends intermittently entirely around the tip of south Florida from Dade County to Lee County. However, in a number of places it has been destroyed in the past 50 to 100 years by fires or by the slowly rising sea. In many places on the earlier U. S. Coast and Geodetic Survey maps it is shown by a dotted line but not named, except that on some sheets a symbol indicating hammock vegetation is used.

FIG. 2.   Remains of a cypress stand in the Fakahatchee Stand some 25 years after
logging, drainage, and repeated fires.

Although not truly hammock vegetation, many tropical hardwood trees, particularly buttonwood, are found here in great abundance.

In places, as in the ENP, the Buttonwood Embankment (elevation 1.5 to 2.0 feet above mean sea level) lies 6 miles inland on the north shore of West Lake, where it is several hundred yards wide. It is well defined on the north shore of several lakes and bays to the east, namely, West Lake, Cuthbert, Seven Palm Lake, Madeira Bay, Joe Bay, and Long Sound (see fig. 1).

In Dade County, south of Black Point, the mangrove forest on the shore of Biscayne Bay formed a very narrow belt and the embankment was only 100 yards inland along much of this coast prior to hurricane Donna in September 1960.

On the inland shore of Whitewater Bay (see fig. 1) there is no distinct embankment except for that of the banks of the numerous freshwater tributaries This area, at one time continuous mangrove forest, is now broken into numerous islands by the rising sea. Several islands have been broken up and disappeared in hurricanes of the past 20 years, leaving only a submerged plug of peat.

In the Lostmans River system the string of lakes and bays extending westward (Lostmans, Onion Key, Alligator, Chevalier, Houston, Oyster, and Sunday Bay) to the Turner River, show a well-developed levee on their landward banks. From here, behind the Ten Thousand Islands, which have been gradually submerging for the past 3,000 years, the embankment lying on the landward bank of the lakes and bays is poorly defined.

In the Naples area it formed at the base of the Coastal Sand Dunes, and here the freshwater marsh is only a narrow strip, at places only a hundred yards wide. In Lee County it forms along the east shore of Estero Bay, where the Freshwater Marsh is fairly wide, just landward.

This embankment behind the saline mangrove swamps was undoubtedly a major physiographic feature in separating the saline and freshwater ecosystems. It was a relatively porous structure, soaked with fresh water and was shallowly transversed by numerous small creeks, ending in small bays. Soil cores at the mouths of these bays often revealed patches of charcoal. Recently, with drainage and drought of the dry season, much of the freshwater marshes was dry, and salt water has flooded the zone, pushed inward by high west to northwest winds. These surges of salt water have materially altered the fauna and flora and, in March 1963, filled with salt water one USGS observation well (P38) in the ENP.

Collier County Marshes

In Monroe and Collier Counties, landward to the Ten Thousand Islands, the freshwater marshes behind the Embankment are still distinct, but not functioning as before. The interior drainage has greatly reduced the fresh water that was normally impounded and has concentrated the overflow in several canals, such as the Barron and Fakha Union, where it is greatly altering the character of the mangrove zone (Carter, 1973). Highway US 41 has formed an embankment bisecting this freshwater marsh. That area seaward to the road will be dominated by red mangrove. If baffles 1.5-2.0 feet in elevation were placed at all the culverts along this section of US 41, the characteristics of the freshwater marshes could be maintained inland to the highway, thus preventing the frequent fires and possibly saving the several patches of virgin cypress there, remnants that escaped the 1945 logging of the great Fakahatchee Cypress Stand. One of these islands of cypress, some 300 acres, was bought by Lester Norris of Naples and in 1971 approved as a National Historic Landmark by the U. S. Department of the Interior. The quality of these trees, many 5 feet in diameter breast high and 100 feet tall, is far superior to that of those remaining in the Cork-screw Swamp to the north (see fig. 2).

In places in Lee and Collier Counties, north of Estero Bay, these fresh-water marshes have been completely altered by dense stands of *Melaleuca* and Australian pine *(Casuarina)*. The native marsh plants are completely suppressed. Low-density housing here might be an improvement over the present worthless environment, as inland drainage will prevent future water-ing of these marshes.

Some Recent Natural Changes

Several examples of the power of these natural forces are evident in southwest Florida, though very scantily investigated at the present time. Along the coastal ridge, especially in Collier County and from North Naples to Fort Myers, at 12 to 15 feet above mean sea level, John Beriault has called attention to the numerous sites of the Caloosa Indians buried under 18 to 24 inches of very fine white sand. These sites were exposed as the Hercules Power Co. salvaged the pine stumps, the remains of logging operations of 50 years ago. From the well-preserved pitch-infiltrated stumps are found special chemicals not found in the fresh pitch collected from living trees. These Indian sites are possibly 1,500 to 2,000 years of age. The ridge must have increased by this elevation entirely from the windblown sand. It would be of great interest to investigate this phenomenon more thoroughly. Could some of the shrubby plants with stems and roots now extending into the soil beneath these Indian sites have adjusted to the gradual rise of the eolian sand and lived throughout the intervening period? This fine eolian sand has proved a very serious annoyance where the land has been bulldozed of every vestige of vegetation prior to the construction of buildings. It is blown like dust by the winter winds and sifts through every crack. On some sites it causes a daily clean-up problem. One redeeming feature is that it serves as an excellent lubricant in moving heavy furniture on terrazzo floors; but it is useless on floors with wall-to-wall carpeting.

A good example of the changing plant flora, in response to a varying water table, is found in the cypress heads and sloughs of southwest Florida. Normally, cypress grows in depressions that hold water for a considerable portion of the year. Slash pine normally grows on higher sites where the water of the summer rainy season remains for only a short period. Many cypress sites show several stages of pine invasion, which are probably good evidence of periods of low rainfall, or of recent drainage.

FIG. 3.   Beach setback in the Cape Sable area of Everglades National Park caused by hurricane Donna in 1960.

Buried Forest

Much of the area east of Naples shows evidence of a buried forest about 2 feet below the present surface. This was first observed in 1972 along US 41 as some excavating was in progress 2 miles east of Four-Corners, Naples. A little later, road repair on US 41 at Big Cypress Bend, some 20 miles east, turned up quantities of buried wood. On both sites, stumps were observed broken off 12 to 18 inches above the root system; others were uprooted. Material from both sites was secured; but has not yet been dated. It is extremely rare to find any buried wood in coastal areas of south Florida. Could these extensive deposits of some 2 feet of shell and sand have been caused by a hurricane of far greater intensity than that of Donna in 1960, which deposited only 4 or 5 inches of sediment where the storm was intense?

Salt Intrusion

Several examples of the price to be paid for ignoring natural processes governing fresh- and saltwater exchange can be cited. The best-known case was the salting of the coastal well fields in Miami, brought on by excessive drainage of the Biscayne aquifer through the coastal drainage canals.

Where the sand bars or oyster bars at the mouths of the estuaries have been destroyed, as in the case of the Gordon River in Collier County, vast quantities of saltwater have pushed far inland. Here, unrestricted tidal movement, plus excessive drainage of the interior wetlands, permitted saltwater to intrude some 5 miles inland in the past few years of exceptionally dry weather. In the ENP a large body of freshwater, known as Lake Ingraham, has been turned into a saltwater flat by the East and Middle Cape Canals constructed prior to 1920. These two narrow and shallow outlets have been gouged out to bedrock and the original cuts through the beach have been greatly widened by the daily tides. Each tide carries massive loads of silt into Florida Bay.

A similar case in the ENP was set up when Coot Bay, an area of freshwater, was connected with Florida Bay, at Flamingo, by the Buttonwood Canal. Saltwater has completely changed the flora and fauna of Coot Bay, and erosion in the canal has widened this waterway to twice its original width along much of its length. In addition, the silt carried into Florida Bay keeps filling the ship channel into Flamingo. This is in process of being corrected.

Beaches

The vanishing beaches of south Florida have become a matter of much concern. Many types of groins, pumping sand back on the beach, and various other means of stopping this erosion have been tested with little success. This erosion appears to be more pronounced in the areas of tall buildings, but it is happening at many places around the tip of Florida, where in the past 100 years the shores have not been encumbered by as much as a squatter's shack. Consequently, setback lines for beach structures have been suggested by several workers (fig. 3). That such structures may be an important factor seems to be supported by the action of Hurricane Donna on the keys of Florida Bay. On several islands where a wall of large mangroves forms the shoreline, the action of the storm waves against these trees dug out a wide moat, removing all the marl and shell to bedrock (Craighead, 1971). A practical treatment for construction setback has been proposed by Tabb et al. (1973).

This wind-wave action against structures on the beach no doubt stirs up the sand and shell mixture and moves it into the coastal longshore drift

FIG. 4.   A Collier County beach, showing emerging mangrove stumps and peat
bed as the sea rises and pushes beach inland.

southward. Similar wind-snow drift patterns are commonly seen after northern blizzards.

An excellent picture of beach recession can be seen along the Gulf shores of Collier County from Barefoot Beach to Keewaydin Island. It is most readily observed where Vanderbilt Beach Road dead-ends at the Gulf. Here, at low tide, numerous mangrove stumps are visible, their roots fixed in several feet of peat. These peat beds and stumps (see fig. 4) are the remains of a living mangrove forest that once grew just behind the beach ridge, which at that time was some 200 feet seaward. The peat is continuous beneath the present beach.

This constant regression of the beaches has been going on regardless of man's structures. Mangrove peat, indicating the former existence of mangrove forests several thousand years ago, has been found over a mile offshore on the west coast. The most reasonable explanation is that a rising sea, about 2.5 inches per 100 years, resulting from the melting of the Arctic and Antarctic glaciers, is slowly driving the beach landward. This was supported by Scholl, Craighead, and Stuiver (1969).

All present evidence suggests that undisturbed beaches, where grasses and trees form a cushion, absorb the sea rise without greatly disturbing conditions, except for their gradual landward replication. It seems ill-advised to spend money on beach structures and developments until the present trend of a rising sea can be shown to have slowed down or reversed.

A serious pest tree over most of south Florida, the Australian pine, has been found to be an excellent stabilizer of new deposits in beach formation. Most native trees are killed by the filling of sand and shell over their root systems. On several beaches where this recent introduction has become established in the past 40 years the tree survives by putting out a new root system just under the surface. Consequently, these very recent beaches are 1-2 feet higher than older formations just to the rear (fig. 5).

G.A.C. Development

The G.A.C. lands, involving some 400 square miles east of Naples and adjacent to the Fakahatchee Stand, were approved for development in 1964, and subsequently were dissected by several large canals draining into the Fakha Union River at Remunda Ranch. In addition, most of the area was subdivided by roads half a mile apart. The groundwater level dropped some 6 to 7 feet, drying out the surface to such an extent that for several years, 1971 to 1975, forest fires devastated nearly three-fourths of the area. The fires were intensified to such an extent that usual control efforts were futile. This area is rapidly becoming worthless for the purposes planned. Most of those amenities man loves to associate with his homesite will be lost.

As one becomes familiar with this area he wonders what flight of imagination prompts its development. Over 40,000 lots have been sold in this maze of wilderness roads, and one cannot help but speculate what it will look like 25-50 years hence. The remains of these roads and canals will probably be pointed out as an example of man's greed and folly, just as are the concrete entrance arches of the 1920 land boom that grace the extensive cattle ranges in the Arcadia region of Florida.

The true values of south Florida's environments are totally obscured by the artificial value of land speculation. We forget that much of these lands are no more suitable for development than are steep mountain slopes or the floodplains of our rivers.

In November 1974, with the assistance of Thomas McDaniels and Richard Woodruff of the Collier County Planning Department, I submitted a report to the Water Management Advisory Board. The following suggestions were made:

First, the canals must be blocked to raise the groundwater levels to that of the cypress sloughs and ponds.

Prescribed burning must be substituted for present fire-control techniques. The small percentage of unburned blocks that so far has escaped should be burned when moist after the first rains, to clear the surface litter and thus prevent wildfires for a year or two.

A forest resource study should be made. There may be large values here in pulpwood and other products that could be used to offset the cost of protection and pay taxes.

This study precipitated an extensive investigation of the area by Collier County authorities. It is hoped that transfers of ownership can be arranged on lands that are under water for nearly half the year to higher lands elsewhere in the county.

Burning

Light burning, controlled burning, or prescribed burning are terms that gradually evolved into a more sophisticated terminology as the value of this practice as a silvicultural tool in forest management became widely accepted across the United States. It originated in California where the private timberland owners, around 1910, developed a practice called "light burning" in the ponderosa pine stands. At that time, the entomologists of the U. S. Department of Agriculture, Division of Forest Insect Investigation, at their Palo Alto Laboratory were surveying the state, federal, and private pine stands to determine the extent of losses caused by the pine bark beetles of the genus *Dendroctonus*. It soon became evident that bark-beetle losses were much lower on these burned-over lands. Subsequently it was found that the same situation existed in the pine forests of the Atlantic Coastal Plain, where the expanding pulpwood and paper interests had adopted this practice.

It was not until some 20 years later, however, that research in cooperation with the U.S.D.A. Asheville, North Carolina, Forest Experiment Station, found a reasonable explanation. A constant association of wood fungi, called bluestains *(Ceratostomella),* and bark beetles was obvious in the dying trees (Craighead, 1928). This suggested that the aid of forest pathologists was needed. Their studies supported the theory that it was actually these bluestains that quickly permeated the sapwood, thus shutting off the movement of water through the stem to the leaves. This happened within 10-14 days after beetle attack. Also, it was shown that these fungi could develop only when the moisture content of the sapwood was below normal, a condi-

FIG. 5.   An Australian pine washed out by a recent storm, showing a second root system after the original was covered by some 18 inches of shell and sand.

tion that developed during drought periods. The repeated fires killed the competing hardwoods, providing more moisture for the pines and thus making them unsuitable to the bark beetles that introduced the fungi that killed the trees.

An interesting sidelight on these findings developed at the U. S. Forest Products Laboratory, Madison, Wisconsin. It was found that each species of bark beetle had its own species of bluestain, as described by Miss Rumbold (1932).

An unexpected example of the operation of this symbiotic relationship occurred here in the Naples Pine Ridge Area during the winter of 1973-74, when many pine trees died that were 100 to 150 years of age. These were cull trees from logging of 50 years ago. At the same time, sinkholes that were reported "never dry" had no water in them. A 2-inch core, sampled from the peat deposits in the bottom of one hole, showed the water table to be approximately 2 feet below mean sea level about a mile inland from the beach. It also suggests that no similar drought has occurred during the life of these 150-year-old trees.

REFERENCES

CARTER, MICHAEL R.; BURNS, L. A.; CAVINDER, T. R.; DUGGER, K. R.; FORE, P. L.; HICKS, D. B.; REVELLS, H. L., and SCHMIDT, T. W.
   1973. Ecosystem analysis of the Big Cypress Swamp and estuaries, 387 pp. U. S. Environmental Agency, Region IV, Atlanta, Georgia.
CRAIGHEAD, FRANK C., Sr.
   1928. Interrelation of tree killing bark beetles *(Dendroctonus)* and blue stains. Journ. Forestry, vol. 26, no. 7, p. 2.
   1964. Land, mangroves and hurricanes.   Bull. Fairchild Trop. Gard., vol. 19, no. 4, pp. 5-32, illus.
   1971. The trees of south Florida, vol. 1, 212 pp.   University of Miami Press.
   1973. The effects of natural forces on the development and maintenance of the Everglades, Florida.   Nat. Geogr. Soc. Res. Rpts., 1966 Projects, pp. 49-67, illus.
   1975. Vanishing beaches: Rushing tides or rising sea.   Naples Star, Feb. 28, 1975.
HEALD, E. J.
   1971. The production of organic detritus in a south Florida estuary.   Univ. Miami Sea Grant Techn. Bull., no. 6, 110 pp.
ODUM, EUGENE P.
   1961. The role of tidal marshes in estuarine production.   The Conservationist, vol. 15, no. 6 (June-July), pp. 12-15.
ODUM, EUGENE P., and DE LA CRUZ, ARMANDO A.
   1967. Particulate organic detritus in Georgia salt marsh estuarine ecosystem. Pp. 383-388 *in* "Estuaries," Amer. Assoc. Adv. Sci. Publ. 83, George H. Lauff, ed. Washington, D. C.
RUMBOLD, CAROLINE T.
   1932. Two blue-staining fungi associated with bark-beetle infections of pines. Journ. Agr. Res., vol. 43, pp. 847-873.
SCHOLL, DAVID W.; CRAIGHEAD, FRANK C., Sr.; and STUIVER, MUNZE
   1969. Florida submergence curve revised: Its relation to coastal sedimentation rates.   Science, vol. 163, no. 3867, pp. 562-564, charts.
TABB, DURBIN C.; HEALD, ERIC J.; and REHRER, R. G.
   1973. Innovations in coastal management.   Proceedings of the Gulf and Caribbean Fisheries Institute, 25th annual session, pp. 175-180.

FRANK C. CRAIGHEAD, Sr.

Biotelemetry Capability for Biological Research

Principal Investigators: John J. Craighead, Montana Cooperative Wildlife Research Unit, University of Montana, Missoula, Montana; Frank C. Craighead, Jr., Environmental Research Institute, Moose, Wyoming; Joel R. Varney and Jay S. Sumner, Montana Cooperative Wildlife Research Unit, Missoula, Montana.

Grant Nos. 805, 1023: To develop a biotelemetry capability for biological research.

The purpose of this project was to continue development of equipment and methods for field monitoring of hibernating bears. Since we were unable to locate a hibernating black bear suitable for field studies, we obtained a male black-bear cub (approximate age 8 months) from the Montana Fish and Game Department in October 1971 and began experiments with a captive animal. On November 11 the animal was placed in a concrete-block building containing 6-by-8-foot cells with steel mesh doors and no windows. Ambient light was reduced to a low level to simulate the interior of a den covered with snow. Enough light entered around the door edges to enable the animal to distinguish between night and day, as would be the case in a natural den. A 3-by-3-by-4-foot wooden box provided an enclosure. Loose straw was put in the cell for bed material. The bear constructed a bed by dragging straw into the box. Food and water were placed in the den until December 15 when the bear had become noticeably lethargic and fed irregularly. Detailed records were kept of the bear's activity and of the den temperature, the bear's body temperature, local barometric pressure, disturbances, and other factors that might influence hibernation behavior.

We immobilized the bear for a temperature-transmitter implant operation by firing a syringe dart containing 45 milligrams of Sernalyn (phencylidine hydrochloride, 100 ml/cc) into the shoulder muscles. An additional 15 milligrams was administered after the initial dose took effect, and the bear was taken to a local veterinary clinic for the operation.

The bear was placed in a slightly head-down position on the operating table to keep excess saliva from blocking air passages, and a 1/8-grain dose of atropine was given to reduce salivation. A patch of hair on the belly was shaved off with an electric clipper, and the area was washed and disinfected. A 10-centimeter incision was then made through the skin and fat layers along the midline from just below the umbilicus to 3 centimeters anterior to the penis. This location was selected because it is relatively free of large blood vessels and should present fewer problems than other areas would if field surgery were attempted.

A small incision was made through the peritoneum into the abdominal cavity, then lengthened with a pair of scissors. The transmitter, which had been sterilized overnight in Zephiran chloride (1:1000), was placed in the abdominal cavity and attached to the peritoneum in four places with nylon sutures. The abdominal cavity was closed with chromic catgut sutures, Furacin powder was sprinkled into the incision, and the skin was sewed together with heavy nylon sutures. A 2-centimeter injection of penicillin-streptomycin was given at the conclusion of the operation. The entire procedure took about 45 minutes.

The bear was immobilized 12 days later (December 27) for examination of the incision and removal of the external stitches. Healing was proceeding normally. A slight inflammation was present in the caudal area of the incision, and so a 2-centimeter injection of Combiotic was given and the area washed with 1 centimeter of Combiotic. Hair regrowth on the belly was slower than expected. The incision was checked again on January 18 and had completely healed.

We removed the transmitter from the animal on April 5 following the same procedure. Examination of the area around the transmitter showed that it had been encapsulated in a thin layer of scar tissue. We found no adverse tissue reaction or inflammation, and it appeared that the implant had been accepted well.

It became apparent during the process of implanting the temperature transmitter in the abdominal cavity that such an operation would be a very ambitious undertaking under adverse field conditions in midwinter. We concluded that it would be preferable to conduct any necessary implant surgery early in the fall when it would be possible to capture and hold the animal for a few days for observation and recovery. This would reduce the risk to the animal and increase our confidence in the data obtained during winter sleep by allowing a longer period between the operation and the beginning of hibernation. Before release, the bear could be fitted with a radio collar and radio-tracked until it entered a den for winter. With the temperature transmitter already implanted there would be no need to do surgery in the field and disruptions of winter sleep would be held to a minimum.

If field surgery is necessary in the future, it would be more practical to implant telemetering devices subcutaneously without attempting to enter the body cavity. Previous research has demonstrated that such surgery is relatively minor and has little effect on the animal even if done in mid-winter. Temperatures obtained from a subcutaneous implant differ somewhat from true deep-body temperature, but these differences can be minimized by selection of the proper implant location (near good blood supply and under a thick coat of fur or layer of fat). It should be possible also to obtain good EKG potentials from a subcutaneous implant by running leads under the skin for short distances from the transmitter.

The temperature sensitive transmitter implanted in the captive bear was a simple 1 MHz blocking oscillator with its pulse rate determined by two thermistors in the collector-base path. A Hg-625R mercury cell provided an estimated lifetime of several years at 37° C. Transmitter components were imbedded in epoxy for mechanical support and protection. The transmitter assembly was then waterproofed with a mixture of beeswax and paraffin. An outer covering of Dow-Corning Type A Medical Silastic was used to prevent tissue reaction when implanted in the bear's body. The completed unit was 4.5 by 2 by 1 centimeter in size and weighed 12.8 grams. It was calibrated in a constant temperature water bath and its thermal time constant was measured by subjecting it to an abrupt temperature change of 10° C. The transmitter was recalibrated in the water bath after removal from the bear. We found no measurable shift in the temperature calibration.

With the bear instrumented and in winter sleep, the signal from the temperature transmitter in its abdominal cavity was picked up by a circular loop antenna (14 turns of No. 24 wire, 20 inches in diameter) placed on the floor of the artificial den directly under the bear's bed. The antenna was connected to a standard broadcast band receiver in an adjoining room by a 30-foot cable. Pulses from the transmitter detected by the receiver were converted to direct current by a pulse rate converter and recorded on a Rustrak model 288 chart recorder at 1 inch per hour chart speed.

Temperature data from the implanted transmitter were recorded continuously for a little over 3 months. As a check on the automatic recording system, manual counts of the transmitter pulse rate were made with a stopwatch during the daily equipment checks. Some gaps occurred in the data during times when the bear was out of his bed or oriented unfavorably to the receiving antenna; they occurred more frequently at the beginning and end of the hibernation period and provided an index of the animal's activity.

Cyclic day-night temperature changes were not pronounced, although they did occur for a few short periods. Such changes were on the order of

0.5 to 1° C. At other times they did not occur at all or, if present, were obscured by larger trends or changes due to other factors.

The largest and most significant changes in body temperature occurred in response to unavoidable disturbances connected with the experiment and were related to the duration and intensity of the disturbance. On three occasions that the bear was immobilized his body temperature rose to 37° C., declining about 2° C. afterward over a period of 3 or 4 days before stabilizing again. During the immobilization on December 27, temperature rose 2° C. in a period of 2 hours.

When the disturbance was less severe (for example, when we entered the den for a minute or two to change charts in the temperature recorder or to repair a disconnected lead) the temperature rise was typically 0.5° C.; it did not behave in a predictable way afterward, sometimes rising and sometimes falling in a period of a few days.

Data gathered during the period between January 24 and February 10 were particularly interesting. A severe storm moved into the Missoula area, with subzero temperatures and high winds. As a result, the temperature in the den began dropping on January 25. The bear's body temperature followed this downward trend until January 27, reaching a low of 31.8° C. This is near the lowest temperatures we are aware of in the literature. Then, although den temperature continued to drop, body temperature rose abruptly to 33° C. This cycle was repeated between January 30 and February 1. We suspect that a spontaneous arousal mechanism was operating, with 32° C. being the lower limit that the bear could safely tolerate; a metabolism increase occurred when this danger point was reached. In general, long-term body-temperature trends followed ambient-temperature variations.

The data obtained on barometric pressure and relative humidity could not be conclusively correlated with changes in body temperatures, but we are inclined to think that variations in barometric pressure had little effect on the body temperature or activity of the bear. No correlation between body temperature and pressure was evident. There was a gradual increase in pressure between February 21 and March 20, which was paralleled by a rise in body temperature, but this was probably due to the den temperature increase during the same period rather than pressure changes.

On three occasions we took a series of rectal-temperature measurements while the bear was immobilized for comparison with the telemetered abdominal-temperature data. The intent was to evaluate the accuracy of rectal-temperature measurements and obtain data for correlation with rectal-temperature data obtained in previous years on other studies. Rectal temperatures were taken with a glass mercury thermometer inserted approximately 9 centimeters into the rectum. The thermometer was allowed to stabilize for 2 minutes after insertion before readings were taken. Abdominal readings were obtained by placing a portable radio next to the bear and counting the transmitter pulse rate with a stopwatch. Rectal-temperature readings ranged from 1.3° C. below to 0.3° C. above the abdominal readings, with the rectal readings being generally lower. Though not sufficient data to make generalizations, the data do indicate the spread to be expected between the two readings. We plan to collect further data in future experiments.

The bear was weighed whenever possible during the experiment to determine the rate of weight loss during hibernation. He weighed 75 pounds when placed in the den in November to acclimatize while feeding was continued. His weight increased to 93.5 pounds at the time of the implant operations on December 15. Food and water were not offered after this time, and the bear became dormant. His weight gradually declined during the winter to 68 pounds when the temperature transmitter was removed on April 5, a weight loss of 25.5 pounds or 27.3 percent of his body weight. During the 112-day period from December 15 to April 6, the average weight loss was 0.228 pound per day. Feeding was resumed on April 7, and the bear's weight had returned to 90.5 pounds by April 19. In 12 days the bear regained weight at an average rate of 1.88 pounds per day. This study and others indicate that bears in winter sleep require no food intake because they metabolize body fat. The daily energy requirements are low, and thus the daily weight losses are also low. This weight loss is largely adipose tissue and the lean body weight remains constant. Since adipose tissue provides approximately 3,500 calories per pound, this supplies the sleeping bear with a more concentrated source of calories than the animal would obtain from its normal diet. Once a captive bear becomes active, it rapidly regains lost body weight if a plentiful supply of food is available. An interesting problem is how the bear manages to accomplish this on a low-calorie diet of roots, tubers, greens, and animal protein. This is especially intriguing when one considers that the digestive tract of the bear is that of a carnivore. Apparently, modifications have evolved that have altered both the digestive and assimilation processes normally encountered in carnivores. Our records show, however, that under wild conditions individual animals encountering poor foraging conditions may require 2 to 3 months to regain body weight, and that weight loss may continue well into the summer.

The bear gradually became less lethargic during March and began leaving the bed for short periods during the latter part of the month to explore the den. On March 19 he located the antenna cable and pulled it loose. Examination showed that it would be necessary to immobilize the bear to repair the damage. Since he was nearly out of hibernation, we decided to terminate the experiment instead. The temperature transmitter was removed from the bear on April 5.

The bear was immobilized again on April 19 to remove the stitches from the abdominal incision. The temperature telemetry transmitter that had been removed earlier was inserted rectally, and a continuous temperature recording was made for 2 hours to observe the effect of the immobilizing drug on temperature regulation. The indicated temperature remained nearly constant at 38.5° C.

The bear was held until June 15, when he was fitted with a radio-location collar and released.

A load-cell weighing system was evaluated for future use in more detailed studies of weight loss and metabolism. It consists of a reinforced plywood platform supported on three load cells, which produce an output voltage proportional to the weight on them. They are connected to read-out equipment that can be located at any desired distance. The system provides both a meter read-out and a continuous chart record of the total weight on the platform. The platform is very solid mechanically compared to a conventional spring or balance system with downward deflection for a 100-pound load being only 0.003 inch. The system is accurate to within 1/2 percent of the full scale load of 100 pounds, or 0.5 pound. Larger loads can be accommodated by using less sensitive load cells.

In future experiments with wild bears in natural dens, a means of measuring shifts of position and movements of the animal within the den will be of value. A certain amount of information about such movements can be obtained with the temperature-monitoring system used in this experiment. The range of the transmitter is limited to about 1 meter, and so no data were obtained when the bear was not lying directly over the loop antenna in his bed. An examination of the temperature record for signal dropouts gave a general indication of the activity or inactivity of the bear. This was not foolproof, however, since signal loss also occurred when the transmitter was aligned orthogonally to the receiving antenna. Some gaps in data occurred as the animal shifted to an unfavorable position while remaining in the bed.

A second activity-monitoring method we evaluated during this experiment was the use of a pressure sensitive mat that caused a switch closure when stepped on by the bear. The mat was placed by the water pan, which was put in the den on March 18 in an attempt to determine when and how often the bear would drink. The results were unsatisfactory, as the bear chewed up the mat and destroyed it almost immediately.

Work was started on a coupled-loop inductive-proximity measuring system, but this was not tested because we decided it would be better to minimize disturbance to the bear. Development will continue on this approach for future den monitoring experiments.

REFERENCES

CRAIGHEAD, FRANK C., JR., and CRAIGHEAD, JOHN J.
  1971a. Study of grizzly bears and other big game species by radiotelemetry. Final report. NSF Research Grant GB-6089 (mimeo).
  1971b. Grizzly bear prehibernation and denning activities as determined by radiotracking. Wildlife Monograph no. 32, 35 pp.
CRAIGHEAD, FRANK C., JR.; CRAIGHEAD, JOHN J.; COTE, C. E.; and BUECHNER, HELMUT K.
  1970. Feasibility of tracking free-roaming animals in natural environments (abstract). Amer. Zool., vol. 10, no. 4, p. 407.
  1971. Satellite tracking of elk. Pp. 99-111 *in* "Animal Orientation and Navigation," NASA SP-262.
CRAIGHEAD, JOHN J., and CRAIGHEAD, FRANK C., JR.
  1971a. Radiotracking and telemetering system for large western mammals. Final report, AEC-RLO-1929-15, 289 pp.
  1971b. Home ranges and activity patterns of nomigratory elk of the Madison Drainage herd as determined by biotelemetry. Wildlife Monograph no. 33, 50 pp.
CRAIGHEAD, JOHN J.; CRAIGHEAD, FRANK C., JR.; and VARNEY, JOEL R.
  1971. Development of satellite-related biotelemetry equipment. Progress Report, NASA Research Grant NGR 27-002-006. 37 pp.
CRAIGHEAD, JOHN J.; CRAIGHEAD, FRANK C., JR.; VARNEY, JOEL R.; and COTE, C. E.
  1971. Satellite monitoring of black bear. BioScience, vol. 21, no. 24, pp. 1206-1211.
REAM, R.; BEALL, B.; and MARCUM, L.
  1971. Sapphire Range elk ecology study — elk, logging, and people: First annual report. School of Forestry, University of Montana, 28 pp.
VARNEY, JOEL R.
  1971. A tracking and telemetry system for wildlife research. National Telemetering Conference Record (Institute of Electrical and Electronic Engineers publ. no. 71 C 10 NTC), pp. 247-252.

JOHN J. CRAIGHEAD
FRANK C. CRAIGHEAD, JR.
JOEL R. VARNEY
JAY S. SUMNER

Potentialities of Satellite Telemetering
of Large Mammals

Principal Investigators: John J. Craighead, Joel R. Varney, and Jay S. Sumner, Montana Cooperative Wildlife Research Unit, University of Montana, Missoula, Montana.

Grant No. 804: To investigate potentialities of satellite telemetering of large mammals and applications of satellite multispectral imagery for mapping wildlife habitat.

Improved classification and mapping of grizzly-bear habitats will permit better estimates of population density and distribution and allow accurate evaluation of the potential effects of changes in land use, hunting regulations, and management policies on existing populations.

A brief investigation was made to determine the extent to which ERTS-1 imagery would be useful in studying vegetative and seasonal factors that influence food availability and bear distribution and behavior. Color composite scenes of a central Montana study area were examined on a color-additive viewer. Portions of 1:1,000,000 positive transparencies of MSS scenes taken in August and October 1972 were used. Altitude overlays were superimposed on the scenes to permit more accurate classification of timber types. A time-lapse method of identifying recent snowfalls was also evaluated.

The results of this brief investigation show that ERTS-1 multispectral scanner imagery can be of considerable value in habitat analysis. Useful information about several aspects of the grizzly's environment can be obtained with minimal cost and effort from a few hours spent examining the imagery. Since we have not had prior photointerpretation experience, we may have overlooked information (of which other investigators are already aware) that could be obtained from the imagery. We plan to continue evaluating this technique in ongoing programs where habitat data are needed.

Areas that consisted of a favorable mixture of alpine meadow and timber stands were easily identified. The distribution of one important food species, white-bark pine *(Pinus albicaulis),* was determined with fair accuracy with the aid of the altitude overlay. Snowfield boundaries could be determined, along with their monthly changes. The information obtained from satellite imagery was sufficient to identify areas potentially suitable as grizzly habitat for closer examination by ground survey.

We feel that satellite imagery is most valuable at present as a supplement to, not a replacement for, field observations by personnel on the ground. Limitations in image resolution and in the kinds of information that can be obtained from multispectral scanning allow much room for error if used alone. The imagery can be used, however, to perform a great deal of initial screening and to select those areas where field effort can be most productively concentrated. In surveying wilderness areas to locate suitable habitat for reintroduction of grizzlies, for example, large portions could, with high confidence, be eliminated from consideration on the basis of the imagery alone. Field work can then be focused on the remaining locations that appear to meet minimum requirements. Examination of satellite imagery at the beginning of a study should thus allow an effective sampling strategy to be developed that will minimize the field effort and over-all program cost.

Using the techniques described, we could rapidly survey the three largest ecosystems in the Western United States (Yellowstone, Selway-Bitterroot, and Bob Marshall) to determine the location and extent of favorable grizzly habitat, to assist in making more accurate estimates of the present grizzly population in these areas, and to locate the most promising sites for reintroduction of grizzly bears. Such information is badly needed and could be obtained with comparatively modest funding. If interpreted in context with the extensive data on grizzly food habits, movements, ranges, and general bear ecology that we have already gathered in Yellowstone National Park, such a survey could provide a scientific basis for habitat management and delineation of initial habitat. It could also provide several western states with a basis for evaluating their hunting regulations and harvest and provide both state and federal agencies with better data than are now available to consider when making management and land-use decisions.

Satellite remote-sensing methods are a valuable addition to the tools of the wildlife researcher and manager in their present state of development. The usefulness of the data from ERTS-1 will probably expand in the near future, as a large number of researchers are presently developing various analysis methods to increase the types and quality of data that can be obtained from the images. This effort should result in additional techniques that would be useful in habitat analysis. For future programs, NASA is planning to develop improved multispectral scanners with 60-foot resolution capability and other radiometric and high-resolution radar imaging devices. Remote sensing will become increasingly valuable in wildlife research and management as this improved equipment becomes available on future satellites.

Computer-assisted analysis of ERTS-1 multispectral imagery and intensive ground truth sampling promise great future potential for more refined and precise vegetation mapping of wildlife habitats. We plan to direct our research efforts along these lines.

REFERENCES

CRAIGHEAD, FRANK C., JR.
  1976. Grizzly bear ranges and movement as determined by radiotracking. Proc. 3rd Int. Conf. on Bear Research and Management. pp. 97-109.
CRAIGHEAD, FRANK C., JR., and CRAIGHEAD, JOHN J.
  1965. Tracking grizzly bears. BioScience, vol. 15, no. 2, pp. 88-92.
  1966. Trailing Yellowstone's grizzlies by radio. Nat. Geogr. Mag., vol. 130, no. 2, pp. 252-267, illus.
  1969. Radiotracking of grizzly bears in Yellowstone National Park, Wyoming, 1964. Nat. Geogr. Soc. Res. Rpts., 1964 Projects, pp. 35-43.
  1970. Radiotracking of grizzly bears in Yellowstone National Park, Wyoming, 1962. Nat. Geogr. Soc. Res. Rpts., 1961-1962 Projects, pp. 63-71, illus.
  1971. Grizzly bear-man relationships in Yellowstone National Park. BioScience, vol. 21, no. 16, pp. 845-857.
  1972a. Radiotracking of grizzly bears in Yellowstone National Park, Wyoming, 1959-1960. Nat. Geogr. Soc. Res. Rpts., 1955-1960 Projects, pp. 55-62, illus.
  1972b. Tuning in on the grizzly. 1973 World Book Science Annual/Science Year, pp. 34-49, illus.
  1972c. Grizzly bear prehibernation and denning activities as determined by radiotracking. Wildl. Monogr. no. 32, 35 pp.
  1973a. Radiotracking of grizzly bears and elk in Yellowstone National Park, Wyoming, 1966. Nat. Geogr. Soc. Res. Rpts., 1966 Projects, pp. 33-48, illus.
  1973b. Studying wildlife by satellite. Nat. Geogr. Mag., vol. 143, no. 1, pp. 120-123, illus.
  1974. Radiotelemetry research on large western mammals in Yellowstone National Park, Wyoming, 1967. Nat. Geogr. Soc. Res. Rpts., 1967 Projects, pp. 35-51, illus.
CRAIGHEAD, FRANK C., JR.; CRAIGHEAD, JOHN J.; and DAVIES, RICHARD S.
  1962. Radiotracking of grizzly bears. Interdisciplinary Conference on the Use of Telemetry Behavior and Physiology in Relation to Ecological Problems. American Museum of Natural History.
CRAIGHEAD, JOHN J.
  1976. Studying grizzly habitat by satellite. Nat. Geogr. Mag., vol. 150, no. 1, pp. 148-158, illus.
CRAIGHEAD, JOHN J., and CRAIGHEAD, FRANK C., JR.
  1960. Knocking out grizzly bears for their own good. Nat. Geogr. Mag., vol. 118, no. 2, pp. 276-289, illus.

CRAIGHEAD, JOHN J.; CRAIGHEAD, FRANK C., JR.; and McCUTCHEN, HENRY E.
   1970. Age determination of grizzly bears from fourth premolar tooth sections.
      Journ. Wildl. Managm., vol. 34, no. 2, pp. 353-363.
CRAIGHEAD, JOHN J.; CRAIGHEAD, FRANK C., JR.; and SUMNER, JAY S.
   1976. Reproductive cycles and rates in the grizzly bear, Ursus arctos horri-
      bilis, of the Yellowstone ecosystem. Proc. 3rd Int. Conf. on Bear
      Research and Management. pp. 337-356.
CRAIGHEAD, JOHN J.; CRAIGHEAD, FRANK C., JR.; VARNEY, JOEL R.; and CORE,
   CHARLES E.
   1971. Satellite monitoring of black bear. BioScience, vol. 21, no. 24, pp.
      1206-1213.
CRAIGHEAD, JOHN J.; HORNOCKER, MAURICE; and CRAIGHEAD, FRANK C., JR.
   1969. Reproductive biology of young female grizzly bears. Journ. Reprod.
      Fert. Suppl., vol. 6, pp. 447-475.
CRAIGHEAD, JOHN J.; HORNOCKER, MAURICE; WOODGERD, W.; and CRAIGHEAD,
   FRANK C., JR.
   ———. Trapping, immobilizing and color-marking grizzly bears. Trans. 25th
      North Amer. Wildl. Conf., pp. 347-363.
CRAIGHEAD, JOHN J.; VARNEY, JOEL R.; and CRAIGHEAD, FRANK C., JR.
   1974. A population analysis of the Yellowstone grizzly bears. Montana Forest
      and Cons. Exp. Stat. Bull. 40, 20 pp. School of Forestry, University of
      Montana, Missoula, Montana.
CRAIGHEAD, JOHN J.; VARNEY, JOEL R.; and SUMNER, JAY S.
   1976. Mapping grizzly bear habitat using LANDSAT multispectral imagery
      and computer assisted technology. Rpt., 129 pp.
CRAIGHEAD, JOHN J.; VARNEY, JOEL R.; CRAIGHEAD, FRANK C., JR.; and SUMNER,
   JAY S.
   1976. Telemetry experiments with a hibernating black bear. Proc. 3rd Int.
      Conf. on Bear Research and Management. pp. 357-371.
JENNESS, ROBERT; ERICKSON, ALBERT W.; and CRAIGHEAD, JOHN J.
   1972. Some comparative aspects of milk from four species of bears. Journ.
      Mamm., vol. 53, no. 1, pp. 34-47.
SUMNER, JAY S., and CRAIGHEAD, JOHN J.
   1973. Grizzly bear habitat survey in the Scapegoat Wilderness, Montana. Res.
      Rpt., 49 pp.
VARNEY, JOEL R.; CRAIGHEAD, JOHN J.; and SUMNER, JAY S.
   1974. An evaluation of the use of ERTS-1 satellite imagery for grizzly bear
      habitat analysis. Proc. Symp. 3d Earth Res. Techn. Satellite, vol. 1,
      pp. 1653-1670.

JOHN J. CRAIGHEAD
JOEL R. VARNEY
JAY S. SUMNER

The Development of an Archeomagnetic Chronology for the New World

Principal Investigator: Robert L. DuBois, University of Oklahoma, Norman, Oklahoma.

Grant Nos. 786, 856:   For a study of the application of archeomagnetic chronology to archeological sites of the New World.

Over the past 9 years more than 350 archeomagnetic samples have been collected from archeological sites in the Southwestern United States. An important aspect of this work there has been the establishment and testing of an archeomagnetic chronology that can be used in the dating of burned archeological features, in most cases, with a precision of ±10 to ±30 years at the 95-percent confidence level. With the feasibility of archeomagnetic dating established by the work in the Southwest, it was natural to attempt to apply this method to other areas in the Western Hemisphere.

For those unfamiliar with the archeomagnetic dating method, a short explanation is presented in Weaver's 1967 article in the *National Geographic*. It has been discussed in more detail by Aitken (1961) and is the subject of an article by DuBois (1974).

In contrast to parts of the Southwest, where tree-ring dating has provided a firm chronology, archeologists working elsewhere in the New World have continually sought solutions to chronological problems. Since the advent of radiocarbon dating, a broad framework of absolute chronology has been established throughout the hemisphere. However, there are still many situations where either this method is not applicable or suitable materials are not available. In addition, a greater degree of precision is needed if some problems are to be investigated.

One important problem in Mesoamerican archeology that archeomagnetic dating could help solve concerns the correlation of the Mayan and Christian calendars. After a short period during which radiocarbon evidence seemed to support a correlation proposed by Spinden, new carbon dates now support the Goodman-Martinez-Thompson correlation, which places events about 260 years later than the Spinden correlation. There is, however, still some archeological evidence from Yucatán that seems to support the Spinden correlation.

To investigate the availability of suitable material for archeomagnetic dating, I visited Mesoamerica and Peru during the summer of 1964, supported by a grant from the University of Arizona and, later, through the University of Oklahoma. I collected samples in Mesoamerica and examined burned areas at archeological sites in both Mesoamerica and Peru. Visits with archeologists in the field and continuing correspondence indicated that additional suitable areas with useful materials were present. Laboratory analysis of the samples collected confirmed preliminary impressions that the samples were satisfactory for dating purposes.

On the basis of this preliminary work the National Geographic Society approved an application for support of the first year's work on "The Development of an Archeomagnetic Chronology for the New World." Emphasis during the early years of this project was on Mesoamerica, but material was collected also in parts of South America where ongoing excavations present a unique opportunity to obtain samples to advance the over-all program.

Archeomagnetic samples were collected in Mesoamerica and Peru throughout the summer of 1969. Additional samples were collected on a trip to Peru during December 1969 and January 1970. The initial processing of all this material in the laboratory collected under the Society's support was completed by March 1970.

By the end of the first year's work on this project, 49 archeomagnetic samples from Mesoamerica and Peru had been collected and measured in the laboratory. We were particularly fortunate in getting material from some of the most important sites in these areas. In all, 33 samples were collected from 11 different sites in Mesoamerica, and 16 came from 7 sites in Peru. The site and approximate temporal distribution of the samples are presented in tables 1 and 2. The approximate age of the samples is based on the archeologists' preliminary evaluation of the associated cultural material. Although these chronological placements in some cases may not be too precise, with this preliminary data it was possible to place special emphasis in subsequent seasons on collecting samples to complete the temporal sequence.

Although a fairly good temporal distribution of samples was obtained in Mesoamerica during the 1969 season, the majority of the samples collected in Peru came from the site of Chan Chan, which was occupied for a period of approximately 200 years. As work on the National Geographic Society–Harvard University–Moche Valley Chan Chan project continues, sites representing all the archeological period in the Moche Valley will be excavated. This will provide a unique opportunity to collect a sequence of

TABLE 1.—SITE AND APPROXIMATE TEMPORAL DISTRIBUTION OF MESOAMERICAN ARCHEOMAGNETIC SAMPLES

	1200	600	BC	AD	600	1200	Early Colonial	Un-Known	Total
Central Mexico									
Teotihuacán				2					2
Tula						1			1
Cholula						2	2		4
UA-1							3		3
Oaxaca									
Monte Alban					1				1
Lambityeco					1	5			6
Tierras Largas	2	2	2					2	8
Brawbehl			2						2
Chiapas									
Mirador				1					1
Guatemala									
Kaminaljuyu					1			3	4
Tikal								1	1
TOTAL	2	2	4	3	3	8	5	6	33

TABLE 2.—SITE AND APPROXIMATE TEMPORAL DISTRIBUTION OF
PERUVIAN ARCHEOMAGNETIC SAMPLES

	1200	600	BC AD	600	1200	Unknown	Total
North Coast							
Chan Chan					9		9
La Cumbre				1			1
Cerro Sechin	1						1
North Highlands							
Chavin		2					2
Central Coast							
Mina Perdida		1					1
Pachacamac					1		1
Cajamarquilla				1			1
TOTAL	1	3		2	10		16

archeomagnetic samples for a 3,000-year period from a very restricted area.

The sample from Tula was particularly important among those collected in Mesoamerica. It came from a piece of fired wall in the Palacio Quemado, which burned when the site was abandoned. Differing interpretations of Aztec legends recorded shortly after the Spanish Conquest place this event between A.D. 1064 and 1168. The archeomagnetic dating method will provide an independent test for this dating problem.

During 1970 additional archeomagnetic samples were collected and measured from the New World. In Southwestern United States, 28 samples were collected from Arizona, New Mexico, and southwest Colorado. The age of these samples ranged from A.D. 1300 to 1900 and from A.D. 600 to 650. These samples provided data to develop further the accuracy and temporal range of the master archeomagnetic curve for this area.

Archeomagnetic samples collected from Mesoamerica and Peru in 1970 totaled 47, of which 25 were from Mesoamerica. A large portion of these samples were from Kaminaljuyu, Guatemala, supplying further data to develop Mesoamerican curves from approximately A.D. 300-900. In Peru, 23 samples were collected from various sites, with an emphasis on Chan Chan and Cerro de la Virgen. The temporal range of these sites is about A.D. 1000 to 1500. Four samples were taken from Tiahuanaco, Bolivia, and range from about 400 B.C. to A.D. 700.

Data were collected from various sites in the Midcontinent to begin acquiring a basis for development of archeomagnetic curves for these areas. A total of 10 samples was taken from areas including Iowa, Oklahoma, Missouri, and Texas.

Although more data were needed to confirm preliminary observations, on the basis of all the samples processed by the end of 1970, it appeared that the master archeomagnetic curve developed for the Southwest of the United States might have some application in Mesoamerica. Because of the limited data, it was impossible to make a statement about the curves.

At the time of this writing (October 1976) several additional seasons have been spent in the field in Mesoamerica and Peru. The results of this work have advanced the development of archeomagnetic polar curves for these two areas.

REFERENCES

AITKEN, MARTIN J.
   1961. Physics and archaeology, 181 pp., illus.   Interscience Publishers, New
       York.
DUBOIS, ROBERT L.
   1974. Secular variation in Southwestern United States as suggested by archeo-
       magnetic studies.   Proceedings of the Takesi Nagata Conference, Uni-
       versity of Pittsburgh, pp. 133-144.
WEAVER, KENNETH F.
   1967. Magnetic clues help date the past.   Nat. Geogr. Mag., vol. 131, no. 5,
       pp. 696-701, illus.

ROBERT L. DUBOIS

Mid-Atlantic and Rift Valley Expedition

Principal Investigator: Harold E. Edgerton, Massachusetts Institute of Technology, Cambridge, Massachusetts.

Grant No. 765: To conduct oceanographic studies aboard the Russian research ship *Akademik Kurchatov* in the mid-Atlantic Rift Valley.

This grant enabled me and my assistants to join the 7,000-ton Russian oceanographic research vessel *Akademik Kurchatov* during a cruise to study the mid-Atlantic Rift Valley. Our participation was at the invitation and under the leadership of the chief scientist of the expedition, Dr. Gleb Udintsev, of the P. P. Shirshov Institute of Oceanology, Academy of Sciences, Moscow. Our main objectives were (1) to take bottom photographs, (2) to make precision instrument-to-bottom measurements by means of pinger sound sources on the camera or heat-flow instruments, and (3) to use a 5KHz sonar pulse to study the bottom and subbottom structure—in the Rift Valley and transition zones.

We sailed from Southampton, England, on July 22, 1969, and left the ship in Boston, Massachusetts, on September 10, after stops at the Canary Islands and Dakar, Africa.

About 170 persons were aboard the vessel, about half of whom were scientists and their assistants; the rest were the ship's crew. In addition to myself there were three Americans aboard—James Sholer, a student of mine in a stroboscopic-light seminar at M.I.T., who was also studying the Russian language; Michael Hobart, another M.I.T. student, who operated the heatflow equipment used on the sediment corer; and Stephen Eittreim, a graduate student at the Lamont-Doherty Laboratory of Columbia University, who joined us at Dakar and who assisted in measuring the scattering of light in the sea. The only other non-Russian aboard was Melville Sarginson of Durham University, England, who was interested in sediments.

Equipment Used

An underwater camera (EG&G model 205) with an underwater light

121

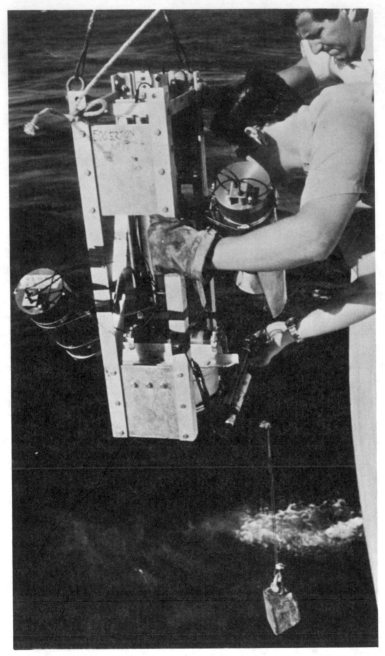

FIG. 1.   Camera and strobe, assembled with pinger, as used aboard the
Akademik Kurchatov. An 8-kilogram lead trip weight hangs below.

(EG&G model 206) of 50-watt-seconds energy was used for photography. This camera exposes about 20 photographs, each being triggered when a bottom-operated switch mechanism touches the bottom. The camera and light were attached on opposite sides of a 12KHz sonar pinger and aimed at approximately 45° to the bottom. A crystal-controlled oscillator was used to set a rate of 1 ping per second. The camera and strobe were activated by means of an underwater contact switch when the bottom-to-lens distance was approximately 1 meter. The combination of a camera system and pinger enables the winch operator to know the distance between camera and bot-

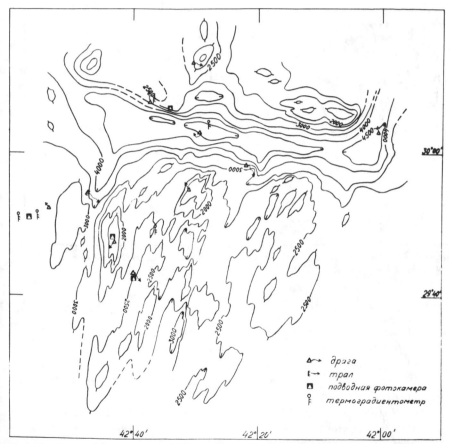

FIG. 2.   Map of Polygon no. 4 as used in September 1969 to locate camera, dredge, and heat-flow lowerings. (Drawn by Natalyna Morova.)

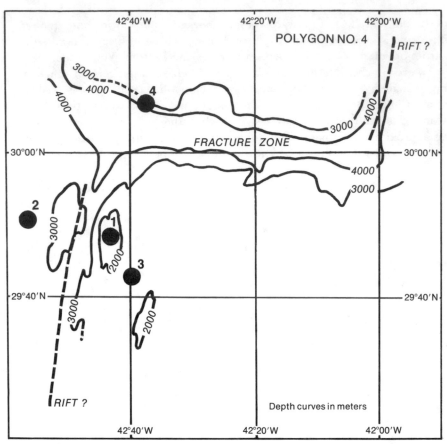

FIG. 3.   Map of Polygon no. 4 illustrating positions of the four camera lowerings
with respect to the Rift Valley and the fracture zone.

tom and thereby to tell when his camera or other instrument is about to strike bottom. He can then pay strict attention to the tensionmeter for direct contact, if he so desires. By knowing if the camera is far from or near to the bottom, he can keep the winch lowering speed at the maximum safe rate before the important contact moment.

One of the several problems when using a pinger for deep-bottom instrumentation is the relative position of the ship and the bottom instrument caused by the influence of wind and ocean currents. A ship usually orients itself perpendicular to the wind and parallel with the waves. Then

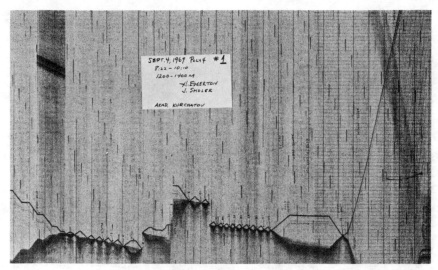

FIG. 4. Pinger record of sonar signals for camera lowering no. 1, plotted on an EPA recorder. The sudden changes may be caused by loss of phase control in the pinger oscillator or counting circuits.

the wire to the instrument trails to the windward. We found that we could not detect the reflected signals from the bottom noise in 3,000 meters of depth when the wire angle was greater than about 15°. The wire angle could be decreased by operating the bow and stern thrusters on the ship. However, the wind was often too great to make a suitable correction. More important, the noise from the thruster propellers entirely blanked out the pinger signals.

Another serious problem was the natural noises on the ship caused by electrical generators and other devices. The *Akademik Kurchatov* was about the noisiest ship I have ever worked on. She has electrical-power generators driven by diesel engines that produce a large continuous noise in the water.

The hydrophone for receiving the reflected sound from the bottom was put about 30 meters below the ship in order to reduce the signal received from the ship's noises. A Russian hydrophone was used. It was shielded from the surface by air-filled acoustical material on the upper side. An English amplifier (Kelvin-Hughes) tuned to 12KHz was used to amplify the signal from the hydrophone. Then the signal was recorded on two recorders. One was a Russian Ladoda (wet-paper type), the other an EPC Lab unit (USA) of the dry type.

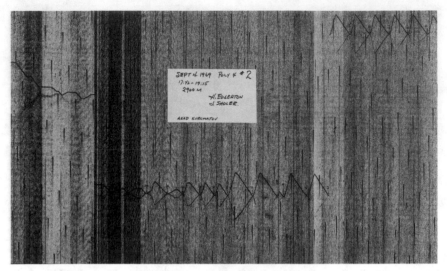

FIG. 5.   Pinger record of sonar signals for camera lowering no. 2.

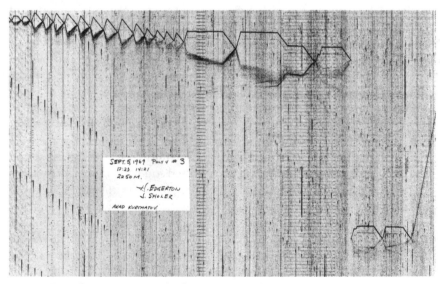

FIG. 6.   Pinger record of sonar signals for camera lowering no. 3.

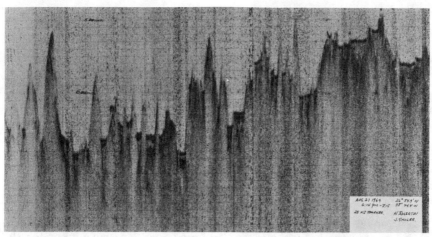

FIG. 7. Seismic record on EPC recorder, 25 KJ sparker. Started at 6:14 p.m.,
August 27, 1969 (26°54.9′ N., 38°44.9′ W., at 11 knots, course 301°); finished at
8:19 a.m., August 28, 1969.

Two types of pingers were used. One was the standard 12KHz (Geodyne Mark I), which uses an ADP crystal array tuned to 12KHz. This is
mounted on a transducer so that the acoustic signal can be directed downward. The timing on the pulses was obtained with clock frequency control
on one unit and by a quartz-crystal oscillator control on another.

An experimental transducer (5KHz Massa, type TR-76) excited by an
EG&G, Geodyne Mark I driver was used in an attempt to penetrate into the
sediments that thinly cover the fracture zone and Rift Valley. This transducer had an oil-immersed pulse transformer arranged to withstand the
tremendous pressures associated with depths of 4,000 meters.

Sonar Results

The sonar results during this expedition did not come up to expectations, since the bottom echo could not always be recorded, the reasons being:

1. The small size of the transducer (especially the 5KHz) precluded
any angular concentrations of the acoustical output.

2. The bottom surface did not produce a vigorous echo if over a rocky
surface at the Rift Valley. The sediments also were too thin and too scattered to act as a specular reflector.

3. The wind caused a velocity of the ship that created a big wire angle, so that the transducer was not directly under the ship.

4. The great depth of the water, 3,000 to 5,000 meters, caused the signal of the bottom echo to be too weak at the surface compared to noise signals created by the ship.

Figure 1 shows the underwater camera and the underwater strobe light as they were used. A photograph is exposed when an 8-kilogram bottom weight touches the bottom and operates a bottom switch to trigger the camera shutter. A 50-watt-second underwater strobe lamp furnishes light to expose Plus-X film with an f.8 Hopkins lens.

Shallow-bottom Photos, Location 21.5° N., 17° 20.2' W.

A sequence of 14 bottom photographs were made on August 12, 1969, when the *Akademik Kurchatov* was tethered to a Russian tanker for the transfer of fuel oil. The depth was 66 meters. Examples were given to Fedor Pasternak, a biologist, to supplement his reports on grab samples.

Deep-bottom Photos

No photos were taken at the Rift Zone (40° N., 24° W.) owing to bad weather conditions and depths greater than our camera's safe depth. For the same reasons, no photographs were made during a survey of the Palmer Ridge area. The Russian stereo camera, which has greater depth capability than ours, may have obtained photos from these two locations. Dr. Udintsev will have information on this result.

Polygon No. 4, Location 30° N., 42° W.

Four sets of photographs were taken. Figure 2, a map of Polygon 4, shows the location of four camera stations and the depths as well as the longitudes and latitudes of the lowerings.

Our report contains three sets of data on each lowering. These are (1) the "cable out" plotted against time, as read at the winch dial; (2) the pinger record of signals vs. time during the camera lowering and operation; and (3) the actual photographs themselves.

There is no way positively to identify a photograph with the sonar records or the "cable-out" records since the camera may skip or double fire when bottom contact is made. The number of useful pictures per lower-

FIG. 8. Bottom photo at camera lowering no. 1 of volcanic rocks at 1,400 meters. Some attached organisms are present.

FIG. 9. Bottom photo at camera lowering no. 4, showing rocks partly covered with sediment at 2,400 meters.

ing varied from 2 to 21, depending upon local conditions. Large wire angles and difficulty of triggering the camera accounted for the variations as well as equipment damaged by bottom contact.

Lowering no. 1, 1,400 meters. Photographs taken in lowering no. 1 showed a lava rock formation at 1,400 meters (fig. 8). Apparently the camera was lowered onto the top of a lava outflow. A lava pillow is shown clearly in the foreground. No sediment is observed. A few living plants or organisms are present. Light can be seen scattered from small particles in the water that are out of focus. These undoubtedly came from a previous lowering and raising of the camera between exposures, disturbing material on the bottom.

The second photo was out of focus because it was triggered too close. This was the last photo taken; the bottom switch at this moment struck a rock and was broken.

Lowering no. 2, 3,000 meters. Only sediments are shown at this 3,000-meter depth area. Most of the photos are out of focus or underexposed. It could be that our trip weight went deeply into the sediment before striking something solid enough to operate it. I observed that the focus is better when there are small stones on the surface of the bottom. Could it be that a stony bottom is more solid and trips the camera earlier in the drop? Take a good look at the pinger record, for example (fig. 4). It shows 21 bottom contacts. The *bottom* signal of pictures 1, 2, and 3 are very weak. The sonar record of the bottom of no. 4 is stronger.

The small rocks on the bottom surface are irregular in shape and black. They are probably lava fragments that cracked off when the hot lava hit the water. Then these were transported by the current and distributed on the bottom. The distribution could be selective according to size if the above mechanism is a true one.

Lowering no. 3, 2,400 meters. This photo sequence took about 50 minutes at the bottom, with the first photo at a cable length of 2,340 meters and the twenty-second photo at 2,475 meters. The photos show sediment and rocks. The sonar record is of special interest, since the bottom echo of the sequence varies in intensity along the sequence (fig. 6).

Lowering no. 4, 3,100 meters on north side of fracture zone. The 12KHz pinger ceased to operate after the second picture because of a puncture of the rubber diaphragm of the transducer. Fortunately the 5KHz pinger had been installed on the cable and was then used for the photo operation. The 5KHz pinger operates at a 2-per-second rate. Also, it was above the camera on the steel cable by some 6 meters. The photos show broken rocks without any sediments. Often the camera was tipped on its side when the

FIG. 10. Bottom photo at camera lowering no. 4 taken in fracture zone at 3,100 meters, where the top of the slope is at a depth of 2,800 meters and the bottom is at 4,000 meters.

photos were made. However, there are usually some small plants on the tops of most of the rocks. The orientation of the plants is assumed to be vertical and therefore shows the orientation of the photographs.

Sonar Records

Sonar records from the 12KHz and 5KHz pingers are shown in figures 4-6. These reveal several interesting effects.

Lowering No. 1. The sonar shows many "camera" contacts with the bottom. However, only two photographs were taken, because the second contact broke the bottom switch.

The sonar record (fig. 4) is unusual at the beginning, since the bottom signal is almost flat whereas it should be a mirror image of the direct signal. I am at a loss to explain this. However, at the end the sonar record for the long, last contact shows a more normal bottom reflection.

Side echoes could be responsible for the flat bottom echo at the first exposures. For example, the pinger could have been in a valley with steep sides.

Lowering no. 2. The sonar signals received from the bottom vary greatly from photo to photo. The signal disappears almost completely in some instances.

None of the photos when the sonar signal was good are in focus. Does this mean that the weight goes into the sediment before tripping or does the weight drag? The photos on the same run, with poor sonar echoes, show a pebbly bottom, which is almost in focus most of the time.

Lowering no. 3. The subbottom or side echoes are very much in evidence in the sonar record. It is believed that the strong signals are due to sediment layers.

Lowering no. 4. The 12KHz pinger ceased to operate when the transducer rubber diaphragm was punctured by a rock. (Note, a metal bumper has been installed on this pinger, after repair, for future expeditions.) However, a 5KHz pinger at 2-per-second rate continued to operate, and so both photo and sonar records were made. The gain control was set too high, causing the record to be too dark.

REFERENCES

EDGERTON, HAROLD E.
    1969. Rift Valley Expedition.   Aquasphere, December, pp. 17-22, illus.
EDGERTON, HAROLD E., and UDINTSEV, GLEB
    1973. Rift Valley observations by camera and pinger.   Deep-Sea Res., vol. 20,
        pp. 669-671, illus.

HAROLD E. EDGERTON

Exploring Subbottom Features of a Harbor
with Sonar and Magnetometer

Principal Investigators: Harold E. Edgerton, Massachusetts Institute of Technology, Cambridge, Massachusetts; and Peter Throckmorton, National Maritime Historical Society, Newcastle, Maine.[1]

Grant Nos. 806, 866:   For sonar search for ancient shipwrecks, Porto Longo, Greece.

Various studies demonstrate that a shipwreck which is covered over by mud or sand, and which remains covered, will be well preserved. An exploration of the harbor of Porto Longo, Sapiéntza Island, in 1963 demonstrated that this state of preservation could be expected even in shallow water, if the right conditions existed. Sapiéntza Island is south of Methone, on the westward arm of the Peloponnesus Peninsula.

The ideal shipwreck lies at a depth of under 20 meters in a reasonably sheltered muddy bay or harbor. At these depths the physiological problems associated with deep diving are absent. The wreck will have been covered over by sand or mud soon after sinking and will be invisible and thus preserved both from destruction by natural forces and from looting by casual skin divers.

Harold Edgerton, one of the writers, has studied the application of depth-finding sonar to the problem of "seeing" with sonar objects which lie below the surface of the sea bed. The sonar used is similar to conventional depth-finding equipment except that the pulse length of the signals is shorter and more powerful and the basic frequency of the pulse is lower, to permit the sound to penetrate below the surface. A permanent record is produced instantly for study. Before our Methone project, several experiments had

---

[1] We acknowledge with thanks the interest and help of Joan Throckmorton, Fred Feyling, Donald Fry, Donald Krotser, Dr. E. T. Hall, William Dixon, and Richard Ely, as well as many persons in Greece.

been made with this instrument in Greece by Professors Marinatos and Edgerton. They had concluded that the sonar was potentially very useful, but that several problems regarding its use had to be solved before attempting to use it on sites such as Helice or the sea battle of Salamis.

In 1969 we received a grant from the National Geographic Society for experimental work with sonar at Porto Longo (see fig. 1), and a preliminary survey was made of the harbor there during October and November of that year.

In 1970 we received a second grant for further research at Porto Longo. This work we carried out in the summer of 1970 using an EG+G 254 recorder, 5-kc and 15-kc transducers, and a 616/B/120 Elsec Proton Magnetometer. The objective of this expedition was to relocate the interesting anomalies of the previous season and pinpoint them with sonar and magnetometer, then to dig with airlifts so as to "see" visually what the sonar and magnetometer had "seen" electronically.

During the first two weeks, H. E. Edgerton directed the work of east-west cuts across the harbor using the 5-kc transducer. The east-west course was chosen because the harbor is much narrower this way and navigation is somewhat simplified. Marks were set on the west shore about every 25 feet and corresponding ones on the east shore to match. The procedure was to make slow (1- to 2-knot) traverses at half-mark intervals up the bay. This work was done mostly in the morning when the wind was light and made course keeping easier. During the day when wind was stronger we worked on targets already found by divers or sonar. The targets were marked first by buoys on the targets. By making several north-south and east-west runs, buoys were placed near the center of an acoustical target. The second method was to outline the target on the bottom by dropping painted rocks when the boundaries of the targets appeared on the record.

When Dr. E. T. Hall arrived in *Blue Bonito,* a magnetic survey of Porto Longo was carried out with the Proton Magnetometer. The survey was done by north-south passes at 10-meter intervals. The north-south direction was chosen because the sensing "fish" had to be streamed about 100 feet behind the boat. The bay being about 4 times as long as wide, the reason for the 10-meter spacing was that it related to the approximate water depth of 10 meters, although this varied greatly.

All records were made in the same direction to facilitate interpretation. The navigation of the boat was shore-controlled by radio.

With the search area about 1 kilometer long and a spacing required between runs, navigation became the critical problem. To overcome it the

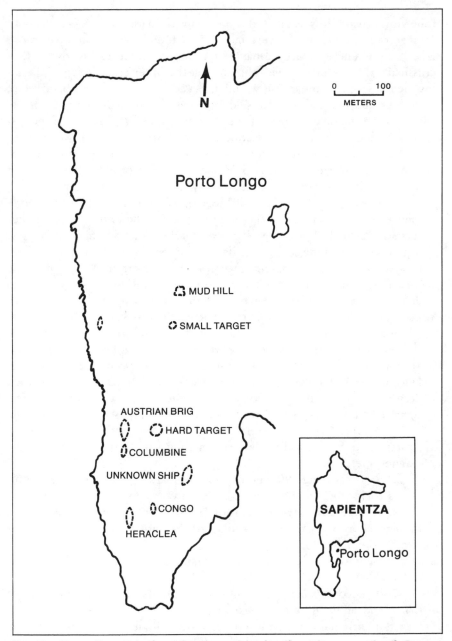

FIG. 1. Porto Longo harbor, Sapiéntza Island, off southwest coast of Greece, showing some of the objects located.

following procedure was devised. The area was divided into 33 lanes about 10 meters apart and marks were made at each end corresponding to those lanes. At one end we placed a man with a transit, and he aligned the vertical crosshairs of his telescope with the mark at the other end. The man operating the telescope on the transit would direct the boat via citizens-band radio, with the result that the boat was seldom, if ever, more than 3 feet off course. This was the major discovery of the expedition, and its use led to the discovery of five of the targets described below, three large and two small.

1. A hard sonar reflection occurred a foot or two beneath the bottom, 120 meters east of mark J. When airlifted it proved to be a pile of limestone ballast blocks. It did not show up on the magnetometer.

2. During a gale in 1824 HMS *Columbine* is known to have gone ashore on the west side of the harbor opposite the entrance. An earlier survey had located wreckage between marks J and K. This consisted of bits of oak planking, copper nails, and other material, obviously from *Columbine,* in about 10 meters of water at the break in the slope where the rock meets the mud of the harbor bottom. Extensive work was done to delineate the extent of the wreck. Although many careful passes were made with the 5-kc and 15-kc transducers, no wreckage could be detected, even when the 15-kc transducer was lowered to within 2 meters of the bottom. Airlifting, however, revealed considerable wreckage, apparently from *Columbine.* It is apparent that the sonar cannot reveal wrecks lying on rock. However, this target was "seen" by the magnetometer, despite confusion from geologic noise which made a definite magnetic signature hard to decipher. A contour map would have solved this problem.

3. A target lying 55 meters east of mark 5½ on the west shore was airlifted and proved to be a layer of medieval potsherds invisible to the magnetometer.

4. A target lying 100 meters opposite mark 5 proved to be an amorphous rock ridge lying northeast to southwest under 4 feet of mud.

5. A large object lying north-south about 100 meters off mark 8½ on the east shore was identified as a late-19th-century wreck. It was "seen" also by the magnetometer.

6. *Congo,* a well-known wreck containing a very prominent, gaseous reflector.

7. A decomposing cargo of grain, lying about 50 meters south of *Congo* and about 80 meters east of mark 17½ on the west shore. This target, a fairly hard reflector with crisp sides, under about 4 feet of mud, proved to be a mass of ballast stones. Its trial magnetometer signal was much confused by geology.

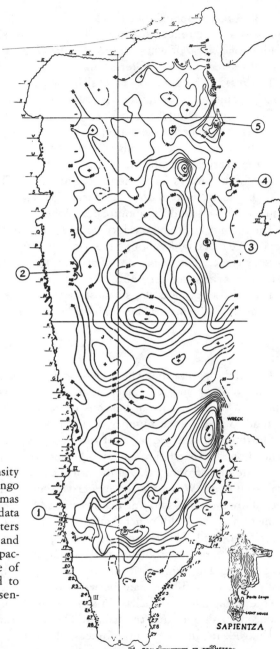

FIG. 2. Magnetic intensity contours of Porto Longo harbor, measured in gammas referred to 44,000 data points spaced every 5 meters along south-north lines and 10 meters east-west. Spacing control by N-S line of sight; variation removed to 0900, August 22, 1970, sensitivity I.S. gammas.

8. A target opposite mark 11 on the west shore and about 75 meters out was a poor reflector, but the buoy, on visual inspection, was in the middle of a circle of white stones. Airlifting to 2 meters revealed nothing. There was no magnetometer signal.

The rest of the area was carefully mapped out, but there was considerable difficulty differentiating between signals and geology. The Cenozoic limestone surrounding the area is not pure, as its appearance would indicate. Considerable magnetite, hematite, and other heavy metals constitute these reefs. The former two minerals caused considerable background variation, making interpretation difficult.

The other targets were identified, however. The first was located opposite the small island on the map (target H). This was buoyed. We dived on it and found a metal door about 6 feet long, 4 feet wide, and 1 inch thick.

The second, target N, was located in 14 meters of water. It turned out to be two large metal tanks about 5 feet on a side. We dived on this, taking only a cursory glance. They were not of archeological interest as they were both steel and appeared modern.

The third target was the smallest and very close to the west shore, opposite mark 2. Owing to the signal received, no investigation was made.

Comment

It seems apparent that whenever one does seismic profiling one is really mapping geology and anomalies in it. Porto Longo is no exception. The harbor is a series of ancient beaches or seismically "hard" geologic zones that tend to give a great number of anomalies.

On the west side are some of the deceptive "beaches." The most pronounced one lies parallel to and at a distance of about 10 feet from the west shore, extending from mark 9 at the north end to where it runs into bedrock at the south end. When viewed in a cross section, this "beach" resembles a wreck. However, it has no side echoes and no hard reflecting boundary. Discrimination is more difficult because the "beaches" occur at the break of bedrock and sand. This is the most likely place for a wreck to occur.

There are other problems with sonar attempts to "see" remains on ancient ships. The remains must not be lying on bedrock, as the sonar is usually unable to differentiate between bedrock and ballast. At the same time the sonar can "see" ballast in sand or mud, but cannot determine the presence of a ship around the ballast. The sonar cannot see wood which is waterlogged; it can "see" only objects which have a significantly different acoustical impedance. It is this change in impedance that causes reflection and thus produces a visual signal.

The final comment is on the problem of navigation, which was not solved satisfactorily during those two weeks. The major difficulty was to return to a target. The system of launching a buoy and then mapping in relation to that buoy worked reasonably well, but the system required a great many buoys all with their tie lines as short as possible. This system would not work well in deeper water. The dropped white stones worked well, in that the results were permanently in place and required no specific direction.

Conclusions

Sonar can find certain categories of targets, especially hard reflectors or gaseous reflectors: cargoes of grain, or a wreck whose hull was filled with seaweed before it became covered over, are ideal targets. One of the results, for instance, of the work done at Porto Longo was the discovery in the Solent of the *Mary Rose,* a battleship of Henry VIII; the seaweed washed into her hold made a fine gaseous reflector.

The magnetometer is capable of seeing nearly any wreck, but only if the geological circumstances are right. In a large area with extensive sediments, the use of the two instruments together is indicated. Neither instrument provides an infallible answer to the problem of the researcher who wants to find ships under the mud, but the two used together under the right circumstances, and after taking into consideration the geology of the area, can be a well-nigh infallible wreck-finding tool if the research team has the time, money, and patience to go about the survey in a correct manner.

HAROLD E. EDGERTON
PETER THROCKMORTON

Archeological and Paleobiological Studies at Stanton's Cave, Grand Canyon National Park, Arizona — A Report of Progress

Principal Investigator: Robert C. Euler, U. S. National Park Service, Grand Canyon National Park, Arizona, and Southern Illinois University, Carbondale, Illinois.

Grant Nos. 753, 896:   Excavation of Grand Canyon's earliest site of human occupation.

Stanton's Cave is a large limestone solution cavern in the Mississippian Redwall formation in the inner gorge of Marble Canyon, an easterly extension of Grand Canyon (figs. 1 and 2). The cave is 44 meters above the level of the Colorado River, 58.8 kilometers below Lees Ferry.

The site is at an elevation of 927 meters. Vegetation is scarce, except at a large spring, Vaseys Paradise, about 200 meters downstream from the cavern. Aside from the exotic tamarisk *(Tamarix chinensis)*, the principal plants outside the cave are agave *(Agave utahensis)*, Mormon tea *(Ephedra* sp.), beavertail cactus *(Opuntia basilaris)*, barrel cactus *(Ferocactus* sp.), sparse small grasses, and, along the river, willow *(Salix* sp.). Animals are not abundant; the only land species observed included bats, lizards, rock squirrels, and snakes. Predominant birds noted were cliff swallows, canyon wrens, hummingbirds, and ravens.

In front of the cave the talus, composed mostly of large blocks of Redwall limestone, slopes steeply at an angle of 32° to the rocky shore of the river.

Foot access to Stanton's Cave is restricted to two routes: down the Colorado River canyon from river kilometer 54, where the canyon walls are broken and faulted; and down South Canyon, a right bank tributary that enters the Colorado a few hundred meters upstream from the cave.

Stanton's Cave is named for the intrepid engineer Robert Brewster Stanton, who, in 1889-1890, surveyed for a water-level railroad route through Grand Canyon (Smith, 1965). In July of 1889, after three men in Stanton's party drowned within five days, he cached his equipment in the cave and hiked out South Canyon to the Mormon settlement at Kanab, Utah. Parenthetically, within six months Stanton was back on the river and successfully completed his survey. There is no indication in Stanton's journal that he observed any cultural remains within the cave, although he did note a pueblo ruin at the mouth of South Canyon as he and his men began their laborious hike out of the gorge (Smith, 1965, p. 89).

It was not until 1939 that prehistoric archeological remains were found in the cavern. These were split willow twig figurines representing some large animal form. In all probability their manufacture involved some form of imitative magic since many of them seem to have been ritually pierced by tiny wooden "spears." In 1963 a figurine from Stanton's Cave was radiocarbon dated at 4095 ± 100 years before present (B.P.), a date that agrees well with radiocarbon age estimates from similar figurines recovered from other caves in Arizona and Nevada. While no diagnostic cultural remains have been recovered in direct association with the figurines, it is postulated that they may have been produced by hunters of the Archaic Pinto Basin Complex. (For details, see Euler and Olson, 1965; McNutt and Euler, 1966; and Euler, 1966.)

Prior to the excavations reported here, no Grand Canyon site (several are known) containing these figurines had been excavated in a scientifically controlled fashion, and the cultural affinities of the artifacts remained hypothetical.

In addition to the presence of figurines in Stanton's Cave, amateur explorers had also reported what later proved to be the remains of Pleistocene fauna in the cavern (Parmalee, 1969).

The scientific import of the site was twofold, for it held promise of yielding more details as to the cultural affinities of the split-twig figurine makers and of providing data regarding the paleo-environment of Grand Canyon from Pleistocene times to the present.

In recent years, prior to the excavations, Stanton's Cave had been visited by thousands of people on Colorado River raft trips as well as by a few hikers and amateur cave explorers and the site was being increasingly disturbed, especially by the latter (Anonymous, 1966).

In order to prevent further vandalism and to recover scientific data, the National Geographic Society provided funds for the construction of a protective fence at the mouth of the cave and, in 1969 and 1970, made grants to the author to conduct archeological and biological excavations there. These excavations were conducted under permits issued by the Department of the Interior and the National Park Service. In addition, some funds to support

FIG. 1. Stanton's Cave (arrow) deep within the inner gorge of Marble Canyon.

laboratory analyses were made available by the National Park Service — Colorado River Research Project. All these sources of support are sincerely acknowledged.

In developing a research design for the project, two goals were set forth. The first was to attempt to locate additional figurines *in direct association with* other diagnostic artifacts to test the validity of our hypothesis that the figurines were made by Pinto Basin hunters. The second was to conduct our excavations with such care stratigraphically that a total ecologically oriented recovery could be made of the biological remains in a datable context.

The 1969 field party, in addition to the author, included Bruce Harrill, assistant archeologist (University of Arizona), Robert Page (then of Prescott College), Larry Powers (Flagstaff, Arizona), John Ware III (then of Prescott College), and Wayne Learn, helicopter pilot (Aerolift Helicopters, Kingman, Arizona). Parenthetically, with the exception of Learn, the field crew was composed of undergraduate college students; the research thus had another goal, that of providing direct field-research experience for these anthropology students, an objective in the finest tradition of scientific education.

Consultants who visited the site during the 1969 excavations were Dr. Paul S. Martin, palynologist (University of Arizona), Dr. Stanley J. Olsen, vertebrate paleontologist (University of Arizona), Dr. David Schleicher, geologist (U. S. Geological Survey), and Dr. Walter W. Taylor, archeologist (Southern Illinois University).

The 1970 field party, again in addition to the author, included: Paul Long, archeologist and photographer (then of Prescott College), Wayne Learn (helicopter pilot), Bruce Harrill, assistant archeologist (then of the Museum of Northern Arizona), Steven Clarke (then of Prescott College), Debbie Westfall (then of Prescott College), Dr. Paul S. Martin, botanist and palynologist (University of Arizona), Martha Ames, palynological assistant (University of Arizona), Dr. C. W. Ferguson, dendrochronologist (University of Arizona), Barney Burns, dendrochronological assistant (University of Arizona), and Dr. Austin Long, radiocarbon specialist (University of Arizona).

Specialized laboratory analyses of the biological material recovered have been and are now being done by Dr. C. W. Ferguson, dendrochronologist (University of Arizona), Dr. Lyndon L. Hargrave, ornithologist (Prescott, Arizona), Amadeo Rea, ornithologist (University of Arizona), Dr. Hildegard Howard, Pleistocene ornithologist (Los Angeles County Museum), Dr. Austin Long, radiocarbon dating (University of Arizona), Dr. Paul S.

Martin, palynologist (University of Arizona), Eleanora Iberall Robbins, paleobotanist (U. S. Geological Survey), Dr. Stanley J. Olsen, mammalogist and herpetologist (University of Arizona), Dr. C. R. Harington, Pleistocene zoologist (National Museums of Canada), Dr. Robert R. Miller, ichthyologist (University of Michigan), Dr. David Schleicher, surficial geologist (U. S. Geological Survey), and Dr. Richard Hevly, botanist (Northern Arizona University).

Each season all field personnel and excavation and camp equipment were taken to the site by helicopter. A camp was established on a sand bar

FIG. 2.   Aerial view of Stanton's Cave, showing Colorado River, historic high-water line, and talus slope entrance to cave.

FIG. 3.   Mapping in main room of Stanton's Cave prior to excavation. Level lines
are for profiles. Note extensive rock fall on floor.

along the river a few hundred meters upstream from the cave. The 1969
excavations continued for 30 days during June and July, and in 1970 the
party was in the field for 7 days in September.

The Excavations

Stanton's Cave is a very large grotto. Its naturally roofed entry is a
steep, rocky talus, 21 meters long and varying in width from 3 to 10 meters.

The main room of the cave is approximately 17 by 44 meters, with a fairly level rock-strewn floor that at its rear begins to slope sharply upward. At that point, a narrow, sloping crawlway provides access to a rear antechamber.

After establishing a map of the cave so that all specimens recovered could be accurately located in horizontal and vertical provenience (see figs. 3 and 4), we made a careful examination of the entire cave for artifacts. None was found in the crawlway or rear antechamber. Therefore, after clearing surface rock, two grid systems were established on the main room floor. One grid, in a north-south direction in the widest part of the room, extended for 12 meters. A second, closer to the entrance and in an east-west direction, covered a length of 8 meters. Each was 1 meter wide. In the 1969 excavations, each square meter was excavated in arbitrary 5-centimeter levels from present floor surface to a depth of 25 centimeters. In some cases, however, because of masses of rock in the east-west trench, 25-centimeter levels had to be employed in preference to the tighter level. Below that, material was removed in arbitrary 25-centimeter levels until bedrock was reached at a maximum depth of 1.5 meters. All excavated material was carefully screened, the 5-centimeter levels through a window screen and the others through a 6-millimeter mesh. In addition, all areas of the main room from the walls extending out approximately 1 meter were excavated to a depth of 5 centimeters.

Subsequent laboratory analyses indicated a need for even more refined vertical controls. Therefore, the 1970 project, in addition to accomplishing specialized biological tasks, included the excavation of a 1-meter-square test (Grid I-I) adjacent to the earlier east-west trench. The fill was removed in 5-centimeter levels from surface to bedrock and *all* cultural and biological specimens were collected after screening through a window-screen-size mesh. Samples of the material that passed through that mesh were taken to the river for recovery of minute specimens by a flotation process.

Findings

While not all of the laboratory analyses are complete at this writing, some preliminary results may be presented.

Archeology. From several unpublished reports it is estimated that approximately 75 to 80 split-twig figurines were removed from Stanton's Cave from 1939 until the beginning of scientific study there in 1969. During the author's initial reconnaissance of the cave in 1963, 10 specimens were recovered. These essentially conformed to previously published descriptions (Euler, 1966); 7 were pierced with wooden twigs.

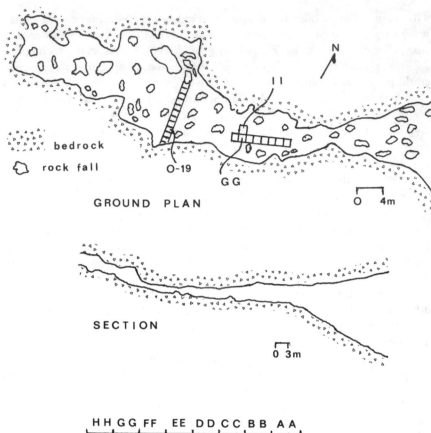

bedrock

rock fall   O-19

GG

GROUND PLAN   O   4m

SECTION

0 3m

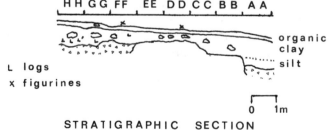

HH GG FF   EE DD CC BB AA

organic
clay

L logs   silt
x figurines

0   1m

STRATIGRAPHIC   SECTION

EAST   TRENCH

FIG. 4.   Ground plan, section, and east trench profile of excavations in Stanton's
Cave.

During the 1969-1970 excavations, an additional 65 figurines were collected, many from their original in situ locations (see figs. 5-8). Virtually all these were grouped in small caches under rock fall and none was found at a depth exceeding 5 centimeters in the loose surface fill of the cave floor. Only 2 were pierced with twig "spears." Several contained deliberately placed pellets of animal dung, probably from the mountain sheep *(Ovis canadensis)*, in the body cavity. These figurines also conformed generally to previous descriptions although a few had "hornlike" appendages woven into the head. Complete specimens ranged in length from 4.8 to 16.6 centimeters and in height from 5.3 to 19.5 centimeters.

No artifacts of human manufacture were found in direct association with the figurines. In fact, only 7 nonfigurine artifacts were recovered during the two seasons of excavation. Of these, 3 were small *Olivella* shell beads in the 0-5-centimeter level of Grid II; one quartzite end scraper came from the 10-15-centimeter level of the same grid; and 1 small, one-hand mano fashioned from a fine-grained, reddish sandstone river cobble was encountered at the 10-centimeter level of Grid II. None of these artifacts is diagnostic as to cultural affinity. In addition, 4 fragmentary corncobs and a few potsherds were found on the surface of the cave floor. It is hypothesized that they may represent a prehistoric Pueblo visit to (but not occupation of) the cave from the Kayenta Anasazi open site a few hundred meters up the canyon. This site was occupied approximately A.D. 1100. There is certainly nothing to indicate that these few artifacts are in any way related to the figurine makers. Hence, the postulate that the figurines were made by Pinto Basin hunters remains hypothetical.

Geology. While the Redwall limestone formation in which the solution cave was formed is relatively well understood (McKee and Gutschick, 1969), the surficial deposits in the cave itself had been unstudied. Schleicher's (1970) preliminary study indicates that "The floor of the cave is underlain by noncohesive clays and silts locally mantled by organic debris." The bedrock floor, as exposed by the excavation, "consists of nonlustrous, apparently degraded flowstone." This, in the north-south trench, "is covered by about 50 centimeters of stony pale brown silt" containing "about 25 percent limestone fragments." Above that are interbedded white and tan clays "dominantly illite." No stalactites, stalagmites, or fresh flowstone were observed, suggesting that "no cave-forming activity has gone on recently." The cave probably formed during the Paleozoic and the silty materials above bedrock "may be river deposits, or they may have been washed in from the rear." However, there is an obvious lack of stratification to them. Schleicher

FIG. 5.   Cache of split-twig figurines *in situ* 5 centimeters below surface, main
room of Stanton's Cave. North arrow is 30 centimeters long.

estimates that, if they are river deposits, "they should be between roughly 1
and 12 million years old. At the same time, the white, tan, and pale gray-
brown clays may be much younger.

Biology. In this preliminary report not all the species of animals and
plants recovered can be mentioned. The discussion therefore centers on
general comments and taxa unusual or important to the project.

Zoology: Almost 2,000 small, mammal bones were collected during the
excavation. Analysis of the 1,208 identifiable specimens (Olsen and Olsen,

FIG. 6.   Typical split-twig figurine from Stanton's Cave.

n.d.) indicated that by far the most common were those of the wood rat *(Neotoma* sp.) and mouse *(Peromyscus* sp.). The ringtail cat *(Bassiriscus astutus)* was also well represented.

From the surface of the cave floor, including pack-rat nests, are bones of the beaver *(Castor canadensis)*, desert shrew *(Notiosorex crawfordi)*, coyote *(Canis latrans)*, gray fox *(Urocyon cineoargenteus)*, raccoon *(Procyon lotor)*, mountain lion or puma *(Felis concolor)*, and muskrat *(Ondatra zibethica)*, in addition to the three most common animals noted above. Of these, only the muskrat is unknown from the area today.

Stratigraphically, the wood rat *(Neotoma)* was found in all levels from the surface to a depth of 125 centimeters. Mice *(Peromyscus)* were found to the 50-centimeter level, as was the case with the river otter *(Lutra canadensis)* and cottontail *(Sylvilagus)*. Bats *(Eptesicus* cf. *fuscus)* occurred to the 25-centimeter level and *(Myotis)* to 20 centimeters. Other species such as the black-tailed jack rabbit *(Lepus californicus)*, porcupine *(Erethizon dorsatum)*, muskrat *(Ondatra zibethica)*, rock ground squirrel *(Citellus)*, coyote *(Canis latrans)*, and ringtail *(Bassiriscus)* were not recovered below the 20-centimeter level.

Large animals, mostly artiodactyls, included the extinct mountain goat *(Oreamnos harringtoni)*, mule deer *(Odocoileus hemionus)*, mountain sheep *(Ovis canadensis)*, bison *(Bison* sp.; almost identical to *B. crassicornis)*, and the recent feral burro *(Equus assinus)* (Harington, 1973).

Most of these were surface recoveries although the goat *(O. harringtoni)* was found stratigraphically at a level of 25-50 centimeters. Other *Oreamnos* sp. remains in younger contexts were nearly as large as those of *O. americanus.*

Parenthetically, in the Carnegie Museum, Pittsburgh, is the phalanx of a Pleistocene camel *(Camelops)* allegedly collected in Stanton's Cave by an amateur cave explorer.

Very few herpetological specimens were recovered. Olsen and Olsen (n.d.) have reported 5 species of lizards, including the chuckwalla *(Sauromalus obesus)*, and 3 species of snakes from the surface of the cave floor. Stratigraphically, the bones of the garter snake *(Thamnophis)* were found in the 0-5-centimeter level, the whiptailed lizard *(Cnemidophorus)* in the 5-10-centimeter level, and the western rattlesnake *(Crotalus)* in the 20-25-centimeter horizon.

Fishes were likewise poorly represented in the collection. Analysis (Miller and Smith, n.d.) revealed 2 species of sucker *(Catostomus discobolus* and *C. latipinnis)* from a stratigraphic context at the 15-20-centimeter level and 3 other species from the surface: the rare humpback chub *(Gila cypha)*, the bonytail chub *(Gila elegans)*, and the Colorado squawfish *(Ptychocheilus lucius)*.

Bird bones in the deposits were numerous. Of approximately 1,000 specimens recovered, some 340 identifiable bones from large birds and a similar number of smaller bones, mostly Passeriformes and small Charadriiformes, have been analyzed (Hargrave and Rea, n.d.; Rea, n.d.; Howard, pers. comm.).

FIG. 7. Split-twig figurine pierced by miniature "spear."

Those in a stratigraphic context included the Pleistocene vulture *(Teratornis merriami)* at the 25-50-centimeter level; the California condor *(Gymnogyps amplus)* at between 5 and 40 centimeters; the great horned owl *(Bubo virginianus)* and the American kestrel *(Falco sparverius)* at 25-50 centimeters; and the common snipe *(Capella gallinago)* at a 15-40-centimeter horizon. More than 22 other species were recovered, many of which were undoubtedly introduced to the cave environment by mammalian predators. A turkey *(Meleagris* sp.) bone, not of the present species *(M. gallopavo)* was found in a surface pack-rat nest. Condors, the vulture *(Teratornis)*, the sage grouse, a Pleistocene turkey, and the black-billed magpie are the only five taxa not represented in the modern avifauna of the region; all the remainder should be commonly encountered in the inner gorge of the Grand Canyon today.

A thorough study of artiodactyl fecal pellets from Stanton's Cave, in an effort to identify epidermal fragments of plants preserved in them, has been completed (Iberall, 1972). From Grid I-I, the most carefully controlled test stratigraphically, almost 5,000 pellets were collected and studied. From these pellets, 53 vascular plants, including 18 grasses, were identified. None of them, according to Iberall, "could be interpreted as cooler or wetter elements."

In addition, measurements of these pellets from different stratigraphic levels indicate that those averaging 0.22 gram may be assigned to *Ovis canadensis* while those averaging 0.50 gram, and found only below the 20 centimeter level, may be assigned to the extinct *Oreamnos harringtoni*.

FIG. 8.   North-south test trench, Stanton's Cave. Note figurine on pedestal (arrow) in left rear, driftwood in lower levels.

Iberall's analyses also suggest that these artiodactyls inhabited the cave during winter or summer when forage was poor elsewhere (Iberall, 1972, p. 45).

Botany: During the two seasons of excavation the field party recovered 2,410 seeds, 46 small fruits, 7 flowers, 28 leaf fragments, and 23 stems or roots (Hevly, 1974). In addition, Martin (1970, pers. comm.) collected several carefully controlled pollen samples from the different stratigraphic levels, from fecal pellets, and from a cranium of the vulture *(Teratornis merriami);* the latter represents the first pollen analysis from an extinct bird.

Altogether, 20 taxa of macroscopic plant remains were identified, most of which can be found today within a short distance of Stanton's Cave, albeit usually in more mesic habitats. In general, *Pinus* and *Opuntia* remains are more common above the 20-centimeter level and *Juniperus* more frequent below that. Hevly (1974, p. 6) has reported: "Assuming that the proportion of seed types is a true reflection of local environments, it would appear that a Juniper Woodland surrounded Stanton's Cave during the period represented by the lower 40-centimeter interval of" Grid I-I. As will be seen below, radiocarbon dates indicate that this deposit is late Pleistocene. Although the seed-bearing strata differed between the excavated north-south and east-west trenches, Hevly has correlated plant identification with radiocarbon dates and has noted the following:

The dramatic change of seed composition revealed in the sediments of Stanton's Cave is not unlike that which has been C_{14} dated between 8,000 and 13,900 B.P. in Late Pleistocene deposits analyzed in nearby areas of the Mohave and Great Basin Deserts by Martin, Sabels, and Shutler (1961), Mehringer (1967a), and by Wells and Berger (1967). Recently available C_{14} dates from Stanton's Cave in fact suggest that the change in seed composition took place after 10,760 ± 200 B.P. (Iberall, 1972). The pale gray-brown clay of the Test Pit and East-West Trench, which contain an abundance of Juniper seed, are, therefore, Late Pleistocene in age. The gray-brown humus of the North-South Trench, which also contains an abundance of Juniper seed, is probably correlative. The dark gray organic material overlying the pale gray-brown clay in the East-West Trench and Test Pit [Grid I-I] has a C_{14} date of 2,450±80 and 5,760± 200 B.P., indicating the existence of a 5,000 year hiatus between the two deposits, not unlike other Southwestern localities which have shown a 1,000 year or more hiatus including the period generally referred to as the Altithermal (Cooley and Hevly, 1964; Haynes, 1968; Hevly, 1966, 1969; Mehringer, 1967b; Mehringer, Martin and Haynes, 1967). The cactus seed rich dark gray organic deposit occupying the upper 10-20 centimeters of the profiles in the East-West Trench and adjoining Test Pit [Grid I-I] was, therefore, deposited at least in part during the Little Ice Age climatic perturbations described by Haynes (1968), Hevly (1964), Mehringer (1967b), Irwin-Williams and Haynes (1970) and by Baumhoff and Heizer (1965).

The analyses of the pollen profiles (fig. 9) from Stanton's Cave (Martin, 1970, pers. comm.) show that "two zones can be recognized above and below the 30-centimeter level. The upper zone contains relatively large numbers of oak and *Ephedra* pollen. The lower zone contains much more *Artemisia,* and also increased numbers of greasewood, birch, and spruce pollen." The lower levels suggest "an environment in which Great Basin sagebrush occurred closer to the cave than it does at present, with water birch also in the vicinity, perhaps at Vaseys Paradise itself." Pollen recovered from the *Teratornis* cranium, which unfortunately was not in situ but in a surface pack-rat nest, indicated that both *Artemisia* and *Juniperus* were dominant. This, according to Martin, matches the 55-centimeter level in Grid GG. He believes this to date from the Wisconsin pluvial, definitely before 11,000 B.P., perhaps closer to 20,000 B.P.

The change in the Stanton's Cave pollen profile from high *Artemisia* in the lower levels to high Chenopodiaceae-Amaranthaceae (Cheno-Ams) suggests to Martin that the Compositae signify wetter conditions and Cheno-Ams a warmer and/or a drier climate.

In addition to the plant and pollen remains described above, the lower levels of the excavations revealed a large number of logs, many resting on bedrock. These were bedded in a manner indentical to modern driftwood on the beaches along the river and had to have been deposited by water action at some time before any of the other deposits were laid down. This wood included Douglas fir *(Pseudotsuga menziesii),* cottonwood *(Populus fremontii?),* and a few other species.

A sample of this driftwood, a piece of Douglas fir (fig. 10), has been radiocarbon dated at "greater than 35,000 years" (Ferguson, 1971, p. 352; see also below).

Schleicher (1970), in recognizing that this driftwood was deposited by the Colorado River, has suggested three possible reasons for such a high water level, at least 44 meters above the present level of the river:

1. lava damming near Toroweap; Hamblin's "F" flow has remnants at an elevation of 3100 ft (about 100 ft higher than Stanton's Cave), and lava flows have been extruded there from about 1.2 million years to about 10,000 years B.P. (Sabels, B. E., as quoted by Damon et al., 1967, p 467).

2. high water levels during or shortly after late Bull Lake (Early Wisconsinin) glaciation (cf Richmond, 1965, Table 2, p 227, and unpub. data), because of high runoff or possible ice damming;

3. temporary ponding by mass-wastage downstream from the cave.

Cooley (1971, pers. comm.) has estimated that if damming is excluded, it would have taken a free flow of the river of at least 10 million cubic feet per second (cfs) to deposit the wood in the cave. The highest flows recorded during the historic period do not exceed 500,000 cfs. While it is possible

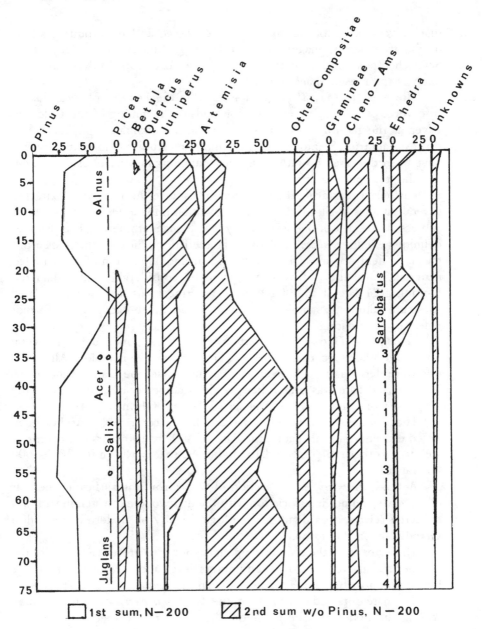

FIG. 9. Pollen profile, Grid GG.

that an extreme runoff during the Pleistocene could have produced a flow of the tremendous magnitude postulated by Cooley, the suggestion of Schleicher positing lava damming from the Toroweap flows seems more likely at the present stage of our research.

However, in May 1976, geologists from the U. S. Geological Survey discovered what may be evidence of landslide damming of the Colorado River at the mouth of Nankoweap Creek, approximately 32 kilometers downstream from Stanton's Cave. If continuing studies demonstrate that to have been the case, this rather than lava damming may have resulted in the ponding that put the driftwood in the cave.

Furthermore, during the same reconnaissance the geologists extracted several samples of silt in which the driftwood is imbedded. These have been subjected to measurement in a cryogenic magnetometer. The samples definitely exhibit reversed polarity characteristics indicating that the earth's magnetic field was most likely reversed during deposition of the sampled material. Thus, the driftwood may well be considerably older than the limiting C-14 date of 35,000 B.P. At this writing, plans are being formulated to secure additional samples to provide an adequate data base for further paleomagnetic dating.

Radiocarbon Dating. Radiocarbon dates were obtained from several levels and other specimens collected. These are shown in table 1. All except one were derived at the University of Arizona Isotope Dating Laboratory. The figurine date was established by the Radiocarbon Laboratory of the University of California, Los Angeles (Euler and Olson, 1965).

These dates are generally stratigraphically compatible. As has been noted elsewhere in this paper, the date of 4095 ± 100 years ago conforms well to all other radiocarbon dated figurines; that is, within the 3000-4000 B.P. range.

A-1184, the *Pinus edulis* section of wood from the surface in the rear of the cave, and not in association with the driftwood excavated in situ, was collected relative to a dendrochronological study of modern driftwood in Grand Canyon (Ferguson, 1971).

The dates from the artiodactyl pellets appear to present a record of the Altithermal above the 20-25-centimeters level and of Pluvial conditions below that horizon, with a hiatus between the two.

The date obtained directly from the *Teratornis merriami* ulna of 15,230 ± 240, the first such date obtained directly from the species, appears to conform well to archeological dated horizons containing bones of this huge bird. At Tule Springs, Nevada, near Las Vegas, stratigraphic Unit E1 at Site 5

FIG. 10.   Cross section of Douglas fir driftwood sample, STC-1, radiocarbon dated at more than 35,000 years ago.

TABLE 1. RADIOCARBON DATES FROM STANTON'S CAVE

Isotope Dating Laboratory No.	*Date Measured (B.P.)*	*Location and Comments*
A1184 (UA)	1500 ±	*Pinus edulis* log on surface in back of cave; not *in situ*.
A1165 (UA)	2450 ± 80	*O. canadensis* dung; 5-10-centimeters, Grid I-I.
741 (UCLA)	4095 ± 100	Split-twig figurine under rock fall on cave floor.
A1166 (UA)	5760 ± 200	*O. canadensis* dung; 15-20 centimeters, Grid I-I.
A1154 (UA)	10760 ± 200	Small fecal pellets; 20-25 centimeters, Grid I-I.
A1155 (UA)	10870 ± 200	Large fecal pellets; 20-25 centimeters, Grid I-I.
A1082 (UA)	13070 ± 470	Small fecal pellets; 20-25 centimeters, Grid AA.
A1132 (UA)	13770 ± 500	Large fecal pellets; 20-25 centimeters, Grid GG.
A1238 (UA)	15230 ± 240	*Teratornis merriami* humerus; unstratified pack rat midden.
A1056 (UA)	>35000	*Pseudotsuga menzeisii* driftwood (SC#1), 68 centimeters level.

(which contained an ulna of *T. merriami*) radiocarbon dated at 13,100 ± 200 and 12,920 ± 220 (Tuohy, pers. comm. and 1967).

Conclusions

It is difficult to draw any firm conclusions at this stage of the analyses. Obviously, Stanton's Cave is an important site, more for its paleoenvironmental and climatic potential than for the cultural data it has yielded.

Yet to be completed are more detailed comparisons of biological specimens recovered within stratigraphic contexts. This includes not only the relationship of one taxon to another, both floral and faunal, but the chronological position of these as well.

Comparison alone, however, is not sufficient. Once the natural relationships are understood and they are put in as precise a time perspective as possible, more detail of the past environment must be reconstructed. Even this is not enough. The biologists must look to the matter of process, and must pose and attempt to answer questions similar to those now being raised by archeologists in other contexts (Plog, 1974). To paraphrase those cultural queries, we need to wring from the Stanton's Cave data information, for example, as to why the environment changed as it did, why there is an apparent hiatus, why some change was slow and some rapid, and whether the data can be replicated elsewhere. These factors are probably due to certain variables and those which are important to paleoenvironmental change must be isolated. Only then will the excavated data from Stanton's Cave be put to its greatest use.

These studies will now go forward, it is to be hoped, so that a final report can be compiled.

REFERENCES

ANONYMOUS
   1966. Split-twig figurines found by the CAG.   Cave Crawlers Gazetteer, vol. 7, no. 4.
BAUMHOFF, M.A., and HEIZER, R. F.
   1965. Postglacial climate and archaeology in the desert West.   Pp. 697-707 *in* "The Quaternary of the United States," H. E. Wright, Jr., and D. G. Frey, eds. Princeton University Press.
COOLEY, M. E., and HEVLY, R. H.
   1964. Geology and depositional environment of Laguna Salada, Arizona.   Pp. 188-200 *in* "Chapters in the Prehistory of Eastern Arizona, II." Paul S. Martin et al., eds. Fieldiana: Anthropology, vol. 55, 261 pp.
EULER, ROBERT C.
   1966. Willow figurines from Arizona.   Nat. Hist., vol. 75, no. 3, pp. 62-67.

EULER, ROBERT C., and OLSON, ALAN P.
  1965. Split-twig figurines from northern Arizona: New radiocarbon dates. Science, vol. 148, pp. 368-369.
FERGUSON, C. W.
  1971. Tree-ring dating of Colorado River driftwood in the Grand Canyon. Pp. 351-356 *in* "Hydrology and Water Resources in Arizona and the Southwest," vol. 1. University of Arizona Press, Tucson.
HARGRAVE, LYNDON L., and REA, AMADEO M.
  1976. The large bird bones from Stanton's Cave, Arizona. Unpublished manuscript.
HARINGTON, C. R.
  1973. Stanton Cave fauna identifications. Unpublished manuscript, dated 1973.
HAYNES, C. VANCE, JR.
  1968. Geochronology and Quaternary alluvium. Pp. 591-631 *in* "Means of Correlation of Quaternary Successions," R. B. Morrison and H. E. Wright, Jr., eds. University of Utah Press, Salt Lake City.
HEVLY, R. H.
  1964. Paleoecology of Laguna Salada. Pp. 171-187 *in* "Chapters in the Prehistory of Eastern Arizona, II," Paul S. Martin, et al., eds. Fieldiana: Anthropology, vol. 55. 261 pp.
  1966. Preliminary pollen analysis of Bonfire Shelter. Pp. 65-178 *in* "Preliminary Study of the Paleoecology of the Amistad Reservoir Area," D. A. Story and V. M. Bryant, Jr. (assemblers). University of Texas Press, Austin.
  1969. Sand Dune Cave pollen studies. Pp. 396-397 *in* "Survey and Excavations North and East of Navajo Mountain, Utah, 1959-1962," A. J. Lindsay, Jr., et al., eds. Museum of Northern Arizona Bulletin 45. Flagstaff.
  1974. Macroscopic plant materials from Stanton's Cave, Arizona. Unpublished manuscript, dated 1974.
IBERALL, ELEANORA ROBERTA
  1972. Paleoecological studies from fecal pellets: Stanton's Cave, Grand Canyon, Arizona. Unpublished M.A. thesis, University of Arizona, Tucson, dated 1972.
IRWIN-WILLIAMS, CYNTHIA, and HAYNES, C. VANCE, JR.
  1970. Climatic change and early population dynamics in the Southwestern United States. Quaternary Res., vol. 1, pp. 59-71.
MARTIN, PAUL S.; SABELS, B.; and SHUTLER, D.
  1961. Rampart Cave coprolite and ecology of the Shasta ground sloth. Amer. Journ. Sci., vol. 259, pp. 102-127.
McKEE, EDWIN D., and GUTSCHICK, R. C.
  1969. History of the Redwall Limestone of northern Arizona. Geol. Soc. Amer. Bull., no. 114, 114 pp.
McNUTT, CHARLES H., and EULER, ROBERT C.
  1966. The Red Butte lithic sites near Grand Canyon, Arizona. Amer. Antiq., vol. 31, no. 3, pp. 410-419.

MEHRINGER, P. J., JR.
  1967a. Pollen analysis of the Tule Springs area, Nevada. Pp. 129-200 *in*
      "Pleistocene Studies in Southern Nevada," H. M. Wormington and D.
      Ellis, eds. Nevada State Mus. Anthrop. Pap., no. 13. Carson City.
  1967b. Pollen analysis and the alluvial chronology. Kiva, vol. 32, no. 3, pp. 96-
      101.
MEHRINGER, P. J., JR.; MARTIN, PAUL S.; and HAYNES, C. VANCE, JR.
  1967. Murray Springs, a mid-postglacial pollen record from southern Arizona.
      Amer. Journ. Sci., vol. 265, pp. 786-797.
MILLER, ROBERT RUSH, and SMITH, GERALD R.
  1973. Fish remains from Stanton's Cave, Grand Canyon of the Colorado,
      Arizona, with observations on the status of *Gila cypha.* Unpublished
      manuscript.
OLSEN, STANLEY J., and OLSEN, JOHN W.
  1975. The herpetofauna of Stanton's Cave. Unpublished manuscript.
  1975. Small mammals from Stanton's Cave, Arizona. Unpublished manuscript.
PARMALEE, PAUL W.
  1969. California condor and other birds from Stanton Cave, Arizona. Journ.
      Arizona Acad. Sci., vol. 5, no. 4, pp. 204-206.
PLOG, FRED T.
  1974. The study of prehistoric change, 199 pp. Academic Press, New York.
REA, AMADEO M.
  1976. The micro-bird bones from Stanton's Cave, Grand Canyon, Arizona.
      Unpublished manuscript.
RICHMOND, GERALD M.
  1965. Glaciation of the Rocky Mountains. Pp. 217-230 *in* "The Quaternary
      of the United States," review volume for VII Congress INQUA,
      Princeton University Press.
SCHLEICHER, DAVID
  1970. Preliminary geologic notes on Stanton's Cave. Unpublished manu-
      script, dated 1970.
SMITH, DWIGHT L., ed.
  1965. Robert Brewster Stanton: Down the Colorado, 237 pp. University of
      Oklahoma Press, Norman.
TUOHY, DONALD R.
  1967. Locality 5 (Cl-248), Tule Springs, Nevada. Pp. 372-393 *in* "Pleistocene
      Studies in Southern Nevada," H. M. Wormington and D. Ellis, eds.
      Nevada State Mus. Anthrop. Pap., no. 13. Carson City.
WELLS, P., and BERGER, R.
  1967. Late Pleistocene history of coniferous woodland in the Mohave Desert.
      Science, vol. 155, pp. 1640-1647.

ROBERT C. EULER

Accomplishments of the Proyecto Andino de Estudios Arqueológicos, 1967-1971

Principal Investigators: Clifford Evans and Betty J. Meggers, Smithsonian Institution, Washington, D. C.

Grant No. 775:   In aid of research on the prehistoric culture development in the Central and North Peruvian highlands.

This research program owes its inception to the initiative of Peruvian archeologist Ramiro Matos Mendieta. During two years in the Smithsonian Institution's Department of Anthropology as a Guggenheim Fellow, he became familiar with the Programa Nacional de Pesquisas Arqueológicas cosponsored by the Smithsonian Institution and the Conselho Nacional de Pesquisas of Brazil. His experience in Peruvian archeology convinced him that a similar collaborative research-training program was badly needed in Peru to overcome the chaotic approach to fieldwork, analysis, and terminology that prevails and constitutes a severe impediment to comparison of data and formulation of interpretations. The 37th International Congress of Americanists in Mar del Plata, Argentina, during September 1966 provided the opportunity to discuss the urgency and feasibility of such a program with other Peruvian archeologists, several of whom wished to participate. Concurrently, it came to our attention that the Ford Foundation was considering expanding its activities in archeology, providing a potential source of long-term financing. As a consequence, a 5-year research proposal was prepared and submitted to the Ford Foundation in 1967. Unfortunately this submission coincided with a policy decision of the Foundation to review its entire overseas commitments, with the result that the application was indefinitely shelved.

In the effort to get the program started, we searched for other sources of support. The generosity of the Kaiser Jeep International Corporation provided gratis three 4-wheel-drive "wagoneer" station wagons, and the W. R. Grace Co. offered 25 percent reduction in transportation costs from New York to Lima. The remaining 75 percent was covered by the Smithsonian Institution. Funds were needed for fees, licensing, insurance, minor

repairs, and maintenance, and the Wenner-Gren Foundation for Anthropological Research provided an emergency grant in November 1967 for
these expenses and to permit initiation of field work.

The decision of the Ford Foundation was made known to us in the
summer of 1968, leaving the project with three vehicles but no means of
utilizing them effectively. This time, the project was rescued by a National
Geographic Society research grant providing sufficient funds to finance
about 60 days of fieldwork for each of the three archeological teams.

A general statement of environmental characteristics and a brief description of each site included in the survey, as well as a map showing site
locations, have been submitted by the investigators of Area 1 and 2 and are
in the files of the project at the Smithsonian Institution. Area 3 produced
many more sites, making such a detailed account more time-consuming than
necessary at present, and generalized reports have been provided. The following résumés have been compiled from these more detailed reports:

Area 1: North Highlands (Departments of Cajamarca and Amazonas)

Investigators: Hermilio Rosas La Noire and Ruth Shady Solís, Museo
Nacional de Antropología, Lima.

Environment: The terrain is very irregular, with precipitous slopes and
deep, narrow valleys. The Andes are lower, however, so that barriers are
less severe than they are farther south. The highest pass is 3,815 meters in
elevation, and there are no permanent snows. Climate is characterized by
two well-defined seasons: a rainy period from November to April and a dry
period from May through October; variations in duration and amount of
precipitation are common. Three major ecological zones can be distinguished: (1) "El Temple," below 2,000 meters elevation in the bottoms of
quebradas and along the rivers, with a warm dry climate; (2) an intermediate
"Quichua" zone, between 2,000 and 2,800 meters elevation; and (3) "La
Jalca," above 2,800 meters, a cold, damp, and continuously cloudy region
favoring pasture and large trees but unsuitable for the kind of agricultural
exploitation possible at comparable or higher altitudes in the central and
southern highlands.

Archeological investigations: Survey has been conducted in two parts of
the area: the Chotano basin in the south and the Utcubamba basin in the
northeast (fig. 1). In spite of severe transportation problems (travel is primarily on horseback or foot), 91 archeological sites have been recorded, of
which 28 have Formative period remains. They concentrate in the intermediate "Quichua" zone, with a sparse representation in the "Temple" but

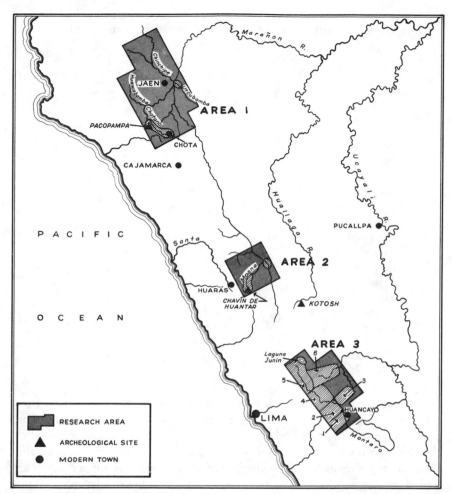

FIG. 1. Map showing areas in Peru surveyed by Proyecto Andino de Estudios Arqueológicos.

none in the "Jalca." (The latter zone produced extensive evidence of later occupation, however, including stone constructions.) A large stepped pyramid composed of three platforms surrounded by remains of galleries, well-cut stones, and other cultural refuse, located near the present village of Pacopampa, appears to represent an important Formative period ceremonial center worthy of more intensive investigation.

TABLE 1.—SUMMARY OF ARCHEOLOGICAL SITES RECORDED BY AREA
AND CULTURAL PERIOD

	Preceramic	Preceramic to Formative	Formative	Post-Formative	Total
Area 1:					
Chotano basin			17	52	69
Utcubamba basin			10	12	22
Subtotal			27	64	91
Area 2:					
Mosna basin	5		19	17	41
Marañon			5	1	6
Subtotal	5		24	18	47
Area 3:					
Region 1	34		4	54	92
Region 2	14		2	10	26
Region 3		6		8	14
Region 4		70	2	28	100
Region 5		48	28	25	101
Region 6		42	6	10	58
Subtotal	48	166	42	135	391
Totals	53	166	93	217	529

Six stratigraphic pits excavated in three sites provide the basis for a relative chronology for the Formative period. Four Formative ceramic complexes have been recognized. The earliest, called Pacopampa, is characterized by incision on polished surfaces, appliqué strips or nubbins, red slipping, and painting in red and white between incisions. Rectilinear motifs are typical; simple bowls and short-necked jars predominate; stirrup-spout jars also occur.

Stratigraphically above this complex is pottery with Chavinoid elements such as stamped circles, feline designs, incisions filled with red pigment, and highly burnished surfaces. A complex related to Pacopampa in the Utcubamba basin has been given the name Bagua; the predominant decoration is zoned red, black, and white painting; incision on plain or red-slipped surfaces also occurs. Following it is the Salado complex, featuring red finger-painted designs.

This preliminary investigation brought to light unusual and important aspects of the local Formative development. Among them are the presence of a well-defined pre-Chavin occupation, characterized by stone constructions and pottery with zoned painted decoration. The closest ceramic parallels are with Chiripa material from the Titicaca basin and Ocucaje and Paracas on the south coast, indicating hitherto unsuspected connections between these areas and the north highlands. Other ceramic characteristics point to Ecuadorian influences, although comparison here suffers from the paucity of data from the southern Ecuadorian highlands. No preceramic sites have been encountered as yet; whether this reflects unfavorable ecological conditions or the difficulties of discovery has yet to be determined.

Eighty percent of the sites (100 percent of those in the Chota area) belong to the Cajamarca or Marañon culture, previously described by Reichlen. They are characterized by a defensive location, on the summits of hills, and by the presence of "chullpas" of dressed stone, which may have served as watchtowers. The exterior walls are ornamented with felines, human faces, and prisoners being devoured by birds. Tombs cut into rock or constructed of enormous slabs are associated. Survivals of Formative period art styles are notable, and the material collected should permit the development of a detailed sequence of development from Formative to Inca times.

Inca remains are rare aside from occasional "tambos," although Inca influence is discernible in the late pottery of the Cajamarca complex.

Area 2: North Central Highlands (Department of Ancash)

Investigator: Hernán Amat Olazaval, Museo de Arqueología de San Marcos, Lima.

Environment: The Mosna flows northeastward from its source in the Cordillera Blanca to the Río Marañon, through a narrow valley. Elevations range from about 2,000 meters to perpetual snows above 4,800 meters. Rainfall is concentrated between September and May; quantity and duration of precipitation tend to increase with elevation. Five general life zones are distinguishable: (1) a narrow band of thorn forest on the slopes between 2,000 and 2,800 meters elevation; (2) dry montane forest between 2,800 and 3,600 meters, with an annual rainfall averaging 500 millimeters and a temperate climate; (3) humid montane forest between 3,600 and 4,000 meters, with winter frost and relatively high humidity prejudicial to agriculture but favorable to grazing animals; (4) páramo between 4,100 and 4,800 meters, with low temperature throughout the year and vegetation dominated by grasses and shrubs; and (5) the snow-capped peaks, which serve as the source of the stream and rivers that provide the water supply essential to exploitation by man of the lower and drier elevations.

Archeological investigations: The survey covered the Mosna basin from the source to its junction with the Marañon. As in Area 1, travel must be by horse or on foot, and the precipitous and irregular nature of the terrain makes it necessary to spend a large amount of time to cover a small horizontal distance. In spite of unfavorable weather conditions created by an unusually prolonged rainy season, 47 sites were visited, half of which had Formative remains. The majority (70 percent) were in zone 2; a few with late occupations occurred in zone 3; none were found in zones 1, 4, and 5.

No evidence was found of pre-Chavín Formative ceramics, in contrast to the situation in Areas 1 and 3. The famous center of Chavín de Huántar is in the middle Mosna basin, and evidence of Chavín occupation extends to the Marañon. All Formative sites continued to be occupied during the following period, but in later times many were abandoned and new settlements tended to be at higher elevations. In addition to surface collections, stratigraphic tests were made at a number of sites and these data combined with results previously obtained from extensive work at Chavín de Huántar have provided a detailed relative chronology from preceramic through Inca. One of the principal goals of research in Area 2 is improved understanding of the distribution and nature of the population that was served by the ceremonial center, and complete analysis of the survey results promises to shed light on this problem.

During the final period of survey, four large rock shelters were discovered near the Laguna de Kanrash at the headwaters of the Mosna at elevations between 4,300 and 4,700 meters, in an environment resembling that of Lauricocha. Preliminary testing revealed mammal bones associated with flake tools and projectile points of Paleo-Indian type.

Area 3: Mantaro Basin in the Central Highlands (Provinces of Hunacavilica and Junín)

Investigator: Ramiro Matos Mendieta, Universidad Nacional del Centro, Huancayo.

Environment: The Mantaro basin is one of the highland regions best suited for human exploitation because it combines a relatively broad and level terrain with fertile soil, equable climate, and moderate rainfall. Agriculture is possible to elevations between 4,200 and 4,500 meters, above which is the puna.

Archeological investigations: Survey has been concentrated in six regions of varying size (fig. 1). Sites of all periods are numerous, with the preceramic and Formative periods particularly well represented. Rock shelters and caves occur in abundance, and preceramic occupation was identified in 214.

Of these, 166 also contain Formative remains; an additional 42 open sites date to the Formative.

Stratigraphic test excavations have been made at four sites in order to gain information on the stratigraphy and cultural change. Pacha-Machay, a rock shelter, was trenched from the talus slope to the center of the floor deposit, revealing stratigraphic accumulation extending from the early pre-ceramic to the end of the Formative, including large quantities of animal bones. Another site in the vicinity contained occupation refuse to a depth of 6.5 meters covering a comparable time period.

Preliminary analysis indicates that the earliest pottery shares many features with the Pre-Chavinoid periods at Kotosh somewhat to the north as well as with early ceramics in the Ayacucho area to the south. Chavinoid influence is also strong. The abundance of dry caves conducive to preservation of perishable plant and animal remains indicates that more intensive excavation of several sites will produce a wealth of data relevant to the process of domestication.

Conferences

The participants have met with the principal investigators on two occasions for clarification and coordination of methods of field work and analysis and for discussion of preliminary results. In August 1968, Meggers, Evans, Matos, Amat, Rosas, and Shady met in Huancayo for two days, and additional time was devoted in Lima to preliminary classification of pottery to resolve analytic problems. The second meeting occurred in August 1970, at which time standardization of terminology for pottery description was discussed. Each team took advantage of the opportunity provided by the 39th International Congress of Americanists, August 2-9, to present a preliminary report on the research results.

A third meeting was scheduled to be held in August 1971.

Publications

Papers were presented at the 39th International Congress of Americanists but not published. Several papers presented at the symposium during the 41st International Congress of Americanists at Mexico City in September 1974 have been published in the proceedings of that Congress.

In order to facilitate standardization of the ceramic classification and description, Meggers and Evans prepared a manual entitled "Potsherd Language and How to Read it," which has been translated into Spanish and distributed widely in Peru and other parts of Latin America.

General Accomplishments

The results of this initial period of investigation have provided a general chronological framework in the three areas and also established a number of preliminary correlations between the successive cultural complexes and different ecological zones, implying changes in subsistence patterns and other aspects of cultural-environmental relations. They have also demonstrated that cultural development over the north and central highlands was far from a unitary phenomenon; a finding that supports the results obtained in Mesoamerica in recent years.

As a consequence of the promising results of these preliminary investigations, an application has been made to the Smithsonian Research Foundation for two years additional support. In Area 1, further survey is planned because most of the region remains unexplored; in Areas 2 and 3, sites have been selected for intensive stratigraphic excavation.

A beginning has also been made toward standardization of methods of classification and terminology, which is vitally needed in Peruvian archeology. Both communication and interpretation are seriously impeded by lack of comparability of data and since this project is the only concrete effort to alleviate this situation, its methodology is beginning to attract the interest of students and young professionals. The long tradition of uncoordinated research in Peru makes standardization a much more difficult task than it was in Brazil, and rapid progress is consequently unlikely. The important thing is that a beginning has been made.

REFERENCES

AMAT O., HERNÁN
   1971. Proyecto Andino de Estudios Arqueológicos; pt. 1: Zona II, Ancash, informe preliminar de exploraciones.   Arqueología y Sociedad, vol. 5, pp. 36-56. Lima.
   1976. Estudios arqueológicos en la cuenca del Mosna y en el alto Marañon. Actas del XLI Congreso Internacional de Americanistas, vol. 3, pp. 532-544. México.
MATOS MENDIETA, RAMIRO
   1970a. El período Formativo en la sierra central.   El Serrano, vol. 19, p. 246.
   1970b. Alfareros y agricultores.   Pp. 34-43 *in* "Pueblos y Culturas de la Sierra Peruana," Duccio Bonavia and Rogger Ravines, eds. Cerro Pasco Corporation, Lima.
   1970c. El período Formativo en el valle del Mantaro.   39th International Congress of Americanists, Actas y Memorias, vol. 3, pp. 41-51, Lima.

1973. Ataura, un sitio Chavín en el valle del Mantaro. Revista del Museo Nacional, vol. 38. Lima.

1976. Estudios arqueológicos en Junín-Peru. Actas del XLI Congreso Internacional de Americanistas, vol. 3, pp. 553-563. México.

ROSAS LA NOIRE, HERMILIO, and SHADY SOLÍS, RUTH

1970a. Pacopampa: Un centro formativo en la sierra nor-peruana. Universidad Nacional Mayor de San Marcos, Lima.

1970b. Pacopampa: Un complejo temprano del período Formativo peruano. Arqueología y Sociedad, vol. 3, pp. 1-16. Lima.

1976. Investigaciones arqueológicas en la cuenca del Chotano. Actas del XLI Congreso Internacional de Americanistas, vol. 3, pp. 564-578. México.

SHADY SOLÍS, RUTH

1971. Bagua: Una secuencia del período formativo en la cuenca inferior del Utcubamba. Master's thesis, Universidad Nacional Mayor de San Marcos, Lima.

1972. La arqueología de la cuenca inferior del Utcubamba. Doctoral thesis, Universidad Nacional Mayor de San Marcos, Lima.

1976. Investigaciones arqueológicas en la cuenca del Utcubamba. Actas del XLI Congreso Internacional de Americanistas, vol. 3, pp. 579-589. México.

CLIFFORD EVANS
BETTY J. MEGGERS

Mountain-gorilla Research, 1969-1970

Principal Investigator: Dian Fossey, Ruhengeri, Rwanda.

Grant Nos. 840, 874.   In aid of long-term field observations of behavioral patterns of the mountain gorilla *(Gorilla gorilla beringei)* in central Africa.

The long-term mountain-gorilla research project came into being because of the late Dr. L. S. B. Leakey, who keenly sought further information concerning the behavior and, in particular, the dynamics of group structure of this unique great ape. The study began in January 1967 in the Parc des Virungas of Zaire (fig. 1) under grants from the Wilkie Brothers Foundation, the African Wildlife Leadership Foundation, and the New York Zoological Society. In July 1967 the work in Zaire had to be terminated and was renewed in the Parc des Volcans of Rwanda in September 1967. The National Geographic Society has been the principal sponsor of the project since that time.

The Karisoke Research Centre is located in terrain similar to that of the initial study site at Kabara in Zaire. The current camp lies within a montane rainforest, at an altitude of 10,000 feet, where gorillas range between 9,000 and 12,000 feet. Through the period 1969-70, research was concentrated upon four main groups of gorillas that ranged over a total of 10.75 square kilometers on the slopes of Mount Visoke and its adjacent saddle area to the south and west of camp. This particular area (fig. 2) may be considered the heartland of the Virunga Mountain range, as nearly all the saddle terrain is comprised of Mounts Visoke, Karisimbi, and Mikeno, leaving only a small portion exposed to cultivated areas.

During the above two years of study, 2.13 square kilometers (19.81 percent) of the combined ranges of the four main study groups were used by more than one group and thus were considered as "overlapping" range areas. Only 0.44 square kilometer (4.00 percent) was used by more than two groups. The general tendency, with time, has been toward a reduction of overlapping ranges because the mechanism of gradual range expansion has provided increased spatial separation between groups. Indicated below

is the amount of the total range used by each group over the 2-year period
and the amount of new terrain used in 1970 that had not been used in 1969:

Group	Total Range 1969-1970 (km²)	New Area Added, 1970 (km²)
4	5.13	2.44
5	3.38	1.25
8	3.69	1.44
9	1.19	0.06
Total	13.39	5.19

Of all range extensions, 4.06 square kilometers (78 percent) occurred
within the saddle terrain; the remainder, on the slopes of Mount Visoke.
There were several obvious reasons for the outstanding influx into the saddle: First, increased surveillance in the form of patrols greatly diminished
the number of encroachers (herdsmen and their cattle, poachers, and trap
setters) who were well established in the saddle when the study began in
1967. Their presence had made the area uninhabitable for the gorillas, at
least during the initial part of the study, and even following a significant
eviction of encroachers the gorillas were apprehensive during the first year
they were observed using this area. Second, the food resources of the saddle
terrain are superior in both quality and quantity to those found on the slopes
of Mount Visoke, which, even in 1967, showed signs of overuse in certain
areas (overlapping range sections in particular). The attraction of "new" terrain offering both a diverse and plentiful food supply was obviously partially responsible for the prolongation of time spent off the Visoke slopes.
It would be erroneous, however, to assume that the saddle was "new" or
unknown to the adult gorillas of the main study groups simply because the
area was not in use at the commencement of the study. Actually, in some
cases involving localized and favored items of food, the gorillas have shown
a remarkable retention of knowledge concerning its whereabouts, suggesting prior knowledge of the terrain. Third, overcrowding on the Visoke
slopes had resulted not only in increasingly inferior food resources but also
in an increased number of agonistic interactions between groups; by expansion of the ranges, interaction frequency was reduced (see Fossey, 1974,
pp. 568-581).

In 1967 the four main study groups were defined within the immediate
study area, and observations continued primarily with the same four groups
throughout 1970. Contacts with the two large "fringe" groups (those whose

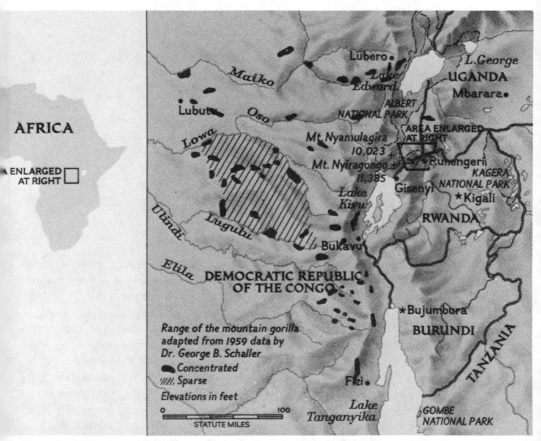

FIG. 1.   Map showing location of the study area in Zaire, Rwanda, and Uganda.

ranges abutted and slightly overlapped on the mountain slopes with the ranges of the main study groups) were reduced in the period 1969-1970. These particular groups, however, were encountered during census work conducted in regions outside the study area during this time and will be discussed under census-work results.

The following table shows the composition of each of the study groups by the end of 1970. As may be seen there were various alterations in group structure over the two-year period, involving mainly births, deaths, and changes in maturation stages (see also fig. 3):

Age/sex class	4	5	8	9	Totals
Silverback	1[a]	2[a]	2[a]	2	7
Blackback	0[a]	0[b]	2	0[b]	2
Adult female	7	5[b]	0	6[b]	18
Young-adult female	0	0	0	0	0
Young-adult male	0	1	0	0	1
Juvenile female	1	3	0	0	4
Juvenile male	1	0	0	0	1
Juvenile ?	0	0	0	4	4
Infant male	2	2	0	0	4
Infant female	1[c]	0[c]	0	0	1
Infant ?	0	0	0	2	2
Totals	13	13	4	14	

[a] 1 in peripheral travel   [b] 1 disappeared   [c] 1 deceased

In Group 4 there were three births during this time, but only one infant survived through the end of 1970. A second disappeared and was assumed dead in its 17th month; the third was considered a nonviable birth. A blackback and the silverback Amok became peripheral to the group; in other words, half or more contacts per month found either the night-nest site or the individual between 300 to 600 feet away from the group. In 1969, after 5 months of peripheral travel Amok became a lone animal—one having no associations with other groups or individuals except for interaction purposes. The only other changes of composition during this time were those concerned with maturation; 2 infants obtained a juvenile status, 3 young-adult females became adults. Thus, from 1969 through 1970 there was an overall gain of 1 individual and a loss of 3 (discounting the nonviable birth).

In May 1968 the group's dominant silverback died. Following his loss the group appeared relatively unstable until September 1969, when it began to attain a more apparent cohesive nature under the leadership of a much younger silverback, "Uncle Bert." The third infant he was known to have sired was the only one surviving by the end of 1970. In March 1969 an older female, Flossie (see figs. 4 and 5), gave birth 10 months after the death of her previous infant, making this the shortest interval of time between births yet recorded. When this infant died, a 12-month lapse occurred before her next parturition (in August 1971). Another adult female of Group 4, Maisie, formed an unusually close relationship with Flossie and one of her young infants several weeks before giving birth herself in October 1969 at the

PARC DES VIRUNGAS
PARC DES VOLCANS
1:50,000

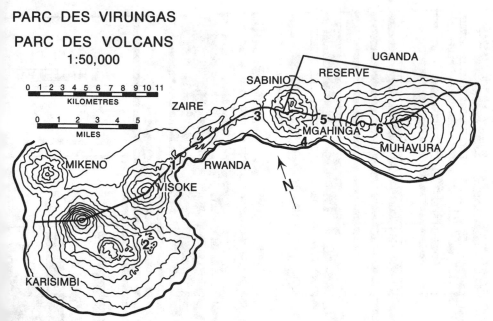

FIG. 2. The six central and eastern mountains of the Virunga volcanoes where the gorillas are distributed within the Parc des Virungas (Zaire), Parc des Volcans (Rwanda), and the Reserve (Uganda).

approximated age of 8 years 10 months (the birth was nonviable). This parturition age, also recorded for another female, has been the youngest yet documented by the study. The mean figure, based upon four primiparous females, was 9 years 8 months.

During 1969 through 1970 Group 4 was known to have had 20 interactions, and all of them were auditory (those in which only vocalizations were exchanged between groups). The fairly low frequency of intergroup interactions was attributed in part to inadequate observations between August through December of 1970, but of more significance was the tendency of Uncle Bert to avoid encounters with other groups, probably because of his lack of experience as a group leader.

During the same period there were 2 births in Group 5, but only 1 survived through the end of 1970. The second disappeared and was assumed dead in its 16th month. The youngest of three silverbacks, Brahms, became peripheral to the group in May 1970 and almost immediately after-

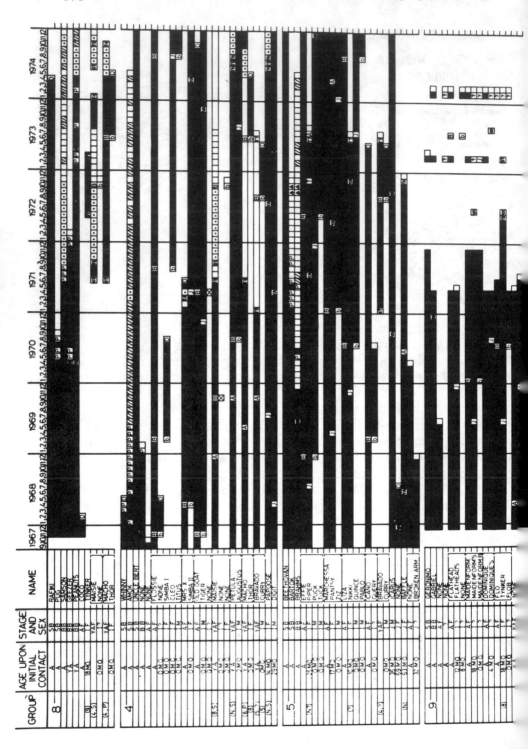

◀ FIG. 3. Changes in composition among the four main Visoke study groups. Definitions:

Group: The group into which the animal was probably born and in which it was first contacted. In brackets, the numbers indicate other group associations, initials indicate silverback associations, and "?" indicates association with unknown social unit.

Ages: Known birth dates shown in figures (ages of infants and juveniles estimated to within 3 months when first contacted); initials indicate young adult (YA) and adult (A) status, but see Amok, below.

Stage and sex: Initials indicate stage when first contacted, namely silverback (SB), blackback (BB), adult female (AF), young adult female (YAF), juvenile (J), infant (I), sex unknown (?).

Names: Brackets enclose name of mother followed by infants in descending age order; "none" signifies unnamed.

Peripheral travel: Half or more monthly contacts found animal and/or its nest 300-600 feet from the group.

Lone travel: Less-than-half to all monthly contacts found animal 600 or more feet from the group.

Amok: (See Mrs. X) the initial A refers to Amok, not Adult.

Nunkie: A lone silverback whose group affiliation was not precisely known.

■ Home group travel		J Juvenile stage (3 years)	
• Transfer group travel		YA Young adult stage (6 years)	
P Peripheral travel		A Adult stage (8 years +)	
▨ Lone travel		BB Blackback stage (8 years)	
▲ Male/male travel		SB Silverback stage (11 years)	
B Parturition		P Peanuts	
b Birth		S Samson	
D Death		A Amok	
⊠ Birth/death		N Nunkie	
T Transfer to __		? Identity uncertain	
T Transfer from __		⬚ Status unknown	

ward traveled as a lone animal. An aged female disappeared in April 1970 and was presumed to have died, though the body was not recovered (in 1975, an old skeleton of an aged female was found in a part of the forest only known to have been used by Group 5). Maturational changes occurred when two infants became juveniles; one juvenile became a young adult and one young adult became an adult. Thus, over the 2-year period there was a gain of one and a loss of three individuals.

Group cohesiveness was stably maintained by the older silverback, Beethoven, with no agonistic behavior observed between him and the two younger silverbacks. The oldest female, Effie, was dominant over the five other adult females of the group. Her two offspring, juvenile Piper and infant Puck, occupied secure positions among their peers. Marchessa, second in line of female dominancy, was far more inconsistent in her interactions with other individuals, and her temperament provoked a considerable number of outbreaks within the group. Two remaining adult females, Liza and Idano, did not share proximity with Beethoven and were more often observed at the edge of the bulk of the group, seldom interacting with other adults.

During 1969 through 1970 Group 5 was known to have had only 7 interactions. This was attributed to the fact that less observation time was given to Group 5 than to other groups, and that fewer groups shared Group 5's range during that period. Five known interactions occurred with Group 4, and Beethoven was responsible for the encounters.

During the period under discussion, Group 8 consisted of only 5 males, 2 blackbacks, and 3 silverbacks. In September 1970, after a 3-month peripheral stage, the silverback Pugnacious left the group completely. One of the blackbacks, Geezer, joined him for 2 months of peripheral travel before returning to the group in June 1970. Both Pugnacious and Geezer were suspected to have had strong kinship ties not shared by other members of Group 8. The changes in maturation during this time involved the transition of 2 young adult males into blackbacks and 1 blackback, Samson, into a silverback. Thus, there were no gains and one loss over the 2-year period.

The relationships between the males of Group 8 began to show slight signs of deterioration during the first half of 1969, when minor altercations were observed between Geezer and Samson and, by the end of the year, between Geezer and Peanuts. During 1970 Samson and Pugnacious were involved in minor skirmishes prior to Pug's departure from the group.

By the end of 1969 and during much of 1970 the group appeared restless and quarrelsome; outbreaks increased in frequency and the animals

FIG. 4. Flossie nursing the newly born Simba I, who died at 6 months.

were easily provoked into bluff charges. It seemed likely that the increasing number of intergroup interactions sought by Group 8 in order to obtain females was the basic reason for the development of intragroup friction, because of the buildup of tension that usually accompanied the interactions. During the 2-year period, Group 8 was known to have had 26 interactions with groups 4 and 9 (9 and 17, respectively). Of these, 12 were auditory, 8 were visual (those in which the groups were within sight of each other), and 6 were physical, where intermingling or approaches to within 15 feet took place between the members of the two distinct social units. Injuries of varying degrees of severity resulted from all 6 physical interactions. It was noticeable that only Pugnacious maintained a wide spatial separation from his group during their encounters. This naturally decreased the risk of his being injured but, more importantly, diminished any chances of his being subjected to misplaced aggression from the group's dominant silverback,

Rafiki. The better-documented of the interactions were those with Group 4, yet only 2 of these (as with Group 9) were known to have occurred when a female was estrous (knowledge based upon both behavior and subsequent parturition). Despite the persistence with which Group 8 followed other groups, they did not obtain any females during the above period.

There were 2 births in Group 9 over the 2-year time span and both infants were believed to have been alive by the end of 1970. One adult female disappeared from the group in June 1969. Transitions in maturation stages were as follows: 4 infants became juveniles; 1 young adult became an adult; 1 blackback became a silverback. Thus, the group was known to have gained 2 individuals and lost none.

The dominant silverback of the group, Geronimo, was estimated to have been about the same age as Beethoven of Group 5 but not as old as Rafiki of Group 8. A close rapport existed between Geronimo and Gabriel, the only other mature male in the group. Of all the groups studied during this period, Group 9 evidenced more cohesion and stability than any of the others. No specific hierarchy was evident among the 5 adult females and their young, but this was possibly because they left the study area before becoming totally habituated; thus certain behavioral tendencies remained inconspicuous.

Group 9 had a total of 25 known interactions during the period 1969-1970 and, as previously mentioned, 19 of them were with Group 8. Geronimo was more experienced than Uncle Bert; however, observations suggeted that he was frequently "intimidated" by Rafiki's persistence on those occasions when an interaction carried over for several days. Also, Geronimo was not supported by Gabriel during interactions and usually "stood his ground" alone to face the 4 males of Group 8 while simultaneously keeping his own group members separated from them. One particular interaction lasted 4 days, during which time a Group 9 female gave birth. There was also a second very young infant in the group, and Peanuts and Geezer seemed very interested in the infants. Leaving Rafiki behind, they followed Group 9 to within several meters. Unexpectedly, Geronimo turned and directly charged them with the apparent intention of causing physical harm. The two young males rapidly retreated, screaming. This brought Rafiki down to charge Geronimo who, in turn, ran back to his own group rather than challenge the older silverback. Group 9 was never observed initiating an interaction or trying to maintain one. Their usual reaction toward avoidance was simply to reverse their trail route away from Group 8, but at more normally paced travel than that observed for Uncle Bert. It was when followed for prolonged periods of time that Group 9 eventually, and very gradually, moved out of the study area to the point where Group 8 turned back and switched their attentions to Group 4. The above social reasons seemed to be the precipitating cause for the dramatic range shift of Group 9.

During the period under discussion, a census was conducted on the Visoke slopes outside the immediate study area; it revealed a total of 45 animals in 5 groups, plus 2 lone silverbacks. This population frequented the western, northern, and northeastern slopes as well as some of the adjacent saddle terrain. The areas covered were poor in contrast with the main study area: the vegetation was inferior in both quality and quantity, and large sections of scrub brush and stunted bamboo were found. Herds of cattle numbering in the hundreds had become permanently established around the base and lower slopes of the mountain and had caused severe damage to the indigenous vegetation. Only in the western sector, in Zaire, and where the subalpine vegetation zones on Visoke were approached, was natural habitat found unspoiled. Two of the groups encountered during the census, Groups 6 and 7, were known from the work of the main study camp, as they previously had interacted with the well-documented groups: Group 6 with Group 5 and Group 7 with Groups 4 and 5. No transfers of females between groups were known to have occurred during these interactions, which took place in the far eastern part of Group 5's range and in the high altitude zones of Group 4's southern range section.

In 1969 a brief recheck was also made within the original study site at Kabara in Zaire. In 1967 a total of 50 animals in 3 groups, 2 lone silverbacks, and a consort pair had been accounted for. In 1969, however, only 20 animals were found from presumably the same 3 groups; two group counts were based upon observations and nest counting and one upon nests alone. By 1969, cattle, poachers, and trap setters had virtually taken over the Kabara area since park guard patrols had ceased because of political upheavals.

In January 1969 an aerial survey made of all the Virunga Mountain reconfirmed the degree to which the Zairoise, Rwandese, and Ugandan sectors of the Virungas had been given over to cattle grazing. By the end of 1970 the only area within the Virungas at least under partial surveillance was that within the immediate study area and it amounted to only a fragment of the entire gorilla habitat.

By December 1969, 10,000 hectares had been taken out of the Parc des Volcans (leaving 15,000 hectares intact) by the Common Market settlement scheme for the cultivation of pyrethrum. The maximum altitude originally planned extended to 2,950 meters, only 50 meters below the

FIG. 5.   Flossie suckling her 6-month-old infant Cleo.

research center, and would have included the majority of the ranges of groups 5 and 6 plus several lesser known groups on Mounts Visoke and Karisimbi. Intervention by the International Union for the Conservation of Nature (IUCN) reduced the planned altitude to 2,700 meters. Group 6 was the most markedly affected of all known groups by the pyrethrum cultivation adjacent to Mount Visoke. Of necessity, they had to relinquish most of their core area on the eastern Visoke slopes and make a substantial range shift toward the west. This move was suspected to have influenced the ranges of other groups on that side of the mountain, resulting in overcrowding and subsequent behavioral adaptations.

In January 1969 it was learned that two young gorillas had been captured on Mount Karisimbi upon request of the Cologne Zoo. There was a 3-week interval between the captures. This factor, in addition to that of the nature of the gorilla, suggests that two separate groups on Karisimbi had to be destroyed in the process of obtaining the young gorillas. The first animal, Coco, was brought to camp on February 24 in critical condition after some 2 weeks' confinement in a small box. The second, Pucker, arrived on March 4 suffering from numerous infected wounds caused by the capture process and subsequent binding of her extremities. Both animals were considered out of danger by March 18 and began playing gently together at that time. Shortly thereafter they were taken into the surrounding forest where feeding and play behavior could be clearly observed as the two immediately "readapted" to their own environment. On those occasions when Groups 4 and 5 were heard vocalizing from the slopes of Visoke, neither Coco nor Pucker showed any hesitancy in running off toward the sounds. However, they were frustrated by the density of the foliage on the mountain slopes which prevented them from reaching the free-living groups. Upon order, both animals had to be relinquished on May 4 to the Cologne Zoo, where they have remained since.

No further gorilla captures have been known to have occurred within the Rwandese sector of the park, nor has the over-all condition of the park deteriorated since 1970. The conservation process has been a gradual but consistent one since that time, making the prospect of gorilla survival, at least within the heartland of the Virungas, a plausibility rather than, as previously thought, an impossibility. The National Geographic Society is to be highly commended for the significant contribution it has made toward the survival of the mountain gorilla.

REFERENCES

FOSSEY, DIAN

    1970. Making friends with mountain gorillas. Nat. Geogr. Mag., vol. 137, no. 1, pp. 48-67.

    1974. Observations on the home range of one group of mountain gorillas *(Gorilla gorilla beringei)*. Anim. Behav., vol. 22, pp. 568-581.

    1976a. Development of the mountain gorilla *(Gorilla gorilla beringei)* through the first thirty-six months. *In* "Perspectives on Human Evolution (Great Apes)," vol. 5, D. Hamburg and J. Goodall, eds. Staples, W. A. Benjamin, Inc., Menlo Park, California.

    1976b. The behaviour of the mountain gorilla. A dissertation submitted to the University of Cambridge for the degree of Doctor of Philosophy. 365 pp., illus. Cambridge University Library Microfilming Service.

    1976c. Mountain-gorilla research, 1967-1968. Nat. Geogr. Soc. Res. Rpts., 1968 Projects, pp. 131-140, illus.

KABAGABO, PH.

    1975. Rapport de mission à la 14e session de l'assemblée générale de l'O.I.A.C. Bull. Agr. Rwanda, April, vol. 2, pp. 110-115.

DIAN FOSSEY

Taxonomic Study of the
Giant Leatherback Turtle (*Dermochelys coriacea*)

Principal Investigator: Wayne F. Frair, The King's College, Briarcliff Manor, New York.

Grant No. 778:   In support of a taxonomic study of the giant leatherback turtle.

The hour was late; the friction-lit surf was sounding along the coast; it was high tide; and there was a brisk breeze from the sea ... a beautiful night for.... Our leader stopped abruptly and shined his light, revealing a fresh exploratory turtle track. "Aitkanti; we come back later," he said.

Thus began our first night on Bigisanti Beach on the coast of Surinam, South America. We had traveled to this remote beach to work with sea turtles, primarily the giant leatherback, *Dermochelys,* which the Surinamese call "Aitkanti." Our mission was to obtain blood samples with a minimum of inconvenience to the turtles while they were on their laying beaches.

Thursday evening, May 8, 1969, our plane had landed in Paramaribo, and we spent the night in a hotel. Friday we visited with the Forest Service and discussed with Dr. A. G. Voorhoeve plans for going to the beach and for obtaining necessary supplies.

One big problem was to locate dry ice needed for preservation of blood samples. After extensive inquiries and traveling, we concluded that dry ice was not available in the whole country of Surinam. Few people even knew what it was, and some had an idea only when we mentioned "liquid carbonic." One store (where the manager could get you "anything") actually had it; but this turned out to be a can of some liquid to be frozen and then carried, as on a picnic, to keep something cool. Before leaving the United States we had inquired about dry ice (solid carbon dioxide); and even though we did not have a definite answer from those we asked, it was our impression that it could be obtained. Another attempt to solve the dry-ice problem was to visit the Surinam Brewery where, after a deposit of 100 guilders and a promise we would return it, Hans Kluijver graciously lent us a cylinder of liquid carbon dioxide for making "do it yourself" dry ice. But there were some technical problems involved in obtaining enough satisfactory solid carbon dioxide from the available liquid material.

187

We knew that there were large liquid carbonic companies in Trinidad because we had checked there during a stopover en route to Surinam. After serious deliberation we decided that Bert Prol, curator of the Ringwood Manor State Park, New Jersey, would fly the 550 miles back to Trinidad for a block of dry ice. He spent a hectic day procuring a crate with a custom-made styrofoam container. With only 60 minutes of freedom left in Trinidad, he finally bought the 70-odd pounds of dry ice and raced back to the airport, arriving with just minutes to spare. Only when he was safely through customs and on his way to Paramaribo at 2230 hours did he breathe easily again.

Another problem would present itself on the jungle beach, for there we would be a considerable distance from such conveniences as running water and electricity. We needed to locate a source of electricity for our centrifuges. Various generators were checked, and at length we obtained a Honda gasoline-powered model from G. Plak of the Forest Service. Our success here insured the use of our centrifuges; however, as a precaution, we borrowed a hand-operated centrifuge from H. E. Lionarons, head of the Fisheries Division. It would be no understatement to record that everyone was most generous and helpful, a fact for which we are indeed grateful.

The blood-taking procedure we were preparing to use basically was the same Dr. Frair has been using for ten years with other species of turtles. This is the cardiac-puncture method in which a needle is inserted directly into the ventricle of the heart and blood is withdrawn. Turtles appear to suffer no adverse consequences from such treatment. Presently the live turtle collection at The King's College contains animals that have been bled periodically for eight years by this method. Before leaving the United States we had some very large needles made especially for this project but later found that it was not necessary to use them, because after turning over the large turtles we could go directly through the plastron rather than having to go into the heart from the region of a leg, which had been feared might be necessary. Finally on Monday we had all our materials ready.

Early Tuesday morning we loaded our gear into a long narrow boat equipped with an outboard motor, operated by August Wolf. Johan Nathaniel was retained by the Forest Service to assist us in loading, unloading, cooking, and other related activities that would be necessary during our undertaking on Bigisanti Beach. The help and cooperation he rendered during our eight-day stay figured greatly in the success of our mission.

We launched out into the Surinam River and sailed past the beautiful shoreline, dotted with a church, homes, and fortifications reminiscent of a previous age. As we churned our way into the Commewijne River, we were

FIG. 1.   Closeup of leatherback head. Note cusps of upper jaw and tears running from eye. (Photo by Joop P. Schultz.)

impressed by the banyan trees with their long roots reaching into the water. Much of the river bank is in a natural state, unchanged by man. Egrets and other types of birds periodically were seen. We motored farther on to the beautiful Warappa River.

An exciting time came as we turned into the Matapicca Creek where the river banks seemed to crawl gradually toward us. We then turned into the Matapicca Canal; here we encountered groups of four-eyed fish (*Anableps*) skimming over the surface of the water and watching us suspiciously with their upper two eyes. Along the banks numerous red Indian crabs were seen scampering and waving their claws. We also encountered two caimans, which simply avoided us. The tide was quite low, resulting in our scraping bottom several times. Once the boat almost capsized.

At a base station on the Matapicca Canal we transferred to a larger ocean-going boat. We plowed eastward along the coast until we came to the remote but charming region of Krofaja Pasi. Here the Forest Service had stationed two men, Louis Radman and A. Wolf, for studying and keeping records of sea-turtle activity. We moved into a small shanty, which housed the five of us in close quarters.

We had a little sleep in preparation for the fascinating activities to come that evening. It was Tuesday night, our first night on the beach. We walked in silence enveloped in the darkness, which occasionally was pierced by brief gleams of the leader's flashlight. Excitement was high when we discovered a fresh exploratory turtle track forming a semicircle back to the sea. It was the area of these tracks to which we were to return later that night to see our first leatherback. About 2 o'clock, Louis, who had turned back ahead of the rest of us, came upon the leatherback in the last stages of her egg-laying. He frantically signaled, shouting "Aitkanti! Aitkanti!"; and we came quickly to wait until she finished this laborious process.

After she had completed laying about 120 eggs and covering the nest, we turned the mammoth animal over and struggled to hold the large fore flippers down while Dr. Frair easily took a blood sample. She was uprighted again and permitted to return to the ocean. However, while moving down the beach, she gave two of us a ride of about 5 meters (16 feet). She appeared to have little trouble carrying the extra 150 kilograms (330 pounds). Her straight-line carapace length was 157 centimeters (5 feet 2 inches); and we estimated her weight to be about 320 kilograms (700 pounds). It was a time of elation observing and photographing this type of turtle, which has been seen by very few Americans. Success on this first night served as a great encouragement to us, because we paced the beach six days before seeing another of these gargantuans. We spent hours of eager anticipation searching for clues to the presence of a leatherback.

On the Wia-Wia Preserve, about 7 miles from our camp, was another Forest Service station. Two Englishmen named Russ Hill and Del Green, who were living here, kept daily records of sea-turtle nesting activities at their region of the beach. Their data were very helpful, and they were happy to cooperate with us.

While we were looking for leatherbacks we came across many green turtles (*Chelonia mydas*) and some olive ridleys (*Lepidochelys olivacea*). Surinam names for these are "krape" and "warana," respectively. As turtles became available, Dr. Frair took blood samples from each. Then when it became daylight, using the gasoline generator, we checked the hematocrits (packed red blood cell volumes), and froze the blood serum or plasma by using dry ice. Some of the blood cells also were frozen in order to release their hemoglobin for further study back in New York. Our gasoline generator performed beautifully; our quantity of dry ice lasted one week. Mr. Prol made another trip back to Paramaribo and obtained from Trinidad an air shipment of more dry ice, which he brought to our jungle station with many difficulties.

FIG. 2. Leatherback turtle during nesting activities. (Photo by Bert Prol.)

During our stay on the edge of the jungle, it was very hot during the day and some nights; it rained every day at some time. Frequently we were caught by sudden showers both during times of light and of darkness. The area is an insect haven; when we were out at night and would put on a light in front of us, the insects would be so thick we hardly could breathe. Dr. Joop P. Schulz likes to speak of insects here being in "industrial quantities." Our bodies became covered with red and itchy blotches. In spite of the fact that the area was so alien to human habitation, it was none the less very beautiful when the air was clear.

Most sunrises and sunsets were majestic to behold. Morningglory plants (*Ipomoea*) covered much of the ground, the flowers adding touches of purple loveliness among the green leaves. Colorful racerunner lizards (*Cnemidophorus*) darted to and fro capturing insects. They even entered our building and seemed to have great delight in walking along the screen and claiming the tasty morsels there.

In addition to the racerunners there were iguanas and some boas. Jaguars are said to live in the jungle and at times are reported to attack laying turtles. We saw the apparent results of these attacks in the form of a few dead and decaying turtles on the beach.

On Monday afternoon, after we had been there almost seven days, we saw our second leatherback. This event was the climax of our trip. It was a momentous encouragement to us especially because of our wearying day and night pace during which we had not shaved and hardly had washed or changed clothes. This second turtle was a large animal. Its length, including head and carapace, was more than 2 meters (greater than 7 feet) and it weighed probably 350 kilograms. The carapace alone was 165 centimeters by straight line. Contrary to the habit of most females of its species, this one came up to lay by daylight. We arrived on the scene just as it began to dig its nest; and we watched and photographed the entire digging, egg-laying, and hole-filling process. These animals are very cautious about coming up on the beach unless they feel that it is safe to do so. Once they have surveyed the situation from the edge of the ocean, they will venture farther and drag their heavy bodies across perhaps 15 meters of sand to a nesting location. Then with the hind flippers they dig a hole about 1 meter deep. Usually leatherbacks will come up when the tide is high, but often they come up when the tide is lower. However, they do not move very far up the beach to lay their eggs. Because of this, leatherback eggs frequently are washed out when the tide rises. Green turtles or ridley turtles go much farther from the edge of the ocean to deposit their eggs.

When this second leatherback had finished her work, we turned her and took a blood sample. Then she was righted and permitted to return to the sea. After plowing down the beach, she hesitated at the surf's edge, inhaled deeply, and plunged in. We watched and strained our eyes until the animal's head was indistinguishable in the myriad waves of the Atlantic.

When the second leatherback crawled back to her watery home, she carried with her the tiny tag that we had fastened to a front flipper. Actually the Forest Service tags all live turtles discovered on this beach. We found several with tags put on by Dr. Peter Pritchard a few years earlier.

After tagging and constant checking of the beach, they have discovered that some green turtles will come up at least five and possibly seven or more times in a single laying season. The interval between layings is about 13 days (10 days for *Dermochelys*). Each time the sea turtle will lay approximately 100 eggs, so that the total in one season may approach 1,000 eggs. Probably the turtles will not lay again for two or three years. Each species of turtle has its particular egglaying season during which its members will be found on the beaches in the greatest numbers.

On Tuesday night, May 19, there seemed to be many turtles coming up to lay. As soon as night began to fall, we could see turtles here and there starting to come up along the beach. We took blood samples from ridleys and greens until it was impossible to keep up with the number of available animals. Then we discovered another leatherback! Its carapace was 155 centimeters long, but it seemed thinner than the others and had bloody stains from some small wounds on the underside. Because the leatherback does not have a hard shell as other sea turtles, it can be injured more readily. On all three of the leatherbacks we saw evidence of former wounds, many of these being on the flippers. It was these broad flat limbs that caused us the greatest amount of trouble while we were taking blood samples, because all the sea turtles thrash them around; and the flippers of the leatherback easily could break a man's arm or leg. It took two men to hold down one front flipper of the active leatherbacks.

After taking blood samples from our third leatherback, we spent most of the night processing the various blood samples and getting them frozen. The boat was scheduled to take us back Wednesday morning; and we left on schedule. Our dry ice was subliming rapidly, but we had an adequate supply for sending some material back to the United States and for retaining the rest frozen until we ourselves could return with it.

Back here in our research laboratory at The King's College, we have been studying proteins of sea-turtle blood in order to gain knowledge that will help in improving the classification system of turtles. Also these studies should aid our understanding of the physiology of these animals. Contrary to what some anatomists have believed, our findings so far suggest a close relation between *Dermochelys* and other marine turtles, for our analytical experiments reveal that *Dermochelys* has blood proteins resembling those of other sea turtles more than fresh-water or land species.

Of all turtles we have tested so far, it has been most interesting to discover that the huge sea turtles (leatherbacks and others) seem to have blood proteins most like our common box *(Terrapene)*, painted *(Chrysemys)*, and snapping *(Chelydra)* turtles. This has not been reported before, and presently we are continuing our experiments to determine if it will be well confirmed.

Another of our recent discoveries never before reported is that the large sea turtles appear to have hematocrits higher than any other turtles in the world. Hematocrit refers to the packed volume of their red blood cells. This means that in a given volume of blood there are more or larger blood cells than other turtles have. This could suggest a greater oxygen-carrying capacity in the circulatory system of large sea turtles. This also is a matter for future research.

There remains a great deal to be learned about turtles, for they generally have been neglected from a scientific standpoint. We hopefully are aiding in man's understanding of these creatures. Even though our laboratory studies are exciting and very important in the expanding of our knowledge of marine and other turtles, we think that many of our most cherished memories are of the God-given beauties of nature. During our recent Surinam safari we were privileged to enjoy many of these in full measure.

REFERENCES

FRAIR, WAYNE F.
> 1971. The world's largest living turtle. Journ. Int. Turtle and Tortoise Soc., vol. 5, no. 2, pp. 22-23, 31, illus.
> 1972. Leatherback: Northward Ho! Aquasphere, vol. 6, no. 3, pp. 12-15, illus.
> 1977. Sea turtle red blood cell parameters correlated with carapace length. Comp. Biochem. Physiol., vol. 56A, pp. 467-472, illus.

FRAIR, WAYNE F.; ACKMAN, R. G.; and MROSOVSKY, N.
> 1972. Body temperature of *Dermochelys coriacea:* Warm turtle from cold water. Science, vol. 177, pp. 791-793

FRAIR, WAYNE F., and PROL, BERT
> 1970. 'Aitkanti' blood sampling. Journ. Int. Turtle and Tortoise Soc., vol. 4, no. 3, pp. 12-15, 33-34, illus.

WAYNE F. FRAIR
BERT PROL

Geophysical and Geologic Investigations of Some "Accidents Circulaires" in Mauritania

Principal Investigator: Robert F. Fudali, National Museum of Natural History, Smithsonian Institution, Washington, D. C.

Grant Nos. 748, 848: For a field and laboratory investigation of several proved and possible meteorite impact structures in northwest Africa.[1]

My special interest over the past several years has involved the geomorphic structures and shock effects created by the high velocity impacts of meteorites and comets with planetary surfaces. Although proved meteorite and cometary impact craters on the earth's surface are rare, we now believe that this may be due merely to their extensive modification since formation by erosive and tectonic forces, both of which are formidable agents of change over geologic time on the earth. On the moon, and to a lesser extent on Mars, where erosive and tectonic forces are much less effective, large circular depressions dominate the landscapes. Many of these are endogenic — volcanoes, collapse calderas, ring dike complexes, etc. — but many, perhaps most, may be of impact origin. The key to understanding the origin and history of these planets will rest largely on our ability to interpret correctly the nature of their circular surface features.

The end of the Apollo program and the minimal nature of the future Martian program clearly prohibit direct determinations of the nature of individual craterforms on the moon and Mars. For the foreseeable future, the identification and understanding of impact craters on these planets will be directly dependent upon our understanding of such features on the earth. This constitutes one reason for studying terrestrial impact structures, but of course we would also like to be able to assess the importance of impact cratering on the past history of the earth itself. The possibility of explaining a number of puzzling features of the geologic record as a result of gigantic

[1] This investigation was also partly supported by funds from the Smithsonian Research Foundation.

impact events is an intriguing one. To these ends it is important to identify all the old impact scars we can find and to try to reconstruct their original morphology. Together with ongoing laboratory studies involving hyper-velocity impact experiments with various projectiles, target rocks, and soils, such field studies, we hope, will give us an idea of the morphological vari-ation that we may expect in impact craters. Eventually, perhaps, these variations may be meaningfully related to variations in the parameters of the target material and the parameters of the impacting body (total kinetic energy, velocity, mass, density, strength, and angle of impact). We also ex-pect the field studies to provide us with some idea of the variation of the planetary bombardment intensity (if any) over geologic time. Finally we would like to know whether or not impacting projectiles sometimes "trig-ger" volcanic and/or tectonic activity.

My own contribution to these problems involves the field investigation of several circular features in northwest Africa, more specifically Mauri-tania. Northwest Africa has been an area of exceptional crustal stability since at least late Precambrian time, and much of it has probably been dry land since the Ordovician. Consequently craters formed over the past 10 million years or so are likely to be excellently preserved, and even craters 300-400 million years old should be at least partially preserved in the rocks of this region.

In 1970 and 1971 my colleague Dr. William A. Cassidy, of the University of Pittsburgh, and I examined four circular features in Mauritania of proven or possible impact origin. The four features are: Aouelloul Crater; Tenoumer Crater; Temimichat Ghallaman Crater; and the Richat Dome. Remarkably, the three craters lie in almost a straight line trending N.35° E. over a dis-tance of several hundred kilometers and the Richat Dome is not far off this trend (fig. 1). There is no evidence to date, however, that the craters are in any way related to one another or to the dome. Aouelloul and Tenoumer are proved meteorite craters and Temimichat is a possible impact crater. The Richat Dome is an old, dissected structural dome of enigmatic origin and is perhaps the most fascinating and certainly the most impressive of the four structures.

The three craters are of particular interest because of their excellent preservation, which gives us the rare opportunity to study their original morphology and subsurface structure with minimal recourse to guesses and extrapolations. Unfortunately they are situated in remote locations that can be reached only by extensive cross-country traverses through truly difficult terrain; and they are all partly filled with sand and silt, which prevents any convenient direct observations of their original morphology. The combined remoteness and inhospitality of the environment rule out the obvious approaches, such as core-drilling and seismic surveys, to obtaining subsurface information. We elected to use a gravimeter in an attempt to delineate the subsurface configurations. This approach worked well. We also ran a single gravity traverse across the Richat Dome in an effort to demonstrate the presence of an igneous intrusion beneath it. In addition to the gravimeters, we used a magnetic gradiometer at Tenoumer, but so far we have been unable to interpret the magnetic data in a meaningful way. Finally we made extensive rock collections at all four structures for laboratory examination and analysis.

Tenoumer

With a rim-crest to rim-crest diameter of 6,300 feet, and a maximum relief of 350 feet, this crater is the largest of the three examined. It is also the most perfectly circular. Shock metamorphic effects in rocks found immediately outside the crater demonstrate an impact origin.

The most straightforward interpretation of the gravity data is that the present crater floor is underlain by 750 feet of sand fill, which in turn rests on a lens of crushed granite country rock extending to a maximum depth of 2,000 feet. This makes the original crater (before infilling of sand) a virtual twin of Meteor Crater, Arizona, if they are both scaled to the same size for comparison.

Immediately outside and obviously structurally controlled by the crater are several sets of concentric outcrops of what appear to be small dike swarms. The dike rocks consist of a glassy, vuggy matrix containing fragments of shocked and partly altered granite country rock (French et al., 1970). The substantial chemical discrepancies between these dike rocks and the essentially granitic country rocks have been a strong argument against their origin by impact-generated melting. However, our work on a total of 11 dike-rock and 25 country-rock specimens from Tenoumer has clearly shown that the dike rocks are impact-generated melts rather than products of subsequent volcanism (Fudali, 1974). Their major element chemistry can be exactly duplicated by the addition of varying amounts of an amphibolite country rock to the various granitic country rocks. Since the local amphibolite occupies only a trivial volume in the granitic terrain, the impact melt must have *preferentially* incorporated this mafic component. This mafic enhancement is theoretically favored both by kinetic and viscosity

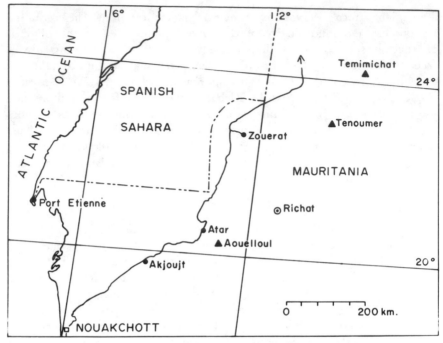

FIG. 1.   Location of the craters studied in Mauritania.

considerations and should be a general operative mechanism in all similar target terrains rather than being specific to Tenoumer. In particular, the many similar country rock/melt rock discrepancies associated with craters on the Canadian Shield are explicable in terms of this mechanism. Contrary to past assertions (see Curry, 1971), the relationships at Tenoumer un-equivocally demonstrate that shock processes are quite capable of producing melt rocks whose individual hand specimen chemical compositions may be radically different from both average and specific country-rock values.

Temimichat Ghallaman

Temimichat is a distinctly hexagonal crater with diameters of 2,100 feet (side to side) and 2,400 feet (apex to apex) and a maximum relief of 125 feet. To date there is no evidence for or against an impact origin. We have microscopically examined 22 sections of 18 different rock specimens from the crater for shock metamorphic effects, with negative results. But we do

FIG. 2.   Photograph of Richat Dome taken from near space on the Apollo 8 mission. (Photographs of the craters Tenoumer, Temimichat, and Aouelloul are published in Fudali and Cassidy, 1972.)

not have access to subsurface samples here such as are supplied by the dikes at Tenoumer. The surface rocks at Tenoumer have also given negative results when examined for shock effects (18 rock samples examined).

The gravity data indicate a remarkably shallow structure for a crater of this diameter. The estimated maximum depth to the original crater floor is only 150 feet (now sand-filled), or about half the depth we would have predicted for an impact crater. Were it not for the fact that Aouelloul (a proved impact crater) has a similar depth/diameter ratio we would consider this configuration at Temimichat to be strong evidence against an impact origin. As it is, the fact is merely equivocal. The crater needs to be core-drilled for definitive evidence.

Aouelloul

Aouelloul is the smallest of the three craters and also the most accessible. Consequently it has been casually studied by a number of scientists, and several established misconceptions in the literature have resulted. These concern its size (most commonly reported as 800 feet in diameter), the stratigraphic sequence at the crater site (most recently reported as Oujeft quartzite overlying Zli sandstone), and the lack of evidence in the rim for an explosive event. Our plane table survey demonstrates a rim crest to rim crest diameter of 1,250-1,300 feet. The actual stratigraphic sequence is Zli sandstone overlying Oujeft quartzite (important to understanding the mechanics of cratering and the formation of impact glass at Aouelloul). And we found a reasonably well-developed, overturned sequence in the northern sector of the rim (Oujeft overlain by Zli overlain by Oujeft), which is good evidence for an explosive event.

The crater is of proven impact origin. The proof consists of a quantity of small glass fragments lying in and around the crater that are chemically identifiable with the Zli sandstone and that contain small metallic spherules of meteoritic nickel-iron. As at Temimichat the gravity data indicate a remarkably shallow structure, with the bottom of the sand fill (the original crater floor) only 100 feet below the level of the present crater floor. Beneath the original crater floor is a lens of brecciated country rock which has a maximum thickness of ~ 300 feet. To date this is the only known impact crater in this size range to exhibit an original depth/diameter ratio which is so small (1/13). Even more unusual, this small depth/diameter ratio is coupled with a rim that is even now moderately high (maximum 100 feet) for a crater of this size, let alone what it was prior to erosion. Taken together the combination of high rim and shallow floor strikingly extends the range in morphology that we may expect impact craters to exhibit.

Richat Dome

The Richat Dome is a large (40 kilometers in diameter), circular, positive geomorphic feature involving a lower Paleozoic stratigraphic sequence of sedimentary rocks. The original dome has been peneplaned and subsequently dissected to its present configuration, which is a series of annular ridges and depressions (corresponding to harder and softer strata respectively); from the air it looks like a slice through an onion. It is an impressive feature, even when viewed by earth-orbiting cameras (fig. 2).

In detail there are a great many complexities and fascinating problems associated with the structure and its constituent rocks, but we have been concerned only with whether or not it could be the highly eroded root structure of a gigantic impact crater. In 1968 we examined the structure and all the important rock types present for both macroscopic and microscopic evidence of shock metamorphism. We found none, and since the exposures are so good we concluded it could not be an ancient impact scar. But negative evidence is never entirely satisfying, and in 1971 we ran a gravity traverse across the structure hoping to delineate an igneous intrusion below the dome. Unfortunately the gravity profile indicates neither a mass excess nor a mass deficit beneath the dome, so that the origin of the updoming event remains obscure.

We did not attempt to examine several other craters reputed to exist in this general region of the Sahara. After examining air photos and talking to pilots and geologists familiar with the reported areas of occurrence we conclude that most of the reports are likely fictitious. But we do feel that an area as large and tectonically stable as the western Sahara should contain more than the three craters so far known, and we plan to continue sporadic aerial reconnaissance as circumstances and finances allow.

REFERENCES

CURRY, K. L.,
  1971. Origin of igneous rocks associated with shock metamorphism as suggested by geochemical investigations of Canadian craters. Journ. Geophys. Res., vol. 76, pp. 5575-5585.
FRENCH, B. M.; HARTUNG, J. B.; SHORT, N. M.; AND DIETZ, R. S.
  1970. Tenoumer crater, Mauritania: Age and petrologic evidence for origin by meteorite impact. Journ. Geophys. Res., vol. 75, no. 23, pp. 4396-4406.
FUDALI, ROBERT F.,
  1974. Genesis of the melt rocks at Tenoumer Crater, Mauritania. Journ. Geophys. Res., vol. 79, pp. 2115-2121.
FUDALI, ROBERT F., and CASSIDY, WILLIAM A.
  1972. Gravity reconnaissance at three Mauritanian craters of explosive origin. Meteoritics, vol. 7, no. 1, pp. 51-70, illus.
  1973. Gravity reconnaissance at Richat. Pp. 77-81 *in* "Contributions a l'Etude de l'Accident Circulaire des Richat (Adrar, Mauritanie)," Th. Monod and C. Pomerol, eds., Sciences de la Terre, Memoire 28.

ROBERT F. FUDALI

Acquisition of Sign Language by a Nonhuman Primate

Principal Investigators: R. Allen Gardner and Beatrice T. Gardner, University of Nevada, Reno, Nevada.

Grant No. 751: To investigate the possibility of sign language being taught to a chimpanzee.

The extent to which another species might be able to use language is a classical problem in comparative psychology. In our approach to this problem we undertook to teach an infant female chimpanzee, named Washoe, to use American Sign Language, the gestural language used by the deaf in North America.

If overlap exists between the linguistic capacities of human beings and other species, we expected to find it among the great apes. The intelligent and social chimpanzee was an obvious choice as a subject for our investigation.

Previous attempts to teach a chimpanzee to use a vocal language such as English (e.g., Hayes and Hayes, 1951) had met with failure and have often been cited as evidence that no significant degree of linguistic capacity is present in any species other than man. But the vocal apparatus of chimpanzees is very different from that of man (Bryan, 1963) and is likely to be a severe handicap in the production of the sounds of human language. More important, the vocal behavior of chimpanzees is very different from that of a man. Undisturbed, chimpanzees are quite silent animals. They do make a variety of sounds, but these generally occur in situations of high excitement and tend to be specific to the exciting situation (Bastian, 1965). Under such conditions it is unlikely that an animal could be trained to make refined use of its vocalizations.

A great deal of evidence based on observations of chimpanzees both in the wild and in the laboratory suggested to us that a language based on gestures should be more suitable for a chimpanzee than one based on speech. Use of the hands is a prominent feature of chimpanzee behavior; manipulatory mechanical problems are their forte. More to the point, even caged laboratory chimpanzees develop begging and like gestures spontaneously

(Yerkes, 1943), while members of well-established wild bands and chimpanzees that have had intensive interaction with human beings display an even wider variety of communicative gestures (van Lawick-Goodall, 1968; Hayes and Nissen, 1971; Kellogg and Kellogg, 1933).

Because American Sign Language (ASL) is a gestural language in current use by human beings, it has the important additional advantage of permitting comparisons between the performance of our subject and that of human children, and the evaluation of our subject's performance by independent observers, fluent in ASL.

Methods

At the outset we were certain that Washoe could learn to make a variety of signs to obtain food, drink, and other goods and services. For the project to be a success we felt something more must be developed. We wanted Washoe to use the sign language to declare her wants both positively and negatively, to describe objects and events, and to ask questions. Therefore, we attempted to provide Washoe with an environment that might be conducive to this sort of communicative behavior.

Washoe lived in a furnished housetrailer located in a large fenced yard. All participants in her training used ASL in her presence as much as possible, and speech was excluded. Whenever Washoe was awake one or more human companions were present, and they attempted to make her environment as intellectually and socially interesting as possible. A great many games and activities were introduced to maximize the amount of interaction between Washoe and these human companions who used ASL extensively in association with objects, activities, and events. In addition, Washoe's companions used ASL to communicate both with her and with one another, so that the chimp's linguistic training became an integral part of daily life and not restricted to special training sessions.

Only a brief summary of the actual teaching methods, recording techniques, and testing procedures will be given here, for these have been described elsewhere (Gardner and Gardner, 1969, 1971, 1973). In the early phases of the project we encouraged any manual play that resembled components of the gestures of sign language, by being as responsive as possible: smiling, clapping, and repeating the gesture that she seemed to have made, much as parents do when children babble. We also introduced new signs by the conventional tactics of instrumental conditioning. Thus, we would select from the responses that Washoe tended to make in a given stimulus situation, a response that resembled an ASL sign that was appropriate to the situation. By administering suitable rewards, we could then shape increasingly closer approximations to the to-be-learned sign.

It soon became obvious that most of the signs we wanted to teach Washoe could not be taught in a reasonable amount of time if we had to rely on trial-and-error alone. The odds of a reasonable approximation to an appropriate sign occurring in an appropriate situation under conditions that would permit us to administer an appropriate reward were entirely too low. Thus, two methods of guidance, modeling and molding, were used to introduce most new signs. We modeled signs in association with their referents during the activities of the day, as well as in special teaching sessions, when we deliberately engaged Washoe's attention in a new referent, and then signed its name. We also introduced new signs by displaying the referent and then holding Washoe's hands in ours, forming her hands into the appropriate configuration, and putting her hands through the required movement.

In the early stages of the project we were able to keep fairly complete records of Washoe's daily signing behavior. But, as the amount of signing and the number of signs to be monitored increased, our attempts to obtain exhaustive records became prohibitively cumbersome. We kept track of the growth of Washoe's vocabulary by recording spontaneous occurrences of signs. The criterion of acquisition was based on the reports of several different observers of the spontaneous and appropriate use of a sign throughout a period of 14 consecutive days.

We also obtained comprehensive samples of signing behavior, comparable to the samples that have been gathered for the analysis of language in young children. During recording sessions, lasting for 1 hour or less, an observer reported everything that Washoe signed, everything signed to Washoe by her companion, and the contextual events surrounding each manual utterance, by whispering into a sensitive microphone attached to a miniature cassette recorder. These comprehensive samples provide data on the use that Washoe made of her vocabulary of signs, which items of vocabulary were used more often than others, how signs were combined, how the signing of her human companion affected Washoe's signing, and so on.

In addition, we developed a testing procedure for the nouns in Washoe's vocabulary, which made use of photographs of objects. The essential features of the vocabulary test were (1) that examples for many different vocabulary items were shown; (2) that several different examples of a given vocabulary item, including some that Washoe had never seen before, were shown; (3) that the examples were presented trial by trial in a random sequence;

and (4) that the sign that Washoe made would be the only information about the photograph she was viewing available to the observer.

A number of other procedures for recording data were developed for particular studies within the project, e.g., a determination of Washoe's preferred hand in signing.

We also kept an extensive motion-picture record of Washoe's signing and of other aspects of her behavior, such as imitation, play, and tool-using. Two special studies within the project required videotape recording of signing.

Results

At the time that we started to receive support for this project from the National Geographic Society (September 1969), Washoe was using a vocabulary of over 80 signs, and she probably understood several times that number. She used her signs very much as young children use words, and this was so both for the way in which she transferred the use of signs to new referents and for the way she combined signs to form sentencelike manual utterances (Brown, 1970; Gardner and Gardner, 1969, 1971, 1973).

During the period of Society support Washoe acquired approximately 50 new signs, by our criterion of reliability. These included signs for objects, actions, and proper names, as well as signs for negation *(no, cannot),* signs for such abstract attributes as *same* and *different,* and the question sign *Who.* (Gardner and Gardner, 1975).

During the period of Society support many formal tests of vocabulary were administered. The percent of items that were correctly named on these tests, ranging between 70 and 90, far exceeded chance expectation and served as evidence that Washoe was using the signs in her vocabulary appropriately. Since Washoe named entirely new photographs of objects on several of these tests, she evidently was using signs as names for referent classes. An analysis of errors in the vocabulary tests showed that these reflected conceptual relations among signs; the common error for a photograph of a dog, for example, would be the sign for another animal such as *cat,* while the common error for pictures of fruit would be the sign for another type of food, such as *meat.* We have recently reported these findings (Gardner and Gardner, 1971, 1974) and are in the process of preparing the report for publication.

During this period we also undertook a number of systematic samples of signing behavior. Very briefly, we sampled Washoe's replies to questions containing the interrogatives *Who, Whose, What,* and *Where.* The results showed that Washoe produced different classes of signs as replies to the different interrogatives, e. g., signs for persons in replies to questions containing *Who,* signs for location in reply to questions containing *Where.* Comparable findings for children have been cited as evidence for the mastery of grammatical classes (Gardner and Gardner, 1975).

Finally, during the period of Society support, Roger Fouts completed his experimental evaluation of teaching methods (Fouts, 1972). He was able to compare the relative effectiveness of three successful techniques for introducing new signs into the vocabulary, and he is presently continuing research on this topic with a larger number of subjects.

We ourselves were sufficiently encouraged by the level of verbal behavior achieved by a very young chimpanzee to plan to undertake further research with more chimpanzees and older chimpanzees in order to investigate the social transmission of sign language, the critical age for sign language acquisition, the effectiveness of different training procedures, and the regularities in the development of concepts and vocabulary.

REFERENCES

BASTIAN, JARVIS R.
    1965. Primate signaling systems and human languages.   Pp. 585-606 *in* "Primate Behavior," I. Devore, ed., 654 pp., illus. Holt, Rinehart & Winston, New York.
BROWN, ROGER
    1970. The first sentences of child and chimpanzee.   Chapt. 8 (pp. 208-231) *in* "Psycholinguistics: Selected Papers," 392 pp. Free Press, New York.
BRYAN, ALAN LYLE
    1963. The essential morphological basis for human culture.   Current Anthrop., vol. 4, pp. 297-306.
FOUTS, R. S.
    1972. The use of guidance in teaching sign language to a chimpanzee.   Journ. Comp. and Physiol. Psych., vol. 80, pp. 515-522.
GARDNER, BEATRICE T., and GARDNER, R. ALLEN
    1971. Two-way communication with an infant chimpanzee.   Pp. 117-184 *in* "Behavior of Nonhuman Primates," vol. 4, Allan M. Schrier and Fred Stollnitz, eds., 239 pp., illus. Academic Press, New York.
    1974. Comparing the early utterances of child and chimpanzee.   Pp. 3-23 *in* "Minnesota Symposium on Child Psychology," vol. 8, Ann Pick, ed. University of Minnesota Press.
    1975. Evidence for sentence constituents in the early utterances of child and chimpanzee.   Journ. Exper. Psych., vol. 104, pp. 244-267.

GARDNER, R. ALLEN, and GARDNER, BEATRICE T.
    1969. Teaching sign language to a chimpanzee.   Science, vol. 165, pp. 664-672.
    1972. Communication with a young chimpanzee: Washoe's vocabulary.   *In*
        "Modeles Animaux du Comportement Humain," R. Chauvin, ed.
        CNRS, Paris.
    1973. Teaching sign language to the chimpanzee, Washoe (16-mm. sound film).
        Psychological Cinema Register, State College, Pennsylvania.
HAYES, KEITH J., and HAYES, CATHERINE
    1951. The intellectual development of a home-raised chimpanzee.   Proc.
        Amer. Philos. Soc., vol. 95, pp. 105-109, illus.
HAYES, KEITH J., and NISSEN, C. H.
    1971. Higher mental functions of a home-raised chimpanzee.   Pp. 59-115 *in*
        "Behavior of Non-human Primates," vol. 4, Allan M. Schrier and Fred
        Stollnitz, eds., 234 pp., illus. Academic Press, New York.
KELLOGG, WINTHROP N., and KELLOGG, LUELLA A.
    1933. The ape and the child: A study of environmental influence upon early
        behavior, 341 pp., illus.   Whittlesey House, New York.
LAWICK-GOODALL, JANE VAN
    1968. The behaviour of free-living chimpanzees in the Gombe Stream Reserve.
        Animal Behavior Monogr., vol. 1, pt. 3, pp. 161-311, illus.
YERKES, ROBERT M.
    1943. Chimpanzees: A laboratory colony, 321 pp., illus.   Yale University Press,
        New Haven, Connecticut.

R. ALLEN GARDNER

BEATRICE T. GARDNER

Aerial Roots of Trees in Coastal Swamps of the Eastern Pacific

Principal Investigator: A. Malcolm Gill, CSIRO Division of Plant Industry, Canberra City, Australia.[1]

Grant No. 807:   In support of a study of the aerial root systems of trees in eastern Pacific coastal swamps.

The tree floras of the world reach a pinnacle of diversity in the Tropics. This variability is most widely appreciated for the tropical rainforest where large numbers of trees intermingle on small tracts, where lianes and epiphytes abound and where growth and decay are always prominent. Other plant communities in the Tropics are usually less spectacular in these respects but may have their own particular features of interest. This is true of the coastal swamps of the Tropics where aerial roots are prominent and diverse in their shapes, sizes, and modes of development (Ogura, 1940; Jenik, 1967, 1973; Gill and Tomlinson, 1975). My objective was to survey this array in terms of morphological development and, partly, function.

The major coastal swamps of the Tropics are the mangrove-dominated plant communities. While taxonomic diversity of mangroves is relatively low in the Americas and West Africa, it is relatively high along the warm shores of the Indian Ocean and the eastern Pacific Ocean. Thus, attention was given to the swamps of the latter region, particularly those in the Philippines, New Guinea, and eastern Australia. Some genera such as *Pandanus* were found to penetrate the mangrove swamps from neighboring less saline swamps and were included in this brief survey because of their spectacular aerial root systems.

High water tables are, perhaps, the most definitive feature of swamps and their presence has several consequences. The emphasis here will be on one of these, soil anaerobioses. Water has a very low oxygen diffusivity and anaerobic conditions develop very rapidly when the soil is flooded

---

[1] This study was carried out while the author was employed by the Fairchild Tropical Garden, Miami, Florida. The assistance of Gerry Goeden during these investigations is much appreciated. Laboratory facilities and transport were kindly supplied by the International Rice Research Institute in the Philippines.

209

(Ponneramperuma, 1972). Oxygen for growth of subterranean roots must then come from external sources. For most woody plants growing in oxygen-deficient soils it may be assumed that oxygen must travel internally in the plant, having entered it from atmospheric sources. Various strategies may be adopted by the plant to link the roots in the anaerobic soil with other plant parts in the air, and many of the early investigators have assumed that aerial roots of swamp plants fulfil such a function. In the present study a survey of aerial root structures among mangroves and other woody swamp plants was made. Also, an attempt was made to gather information pertinent to the possible roles of the aerial roots of *Ceriops* and *Bruguiera*.

Methods

Aerial roots were observed in the field in the genera *Rhizophora, Bruguiera,* and *Ceriops* (Rhizophoraceae), *Xylocarpus* spp. (Meliaceae), *Lumnitzera* (Combretaceae), *Avicennia* spp. (Avicenniaceae), *Sonneratia* (Sonneratiaceae), *Acanthus* (Acanthaceae), and *Pandanus* (Pandanaceae). These observations were necessarily superficial but provided some useful data on growth and development.

Anticipating a possible role in gas exchange for the aerial roots of *Ceriops* and *Bruguiera,* we made a series of measurements on stems and aerial roots at different stages of development in order to ascertain the volumes of gas spaces in the tissues. Weights of excised tissues were recorded before and after infiltration with water under vacuum. Volumes of tissues were measured by water displacement. In this way the volumes of gas spaces in irregularly shaped tissues could be measured.

Results

Root System Variety. Part of the array of root structures observed will be summarized below; although some of these observations have been published (Gill, 1975; Gill and Tomlinson, 1975), this repetition is made to facilitate later discussion. A general semipopular and wide-ranging account of observations made during the course of this work has been published also (Gill, 1970), but the details of results on the root systems of *Ceriops* and *Bruguiera* have not been reported by me previously.

Avicennia *spp.:*
Aerial roots arose vertically as lateral roots from major horizontal subterranean roots. Branching of the aerial portion was rare and, when apparent,

FIG. 1. Developmental stages of the *Ceriops*-type root system at the base of the stem. On the left are two seedlings with small-diameter roots emergent from the hypocotyl. On the right are two plants with some aerial roots removed to show the hypocotyl (arrows) from which they have grown.

was always the result of injury. The aerial roots were usually pencil-like in size and shape and had limited growth. Secondary thickening of the aerial roots was usually slight but the typical "anomalous" secondary thickening of the stem (Gill, 1971) was repeated in the major horizontal roots that supported them. Aerial roots sometimes developed on the stem and grew downward. Vertically growing aerial roots of the *Avicennia* type varied in length from a few centimeters to 2 meters, the maximum being observed in *Sonneratia* in New Guinea.

Xylocarpus *spp.:*

The conspicuous feature of the root systems of these species was the asymmetric development of secondary tissues from major horizontal subterranean roots. In *X. moluccensis* conical projections of secondary tissues appeared above the substrate from the upper sides of subterranean waves in the parent root. In *X. granatum,* secondary thickening proceeded all along the upper side of the parent root to form an aerial slab of secondary tissues.

F**IG**. 2.   Four stages of development of the looped aerial root: *(a)* Root emergence from the soil and beginning of apex return to the substrate *(upper left); (b)* return to soil completed *(upper right); (c)* and *(d)* later stages.

Pandanus *sp.:*

This species was found near Lae, New Guinea, intermingling with the mangroves *Sonneratia* and *Bruguiera*. Festoons of aerial roots hung curtain-like down to the soil. Rows of very short, sharp, lateral roots were present on these aerial roots, which were about 2-4 centimeters in diameter. Upon penetration of the muddy substratum, major axes apparently gave rise to relatively large-diameter, aerial laterals, which grew down to the substrate. Another type of aerial root in these species had a subterranean origin. These were roots of only about 2 millimeters in diameter emerging vertically for only a few centimeters. They had well-developed lateral roots formed without the stimulus of injury, and these had a tendency to be oriented vertically.

Rhizophora *spp.* (see also Gill and Tomlinson, 1969):

Aerial roots in this species always arose aerially from stems, branches, or secondarily thickened aerial roots and usually arose at right angles to the parent tissue. No lateral root formed in unanchored aerial roots, unless injured, but lateral roots were formed readily in soil. After secondary thickening in the aerial portion of the anchored root, further aerial roots were formed which repeated the cycle of development shown by the parent; in this way a series of root arches was built up. Secondary thickening occurred preferentially along the upper surfaces leaving the anchored-root columns largely free of secondary development.

Bruguiera *and* Ceriops:

Early development of plants of these genera was similar to that observed in *Rhizophora mangle* L. (Gill and Tomlinson, 1969).

Roots about 1-2 millimeters in diameter emerged from the distal end of the propagule's hypocotyl (fig. 1), which became erect and began to expand leaves. With further growth, aerial roots about 5-8 millimeters in diameter formed close together at the base of the stem in a generally acropetal sequence and grew down to the substrate at an angle of about 45° (fig. 1). Subterranean roots tended to grow horizontally upon entry into the soil, so that the root system had a splayed appearance near the base of the stem. Secondary thickening tended to proceed preferentially in the uppermost (youngest) roots and a root buttress may be formed. As secondary thickening was greatest in the uppermost aerial roots it was bypassed in the lower stem and lower aerial roots.

Major horizontal roots, under some conditions, turned upward, grew out of the soil for about 10-15 centimeters, but returned to the soil again. In this way an aerial loop was formed in the root system (fig. 2). On the approach side of the loop the axis diameter was usually about 25 percent smaller than that of the exit side. Lateral roots on the approach side were also smaller than those on the exit side (fig. 2) where a group of large diameter lateral roots sometimes formed near the point of root re-entry into the substrate.

Secondary thickening took place in the loop in preference to the subterranean roots and, in addition, took place preferentially on the upper side of the loop, thus forming a flattened plate or knob of secondary tissue (fig. 3). New adventitious laterals arose from this and usually grew out in the same direction taken by the parent root. Further laterals arose from these roots upon their secondary thickening.

Gas Content. Gas content declined from the lower to the upper stem, and all these values were relatively low. This suggested that gas transport from the leaves to the roots was most unlikely.

To assess the possibility of the stem *base* being a source area for aerating underground roots a series of gas-content determinations was made for stem sections 10-20 centimeters above ground level (above all aerial roots). For stems with cross-sectional areas of 1.0, 2.3, and 11.0 square centimeters gas cross-sectional areas were 13, 14, and 33 square millimeters. Thus, with secondary thickening, the cross-sectional area capable of transferring gas increased.

Young aerial roots originating from the stem had relatively high gas content (30-40 percent), but this percentage dropped as secondary thickening proceeded. (As in stems, however, the actual cross-sectional area occupied by gas increased.) Similarly, young looped aerial roots had about 30-35 percent gas content, but this dropped to a more-or-less constant value of 18-26 percent in both *Bruguiera* and *Ceriops* roots up to 400 milliliters in volume. Subterranean roots underwent little secondary thickening and tended to maintain high gas content of 45-60 percent.

Discussion

The function of the aerial roots of swamp plants has been assumed to be one of aeration of subterranean roots. This has been demonstrated for the aerial roots of *Rhizophora mangle* and *Avicennia germinans* (syn. *A. nitida*) in Florida by Scholander et al. (1955), although these roots are vastly different morphologically. Generalization on the basis of Scholander's studies (loc. cit.) to all the aerial roots described here would seem premature in the light of the work of Kramer et al. (1952), who looked at aerial roots of the *Xylocarpus moluccensis* type in *Taxodium distichum*. These authors were unable to demonstrate a gas-exchange role in these woody roots. Later, the evidence for such a function being fulfilled by the aerial roots of *Ceriops* and *Bruguiera* will be examined.

Some, but not all, of the variation in root systems of swamp plants can be due to variation in environment. For example, the looped aerial roots of *Bruguiera* and *Ceriops* appear to form only when the root system is waterlogged. This is true also of the small erect and branched aerial roots of *Pandanus* but not of the larger-diameter descending aerial roots of the same species. In *Lumnitzera racemosa* at Darwin, Australia, looped aerial roots (superficially similar to those in *Ceriops* but differing in origin and diameter) formed only in narrow drainage channels and not on the broader, flatter slopes of channel catchments. By way of contrast, the aerial roots of *Rhizophora* and *Avicennia* are formed wherever these species occur.

Among root systems of the mangrove genera of the family Rhizophoraceae there appear to be a number of common properties. These occur in *Rhizophora* spp. and in *Ceriops* and *Bruguiera* in waterlogged soils (but their applicability to *Kandelia* is unknown). These properties are:

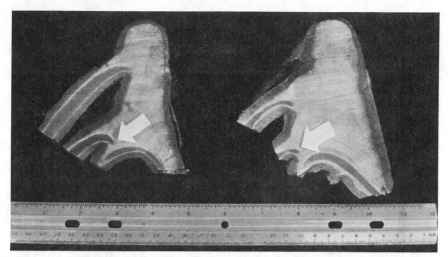

FIG. 3. Longitudinal sections of looped aerial roots showing arched medulla of original root *(at bases of sections)* and adventitious external roots *(arrows)* arising from the secondarily thickened tissues.

(1) no secondary thickening (or, at least, very markedly reduced secondary thickening) in roots in a waterlogged environment;

(2) lateral root formation in primary aerial roots absent unless the roots are injured;

(3) lateral root diameter upon entry into the substrate often initially large but soon decreasing;

(4) eccentric secondary thickening of aerial roots on upper sides;

(5) adventitious lateral roots formed on secondarily thickened aerial roots in the absence of injury.

Despite these similarities, the root systems of *Rhizophora* and of *Ceriops* are vastly different. In its simplest form the root system of *Rhizophora* can be visualized as a set of secondarily thickened arches supported by minimally thickened columns that extend vertically down into the soil to limited depths. This contrasts with the buttressed base of *Ceriops,* and the minimally thickened horizontal subterranean roots with secondarily thickened aerial projections emergent from the soil.

For *Ceriops,* the following *interpretation* of the root system is offered. Secondary thickening is normal in subterranean roots in aerobic soils but is lacking in anaerobic soils where ramification of the root system is restricted as it is in monocotyledons. As oxygen supplies to the subterranean root apex decline (being supported by oxygen from stem-borne aerial roots) the apex is induced to grow upward as do subterranean roots of *Pandanus* in waterlogged soil. Reaching the atmosphere, aeration improves and, unlike *Pandanus*, the apex returns to the soil. With the improved aeration, root diameter increases and the size of lateral roots is enhanced. With secondary thickening, enhanced by the aerobic milieu, new adventitious laterals are formed that may further explore the surrounding soil volume. Thus, these aerial roots may be regarded as centers for the ramification of the root system. If such views are correct any system of aeration of subterranean roots may be viewed as a system of gas-exchange areas (aerial roots on the stem or looped aerial roots) with distal subterranean zones of utilization (of oxygen) and production (of carbon dioxide). But these comments presuppose a role of these aerial roots in gas exchange, and so this topic is now examined in more detail.

To have a role in subterranean root aeration, a structure must be exposed to air, have zones of gas exchange between root tissues and the atmosphere, and must have a network of gas conduits linking the aerial and subterranean structures. Aerial roots fill the first requirement by definition, and in *Ceriops* and *Bruguiera* these have large lenticels — likely portholes of gas exchange. After secondary thickening these areas become quite large, particularly in *Ceriops*. Tissues in these areas appear to be deciduous and water repellent, two properties unfavorable to algae and shellfish, which might otherwise colonize them and interfere with any gas-exchange function.

Gas capacity of the roots provides a guide, but a guide only, to root potential for gas transport (because the gas spaces may lack interconnections). In the subterranean roots there is little doubt that the high gas volumes are interconnected because one can blow through root segments as if through a straw. The gas volume in the root-borne aerial roots, however, varies according to the degree of secondary development — dropping from about 30-35 percent to a more-or-less constant value of 18-26 percent in both *Bruguiera* and *Ceriops* specimens. The gas capacities of the roots do not appear to be prohibitively low for a gas-exchange function. Schimper (1903) suggested that the aerial roots of *Bruguiera* produced such large amounts of carbon dioxide that some of it must have come from subterranean roots.

In addition to the functions suggested above, the aerial roots may also aid the plant in adjusting to sedimentation. New soil layers may be exploited by sending out new aerial roots from the stem or from the aerial root loops. Such adjustment has been described for *Bruguiera* by Troll and Dragendorff (1931) and for *Mitragyna* by Jenik (1973). Other aerial roots such as those described earlier may also provide a similar function. This may be a major function for aerial roots of *Taxodium* and *Xylocarpus* for which no gas exchange function has yet been demonstrated.

REFERENCES

GILL, A. MALCOLM
  1970. The mangrove fringe of the Eastern Pacific. Fairchild Trop. Gard. Bull., vol. 25, no. 3, pp. 7-11.
  1971. Endogenous control of growth ring formation in *Avicennia.* Forest Sci., vol. 17, pp. 462-465.
  1975. Australia's mangrove enclaves: A coastal resource. Proc. Ecol. Soc. Australia, vol. 8, pp. 129-146.
GILL, A. MALCOLM, and TOMLINSON, P. BARRY
  1969. Studies on the growth of red mangrove *(Rhizophora mangle* L.): I, Habit and general morphology. Biotropica, vol. 1, pp. 1-9.
  1975. Aerial roots: An array of forms and functions. Pp. 237-260 *in* "The Development and Function of Roots," J. G. Torrey and D. T. Clarkson, eds. Third Cabot Foundation of Harvard University Symposium. Academic Press, London.
JENIK, J.
  1967. Root adaptations in West African trees. Journ. Linn. Soc. (Bot.), vol. 60, pp. 25-29.
  1973. Root system of tropical trees, 8: Stilt roots and allied adaptations. Preslia (Praha), vol. 45, pp. 250-264.
KRAMER, PAUL J.; RILEY, W. S.; and BANNISTER, THOMAS T.
  1952. Gas exchange of cypress knees. Ecology, vol. 33, pp. 117-121.
METCALFE, C. R.
  1931. The breathing roots of *Sonneratia* and *Bruguiera:* A review of the recent work by Troll and Dragendorff. Bull. Misc. Inform. Roy. Bot. Gard. Kew, vol. 65, pp. 465-467.
OGURA, Y.
  1940. On the types of abnormal roots in mangrove and swamp plants. Bot. Mag. Tokyo, vol. 54, pp. 389-404.
PONNERAMPERUMA, F. N.
  1972. The chemistry of submerged soils. Adv. Agron., vol. 24, pp. 29-96.
SCHIMPER, A. F. W.
  1903. Plant geography upon a physiological basis, 839 pp. Oxford University Press.
SCHOLANDER, PER F.; VAN DAM, LEVIE; and SCHOLANDER, S. I.
  1935. Gas exchange in the roots of mangroves. Amer. Journ. Bot., vol. 62, pp. 92-98.
TROLL, W., and DRAGENDORFF, O.
  1931. Ueber die Luftwurzeln von *Sonneratia* Linn.f. und ihre biologische Bedeutung (mit einem rechnerischen Anhang von H. Fromherz). Planta Archiv. wiss. Bot., vol. 12, pp. 311-473. (See Metcalfe, 1931.)

A. MALCOLM GILL

Flora of the Cape Region, Baja California Sur

Principal Investigators: Amy Jean Gilmartin and Mary L. Neighbours, Washington
State University, Pullman, Washington.

Grant No. 780:   In support of research on the plants of Baja California: A
study of variability in time and space.

A list of flowering plants from the Cape Region, Baja California Sur,
was compiled by the authors over a period of several years in order to
establish the present floristic assemblage. It is based in part upon field work
carried out during the summer of 1969 by the senior author and in the
summer of 1972 by both authors, plus trips during the springs of 1969 and
1974. The study area at the tip of the Peninsula includes 7,500 square
kilometers between lat. 22°52' and 24°10' N. and elevations ranging from
sea level to 2,200 meters.

The field work was complemented by herbarium studies carried out by
both authors from August 1972 through January 1973 at the Herbarium of
the University of California in Berkeley (UC). The largest single holdings
of plants from the study area are housed at the U. C. Herbarium. The present
paper represents a report of work-in-progress on the flora of the Cape
Region. It does not represent the completion of the floristic study of the
Cape Region, which will involve at least several more years of study. It is
the portion that we were able to complete with the support of the Society's
grant.

The systematic annotated list itself, occupying 43 single-spaced type-
written pages, is too long for reproducing here; copies are on file in the
National Geographic Society Library, Washington, D. C., and in the University of California Herbarium, Berkeley, or are available from the authors.

There is at present no other compilation of our current state of floristic
knowledge concerning this particular area, although there is considerable
herbarium material now available. A comprehensive list was prepared more
than 85 years ago by Brandegee (1891), a botanist with the California Academy of Sciences. Our current annotated list provides resource information

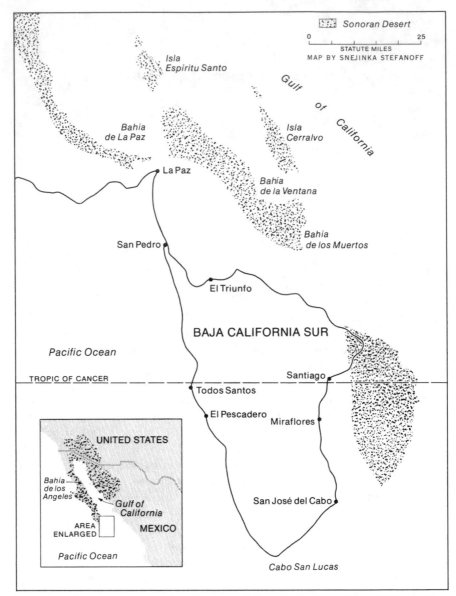

FIG. 1. Map showing the Cape Region of the peninsula of Baja California Sur, including Isla Espíritu Santo north of La Paz to Cabo San Lucas.

in a convenient form to biologists working with this and neighboring floras and faunas. The species list of Hastings et al. (1972) on punch cards includes more than 1,500 species for the Sonoran Desert as a whole, and Shreve and Wiggins (1964) include more than 3,000 species and varieties also largely from the Sonoran Desert, but only a portion of the Cape Region can be considered Sonoran Desert (see discussion below).

The rate of development of the area has stepped up severalfold with the recent completion (December 1973) of the paved transpeninsular highway that now runs the length of the Baja Peninsula, a distance of more than 1,500 kilometers. Currently, the desire for expanded tourism within the Cape Region, particularly La Paz in the northern portion and San José del Cabo at the tip (see map), has engendered political pressure for doubling the number of head of cattle in order to supply the burgeoning human population. It was learned from a newspaper report of July 1972 in La Paz that governmental engineers had been asked by the Territorial Government to study the feasibility of doing this from the viewpoint of water resources. The trend toward doubling the human population suggests that by 1985 there may well be 100,000 people in the Cape Region. It is therefore important to record now the status of the flora.

Plant introductions (e.g., St. Johnswort, genus *Hypericum*) now present in the area have a way of usurping certain habitats, while some native species may be found to be much more rare today than they were during the times of Brandegee's field work at the turn of the century (Brandegee 1891, 1892a,b, 1894, 1903). *Dryopetalon crenatum* (Brand.) Rollins (Cruciferae), for example, was collected several times by Brandegee, was noted by him (1891) to be common at moderate elevations, and was collected by C. A. Purpus in 1902 from near the Cape. It has rarely been collected subsequently.

The annotated list is organized alphabetically by family and within each family alphabetically by genus and species. Information for each specimen citation is organized in the following format: Name of species and author, habit of plant, degree of abundance, vegetation type, locality, altitude, date collected, state of the plant (that is, is it in flower, fruit, leaf?), the collector, collector's number; when known, the common name is included and immediately follows the species name. Collections made by Gilmartin are in the custody of the senior author and eventually will be turned over to the U. C. Herbarium (or to the combined U. C., Dudley, and California Academy of sciences Herbarium when this is created).

Each specimen included in the list was examined by the authors unless otherwise stated. An effort was made to examine critically all specimens originating from the Cape Region that are housed in the U. C. Herbarium. However, time did not permit examining all the Cape Region specimens of the large family Compositae or all portions of the Leguminosae, and the specimen citations are incomplete in these two families and in the Gramineae, Acanthaceae, Labiatae, Rubiaceae, Scrophulariaceae, and Solanceae.

The system of classification followed is that of Cronquist as tabulated by Becker (1973). The synonymy in Shreve and Wiggins (1964) was followed whenever possible.

The Cape Region consists mostly of scrub type of tropical deciduous forest, termed xeric forest by Shreve (Shreve and Wiggins, 1964), and pockets of vegetation of the Sonora Desert type. Shreve notes that the distribution of what he terms Central Gulf Coast type of Sonoran Desert includes a broken strip just along the coast from Bahía de Los Angeles on the gulf at lat. 29° N. to San José del Cabo (see map). A few of the common trees and shrubs of the Central Gulf Coast division of the Sonoran Desert as discussed by Shreve include *Bursera microphylla, Jatropha cinerea, Cercidium floridum, Maytenus phyllanthoides, Stegnosperma halimifolium,* and *Solanum hindsianum.* It is our observation that pieces of Sonoran Desert are also present scattered in other than strictly eastern coastal portions of the Cape Region; for example, on some of the hills west of Santiago and some areas south of Todos Santos.

In all, 732 species of flowering plants and ferns were listed by Brandegee (1892b) from the Cape Region. His lists are based upon plants collected by R. B. Hinds in 1839, by John Xantus from 1859 to 1860, by Edward Palmer in 1890, and many collected by Brandegee between 1889 and 1892 (Brandegee, 1891, 1892a). Subsequently Brandegee (1894, 1903) collected specimens of a small number of additional species.

Our list includes 368 species. Table 1 lists 51 species that are present now but that do not appear to have been noted in the Cape Region by Brandegee or other early botanical collectors. Table 1 was compiled by comparing the authors' annotated list of 368 species with the lists prepared by Brandegee (1891, 1892a,b). An effort has been made to include in table 1 only those taxa that were not noted by Brandegee. It is possible that a few species he included may be found in table 1 if we did not correctly trace the synonymy. In addition, his determinations were sometimes tentative, and we were not able to examine all his herbarium material. Most of Brandegee's collections at the California Academy Herbarium were destroyed in 1906 (Johnson, 1958). The species in table 1, however, can be considered to be that part of the present assemblage of flowering plants of the Cape Region that probably were not a conspicuous element of the flora at the turn of the century. A few of these may have been present then but are so closely related to other species included at the time that they may have been ignored by early workers. For example, *Boerhaavia maculata* Standl. and *Colubrina californica* Johnston were not included by Brandegee but are closely related to species he did include. Others not in Brandegee's list, e.g., *Anagallis arvensis* L., *Crescentia alata* HBK, *Nicotiana glauca* Grahm., and *Psidium guajava* L., are probably more recent introductions or escapes from cultivations.

Brandegee (1892b) includes several common species that he states must have been introduced, such as *Malva borealis* (not *M. miceensis* All.), *Polygonum acre* (not *P. punctatum* Ell.), and *Xanthium strumarium* L. Interestingly, our collections to date do not include these particular species.

We wish to express sincere appreciation to the Director General de Approvechamientos Forestales, México, for permission to collect and to the staff of the Herbarium at the University of California at Berkeley for making their facilities freely available. Special thanks are due also to Annetta Carter, Lincoln Constance, and John Strother.

TABLE 1. SPECIES OF THE FLORA OF THE CAPE REGION, BAJA CALIFORNIA SUR, PRESENT NOW BUT NOT NOTED BY BOTANICAL COLLECTORS AT THE TURN OF THE CENTURY.

Family	*Species*
Amaryllidaceae	*Crinum erubescens* Ait.
Asclepiadaceae	*Asclepias curassavica* L.
Bignoniaceae	*Crescentia alata* HBK
Boraginaceae	*Heliotropium hintonii* (Johnston) Johnston
"	*Tournefortia hartwegiana* Steudel
Celastraceae	*Schaefferia cuneifolia* Gray
"	*Schaefferia shrevei* Lundell
Chenopodiaceae	*Salicornia europaea* L.
"	*Salicornia pacifica* Standl.
Compositae	*Ambrosia psilostachya* DC
"	*Ambrosia pumila* (Nutt.) Gray
"	*Palafoxia linearis* (Cav.) Laq. var. *linearis*
"	*Pluchea salicifolia* (Mill.) Blake
Cruciferae	*Lepidium thurberi* Wooton
Ebenaceae	*Diospyros californica* (Brand.) Johnston var. *tonsa* Johnston
Euphorbiaceae	*Phyllanthus acuminatus* Vahl
Fouquieriaceae	*Fouquieria burragei* Rose

Gramineae	*Chloris cucullata* Bisch.
"	*Eragrostis intermedia* Hitch.
"	*Eragrostis viscosa* (Retz.) Trin.
"	*Muhlenbergia parviglumis* Vasey
"	*Panicum arizonicum* Scribn. & Merr.
"	*Piptochaetium fimbriatum* (HBK) Hitch.
"	*Rhynchelytrum repens* (Willd.) Hubb.
"	*Tragus berteronianus* Schult.
Labiatae	*Hyptis tephrodes* Gray
"	*Salvia pinguifolia* (Fern.) Woot. & Standl.
"	*Teucrium canadense* L. var. *angustatum* Gray
Leguminosae	*Albizzia sinaloensis* B. & R.
"	*Medicago sativa* L.
"	*Mimosa dysocarpa* Benth.
"	*Mimosa margaritae* Rose
"	*Pithecellobium undulatum* (B. & R.) Gentry
"	*Willardia mexicana* (Wats.) Rose
Liliaceae	*Chlorogalum parviflorum* Wats.
Malvaceae	*Bastardia bivalvis* (Cav.) HBK
Myrtaceae	*Psidium guajava* L.
Nyctaginaceae	*Boerhaavia maculata* Standl.
Olacaceae	*Ximenia parviflora* Benth. var. *glauca* De Fil.
Onagraceae	*Oenothera tetraptera* Cav.
Primulaceae	*Anagallis arvensis* L.
Rhamnaceae	*Colubrina californica* Johnston
Rubiaceae	*Crusea subulata* (Pavon) Gray
Rutaceae	*Zanthoxylum sonorense* Lundell.
Solanaceae	*Nicotiana glauca* Grahm.
"	*Physalis leptophylla* Rob. & Greenm.
"	*Solanum nodiflorum* Jacq.
Tiliaceae	*Triumfetta acracantha* Hochr.
Typhaceae	*Typha latifolia* L.
Umbelliferae	*Apium leptophyllum* (Pers.) Muell. ex Benth. ex Muell.
Zygophyllaceae	*Tribulus terrestris* L.

REFERENCES

BECKER, K. M.
1973. A comparison of angiosperm classification systems. Taxon, vol. 22, no. 1, pp. 19-50.

BRANDEGEE, T. S.
1891. Flora of the Cape District of Baja California. Proc. California Acad. Sci., ser. 2, vol. 3, pp. 108-182.

1892a. Additions to the flora of the Cape Region of Baja California. Proc. California Acad. Sci., ser. 2, vol. 3, pp. 218-227.

1892b. A distribution of the flora of the Cape Region of Baja California. Zoe, vol. 3, pp. 223-231.

1894. Additions to the flora of the Cape Region of Baja California. Zoe, vol. 4, pp. 398-408.

1903. Notes and new species of Lower California plants. Zoe, vol. 5, pp. 155-177.

HASTINGS, JAMES R.; TURNER, RAYMOND; and WARREN, D. K.
1972. An atlas of some plant distributions in the Sonoran Desert. Univ. Arizona Inst. Atmosph. Physics Techn. Rpt. no. 21, 255 pp.

JOHNSON, BETTY H.
1958. The botany of the California Academy of Sciences Expedition to Baja California in 1941. Wasmann Journ. Biol., vol. 16, no. 2, pp. 217-315.

SHREVE, F., and WIGGINS, I. L.
1964. Vegetation and flora of the Sonoran Desert, 2 vols., 1,740 pp. Stanford University Press.

AMY JEAN GILMARTIN
MARY L. NEIGHBOURS

National Geographic Society—Bishop Museum
New Guinea Entomological Expedition

Principal Investigator: J. Linsley Gressitt, Bernice P. Bishop Museum, Honolulu, Hawaii.

Grant No. 754: To conduct biogeographical investigations in the eastern-most portion of the Trust Territory of Northeast New Guinea, with special reference to the insect fauna.

The National Geographic Society—Bishop Museum New Guinea Entomological Expedition, organized by me with other members of the Entomology Department of Bishop Museum in Honolulu, took place during the latter half of 1969, with some phases continuing into 1970. Headquarters for the operations were located at Bishop Museum New Guinea Field Station (now Wau Ecology Institute), located at Wau, just above the Bulolo Gorge in Morobe District, south of Lae.

Among the aims of the expedition was the gathering of specimens and information relating to the nature of the insect fauna of a limited portion of Northeast New Guinea (Trust Territory assigned to Australia). In particular, emphasis was primarily on plant-feeding insects, especially beetles, and secondarily on bees and on soil arthropods. The geographical scope consisted of the easternmost part of Northeast New Guinea, mostly south of Bulolo, Wau, Lake Triste, and Garaina. These objectives fell within the general field of biogeography, which embraces such questions as why a given group of animals or plants occurs where it does (or did in the past) or why it is absent from an area.

Several persons participated in the field work at different periods: During July and August my wife and youngest daughter and I worked in several of the areas. We were joined late in July by Dr. Yoshihiro Hirashima, and a little later by Prof. Janos Balogh, after which my wife and daughter returned to Hawaii. After I left a few weeks later, Balogh and Hirashima continued for a further few weeks. Mr. and Mrs. Josef Sedlacek were in the area for a few months and were joined by their son for part of the time. The members and their affiliations are listed below.

227

J. Linsley Gressitt: Chairman, Entomology Department, Bishop Museum, Honolulu — 2 months.

Margaret Gressitt: Wife — 1 month

Ellyn Gressitt: Daughter (student) — 1 month

Janos Balogh: Professor of Zoology, R. Eötvos University, Budapest, Hungary — 3 months.

Yoshihiro Hirashima: Associate Professor (now Professor) of Entomology, Kyushu University, Fukuoka, Japan — 3 months.

Josef Sedlacek: Resident entomologist, Bishop Museum Field Station, Wau, New Guinea — 5 months.

Marie Sedlacek: Field assistant in entomology — 5 months

J. H. Sedlacek: Son (student) — 2 months

Abid Beg Mirza: Pakistani animal collector (funded from other sources), attached to Bishop Museum Field Station.

Field Methods

Various collecting methods were utilized to gather specimens for study. As far as possible, material was carefully collected with host or microenvironment documentation, to provide the greatest amount possible of ecological data. In addition, some mass-collecting methods were used, such as trapping with Malaise traps, lights, and funnels. Since Professor Balogh's area of study is soil- and litter-inhabiting mites and small spiders, great quantities of forest litter and similar material were collected and processed through Berlese funnels to extract the mites, springtails, and various other soil insects, arthropods, earthworms, and other lower animals. Forty funnels were used simultaneously to extract the material in the field. Dr. Hirashima, being a bee specialist, searched for bee nests of various types and accumulated specimens and photographs. In my own work host-association of plant-feeding beetles was the primary objective. Particular emphasis was put on insects of *Nothofagus,* the southern beech, and of associated plants in the moss forest. In this environment study was continued on the epizoic symbiosis, described below.

Investigations of areas involving more than a day's walk away from roads were achieved by the use of trained field assistants at the field station, hiring extra porters as needed, and going by foot, carrying camping equipment and supplies, to the object areas. Starts were made by vehicles, to the end of roads, as at Edie Creek, the Upper Watut Valley, and the end of the road east of Kaisenik (east of Wau), as well as from Garaina.

Itinerary

During the early part of July, my wife, our daughter, and I worked around Wau, site of the Bishop Museum Field Station. We made plans and arrangements for the various phases of the expedition and studied moss-forest insects on Mount Kaindi. Next we made a trip of a few days to Garaina, at the eastern end of the area outlined for study. From there we intended to stop at Bapi, partway back to Wau, but weather, and the imminent arrival in Wau of other members of the team, necessitated cancellation of that stop. Late in July Abid Beg Mirza, animal and parasite collector, funded under other auspices, did some of the preliminary reconnaissance in the study area (to Kujeru and part of the Bulldog Road on the south slope of the divide). Next Dr. Hirashima arrived, and he and my family made a 3-day trip to the top of the divide on the Bulldog Road, south of Edie Creek and Mount Kaindi.

In the meantime Professor Balogh arrived in Port Moresby; Mr. and Mrs. Sedlacek left Wau for a period in the upper Fly River, and they met at Mount Hagen, Balogh spending a week with the Sedlaceks and then proceeding to Goroka to meet Hirashima for the Mount Wilhelm trip. During that week my wife, daughter, and I flew to Mount Wilhelm, dropping Hirashima at Aiyura for a few days' work. The latter then proceeded to Goroka, met Balogh, and the two flew to Mount Wilhelm, my wife and daughter leaving Keglsugl on the same plane that brought them. I then went back to the research station (Australian National University — partly funded by Bishop Museum) on Mount Wilhelm with Balogh and Hirashima. After several successful days there, including a climb to the summit and along part of the side ridge, we descended and proceeded to Angoram on the Sepik River for a few days. Following this we returned to Wau and work proceeded in the main study area. Further work was done in the Wau area and in the western end of the Owen Stanley Mountains after I returned to Honolulu. After some weeks the Sedlaceks returned to Wau and worked in the study area. Late in the year their son came back during vacation from college, and work proceeded in the Kaindi, Bulldog, Kujeru, and Garaina areas.

Early in 1970 I returned to Wau and made two more attempts to reach the summit of Mount Amingwiwa. My first attempts had commenced in 1966. On the fifth try I finally reached the summit, which proved to be not quite as high as anticipated — somewhat less than 12,000 feet. I also made a trip by foot partway to the Kujeru area during 1970.

Environment

The montane environments of New Guinea are rich and diverse in flora and fauna. It is here that a great majority of the endemic New Guinea species occur. Many of the species occurring in the lowlands are widespread ones extending for great distances, even onto neighboring island groups such as the Moluccas, Schouten Islands, or Bismarcks (though species on the last usually differ from those on the New Guinea mainland). On the other hand, the montane species are often local endemics, so that different species occur on different mountain ranges to a great extent.

The studies were based at Wau, at the Bishop Museum Field Station. Here, in the upper edge of the *Araucaria* zone, in lower montane rainforest, there is an arboretum containing many of the local trees and other plants, partly identified. The lower montane rainforest is exceedingly rich and diverse in species. It is rather disturbed in the Wau Valley bottom, but in the Bulolo Gorge and some continuous slopes from there up to Mount Missim on the north and the Bulolo-Watut divide to the south there are reasonably undisturbed sections. Above the station at Wau, on the slopes of both Mount Kaindi and Mount Missim, the oak forests are well represented above the *Araucaria* zone and below the *Nothofagus* zone. The oak zone may be fairly pure or may be mixed or replaced by diverse midmontane rainforest.

Mount Kaindi. The summit of this small mountain (2,350 meters altitude) immediately south of Wau, together with the Edie Creek area, a spacious upland valley on the west flank of the mountain, 300-500 meters lower than the summit, provides a highly diverse main study area. These areas are in the *Nothofagus* zone and lower moss-forest portion, or upper middle montane rainforest. Kaindi, a north-south ridge with a rise at each end, is nearly the same altitude in between. The road from Wau reaches the ridge just south of the north peak, which is still largely covered with forest. The south peak is cleared and leveled and has a telephone repeater station, some second-growth forest, and some remnant nearly pure *Nothofagus* forest. Along the 2-kilometer ridge between north and south summits there are some large *Nothofagus* and other trees — in places fairly natural and elsewhere occurring as fragments of disturbed forest.

The natural forest here, as on the north summit, is fairly dense, highly varied in composition, and wet and mossy. The larger trees are about 40 meters tall and bear numerous epiphytes. *Nothofagus* makes up nearly 40 percent of the biomass on the ridge. It is a common tendency of *Nothofagus* to dominate on ridges and low summit areas.

Other important trees in this forest include several species of Elaeo-carpaceae, including *Elaeocarpus, Sericolea,* and *Sloanea,* but many of them are not yet identified. Others are Rutaceae, including *Evodia* of several species, *Melicope,* and *Atlantia.* Also *Cryptocarya* in the Lauraceae; *Eurya, Aridisia, Macaranga, Archboldiodendron, Quercus,* and *Castanopsis; Drimys* (Winter-aceae), *Aralia, Podocarpus,* and four species of *Rubus.* Among the epiphytes are *Freycinetia* and many other vines, orchids, bryophytes, and lichens.

Bulldog Road. Higher up, along the Bulldog Road to the south of Kaindi and Edie Creek, there are many species of rhododendron and relatives. Just below the summits (3,250 meters) near the highest point in the road (3,050 meters) moss forest attains superlative proportions, with very thick moss and hepatic growth.

Mount Amingwiwa is the highest point of a forbidding mountain range lying along the backbone of New Guinea between the Eastern Highlands of the broad central part of the island and the Owen Stanley Mountains of the slender eastern portion. This range is shorter and much less known than the Owen Stanleys but is less than 2,000 feet lower than the latter. New Guinea is one of the four major wet tropical areas of the world, and its mountains are difficult to climb where trails do not exist. (Many Japanese soldiers died crossing the Owen Stanley Mountains during World War II.)

Mount Amingwiwa and its range are not named or indicated on most maps but are near some well-known landmarks. They are southwest of Bulolo and Wau, which are south of Lae at the inner end of the Huon Gulf. Both Bulolo and Wau are gold-mining and lumbering centers. Edie Creek, site of the richest gold strikes in New Guinea, and still producing, is near the top of Mount Kaindi, just south of Wau. At Bulolo large dredges may still be seen in the valley, and there is one of them at Wau, but other methods of mining are used now.

One of the greatest stands of *Araucaria* trees occurs in the Wau-Bulolo Valley and nearby valleys such as the Watut. Many of the trees have been lumbered, but new forests are being planted, which include both species of New Guinea *Araucaria* — the klinkii pine and the hoop pine.

This area has a great history, for the gold was discovered over four decades ago, before there were roads or airfields in the area. In general in interior New Guinea the construction of airfields preceded that of roads. The miners came over the mountains from the coast and built airstrips. Then the huge gold dredges were cut up in pieces, carried inland in 3-motored Fokker planes, and then welded together again. For quite a period, while the gold rush continued at a very high pitch, Wau had the busiest airstrip in the world. Then there were two hotels at Wau and one at Edie

Creek, besides many shacks. Errol Flynn was one of the many colorful characters attracted to the scene. During World War II, the Wau-Edie Creek area played an important role. The only road ever built across New Guinea was constructed from Bulldog on a river estuary on the south coast to Wau via Edie Creek. Later it was extended to Bulolo and Wau from Lae.

The Bulldog Road was built by Australians and Americans for transport of war supplies to the north coast after most of the airfields had been lost to the Japanese. American jeeps with trailers transported war supplies. After airfields in the north were retaken, the road was no longer needed. Having been hurriedly built on steep slopes, it suffered many landslides and so would have been too expensive to maintain as a cross-island highway. Thus, there is no road across the island, but one planned will probably go through Wau and eastward. The Bulldog Road continues from the Edie Creek Road from Wau. A branch was built to the top of Mount Kaindi, where a repeater station was constructed. In 1971, as a result of a worsening landslide of long history, a detour was constructed, which shortens the distance to Kaindi but lengthens the road from Wau to Edie Creek.

Ascent of Mount Amingwiwa. Our first attempt to scale this mountain, which is part of a range extending from northwest to southeast, was made from near the highest point of the Bulldog Road, which crosses the southeast end of the range; but the distance was too great for us to get very far. The second try was from Edie Creek via the uppermost village in the Watut Valley, opposite the summit. On this 4-day trip we did get fairly high, but still within the forest. We made the third attempt from farther down the Watut, approaching by road via Bulolo. We got onto a main side ridge, leading toward the northwest end of the higher part of the range. The direction and progress were fairly good, and we found a trail partway, but some errors were made and the five days did not enable us to reach the main ridge. We made the fourth try again from Edie Creek, traversing the Bulldog Road a few kilometers, then dropping down quite far up the Watut, and immediately taking a ridge on the other side of the river. This got us to the main ridge, but a long distance from the top, and we found largely dense scrub rather than grassland in that section and had to return without getting very far on the main ridge during the 5-day trip. For the fifth and successful climb we chose the same route as the third, making better headway with our former trail and avoiding the earlier errors that involved some obstructions and circling. We reached the summit very late on the second day and camped for a cold and windy night with limited shelter. During the trip we experienced considerable rain and mist.

The lower ridges are covered with deep rainforest of highly varied nature, sprinkled with large *Araucaria* trees at the base. Higher on the side ridges we found prominent stands of *Nothofagus* (southern beech), thickly clothed with moss and other epiphytic growth. At just over 2,000 meters altitude the forest became much lower and the slope steepened as we reached the side of the main ridge. Shortly we reached open country, consisting of *Danthonia* tussock-grassland, in part replaced by tall *Gahnia*-like sedge, also in tussock form. Often there were small shallow ponds surrounded by more tundralike growth of shorter sedges and grasses, with much moss and lichen. Still higher there was some true tundra. Throughout the grassland and tundra the ground was very wet and soft. As we got higher on the main ridge, the ascent was more gradual. There was constant alternation between grassland and stunted forest, with higher trees in protected areas. Although there was tundra at the summit, with small ponds right to the top, forest also extended to within a few meters of the summit and the main ridge, in ravines. The summit was well under 3,500 meters altitude according to my altimeter, but it is higher than 12,000 feet according to other information and from comparison with the peaks at the top of the Bulldog Road.

Palms and tree ferns drop out at much lower altitudes, but *Pandanus* was common, often standing above some of the stunted forests at about 3,000 meters.

Other areas. The areas around Kujeru and Garaina that we investigated are partly of lower altitude than Mount Kaindi and possess some different elements, and the variety of lowland and lower montane elements is greater. On the way to the Kujeru area the oak forests dominate on the low ridges, which are mostly too low for *Nothofagus*. The Waria Valley around Garaina has a more tropical aspect, with elements not seen at Wau and apparently somewhat different from Bulolo. On the approaches to the Owen Stanley Mountains several montane zones are passed through, but the approach route from Garaina is well populated and much of the forest is gone. Higher on the mountains the insect species, and probably many of the plants, are different from those in the Bulldog-Amingwiwa area.

Epizoic Symbiosis

This phenomenon, the symbiotic existence of animals and plants on the bodies of living animals, is widely developed in marine environments, but perhaps nowhere is it so highly developed among land animals as in the upper montane areas of New Guinea. Its full expression involves the existence together on the backs of large weevils of representatives of a number of families of algae, diatoms, fungi, lichens, liverworts, and mosses — and even a fern gametophyte — with Protozoa, rotifers, nematodes, phytophagous and predaceous mites, as well as parasitic mites, and bark lice. How this ecosystem developed is interesting to speculate. The weevils appear to be modified to encourage the growth of the plants and to protect them and foster the existence of the phytophagous mites, in particular. The plants would appear to provide some protection in camouflaging the weevils, but it is not clear what they would be protected against. The only suspected enemies of the large weevils are nocturnal predaceous marsupials.

Three subfamilies of weevils are involved in the relationship, but the full expression is usually found only in the very large *Gymnopholus* weevils. Most of the groups of plants and animals have been found at one time or another on the *Pantorhytes* weevils and the larger cryptorhynchine weevils, but rarely have all the elements been found together on these two groups of weevils.

It is suspected that among the important factors in the evolution of this ecosystem are the lack of a dry season and the prevailing high humidity and frequency of fog in the montane environment where it has developed. The cryptogamic plants represented on the weevils thrive in such damp environments. Among the animals, the rotifers and nematodes require a practically aquatic environment to exist. When not actually wet the rotifers contract and become like shriveled shells. In this condition they are pink and visible under a hand lens, whereas when wet and active they are colorless, semitransparent, and hard to see. They are easily confused with the plant growth around or beneath them.

This assemblage is believed to include the only known occurrence of moss on living animals, the only occurrence of lichens on insects, the only plant-feeding mites living on the bodies of animals, and the only occurrence of rotifers on land animals, as well as the probably sole records of some of the other occurrences.

Biogeography of New Guinea

New Guinea holds a key position in biotic relationships between southeast Asia, Australia, the Pacific islands and New Zealand, Antarctica, and southern South America. It has been a pivoting point on dispersal routes and a source area for oceanic fauna. It has served as a way point for movement of plants and animals between the East Indies and Australia. There are said to have been no direct connections between Australia and New Zealand, but rather connections of New Zealand and New Guinea via the Melanesian arcs, partly through New Caledonia, and again from New Guinea to Australia, partly during late connections in the Pleistocene. Some of those connections may have been just to the south of New Guinea. Much of the Polynesian fauna has come from the New Guinea area, becoming more depauperate among the more eastern islands. There is a sudden impoverishment at the break between the Solomon Islands and the New Hebrides. This line marks the division between continental and oceanic islands, the latter including New Hebrides, Fiji, and others to the east. The Solomons' biota is related to that of New Guinea, but with some endemic features.

The New Guinea biota has been classified by some as included in the Australian Region and by others as part of the Oriental Region, which to some reaches only to the Wallace Line. Among vertebrate animals the New Guinea fauna is primarily Australian in relationship. However, for insects and other invertebrate groups, and also most plant groups, New Guinea is more closely related to the Oriental Region. Within New Guinea Australian elements dominate in the southern portions with savanna country and seasonal rainfall. In the interior montane portions and northern lowlands, Oriental elements are more conspicuous. The contrast in relationships is both ecological and historical. The rainforests of the north and the mountains provide environments (and plants) more similar to those of Indonesia, whereas the southern savanna country is like much of Australia. The rainforests of Queensland present a depauperate version of the New Guinea rainforest biota. In general, plants and insects can easily cross short water barriers where most land vertebrates cannot. Thus, insects readily dispersed among the islands in similar climate and vegetation, whereas the mammals and other vertebrates would have been able to pass between New Guinea and Australia only during periods of actual connection, which did exist in both Pliocene and Pleistocene. If there had been continuous connections across the island areas of southeast Asia to New Guinea in late Tertiary, then more groups of mammals should occur in New Guinea. As the stepping-stone islands were mostly of relatively low altitude, alpine forms are largely lacking from New Guinea. Many of the high-altitude insects in New Guinea are derived from lowland forms. On the other hand, some of the high-altitude plants are closely related to forms in New Zealand, Tasmania, and still more southern islands.

A number of plant groups are known to extend from New Guinea to South America, through New Caledonia, New Zealand, Australia, and/or Tasmania, and as fossils in Antarctica. Among plants with this distribution is *Nothofagus,* now found in all those areas, except Antarctica as fossils only. *Araucaria* has the same distribution except that it occurs only as fossils in both New Zealand and Antarctica. Members of the Winteraceae and others have similar occurrence. These facts strongly suggest that the areas were connected and, together with many other data recently increasingly coming to light, demonstrate that all these regions, and earlier southern Africa, were united in Gondwanaland, which broke up during the Mesozoic with continental drift.

Insect fauna. Not only is the general insect fauna of New Guinea very rich and diverse, but also the montane areas have high endemicity as between each other. Probably many of these mountains were separate islands during the Pleistocene. The insect fauna of the portion of New Guinea forming the scope of this project is likewise highly diverse, and many more species have been found in the limited area than were expected. The reasons for the diversity are by no means clear at this time, and much more local study and comparisons with analogous environments in other parts of New Guinea will be required. Special attention is planned for the insects associated with *Nothofagus*. It will be interesting to see what parallels might exist between the distribution of the insects and their relatives and that of the southern beech.

Results

During the several months of the expedition, many thousands of insects and other arthropods were collected. These have been partly processed in Honolulu and partly (soil fauna) in Budapest. Some of this material is under study, but much of it waits for specialists and funds to become available before studies can continue. The bees are being studied by Dr. Hirashima. Certain groups of mites and spiders are being studied by Professor Balogh, but the extent of the material is such that the studies will take a long time to complete, even for limited groups. Professor Balogh expressed the opinion that as the result of his three trips to New Guinea (he will make his fourth visit in 1972) the soil arthropod fauna of the New Guinea mountains was better collected than that of North America to date.

In my own field, much useful material was obtained to supplement data and fill gaps in the collections, already obtained by the Bishop Museum. Research on this material continues, but because of the bulk of study material much time will be needed to complete even the leaf-beetle studies alone.

REFERENCES

GRESSITT, J. LINSLEY

1971a. (With J. Sedlacek.) Papuan weevil genus *Gymnopholus:* Second supplement with studies in epizoic symbiosis. Pacific Ins., vol. 12, no. 4, pp. 753-762, illus.

1971b. Chrysomelid beetles from the Papuan Subregion, 7. Pacific Ins., vol. 13, no. 3-4, pp. 607-609, illus.

1971c. Relative faunal disharmony of insects on Pacific islands. Entomological Essays Commemorating Retirement of Prof. K. Yasumatsu, pp. 15-24.

1972a. Beetles. Encyclopedia of New Guinea, pp. 63-66. University of Melbourne Press and University of Papua New Guinea.

1972b. Insects and relatives. Ibid., pp. 564-573, illus.

1973. (With A. C. Ziegler.) The effect on fauna of the loss of forests in New Guinea. Pp. 117-122 in "Nature Conservation in the Pacific," A. B. Costin and R. H. Groves, eds. Australian National University Press.

1974a. Insect biogeography. Ann. Rev. Ent., vol. 19, pp. 293-321.

1974b. Wau Ecology Institute: First biennial report, October 1971 to December 1973, 14 pp.

1974c. (With A. Hart.) Chrysomelid beetles from the Papuan Subregion, 8 (Chrysomelinae, 1). Pacific Ins., vol. 16, nos. 2-3, pp. 261-306, illus.

J. LINSLEY GRESSITT

Archeological Investigations at the Murray Springs Site, Arizona, 1969

Principal Investigator: C. Vance Haynes, Southern Methodist University, Dallas, Texas.

Grant No. 760:   For continuation of archeological excavations at the mammoth-kill site near Murray Springs, Arizona.

In 1969 at the Murray Springs Clovis site, Arizona (see fig. 1), excavations were continued to the west and south. More bison skeletons were found as well as some bones of a horse that may be part of the same animal found in 1968 (Haynes, 1976). Numerous depressions in the western part of the site are smaller than the mammoth tracks and are believed to have been made by bison or possibly horses.

Tools found in these areas include two broken Clovis points, a blade, and two fluted bifaces, one of which may be a knife. The other is a bifacial preform that was broken by the faulty removal of the channel flake. The two halves were found 10 meters apart. Fewer flakes were found than in the previous two years.

Ancient channel sand was found to extend up the sloping banks of an ancient stream and to contain more mammoth-track depressions in and around a much larger and deeper depression within the channel (fig. 2). These features indicate that the spring run was not flowing, and the most logical explanation for the large depression and channel sand upslope is a water hole dug by an animal, probably mammoth (fig. 3).

Southwestward from the main site the Clovis occupation surface conforms to the modern surface, which rises to a small hill. On the surface between the hill and the arroyo we found three end scrapers, two bifacial flakes, and dozens of flakes of materials that match those found buried at the main site. Approximately 600 square meters of this surface were cleared, raked, and screened, yielding a few more flakes.

Geological investigations this year included the excavation and mapping of 530 meters of additional backhoe trenches as well as the continuation of geologic mapping on low-altitude aerial photographs provided by

FIG. 1.   Air view of Murray Springs Clovis site, 1967, looking to the southwest. Excavations, lower right, are at junction of the main arroyo and the easternmost of two undissected swales.

FIG. 2.   Numerous small depressions between a "fossile" spring run and a mammoth skeleton are believed to be tracks of Pleistocene elephants. Clovis projectile points and tools in close association with this one indicate killing and butchering on the spot.

FIG. 3. Cross section of an exceptionally low area along the spring run reveals mammoth-track depressions and channel sand perched anomalously on the sloping banks of the channel. Either man or mammoths are believed to have scooped a shallow well in the moist stream-bed. Subsequent filling by organic clay and laminated marl suggests ponding or low energy discharge soon after Clovis hunters left the area.

the U. S. Army Combat Surveillance School at Fort Huachuca. Except for field checking and drafting the large-scale mapping of the arroyo is complete.

In the course of extending a stratigraphic trench to the north numerous teeth of horse, bison, camel, and mammoth were encountered in a coarse sand underlying the black mat at a depth of 2 to 3 meters below the present surface. The sorting, rounding, and polish exhibited by the sand, as well as its localized horizontal extent, indicate that it is the conduit of an ancient spring in which only the teeth of trapped animals survived the grinding and polishing action of the roiling spring discharge.

The stratigraphic position of this spring deposit immediately below the black mat is evidence that the spring could have been active at the time Clovis hunters were in the area, but no artifacts were found in the sand brought out of the trench by the backhoe. It is also possible that the spring was active a few hundred years before the Clovis occupation of the main site area, in which case the spring deposit offers an excellent prospect for finding evidence of an earlier occupation.

The assistant director of the Murray Springs Project and foreman of the excavations since 1966, E. T. Hemmings, has completed a Ph.D. dissertation at the University of Arizona on the archeology of the Murray Springs site (Hemmings, 1970, p. 196). A condensed version will be published in a scientific journal along with a report on the geology of the site area by Vance Haynes, director of the project. Archeological and geological work was supported by the National Geographic Society and the National Science Foundation in grants to Haynes.

REFERENCES

HAYNES, C. VANCE
    1976. Archeological investigations at the Murray Springs site, Arizona, 1968. Nat. Geogr. Soc. Res. Rpts., 1968 Projects, pp. 165-171, maps.
HEMMINGS, E. THOMAS
    1970. Early man in the San Pedro Valley, Arizona, 236 pp.   Ph.D. Dissertation, University of Arizona, Tucson.

                                                    C. VANCE HAYNES

Magnetometer Survey of the La Venta Pyramid

Principal Investigator: Robert F. Heizer, University of California, Berkeley, California.

Grant Nos. 777, 800, 816.   For a cesium magnetometer survey of the great La Venta pyramid in Mexico.

During our investigations of July 1967 at La Venta for the purpose of collecting charcoal samples for radiocarbon dating (Heizer, Drucker, and Graham, 1968) we observed that the large earth pyramid at the site was of a form quite different from what we had represented it to be, based on our topographic survey of 1955 (Drucker, Heizer, and Squier, 1959: Frontis-piece). Rather than having the rectangular base plan we had assumed, the pyramid was in fact circular, and the sides were "fluted" with an alternating series of ridges and valleys (Heizer and Drucker, 1968; Heizer, Graham, and Napton, 1968).

The earlier excavations at La Venta had not included the body of the pyramid—a formidably large mass of clay whose mass amounts to about 3½ million cubic feet. After we had cleared the surface of the pyramid of vegetation in 1968 in order to make a contour map we were curious about whether there might be internal structures. Local relations with municipal authorities (briefly recounted in Heizer, Graham, and Napton, 1968) were not very cordial ones, and we were careful to observe the requirement laid down by the Delegado Municipal (despite an authorization allowing us to do so issued by the Instituto Nacional de Antropología e Historia of the Republic of Mexico) not to excavate in the pyramid. The municipal author-ities believed that we were actually searching for buried treasure and were determined to prevent any excavations they thought might bring this to light.

As an alternative to excavation we decided to "look into" the pyramid with a high-sensitivity difference magnetometer. The equipment used was selected after laboratory tests of the magnetic properties of La Venta soils and Tuxtla Mountains basalt that was so much used for sculpture and archi-tectural embellishment at the La Venta site (Williams and Heizer, 1965).

Because two detailed reports on the survey itself, carried out in May 1969, have been published (Morrison, Clewlow, and Heizer, 1969;

Morrison, Benavente, Clewlow, and Heizer, 1970) there is no need to provide the details here.

The entire pyramid was systematically examined with the roving cesium sensor at 3.0-meter intervals and the magnetic values were recorded directly on radially scaled graph paper. Two main findings emerged. The outer surface of the pyramid consists of a mantle of unknown thickness of red clay, which is notably magnetic. This suggests that the pyramid was, like so many Mesoamerican pyramids, resurfaced on occasion and is, therefore, not a single-event construction but a structure that was enlarged at least once and probably several times during the period the site was in use — that is, 1000 B.C. to 600 B.C. (Berger, Graham, and Heizer, 1967). The second finding from the magnetometer survey is that there is a definite buried magnetic anomaly lying 1 to 2 meters below the surface in the top of the pyramid. It was not possible to check this by test excavation, but a computer model indicates that it might be made of basalt and measure 10 by 10 meters on the sides with walls on the north and east sides. The magnetometer data suggest strongly that there is a second structure lying at a greater depth.

Except by excavation there is, of course, no way of determining what the buried structure(s) in the top of the La Venta pyramid are. Local residents and officials in the town of La Venta do not look favorably upon outsiders excavating in the site, and many persons believe that a great treasure lies hidden within the pyramid. Whoever undertakes to verify the magnetometer survey findings will have to be a brave man with plenty of protection.

REFERENCES

BERGER, RAINER; GRAHAM, J. A.; and HEIZER, ROBERT F.
  1967. A reconsideration of the age of the La Venta site.   Contr. Univ. California Archaeol. Res. Fac., no. 3, pp. 1-24, illus.
DRUCKER, PHILIP; HEIZER, ROBERT F.; and SQUIER, ROBERT J.
  1959. Excavations at La Venta, Tabasco, 1955.   Bur. Amer. Ethnol. Bull. 170, 312 pp., illus.
HEIZER, ROBERT F., and DRUCKER, PHILIP
  1968. The La Venta fluted pyramid.   Antiquity, vol. 42, pp. 52-56, illus.
HEIZER, ROBERT F.; DRUCKER, PHILIP; and GRAHAM, J. A.
  1968. Investigations at La Venta, 1968.   Contr. Univ. California Archaeol. Res. Fac., no. 5, pp. 1-34, illus.
HEIZER, ROBERT F.; GRAHAM, J. A.; and NAPTON, L. K.
  1968. The 1968 investigations at La Venta.   Contr. Univ. California Archaeol. Res. Fac., no. 5, pp. 127-154, illus.
MORRISON, FRANK; BENAVENTE, JOSÉ; CLEWLOW, C. W., JR.; and HEIZER, ROBERT F.
  1970. Magnetometer evidence of a structure within the La Venta pyramid. Science, vol. 167, pp. 1488-1490, illus.
WILLIAMS, HOWEL, and HEIZER, ROBERT F.
  1965. Sources of rocks used in Olmec monuments.   Contr. Univ. California Archaeol. Res. Fac., no. 1, pp. 1-40, illus.

ROBERT F. HEIZER
PHILIP DRUCKER

Study of the Minor Planet Geographos

Principal Investigator: Samuel Herrick, Jr. (1911-1974),[1] University of California, Los Angeles, California.

Grant Nos. 745,[2] 746:   In support of studies of the orbits of Geographos and other close-approach minor planets.

A few years ago a guest asked about my work and what it was. It seemed appropriate on the occasion to answer: "I use positions observations of a minor planet or satellite to determine its orbit, so that I can predict where it will be seen again, so that the observer can make more observations, so that I can improve the orbit, so that..."

Today the foregoing is greatly amended.

The minor planets (*alias* asteriods, *alias* planetoids) are of growing interest because they were "present at creation." Unlike Alfonso El Sabio they were able to participate in the ordering of the heavenly bodies, and tomorrow they will tell us much about what happened, including many things that the moon and the major planets have forgotten. The close-approach minor planets will be especially attractive for the future exploration that will open an almost totally sealed book.

Before we can send an expedition to land on, or even fly by, a minor planet, however, we must know where it is and where it is going. For those that cross the earth's orbit, moreover, ones such as Geographos, Icarus, and Toro, which do so now, and ones such as Betulia, which will do so in the future, we must know whether their inexorable collisions with the earth will be tomorrow or 10 million years from now. Accordingly the layman can savor a part of the fascination of orbit determination.

Perhaps he can also appreciate the interplay between the orbit analyst

---

[1] Dr. Herrick died on March 21, 1974.

[2] Grant no. 745 was made in the name of Mrs. Betty Mintz, of the U. S. Naval Observatory, Washington, D. C., for observations of the minor planet Geographos in an observatory in the Southern Hemisphere, while Dr. Herrick made his in the Northern Hemisphere. Both sets of observations were correlated by Dr. Herrick.

—EDITOR.

and the observer, in which the former seeks to make his predictions, and the latter his (or her!) observations, as accurate as possible. Thus, in 1968 when Icarus was due to appear above the northern horizon at the start of its streaking across the sky, and the first observations were made by the superbly dextrous observer Dr. Elizabeth Roemer of the University of Arizona, she was faced with a pressing need both for accurate prediction and for new telescopic techniques to meet the challenge of its unprecedentedly rapid motion. Thus also Dr. Richard M. Goldstein of Goldstone made excellent use of our accurate predictions to detect the first faint radar returns ever received from a tiny planet — and to find them within a matter of seconds!

The relationship between orbits and observations outlined in the foregoing reminds one of the well-known question about the chicken and the egg. But on the more important matter of the perfection of the process there are differences. Nature has had a billion years, more or less, for eggspensive egg-sperimentation. The recent addition of an outlet in space navigation, however, forces man to speed up his improvement of his processes and to precede experimentation with materials — and even lives — by mathematical experimentation in orbit determination. It is this area that has been the focus of our work under the grant (Herrick, 1972; Herrick, Reichert, Thompson, and Tiffany, 1968-71, 1969-70), and of some of the related work (e.g., Liu, 1970); other related work has been concerned with physical laws (Shapiro, Smith, Ash, and Herrick, 1971) or has made use of our elements and ephemerides (Naef, 1969; Meeus and Können, 1970).

In an old, established field such as celestial mechanics there exists always the possibility that methods have entered a state of thralldom in relation to the discoveries of bygone years. Accordingly we have not hesitated to question methods and procedures based upon classical theory as well as those developed in ignorance of it. Examples are in the rendezvous problem and in perturbation theory, both of which are indispensable to landings on, or returns from, minor planets. Lambert-Euler theory has been found to be deficient for the former, and alternatives to the limited Lagrange-Hamilton-Jacobi mechanics are being explored for the latter.

Minor planets differ from meteorites in size and in the important fact that they can be seen before they collide with the earth, so that collisions can be predicted. Additional similarities and differences depend for the present upon theories of the origin of the solar system. The possibility of a common origin for minor planets and meteorites (especially siderites) implies the possibility that the former contain treasure houses of nickel and of heavier elements that are rare on the earth's surface because they are locked in the earth's core: rhenium, osmium, iridium, platinum, gold, etc. They almost surely do not contain, however, the fossil fuels that the present exploitation of the earth is wantonly squandering.

Speculation on the possibility of landing a portion of Geographos on the surface of the earth at the time of our contract-predicted record close approach (August 25, 1994) is not itself made a part of this report to the National Geographic Society. Whereas it might vastly increase the mineral resources of the earth, and incidentally dig a new Atlantic-Pacific Canal in northwestern Colombia (dreamt of since 1540), it would certainly wipe out a whole slough of ecology. With tongue in cheek the principal investigator shoulders the burden unsupported!

REFERENCES

HERRICK, SAMUEL
    1972. Astrodynamics, vol. 2, 348 pp.   Van Nostrand Reinhold, London. (Contains much of the mathematical experimentation supported by NGS.)
HERRICK, SAMUEL, and, variously, REICHERT, RALPH J.; THOMPSON, PAUL A.; and TIFFANY, PAUL C.
    1968-1971. Elements, ephemerides, and residuals.   Minor Planet Circulars, Cincinnati, nos. 2902-2906, 2964, 2965, 3105, 3106. (5 for Geographos, 3 for Icarus, 5 for Betulia, 4 for Toro.)
    1969-1970. Elements and ephemerides of Icarus, Geographos, Betulia, and Toro.   Ephemerides of Minor Planets for 1970, 1971. Institute of Theoretical Astronomy, Leningrad.
    1969-1971. Ephemerides.   International Astronomical Union Circulars, nos. 2131, 2147, 2149, 2171. Smithsonian Astrophysical Observatory, Cambridge, Massachusetts. (2 for Geographos, 1 each for Icarus and Toro.)
LIU, ANTHONY S.
    1970. Variational equations derived from the Herrick Variation of Parameters Method.   Journ. Astron. Sci., vol. 17, no. 4, pp. 185-217.
MEEUS, JEAN, and KÖNNEN, G. P.
    1970. Les petites planètes Icarus, Geographos et Toro.   L'Astronomie, vol. 84, pp. 390-396.
NAEF, ROBERT A.
    1969. Grosse Annaherung des Planetoiden (1620) Geographos an die Erde. Orion, Der Sternenhimmel, pp. 43, 106, 112, 117, 118, 121, 122.
SHAPIRO, IRWIN I.; SMITH, WILLIAM B.; ASH, MICHAEL E.; and HERRICK, SAMUEL
    1971. General relativity and the orbit of Icarus.   Astron. Journ., vol. 76, no. 7, pp. 588-606.

SAMUEL HERRICK, JR.

Ecology and Reproductive Behavior of the Gray Gull of Chile and of the Red-tailed Tropicbird and White Tern of Midway Island

Principal Investigator: Thomas R. Howell, University of California, Los Angeles, California.

Grant No. 819:   For a study of the ecology and behavior of three unusual sea birds *(Larus modestus, Phaethon rubricauda,* and *Gygis alba).*

ECOLOGY AND REPRODUCTIVE BEHAVIOR OF THE GRAY GULL IN NORTHERN CHILE

The gray gull *(Larus modestus)* is found only on the Pacific coast of South America from Peru to southern Chile, and within this range it is the most common species of gull. Despite its abundance, the nesting locations and nesting habits were still unknown to science at the time of Murphy's (1936) classic work on the oceanic birds of South America. The nest and eggs were not described until 1945 (Goodall, Philippi, and Johnson, 1945), and the full story of the discovery of nesting colonies in the extreme deserts of northern Chile is retold by Johnson (1967). Through Mr. Johnson's cooperation, I was able to visit one of these colonies in November and December 1968. At that time the birds were just starting to lay eggs, and the chicks, their adaptations to the desert, and their parental care remained completely unknown. The National Geographic Society research grant enabled me to study the means by which a sea bird reproduces successfully in the most barren and (otherwise) lifeless desert in the world.

In January 1970 I returned to Chile and revisited the same nesting colony near Pedro de Valdivia, Province of Antofagasta, that I had visited alone in 1968. This time I was accompanied by Braulio Araya M. of the Departmento de Oceanología, Universidad de Chile, Viña del Mar, and by William R. Millie, a veteran Chilean naturalist living in Vallenar. We camped in the desert 18 kilometers west-northwest of Pedro de Valdivia, elevation 5,400 feet, near Cerro Colupo and about 30 kilometers east of the coast.

251

Close observation of the birds required the use of a blind both day and night. We were equipped with a multichannel battery-operated thermistor thermometer with a variety of sensing probes, a sling psychrometer for measuring relative humidity, a wind gauge, and still and motion-picture cameras with telephoto lenses.

Environmental conditions. In this part of Chile rain falls only at irregular intervals of many years or not at all within recorded history. Except where water is brought in by man, there is no vegetation at all, and thus not even the beginning of a food chain is possible. Hence no animals — not even the smallest insects — can survive there except those capable of traveling long distances to other places where life can be permanently sustained.

At the time of my visits air temperatures ranged from a low of about 2.5° C. at night to a high of about 38° C. at about midday. Surface temperatures in the sun were of course much higher and were often in excess of 50° C. at midday. Relative humidities as low as 8 percent were sometimes recorded. In the afternoons strong and continuous winds reached velocities of about 20 miles per hour, but the air was usually calm in the morning and after dark, or with only light breezes. The surface of the soil is sandy with a great deal of rock rubble, but in some places the sand is so fine that it has a powdery texture.

The coastal region where the birds feed and carry on much of their mating activity is also virtually rainless and largely devoid of terrestrial vegetation. The terrain is both rocky and sandy, and marine life is abundant in the intertidal zone and the offshore waters. The coast in the vicinity of the city of Antofagasta provides excellent opportunities for observing gulls.

Behavior on the coast. Moynihan (1962) described in detail the courtship and aggressive postures (fig. 3) and the vocalizations of gray gulls that he observed at Antofagasta. Both Moynihan and Johnson (1967) noted that the gulls are numerous and active along the coast during the breeding season until sundown, when they gather in large wheeling flocks and disappear in the darkness, presumably heading for the interior. They return again to the coast shortly after dawn and resume feeding and courtship behavior (if during the appropriate months). Like most other species of *Larus,* these gulls are opportunistic feeders, but they also feed by probing vigorously in the sand as the waves recede, in the manner of small sandpipers. In this way they obtain burrowing sand crabs *(Emerita* sp.), which are abundant in such habitats. The aggressive and courtship behavior along the coast is similar to that described by N. Tinbergen in his classic studies on the herring gull *(Larus argentatus).* In the gray gull, however, transient territories are established on the daytime coastal gathering places, and a great deal of courtship and copulation takes place there, far from the nest site in the desert.

Behavior in the desert. Moynihan did not visit any nesting colonies, and the only published observations are those summarized by Johnson (1967). The visits of Johnson and his colleagues were brief—primarily to collect specimens of eggs—and there was little time for study of behavior. Noting that the eggs are exceptionally pale in color for a gull, Johnson suggested to me (personal communication) that this might reflect enough heat to enable the parents to leave the eggs exposed to the sun for long periods while the adult birds flew to the coast for food. One of my objectives was to check this hypothesis and also to ascertain if either the birds or the eggs had any unusual physiological adaptations to desert conditions. My findings from both the 1968 and 1970 trips are summarized in the following account.

For at least 11 days prior to egg-laying, gulls are sporadically present in the nesting area during the day and regularly at night. In this pre-egg stage there is some territorial and courtship behavior during the day but much more at night. Surface temperatures increase markedly by midmorning and the temperature of the sand may exceed 50° C. The rock surfaces—especially those with a white coating of guano—reflect much more solar heat and their temperatures do not exceed 43° C. By the latter part of the morning most birds have forsaken activities on the sand and stand on rocks with their feet shaded by their own bodies. As the heat becomes more intense the plumage on the dorsum is raised and ruffled, providing increased insulation against absorption of solar heat; the birds may also pant. Shortly after midday a strong wind springs up suddenly, and all the birds turn and face into it. Surface temperatures soon drop to tolerable levels and activities on the sand may commence again. By sundown most activity has ceased, and the colony is largely quiet for the first hour or hour and a half after dark.

At about that time birds begin to arrive from the coast and nocturnal activity begins dramatically. The previously quiet desert resounds with the cries of thousands of gulls, and the noise continues unabated until dawn. One hears the entire vocal repertoire of the species, with the loud 7-note Long Call (fig. 1) and the weird, moaning Mew Call being most noticeable. All the vocalizations and the behavior associated with each are described in detail by Moynihan (1962), and when used here are capitalized. The fact that all are heard in the desert at night indicates that a full range of aggressive, territorial, and mating behavior takes place then. Unfortunately, the birds are extremely wary at night and immediately take wing with a chorus of alarm calls at any disturbance, including the beam of a flashlight. All nocturnal

FIG. 2.   Gray gull shading recently hatched chick during peak of midday heat.

FIG. 1.   Gray gull giving long call while standing on rock, shading chick and its own feet.

observations had to be made from a blind by moonlight, but in the clear desert air a full moon provides excellent visibility at close range.

On the night of January 24-25, 1970, we kept an all-night watch on a group of birds that included one highly territorial (presumed) male. He constantly patrolled an area about 10 by 2.5 meters, giving Long Calls directed toward any bird on the wing and running toward any that approached on the ground. He then assumed an Upright or Low Oblique threat position and attacked if the invader did not assume a submissive posture in response. At least one individual, presumably a female, responded with a crouching, head-down, tail-up posture that simulated the start of making a nest scrape. The presumed male would then adopt the same pose, and both birds sometimes then actually began scrape-making. They made five nest scrapes within the territory. At least two other actively defended territories abutted this one, and the behavior of the other birds seemed to be the same insofar as we could see by moonlight.

The nest is a simple scrape in the sand without an assemblage of pebbles or any other materials, and of course no other materials are available. When the first egg is laid and incubation begins, the birds so occupied

FIG. 3.   Male gray gull (left) in aggressive posture; female (right) incubating eggs.

appear to withdraw from territorial defense except for a radius of about 0.5 meter around the nest. Egg-laying is not especially synchronous throughout the colony, and an actively territorial bird may end up nesting within 1 meter of a bird already on eggs, and another pair may then nest well within his former hotly defended territory. We censused a 100-by-100-meter quadrant and found 110 nests with eggs within it.

A count of the number of eggs in 182 completed nests showed about 52 percent with 2 eggs, 47 percent with 1 egg, and 1 percent with 3 eggs. Several freshly dead adult birds found in the colony had distinctly 2-part incubation patches. Virtually all other species of *Larus* have a 3-egg clutch predominating and have a 3-part incubation patch. Incubation begins with the laying of the first egg, and the second (if produced) is laid after a 2-day interval. The incubation period is 29 to 32 days, determined from marked eggs. Adults weigh about 400 and 350 grams (males and females, respectively), and fresh eggs weigh from 42 to 62 grams, averaging about 52 grams. Both parents appear to share the duties of incubation equally, and the eggs are never spontaneously left uncovered for more than a few minutes. We saw change-overs at the nest only at night, usually between 1 or 2 hours after dark when birds first returned from the coast, but sometimes as late as 2 hours before dawn. The arriving bird alights in the vicinity of its nest and may walk directly to it or may wander around to several nests before coming to its own. Vocalizations are frequent by the birds on the nest and those arriving, and this may provide means of recognition, but there is no elaborate nest-relief ceremony. The relieved bird may fly off at once or may remain in the area, even into the next morning. We could not tell if relieved birds headed for the coast at once, but we camped on the beach west of the nesting colony and found that gulls arrived from somewhere and began feeding at about midnight and thereafter. Apparently the duration of each parent's session of incubation is about 24 hours.

The eggs are much paler than those of most gulls, and although the parents do not leave them uncovered for long periods during the day I conducted tests to see if an egg could be left for long periods in the sun without overheating. I implanted a thermistor probe in a fresh egg, placed it in an empty nest scrape in the sun, and recorded temperatures at regular intervals. The internal temperature rose rapidly and reached a high of 45° C. before the start of the afternoon wind. This temperature is near the denaturation point of some protein and is either lethal or causes severe pathological effects to embryos of the domestic fowl; it is extremely unlikely that gray-gull eggs could be safely left in the sun long enough for the parent to fly to the coast and return.

The incubating birds face severe heat stress during the latter part of the morning. At this time they stand up in the nest and shade the egg, meanwhile letting their wings droop, ruffling out the dorsal plumage and panting (fig. 2). Thermistor probes implanted in eggs in nests showed that the internal egg temperature varies only between $33.0°$ and $38.0°$ C. whether the bird is sitting tight in the near-freezing predawn cold or shading the egg in the intense midday heat. When the afternoon wind begins the birds turn to face into it; as the ambient temperature declines they again settle on to the eggs.

Newly hatched chicks weigh about 34 grams. Their pattern of markings is similar to that of other gulls—irregular dark spots on a light background—but the overall tone is grayish and the spots are blurry. They appear somewhat "smoky" and match the prevailing grayish hue of the substrate. The chicks that we observed in 1970 were the first ones of this species ever seen by ornithologists, and a sample of specimens of different ages was obtained by picking up chicks that had died of natural causes.

Care of chicks for the first days is similar to care of the eggs; they are brooded or shaded more or less constantly by one or the other parent. An adult arriving at night soon disgorges semidigested pieces of fish, which are picked up and eaten by the chick. The parent retains enough to continue occasional feedings even as late as the following afternoon. The chick solicits feeding by rapid nibbling of the parent's bill, which in this species is uniform black without a "target" such as the red spot on the herring gull's mandible. The all-black bill contrasts sharply with the pure-white head and may provide maximum visibility during nocturnal feedings.

Within a day or two after the chicks hatch the parent does not remain continuously at the nest and chicks may wander several meters away from the scrape. This is hazardous because of exposure to heat stress and to attacks by adult birds. Observations of marked chicks and individually recognizable adults gave the following general picture. An adult bird returns to its nest scrape and broods or shades it, but it will not move to brood or shade a chick even if the latter is only a few centimeters away in full view. Chicks of any age that have left the nest scrape must seek shelter under an adult, for there is virtually no other shade during the hottest part of the day. Adults, however, usually attack with strong pecks any chick that approaches, including their own. The chick's response is to assume an extremely submissive posture, tucking its bill completely under its body and remaining motionless. This seems to blunt the aggressive impulse of the adult and stops the attack. After a few minutes the chick gradually brings its head upright again and advances toward the adult as far as it can before being attacked again. By such a series of advances the chick usually gets into the nest scrape under the adult, often when the latter is turned the other way. Once the chick is under the adult—even if it is not its own parent and even if one or more chicks are already there—it is immediately accepted by the adult and will be brooded and even fed. One marked chick turned up in three different nests on different days, and some adults known to have hatched only a single chick were found brooding two or three. At least at early chick ages, both adults and chicks behave as though they do not distinguish between individuals. In the gray gull there is little or no vocal communication between adults and chicks; the chicks cheep softly at times but are not audible except at very close range; the adults do not direct any vocalization to the chicks. In most other species of gulls vocal signals are an important means of individual recognition between parent and offspring.

Mortality is high among chicks, and although we only once saw an adult kill a chick directly, we saw chicks die of heat stress because adult attacks kept them from getting to shade in time. The wanderings of young chicks seem to be random, and many perish from inability to find shade even though adult aggression is not involved. Carcasses of young birds of all ages are scattered throughout the colony, mostly with no apparent wounds. Again unlike most other gulls, the gray gull is distinctly nonpredatory on its own species. We never saw one eat an intact egg or a chick although the opportunities to do so are virtually limitless. In the absence of contrary evidence, we assume that mortality of the young is chiefly caused by environmental stress or by starvation. The latter would be inevitable if one parent disappears, for one adult alone could not shelter and feed a chick to the age of self-sufficiency. In this species, of course, young birds must be cared for until they are able to fly a minimum of 30 kilometers to the coast.

We conducted experiments on the ability of chicks of different ages to cope with heat stress. One group of 10 chicks weighing from 27 (recently hatched) to 226 grams was confined in a small stone corral exposed to the late morning and midday sun, with no wind. Air temperatures in the shade were 25.0° to 30.2° C., but air temperatures in the sun ranged from 27.9° to 40.0° C. and substrate temperatures in the sun were 30.0° to > 50° C. The smallest chick did not seek shade but moved at random; its body temperature rose from an initial 39.1° to 44.9° C. in 35 minutes, and it would undoubtedly have died had I not removed it to shade. All the others actively sought what little shade the enclosure provided, and all panted vigorously with wide-gaping beaks. One that initially weighed 45 grams with a body temperature of 39.2° C. rose to a body temperature of 47.5° C. in 95 minutes; this proved fatal. Another with an initial weight of 75 grams and a body temperature of 38.3° C. also rose during 95 minutes of exposure to a body temperature of 47° C. and died. Three others, weighing 70 to 100 grams, all showed markedly elevated body temperatures and probably would have died if not removed to shade. Four others weighing 165 to 226 grams maintained body temperatures lower than 43° C. even after 3 hours of exposure. In another experiment, two chicks weighing 31 and 60 grams were corralled in full sun but in midafternoon when the wind blew 535 to 900 feet per minute. Their initial temperatures in their nest site were 42.0° and 42.2° C. After 35 minutes the 60-gram bird had reduced its body temperature to 40.8° C., and the smaller chick, after an initial rise to 43.0° C., brought its temperature down to 42.0° C. again. Both birds panted continuously.

These results suggest that chicks weighing less than 100 grams are in serious danger of dying from heat stress if exposed for an hour or more to late morning and midday sun, but larger chicks can maintain a safe body temperature by panting. Once the afternoon wind has begun, even small chicks can maintain a safe body temperature even though exposed to the sun. Evaporative cooling must rapidly deplete the body water of the birds, however, and this must limit the duration of effective panting.

Both parents of older chicks are often absent from the nest site during the day and may be on the coast or possibly elsewhere in the colony. These older chicks often stand on rocks as do the adult birds, thus reducing heat loading by conduction from the substrate. The time required for the young birds to reach the stage of leaving the colony remains to be determined.

Predation. The most obvious advantage to nesting in the desert is the virtual absence of predators. A single peregrine falcon *(Falco peregrinus)* was present in both 1968 and 1970. It lacked the distinctive face markings of the resident Chilean subspecies *(F. p. cassini)* and was presumably a migrant from North America. The falcon often swooped over the colony and scared up a flock of gulls, but it seldom seemed to make a serious attempt to strike one. A few freshly dead adult gulls found in the colony may have been killed by this falcon, but its effect on the numbers of gulls was practically nil. An Andean condor *(Vultur gryphus)* occasionally soared over the colony but never alighted. Turkey vultures *(Cathartes aura)* were almost daily visitors and sometimes caused alarm when they came down to the ground. Possibly these vultures eat eggs or chicks, but we found no sure evidence of this. Some kind of fox, *Dusicyon* sp., does reach the colony, for we found a mummified carcass of one and also some fresh footprints. Occasional panicky upflights during the night may have been caused by a fox, but this is only a guess. The area could not support a fox except during the gull's nesting season, and probably few individuals ever reach the colony; it is unlikely that foxes exert much predation pressure. I know of no other potential predators except man, and at least in 1968 and 1970 there was no human disturbance other than our field party.

Colony size. The area occupied by groups of nesting gulls was about 5.5 kilometers long and 1 kilometer wide. Birds were not uniformly distributed throughout this area, and it is difficult to estimate accurately the number of pairs nesting. The 100-by-100-meter (0.01 square kilometer) plot that we censused included 110 nests with eggs; that same density throughout the colony would mean 11,000 nests per square kilometer or 60,500 nests in 5.5 square kilometers. As there was no such uniform high density, I estimate that perhaps 10,000 pairs were nesting in this colony. Interestingly, Goodall, Philippi, and Johnson (1945) estimated the area of the colony as 5 square kilometers some 27 years earlier.

Discussion and conclusions. The colony between Cerro Colupo and the town of Pedro de Valdivia is the only one that has been extensively studied. Others have been reliably reported to exist as much as 60 miles inland, and there must be many scattered throughout northern Chile and possibly southern Peru. The Colupo colony existed at least 28 years ago (Johnson, 1967) and must therefore represent a long-term success. One of the important climatic factors in this colony is the apparently infallible afternoon wind that halts the rise in temperature and brings it down below stressful levels, and one wonders if nesting could be successful without the wind. Perhaps nesting colonies are restricted to sites where the land-form and local climatic conditions produce such regular winds. I found no evidence that either the eggs, chicks, or adults have any special physiological adaptations to heat stress, and their adjustments to desert conditions seem largely behavioral.

How and when desert nesting by this species originated are matters of speculation, but there is no doubt that the principal advantage is virtual freedom from predation. The large aggressive kelp gull *(Larus dominicanus)* dominates the coast and offshore islets and would probably doom any attempt by gray gulls to nest in such places by preempting the most favorable sites and by predation on eggs and chicks. Kelp gulls even interfere with coastal pairing activities of gray gulls by rushing in to seize fish being transferred from male to female during courtship feeding. By nesting in desert sites gray gulls avoid all interspecific competition for sites and are only slightly affected by predators, if at all. The price of this "security" is severe environmental stress that takes a heavy toll of young birds before they reach self-sufficiency. The Colupo colony is littered with desiccated carcasses of young birds of all ages, possibly the accumulation of many years as the extreme dryness prevents rapid decomposition. However, the over-all success of the gray gull's unusual reproductive strategy is demonstrated by its status as the most abundant gull along the entire Pacific coast of South America.

REFERENCES

GOODALL, J. D.; PHILIPPI B., R. A.; and JOHNSON, A. W.
  1945. Nesting habits of the Peruvian gray gull.   Auk, vol. 62, pp. 450-451, illus.
JOHNSON, A. W.
  1967. The birds of Chile and adjacent regions of Argentina, Bolivia and Peru,
    vol. 2, 448 pp., illus.   Platt Establecimientos Gráficos, Buenos Aires.
MOYNIHAN, MARTIN
  1962. Hostile and sexual behavior patterns of South American and Pacific Laridae, 354 pp., illus.   E. J. Brill, Leiden.
MURPHY, ROBERT CUSHMAN
  1936. Oceanic birds of South America, vol. 2, 1,245 pp., illus.   American Museum of Natural History, New York.

REPRODUCTIVE BEHAVIOR AND MORPHOLOGICAL ADAPTATIONS OF THE RED-TAILED TROPICBIRD

The tropicbirds (Phaethontidae) comprise a small and aberrant family within the order Pelecaniformes. Most authorities recognize only three species, all of which are similar — the white-tailed *(Phaethon lepturus)*, the red-billed *(P. aethereus)*, and the red-tailed *(P. rubricauda)*. As their name implies, they are found primarily in tropical areas of the world's oceans and usually nest on islands that lack native mammalian predators. The red-tailed tropicbird breeds abundantly on Midway Island and several others in the Hawaiian chain. The adults have satiny white plumage with a few small black markings on the face, wings, and flanks, and there are two slender, elongate, bright-red tail feathers; the bill is bright red. The sexes are identical in external appearance. The most remarkable anatomical specialization of tropicbirds is the proportionately small size of the pelvis and hindlimbs, which

FIG. 4.   Five tropicbirds in aerial display.

FIG. 5.   Pair of tropicbirds in aerial display. Note tail-twitching by bird at left.

makes them essentially "walkless" just as some other birds are flightless. Landings are often awkward and the birds move on land only by a series of lurches. They are strong fliers, however, and can take off from the ground with powerful wing-beats. Tropicbirds feed on fish and squid, which they obtain by plunge-diving. They swim buoyantly, using their small but fully webbed feet.

The red-tailed tropicbird is the only species that nests regularly on Midway although whitetails are occasional visitors, and from this point on "tropicbird" refers to the red-tailed species unless otherwise mentioned. A few tropicbirds occur on Midway at all times of year, but the peak of breeding activity is in May and June.

The courtship flights of prenesting birds are spectacular and are most frequent in the early afternoon. The basic pattern is as follows: The two members of a (prospective) pair fly slowly into the wind, often gliding, one above the other. The upper bird tilts vertically and begins rapid wing-beats as in hovering; as a result, it moves upward and is carried backward by the wind. At the peak of this ascent it remains in the same place for a few moments, and the long red tail feathers are rapidly switched to one or the other side, or to both sides alternately (fig. 5). Then the bird tips forward, sets its wings partly spread, and glides forward and downward at such an angle that it passes under the second bird. As this happens the latter begins the hover-upward-and-backward phase and then glides down under the first bird. Thus, the two birds alternately describe vertical circles in the air. After a number of such flights, both birds may go into a long, shallow glide, one above the other and both with their wings identically set. Usually many pairs display in the same area, and often three or four birds are involved with one another in circle-glide displays before sorting out into pairs (figs. 4-6). The displays are accompanied by a series of loud and raucous calls that attract attention to the group. Fleet (1972), observing marked birds on Kure Atoll, determined that only those birds that did not yet have nests and eggs participate in the aerial display.

Sites for nests may be prospected for weeks in advance, and the nest itself is only a shallow scrape in the sand. A bird may use its bill to loosen the substrate if necessary, and then it kicks sand out to the side while turning around on the site. The nest is always in part or full shade, under vegetation or (on Midway) beside a building that provides shade. The clutch is invariably a single egg, which varies in color from almost pure white to densely and finely speckled with purplish brown to heavily blotched with blackish purple. The incubation period is long, about 44 days. Like other pelecaniform birds, tropicbirds have no incubation patch (ventral area of skin from which feathers are molted) but tuck the egg well under the fully feathered abdomen with the bill (fig. 11). By placing a thermistor thermometer probe in an egg and then placing this under an incubating bird, I recorded a consistent incubation temperature of 37.0° C. Air temperature in the shade by this nest was between 24.5 and 25.2° C. The bird may place one or both feet, or neither, on the egg while incubating, and I doubt that the small feet make any important thermal contribution.

Unlike the naked hatchlings of other pelecaniform birds, the tropicbird chick is covered with long, fine, grayish down (fig. 10). Newly hatched chicks usually keep their eyes closed but can open them halfway. The chicks also give faint cheeps and can right themselves if turned on their backs. They make no attempt to walk or lurch and may not be able to do either. Even with the eyes half open they do not respond to the sight of an object brought close to the bill, but if touched at the base of the bill the chick immediately gapes and tries to swallow the object touching it. In feeding, the adult gently touches the base of the chick's bill with its bill tip, and the chick gapes and gulps down the adult's bill (fig. 12). Tactile rather than visual stimuli are apparently the most important in eliciting the feeding response of the chick. The adult orients its mandibles at right angles to those of the chick and then regurgitates food into the chick's gullet. In all other pelecaniform birds, the chicks obtain food by reaching into the bill and throat of the adult.

Young chicks are at first brooded under the parent's body but after a few days of growth are brooded under one wing. A parent broods the chick at night but leaves for many hours during the day to go out to sea for food. The long down diminishes heat loss to the surrounding air which, at about 25° C., is well below the body temperature (38° C.) of a brooded chick. The dense down may also possibly prevent soaking and dangerous chilling by rain if this falls during the parent's absence.

I recorded presunrise and postsunset weights for a series of five newly or recently hatched chicks for as long as 15 days (fig. 9). These measurements give an indication of the amount of food given during the day and the net gain per 24-hour period. The graphs for weight gain of two chicks in different nests over the same period (May 31 to June 14) show how remarkably similar the pattern is and how large are some of the daily food intakes—sometimes almost one-half of the chick's weight at the start of the day. A few records in which the chick gained between the last weighing (postsunset) and the first (presunrise) of the next day indicate that some nocturnal feeding of chicks takes place.

Fig. 6. Tropicbird in hovering flight.

I had to leave Midway in mid-June and thus did not follow the long period of nestling care to completion. There was so little mortality of young up to that point that fledging success is probably very high. Fleet (1972) reported that predation by rats on young chicks less than 17 days old was the principal cause of heavy mortality on Kure Atoll, but rats are well-controlled on Midway by a poisoning program and seem not to be an important predator there. No other potential predators are present except man, who sometimes destroys nests accidentally or in the course of Navy operations. Occasionally a disgruntled and frustrated Midway resident goes on a wanton killing spree but if caught is always heavily fined and thrown into the brig.

The Laysan albatross *(Diomedea immutabilis),* an abundant breeding species on Midway, causes a few tropicbird nesting failures. The albatrosses are attracted to the red tail feathers and bills of the tropicbirds and often approach and nibble at these brightly colored parts. This action usually elicits a furious attack by the tropicbird on the much larger albatross, and the former may lunge or be lifted off the ground and fall back on its own

FIG. 7.   Tropicbird on nest threatening curious Laysan albatross; bird's egg behind
its right wing.

egg and break it. There is no aggression by the albatross — only apparent
curiosity (figs. 7, 8).

The vocalizations of the tropicbirds are distinctive and specific for different situations. A harsh snarl is given by a tropicbird when approached
too closely by some species — albatross, man, etc. — other than its own. One
set of calls is given by birds on the ground, and they respond to a tape recording of such a call by an exact repetition of it. Another set of calls is given
by birds in flight.

In view of the great variability in egg color and the fact that only one
egg makes up the full clutch, I carried out tests to see if incubating birds
retrieved their own egg if given a choice of their own or an extra egg borrowed from another nest. Tropicbirds are usually quick and skillful retriev-
ers of displaced eggs (Howell and Bartholomew, 1969). In these tests I
moved the incubating bird about 30 centimeters back from its nest, then
placed its own egg and an extra egg each 8 to 10 centimeters from the nest
scrape and in front of it in relation to the bird, about 15 centimeters apart.
The bird was then scored as it did one of the following: (1) retrieved own
egg only or own egg first, then extra; (2) retrieved extra only or extra, then

Fig. 8.   Pair of tropicbirds at nest site. The bird excavating the nest scrape is
snarling at the albatross, and its mate appears startled.

own; (3) retrieved neither. Results were: category (1): 27; category (2):
8; category (3): 4. This suggests that tropicbirds usually recognize their own
eggs, but the conclusion must remain tentative as the duration of incubation
at the time of the test, the sex of the incubating bird, and possible subtle
position effects could not be known.

An intriguing question about tropicbirds is "Why have they virtually
lost the ability to walk?" There is no evident advantage to walklessness; on
the contrary, the birds seem distinctly handicapped by their clumsiness on
land. The anatomical modifications that result in walklessness must confer
some other advantage, something that outweighs the drawbacks of the difficult landings and the awkward terrestrial locomotion. In the nonbreeding season, which is most of the year, tropicbirds seldom if ever come to
land. Therefore, it is likely that the putative advantages are associated with
flight or swimming and diving. Tropicbirds rest easily on the water but they
neither swim very far nor dive from the surface. In feeding they plunge
into the water from the air but probably do not dive as deeply as do the
boobies (Sulidae). It is difficult to believe that the tropicbirds' relatively
small feet and hindlimbs enhance their ability to swim at or below the surface, and other birds that are expert in these activities have either "normal"

or proportionately large feet. Loons (Gaviidae) and grebes (Podicipedidae) move awkwardly on land, as their hindlimbs are placed relatively far posteriorly, but the feet are large and these birds are powerful swimmers and deep divers from the surface. It seems most likely that the tropicbirds' hindlimb modifications are associated with some advantage in flight.

To investigate this possibility, I compared measurements of the tropicbirds with the royal tern *(Sterna maxima),* a species of similar external dimensions that inhabits the coastal areas of North America. The relevant measurements are given in tables 1 and 2. The figures are necessarily based on small samples and are not definitive mean measurements. They are rounded off to the nearest whole number but are well within the range of variation indicated by the sample and are adequate for present purposes.

The skeletal weights are taken from thoroughly cleaned complete skeletons. As noted, the total body weight of the tropicbird is much greater than that of the royal tern, but the skeleton weights of the two are nearly identical, indicating that the greater body weight of the tropicbird is caused by more bulky musculature. Compared to the tern, the greater weight of the tropicbirds' pectoral girdle bones and the lesser weight of its hindlimb bones and equal weights of the pelvis-synsacrum in the two species indicate that the tropicbird is proportionately heavier in the pectoral region. This suggestion is supported by the linear measurements of the hindlimbs and forelimbs. The former are shorter in all elements in the tropicbird despite its greater total body weight, and in the forelimb all elements are shorter in the tropicbird than in the tern except the humerus, which in the tropicbird is slightly longer and also more robust. In both birds the skulls including bill are about the same length, but the tropicbird skull is broader posteriorly.

The term "posterior back length" refers to the combined anteroposterior length of the five vertebrae anterior to those included in the pelvic girdle. Avian morphologists often use this measurement as a standard of comparison with other skeletal elements on the assumption that these vertebrae are the least likely to show adaptive changes in linear dimensions. Thus, they constitute a conservative index of general body size, and the ratio of this measurement to those of other skeletal elements indicates whether or not the latter have undergone an adaptive increase or decrease relative to over-all body size. Table 2 suggests that the hindlimb elements in tropicbirds are relatively reduced as compared to those of the royal tern, which confirms the intuitive impression.

Comparison of the two forms shows that the tropicbird is more massive anteriorly, with greater bulk in the pectoral area and shorter distal elements of the wings, and is as small as or smaller posteriorly than the tern although

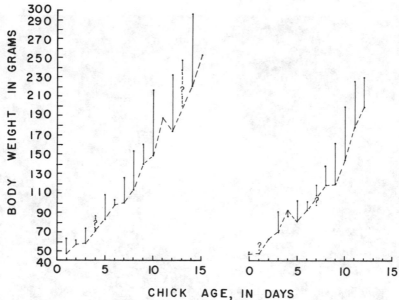

FIG. 9. Growth of two red-tailed tropicbird chicks in different nests on Midway Island. Weights of chick on left began on May 31, 1970, the day after hatching; weights of chick on right began on June 2, 1970, the day of hatching. Points connected by the dashed line are weights recorded (usually) before sunrise. Vertical lines connect presunrise with postsunset weights on the same day. Question marks indicate either that the postsunset weighing was missed or that the chick was fed prior to the presunrise weighing; vertical dashed lines are estimates of what the weights would have been under usual conditions.

their total anteroposterior length (exclusive of elongate feathers) is about the same. The proportions of the tropicbird suggest that it has reduced its total weight at the expense of its pelvic and hindlimb region. Considering the problems that this poses for landing and terrestrial locomotion, I conclude that the most probable compensating advantage seems to be in facilitating hovering flight. The robust pectoral region, the relatively large humerus, and relatively shorter distal wing elements support this suggestion, as all these features would make strong, rapid wing-beats easier than would be the case with longer wings and less massive pectoral musculature. The relatively reduced mass of the posterior body would mean less weight to support while hovering as compared to a "normally" proportioned bird.

FIG. 10. Tropicbird chick.

What could be the advantages associated with facility in hovering? There are few published accounts of tropicbird feeding techniques, and I was never able to observe feeding from the shores of Midway Island or from a boat on several offshore trips. Hovering or stalling before plunge-diving may often be used, but this is uncertain. There is no doubt, however, that hovering is important in courtship display. If the birds that are most effective in displays are those that are best at hovering, those would be most likely to secure mates and selection would favor adaptations that facilitate hovering. If this were not counteracted by selection against reduced facility in terrestrial locomotion, the ultimate result would be diminution in size of the pelvis-hindlimbs to the point at which movement on land was just adequate to accomplish successful breeding. Relatively strong pectoral musculature and reduced posterior body weight would help to compensate for reduced leg-action in take-offs from land, and better hovering ability would ease the impact of landings with reduced "landing gear." Thus, the process

FIG. 11. Tropicbird tucking egg under abdomen.

of posterior body-part reduction, once started, would be self-reinforcing up to the point at which reproductive success began to diminish. As tropicbirds do not seem to be handicapped by reduced hindlimbs in obtaining food and can locomote adequately for breeding on predator-free islands, they may represent the end result of such an evolutionary process. Predatory rats were not present on many oceanic islands before relatively recent introductions by man, and even the rats are ineffective against young tropicbirds older than about two weeks posthatching.

The small hindlimbs may possibly aid in aerial maneuverability as they can be moved through a wide arc. Tropicbirds in long direct flights usually have the feet tucked out of sight in the body plumage, but in display flights the feet are prominent during maneuvers. The hindlimbs are rotated so that the webbed feet are almost vertically oriented and then apparently used as rudders, and while oriented this way the feet may even be raised above the dorsal surface of the body. The feet are also extended laterally, often independently on either side, in many positions during the hovering maneuvers

FIG. 12.　Adult tropicbird feeding chick.

of display flight. However, whether or not the reduced size of the hindlimbs is associated with a wider range of movement is as yet undetermined.

Because tropicbirds differ in several respects from the more typical pelecaniform birds, their assignment to that order has often been questioned. My opinion is that they are a distinctive offshoot of the order Pelecaniformes that shows convergence with some of the terns (Charadriiformes; Laridae; Sterninae).

Most species of terns inhabit inland waters or continental coasts. The pelagic terns such as the white *(Gygis alba)*, sooty *(Sterna fuscata)*, and noddy *(Anous* sp.) do not plunge-dive but catch their food at the surface. Of the large terns that plunge into the water, only *Sterna bergii* has a wide range beyond the continental coasts. I suggest that the tropicbirds fill a feeding niche between that of the large terns that catch surface or subsurface prey and that of the larger, deeper-diving boobies, which can take fish that are too big for tropicbirds. The latter are thus convergent toward the terns but, compared to them, feed by plunge-diving from greater heights with deeper penetration below the surface. Despite some superficial resemblances to terns, tropicbirds show affinity to the Pelecaniformes by a number of characteristics including totipalmate feet, absence of an incubation patch, and location of the nasal salt-excreting gland between the eye and the nasal cavity instead of in a supraorbital fossa. The tropicbirds' unique specializations, which are still incompletely studied, suggest that the group could have evolved and persisted only by nesting (for the most part) on oceanic islands without native terrestrial predators.

TABLE 1. BODY AND SKELETAL WEIGHTS (IN GRAMS)

	Red-tailed tropicbird	Royal tern
Total body	612	495
Total skeleton	37	35
Skeleton ÷ body	0.06	0.07
Femur, tibiotarsus, tarsometatarsus	0.81	1.35
Pectoral girdle	5.8	4.5
Pelvis and synsacrum	2.15	2.15
Pelvis-synsacrum ÷ total body	0.058	0.061

TABLE 2. LENGTHS (IN MILLIMETERS) OF BONES AND WING
(CARPAL JOINT TO LONGEST PRIMARY)

	Red-tailed tropicbird	Royal tern
Femur	37	42
Tibiotarsus	56	70
Tarsometatarsus	28	37
Total	121	149
Posterior back length	37	33
Posterior back length ÷ femur-tibiotarsus	0.31	0.22
Humerus	98	95
Ulna	107	121
Carpametacarpus	51	57
Total	256	273
Wing	330	375

REFERENCES

FLEET, ROBERT R.
1972. Nesting success of the red-tailed tropicbird on Kure Atoll. Auk, vol. 89, pp. 651-659, charts.
HOWELL, THOMAS R., and BARTHOLOMEW, GEORGE A.
1969. Experiments on nesting behavior of the red-tailed tropicbird, *Phaethon rubricauda*. Condor, vol. 71, pp. 113-119, illus.

ECOLOGY AND REPRODUCTIVE BEHAVIOR OF THE WHITE, OR FAIRY, TERN

The white, or fairy, tern *(Gygis alba)* ranges throughout the tropical Pacific, Indian, and South Atlantic Oceans, breeding only on small islands where terrestrial predators are scarce or absent. The bird is very striking in appearance — pure white plumage except for a narrow black eye ring, bill deep blue basally and black on the distal half — and has even more striking nesting habits. No nest of any kind is constructed, and the single egg is laid on a bare branch or fork, on a rock ledge, or on a variety of man-made structures. Incubating birds usually allow a very close approach, and one may often touch the bird without its leaving. All these factors have made the white tern a familiar species to visitors to tropical islands, but there have been surprisingly few studies of it beyond general and anecdotal accounts. The most important publications are those of Moynihan (1962) on hostile and sexual behavior patterns, Dorward (1963) on the natural history of the population on Ascension Island, and Ashmole and Ashmole's studies on food habits (1967) and Ashmole's on molt (1968).

Midway Island, in the Leeward chain of the Hawaiian Islands, offers almost ideal conditions for detailed study of this species. White terns are abundant there and nest in many accessible locations; this fact permits marking of individual birds and regular long-term monitoring of mating behavior, care of the egg and chick, growth rates of the chick, thermoregulatory capacity, and many other important aspects of the birds' biology. With support from the National Geographic Society I spent the period from March 6 to June 14, 1970, on Midway, dividing my research time between the white tern and the red-tailed tropicbird *(Phaethon rubricauda)*.

Moynihan (1962) described accurately and fully the high flights and wandering flights of the white tern associated with pair formation, and Dorward (1963) provided a good general summary of the life history. However, neither of these authors marked individual birds, and they were thus unable to distinguish (except during copulation or egg-laying) male from female, as the sexes are identical externally. I used quick-drying model-airplane paint in several colors to mark adult birds, both those already with an egg and those in the pre-egg stage; in the latter instance I usually could tell by subsequent behavior which was male and which female, and in other cases where this was not possible I was able to tell individuals of the pair apart and thus delimit precisely their roles in incubation and care of the young.

Pairing and nest-site selection. I have nothing of importance to add to

Moynihan's (1962) description of high flights and wandering flights, which (as in many other terns) seem to be important in establishing and securing a pair bond. Preening of each other by members of a pair (or potential pair) is a conspicuous and elaborate procedure. It is confined to the head entirely, and one bird grooms the other with slight and gentle openings and closings of its bill. The preened bird assumes "ecstatic" postures reminiscent of a cat having its chin stroked—the head is raised, the eyes closed, and the birds appear to be in a trancelike state. The head is slowly turned at virtually all angles, and the preening bird seems to pay particular attention to the region around the base of the bill and the contrasting black eye ring. Either sex may preen its (potential) mate, and often one bird that has been preened will then preen the former preener. I suspect that, in this and in other nondimorphic sea birds, face-and-head preening serves to facilitate individual recognition.

Following preening or not, one or both members of a pair may point the bill down, close the eyes, and rock slightly while making soft clucking sounds in rhythm with the rocking. If both birds do this, the rhythm is not coordinated except coincidentally.

A male usually gives several pecks at a female's scapular and nape region—harder than in mere preening—as a prelude to mounting. If the female is receptive, he mounts and may tread on her scapular region for a full minute, as though getting his balance, before attempting cloacal contact. During this treading, he must force her to droop her wings slightly so that by vigorous wagging of his lowered tail he is able to displace her rectrices laterally and then force them up as he lowers his. Usually the male remains mounted for several minutes and makes several copulation attempts. After he dismounts, there is much feather ruffling and self-preening, then preening of the female by the male. (Fig. 13.)

Both members of a pair appear to participate equally in nest-site selection. One or both birds walk back and forth over the prospective site with quick short steps, as though testing the substrate for suitability. Then the tail and undertail coverts are lowered and waggled from side to side, giving the illusion that an egg is about to be laid. However, the male as well as the female does this, and it provides no assurance that the site will actually be used or, if so, how soon. Some pairs prospected a given site for several weeks and never laid an egg there, or if they did it might fall off after the first or second day; others laid eggs on sites where a bird had not been seen before although the site was in a well-watched area. Sometimes presumably quickly chosen sites were successful, sometimes not. After high winds, a

FIG. 13.   White terns in mating positions.

considerable number of fallen eggs of all stages of incubation were found on the ground, suggesting that almost no site is permanently "safe." If an egg is lost, the pair may lay another at the same or a different site within about 10 days.

There seem to be two major criteria for selection of a site — it must be off the ground and it must be at an edge. White terns nest abundantly on buildings, but always at the edge if on a roof, ledge, or other structure with extensive surface area. Too much exposure could not be the sole reason for avoidance of nonedge situations, for the inner portions of wide window ledges provided the same gravelly surfaces and much more shelter from the weather than did the edge. Natural sites, of course, might have 360° of edge.

I found one nest on the ground in a slight hollow among twigs and needles at the base of a *Casuarina* tree. The egg did not hatch until after my departure, but I received word that the chick hatched and was banded before fledging. This is the first known instance of successful ground-nesting in the white tern, and the few other reports of eggs on the ground indicate that such behavior is very rare.

Dorward (1963, p. 367) mentioned that "a series of experiments in which the eggs were removed from their original site indicated that the bird's attachment was to the site rather than to the egg, which was ignored even when only two or three inches away." No other details are given. I carried out similar experiments, usually with birds nesting on roof or ledge edges, moving the egg about 15 centimeters to the left or right of the original site but keeping it at the edge and on a uniform substrate. In 20 tests only one bird settled ultimately on the empty site instead of the egg, and that test was at a site on a branch where substrate and foliage cover were not uniform. Two other birds shifted back and forth between the egg and the site, but all the rest settled ultimately on the displaced egg although most went sooner or later to the original site and made settling motions there. As expected in view of the usual natural sites, egg-retrieval movements are minimal or absent in this species.

White terns are highly aggressive and immediately threaten or attack any bird other than the mate that alights within about a meter's distance. One meter (about five tern-body-lengths) is thus the usual minimum distance between nests, but some may be as close as two tern-lengths (about 0.5 meter) especially if a branch or other object screens the birds from one another. Closer proximity leads to violent fights that doubtless make nesting success improbable.

The incubation period is about 36 days, varying slightly with different pairs and perhaps according to exposure of the site. An egg laid in the fork of a small branch, with the bottom half constantly exposed, required 39 days to hatch. Two pairs for which my records are most complete both required 866 hours (36.1 days) $\pm$ 7 hours, the latter representing the sum of my uncertainties as to the exact hour of laying and of the full opening of the shell. The female assumes the first span of incubation and is relieved by her mate after about one or two days. The egg is never left uncovered except during the first one to four days when an unrelieved adult may go off and leave it exposed for as long as 6-12 hours; eggs left alone at this early stage will still produce a healthy chick. The usual incubation stint is about two days, and nest relief may occur at any hour of the day or night. Neither adult feeds the other. Incubation temperatures recorded from inside the egg were between 35.5° and 36° C. The egg is usually elliptical and only seldom is it detectably more pointed at one end. Usually one end is more heavily pigmented than the other, however, and this end contains the air cell and is the site of pipping. The chick hatches while completely covered by the adult, and the weight at hatching is about 13 grams. Even before its down dries, the chick clings tenaciously to anything contacting its long toes and sharp claws. They can hold on to a stick or finger and be rotated upside down without falling off. When first hatched, however, they are brooded continuously by whichever parent is present except when the parent attacks intruders (fig. 15). Adults that were so placid as to allow me to feel under them to see if the egg was pipped became fierce defenders that flew at my head and attacked me with sharp pecks to the scalp the day after the chick had hatched. This extreme aggressiveness usually subsides after a few days.

By the second day after the chick hatches, adults do not wait to be relieved by a mate but leave the chick unattended as they fly off to obtain food. This absence took 10 minutes at a minimum and was usually much longer, even several hours' duration. If the nest site was on a building and exposed to hot sun, the young chick would walk several meters to find shade if possible. If a rainstorm comes up during the parent's absence, the chick does not move to shelter (even if possible) and may become so soaked and chilled that it falls from the site or dies of exposure before the adult returns. Adults may wander far for food, and I saw no evidence that they hurry back to the chick in case of bad weather. Once a chick falls down below the nest site, the adult no longer attends it even though it may be in plain sight and active on the ground below the site in fair weather. The principal cause of mortality of chicks in the prefledging stage is ultimate starvation and/or death from exposure as a result of wind and rain storms while the adult is away. Sometimes I took inside my room rain-soaked chicks that were on the verge of death from exposure, dried them off, and returned them to their nests after the rain. They recovered well, and often an adult was waiting at the site with food by that time. All such chicks were at once accepted back by the parent.

Food for the chicks consists of small fish and squid — as many as 15 — lined up crosswise in the adult's beak. These are presented to the chick still held in the bill, and the chick pecks, grasps, tugs one loose, and swallows it. They are usually taken singly and in order from tip to base of the adult's bill. The chick does not always grasp the head end of a fish and it may manipulate it until it can be swallowed head first. Sometimes, though, a fish is swallowed tail first with no ill effects. If a fish is dropped at the site, the parent picks it up and presents it again; if it falls down below, it is abandoned. Often a fish is too large in some dimension to be swallowed, but the chick will try repeatedly and may be aided by the adult, which will hold up the distal end. The end of a fish or squid too long to get down all at once protrudes from the chick's mouth until it can be completely swallowed.

I kept daily records of the weight gained by the chick at several different nest sites from the time of hatching until nearly adult weight was reached. I did this by weighing the chick before its first feeding of the day — usually at

FIG. 14. White tern and its egg.

about dawn, when the parent departed — and after its last feeding as indicated by the presence of a brooding parent after dark. Feeding schedules are erratic as is the daily (24-hour) change in weight of the chick; several days of small but steady weight gain may be followed by a loss and then a sharp increase. A chick at the end of the daylight hours may weigh half again as much as it did at dawn, but most of this weight is lost during the night. I recorded no overnight gain greater than one-sixth of the body weight 24 hours earlier. Chicks require about one month to reach a weight that fluctuates around 90 grams, which is about the lower limit of weight of a fledged juvenile. However, the parents continue to feed young birds at the nest site for another month and the young may be fed for still another month after leaving the nest site but before they go out to sea on their own.

For the first few days after hatching, chicks are tolerant of any adult bird that comes to the nest site whether or not it is a parent. Such visitors are not infrequent, and they often approach, preen, and even brood a small chick. If a parent returns when an adult visitor is present, the latter is quickly attacked and routed. After the first few posthatching days, however, chicks become very aggressive toward nonparent adults or juveniles that approach, and succeed in driving them away. Approaching nonparent adults generally exhibit a nervous appearance, which may be the clue by which the chicks recognize them as nonparents, and they usually give way quickly before the aggressive posture of even a small chick.

Although adults have a distinctive repertoire of vocal signals (Moynihan, 1962), there is virtually no vocal communication between adults and chicks. The latter may cheep softly when closely approached, but there is no vocal response from the adult even if it is not carrying food. Yet, when chicks as young as 3 days old moved several meters away from the original nest site, returning parents went unerringly to their own chick although other un-attended chicks were also present a few meters away. I never saw one of my marked adults go to a chick not its own under natural circumstances, even if its chick had voluntarily moved away as mentioned. Of course, such move-ments rarely occur and may be impossible except when the nest is on a man-made structure, but this situation is frequent on Midway.

Despite these indications that parents recognize their own chick away from the nest site, they will accept and raise a chick other than their own if it is substituted for their own at their site. This was most strikingly demon-strated at one site where a frail, 11-day-old chick weighing 19 grams died after exposure to rain. I replaced it 1.5 hours later with a large but still downy hand-fed chick that was somewhat overweight at 95 grams. A parent had by then returned near the site with fish in its beak, and within 5 minutes this adult approached the new, large chick — hesitantly at first — and fed it as it pecked eagerly at the proffered fish. Both parents subsequently cooperated in raising this chick to successful fledging; it initially lost weight under their feeding regime but ultimately gained it back and appeared healthy and strong.

The fact that adults accept a new chick in place of their own at the nest site does not necessarily mean that they do not or cannot recognize their own. Choice experiments were not generally successful for two reasons. Chicks more than a few days old were often aggressive and drove an intro-duced chick away from their nest site. If two younger chicks were placed together at a nest site, the more vigorous of the two got all the food from the returning parent, whether or not this chick was the parent's own. This suggests that adults do not distinguish individual chicks at an early age, and it also shows that their feeding method virtually precludes the possibility of raising two or more chicks. As the adult holds food in its bill until the last piece is consumed and as not enough food can be carried to sate the appetite of any but the smallest chicks, one gets all the food and the other becomes

FIG. 15.   Adult white tern brooding chick under one wing.

weaker and soon starves. Thus, even in the unlikely event that a white tern could balance and incubate two eggs, it could probably raise only one chick.

After feeding a chick the parent often preens it extensively about the face. This is a part of its plumage that the chick cannot preen itself although it is most likely to be soiled during feeding. The motions and postures of both birds are similar to those shown by mutually preening adults, and this suggests that the latter behavior is a ritualized derivative of chick-preening.

As juvenile birds approach the stage of their first flight, they often extend and flap their wings while remaining in place. Fledging — departure from the nest site — seems to be a critical point in survival of the young bird. The first flight usually occurs when the parents are absent, and if the juvenile merely flutters down to the ground or glides away some distance from the site and is unable to fly back up to its vicinity, it has a poor chance of being located by a returning parent. If subsequent flights take it farther from the nest, it will probably never be found and will starve. Those strong enough to fly up to a point above the nest site, or to return to its level from below, have a much better chance of recontacting their parents and being fed to the age of self-sufficiency. The fact that adults seem not to respond to an egg, chick, or juvenile that drops below the nest site suggests adaptive behavior, as a "fallen offspring" at any stage is probably a poor survival risk.

I was not able to follow the activities of any juveniles to the stage of self-sufficiency, but the number of carcasses around the island indicates that many perish before that stage is reached. On Midway these terns have no native predators, and the chief sources of mortality of the eggs and young are wind, rain, and starvation. At least two chicks were attacked by ants (doubtless introduced by man) and would have been killed had I not intervened. House mice *(Mus musculus)* are not a problem, perhaps because the terns' eggs are almost never unattended at night, and house rats *(Rattus rattus)* are rigorously controlled by Navy personnel. In the case of the white tern, human activity — planting of *Casuarina* trees and construction of buildings — has inadvertently but unquestionably favored an increase in the bird's abundance on Midway Island by the great increase in potential nest sites.

The white tern must have had an intriguing evolutionary history, about which we have few clues. As this species almost never nests on the ground even with limitless sites and an absence of predators, it was probably derived from tree- or cliff-nesting ancestors. The noddy terns *(Anous)* are the only other tree-nesting terns, and they always *(A. tenuirostris)* or usually *(A. stolidus)* use vegetation or feathers in their nests. Possibly the white tern's nonuse of nesting materials evolved as an adaptation to nesting on islands where vegetation that could be used for nest construction was scarce or absent. This would have enabled them to exploit sites such as raised coral formations or volcanic rock that were unsuitable for other tern species. If so, selection would favor adaptations for tight clinging of chicks to the substrate that would also be pre-adaptive for "nestless" nesting in trees as well.

Although white terns often nest in fairly close proximity to one another, they are not as colonial or sociable as most other terns. Often a single pair nests successfully in a site far from any others, or a few pairs are sparsely and randomly distributed about an area. Even when they nest in assemblages, as mentioned, pairs are seldom closer than 1 meter to one another. I watched closely two sites only about 0.5 meter apart and noted the associated problems. In one case adults returning with food were often attacked by the closest neighbor and robbed of their fish; a chick in one such nest died, and its low weight at death suggested starvation. In the other site, I saw an adult seize the tail of a squid protruding from a neighboring chick's mouth and remove it for its own use. Too-close nesting appears inimical to adequate feeding of young. Even away from the nest sites, white terns are not very sociable. They never gather in resting flocks as do the noddy-tern species, and one often sees midair fights in which both adversaries fall fluttering to the ground with locked beaks. The white tern's usual (but not invariable) lack of aggression toward humans has given it a reputation for gentleness, but this is not expressed intraspecifically except between mates. Its small number of displays expressing degrees of hostility and aggressiveness is associated not with a peaceful disposition but with a readiness to attack any bird that gets closer than about five tern-lengths away. The birds quickly space themselves out and avoid fights by keeping a safe distance rather than by using subtle behavioral signals. When mates approach each other, a bill-down posture is adopted by one or both birds that I believe indicates nonaggression; this is often followed by face-preening that may confirm individual recognition and further diminish aggressive drives. The white tern's rule of pollex seems to be "if it approaches, raise wings, squawk, and prepare to attack; if it then acts like a mate, preen it." The end result often suggests, deceptively, a placid nonhostile assemblage, especially among mated and incubating birds. Random wanderings would produce aggressive responses and are avoided; this may have prompted Dorward's (1963) comment that, in their domestic life, these terns "have perfected, behaviorally speaking, the art of doing almost nothing."

Lack (1967) provided a series of curves relating egg weight to its percent of adult body weight and to the incubation period — and also the incubation period to fledging period. The weight of a fresh white-tern egg is about 22 grams, making it about 19 percent of adult body weight and thus similar to the proportions of other gulls and terns. The incubation period is much longer in proportion to egg weight than in most (but not all) birds in this group, but the relation of incubation period to fledging period is similar to the others. Possibly the long incubation period in relation to egg size is associated with precocial development at hatching that enables the chick to hold on to its nest site (usually) with a tenacity lacking in other tern chicks, including the tree-nesting noddies. In other respects, the white tern seems to fit the characteristics outlined by Lack for offshore-feeding terns.

Moynihan (1962) proposed that *Gygis* be synonymized with *Anous* and that the species *alba* be known as the white noddy. I feel that the numerous differences in morphology of both adults and chicks and also in behavior are sufficient to distinguish two genera, and thus I retain *Gygis*. Moynihan informs me that the blue-gray noddy, *Procelsterna (=Anous?) cerulea,* bridges the gap between the genera, but unfortunately I have no experience with that form. In any case, the white tern remains an exceptionally interesting and attractive subject for study and one about which there is still much to learn.

REFERENCES

ASHMOLE, N. PHILIP

1968. Breeding and molt in the white tern *(Gygis alba)* on Christmas Island, Pacific Ocean. Condor, vol. 70, pp. 35-55, charts.

ASHMOLE, N. PHILIP, and ASHMOLE, MYRTLE J.

1967. Comparative feeding ecology of sea birds of a tropical oceanic island. Peabody Mus. Nat. Hist. Yale Univ. Bull. 24, 131 pp., charts.

DORWARD, D. F.

1963. The fairy tern *Gygis alba* on Ascension Island. Ibis, vol. 103b, pp. 365-378.

LACK, DAVID

1967. Interrelationships in breeding adaptations as shown by marine birds. Proc. XIV Int. Orn. Congr., pp. 3-42, charts. Blackwell Scientific Publications, Oxford and Edinburgh.

MOYNIHAN, MARTIN H.

1962. Hostile and sexual behavior patterns of South American and Pacific Laridae, 365 pp., illus. E. J. Brill, Leiden.

THOMAS R. HOWELL

Orientation of Migrating Larval, Postlarval, and Juvenile Pink Shrimp, 1969

Principal Investigator: David A. Hughes, Rosenstiel School of Marine and Atmospheric Science, University of Miami, Miami, Florida.

Grant No. 776:   In support of continued research on the mechanisms underlying the migrations of pink shrimp *(Penaeus duorarum).*

This is the concluding report concerning a project initiated in 1964 and undertaken intermittently until midyear 1970. The objective was to determine the mechanisms underlying the migrations carried out by pink shrimp. These migrations involve displacement of larval stages from offshore waters within the Gulf of Mexico, where they are spawned, to inshore "nursery areas," often deep within the Everglades, where they undergo rapid growth for a period of 4 to 6 months, and their subsequent return, as subadults, to deeper waters.

Earlier studies on this project showed that most activities of shrimp are influenced by biological timing mechanisms. This influence is most clearly manifested in the periods of activity and inactivity that coincide with night and day, respectively, and are under endogenous control. An internal "clock" triggers the emergence and burrowing of shrimp, enabling the entire population to emerge from the sand at approximately the same time each evening and reburrow at dawn. The internal clock enforces this pattern of behavior for at least a week even when, by exposing the shrimp to constant light conditions in the laboratory, they are unable to distinguish day from night (Hughes, 1967a, 1968, 1971).

Considerable attention has been given to the method whereby postlarval and subadult shrimp distinguish between and utilize flood and ebb tides for their respective inshore and offshore movements. It was found that both postlarvae and subadults could perceive small changes in salinity, far smaller than those usually occurring between tides in areas such as the Everglades, where considerable amounts of fresh water drain from land to sea. It was deduced from these experiments that appropriate behavioral changes, occurring in response to the perception by the shrimp of salinity changes, enabled the shrimp to use one or another tide for displacement in one direction while largely avoiding displacement by the alternate tide. In this way, progress either inshore (postlarvae) or offshore (subadults) takes place as a series of steplike movements in phase with the tide (Hughes, 1967b, 1969a, 1972).

Subsequent studies were largely aimed at determining the way in which internal timing mechanisms facilitate use of tides. A very striking relationship was found in the laboratory between the times of upstream and downstream swimming of postlarvae in a current chamber and the times of flood and ebb tide in the area from which the postlarvae had been collected. In the absence of any external cue with which to distinguish one tide from another, postlarvae would, for a few days following collection from nature, swim upstream during the time of the flood tides and downstream during ebb tide. Upstream swimming involved considerable activity whereas downstream swimming was largely passive, the postlarvae being transported at the same velocity as the current. It was postulated that their activity during the flood tide served to maintain them within the water column where the tide would displace them inshore, but during their inactive period they would evade displacement by remaining on the substrate.

Further studies were carried out on the endogenous control of swimming in subadults. Evidence of this control was mentioned in an earlier report (Hughes, 1969b). Results confirmed the earlier evidence, based on current chamber studies, which had suggested that swimming, with respect to up and downstream orientation, was a function of entrainment derived from some aspect of the tidal regime existing in nature at the time of collection. Shrimp collected from ebb tides occurring early in the evening would, the following night in the current chamber, swim downstream during the early part of the evening (i.e., for the duration of the ebb tide) and then reverse direction to swim upstream for the remainder of the night. On the other hand, those collected from ebb tides occurring late in the evening swam upstream throughout the following night. No explanation for this difference is yet apparent, although it is probably significant that downstream swimming occurs only during ebb tides when it would be adaptive in nature. The fact that it does not occur at the time of all ebb tides is puzzling and makes difficult any explanation based only in terms of a tidal rhythm. There is one major advantage to endogenous control of tide-associated displacements over simple exogenous control, in which the animal responds directly to changes in water quality. This concerns the problem faced by an animal, transported within a particular water mass, in determining the end or beginning of a particular tide. With change of tide the entire water mass will begin to move in the opposite direction, and there may be little or no change in water quality to indicate tide change. This problem is, however, avoided if, by responding to internal cues, the shrimp carries out appropriate behavioural changes at approximately the time of change of tide.

It is probable that the displacements of both the early larval stage shrimp and subadults in offshore waters, beyond the influence of ebb and flood tides, are effected passively by prevailing currents. Suitable currents appear to exist for these purposes in the Gulf of Mexico and vicinity of the Everglades. Therefore, with the explanation derived from this project, for the mechanism whereby the movements within inshore waters are undertaken, we are probably within reach of an understanding of the entire migration.

REFERENCES

HUGHES, DAVID A.

1967a. Factors controlling the time of emergence of pink shrimp, *Penaeus duorarum.* Contribution to FAO World Scientific Conference on the Biology and Culture of Shrimps and Prawns, Mexico City, 1967.

1967b. On the mechanisms underlying tide-associated movements of *Penaeus duorarum.* Contribution to FAO World Scientific Conference on the Biology and Culture of Shrimps and Prawns, Mexico City, 1967.

1968. Factors controlling emergence of pink shrimp *(Penaeus duorarum)* from the substrate. Biol. Bull., vol. 134, pp. 48-59.

1969a. Responses to salinity change as a tidal transport mechanism of pink shrimp, *Penaeus duorarum.* Biol. Bull., vol. 136, pp. 43-53.

1969b. Evidence for the endogenous control of swimming in pink shrimp, *Penaeus duorarum.* Biol. Bull., vol. 136, pp. 398-404.

1971. Orientation of migrating larval, postlarval, and juvenile pink shrimp, 1965. Nat. Geogr. Soc. Res. Rpts., 1965 Projects, pp. 109-112.

1972. On the endogenous control of tide-associated displacements of pink shrimp, *Penaeus duorarum* Burkenroad. Biol. Bull., vol. 142, pp. 271-280, illus.

1973. Orientations of migrating pink shrimp. Nat. Geogr. Soc. Res. Rpts., 1966 Projects, pp. 127-129.

1974. Orientation of migrating pink shrimp. Nat. Geogr. Soc. Res. Rpts., 1967 Projects, pp. 169-171.

DAVID A. HUGHES

Cyprus Underwater Archeological Search, 1969

Principal Investigator: Michael L. Katzev, University Museum, University of Pennsylvania, Philadelphia, Pennsylvania; and Oberlin College, Oberlin, Ohio.[1]

Grant No. 767:   For continuation of excavation of ancient shipwreck off the coast of Cyprus, near Kyrenia.

The expedition accomplished, in essence, double its projected goal, compressing what was intended as two seasons of diving into one expanded campaign of 5 months. The goal projected had been the clearing and removal of the considerable cargo and cabin equipment that remained *in situ* after the first season's excavation (Katzev, M. L., 1976). However, through a unique combination of the skill of our crew members and excellent weather the expedition proceeded so rapidly as to be able to undertake a great deal more than this.

Preparation of equipment for the summer's work began May 12 under the supervision of Dr. David Owen, the project's assistant director. Our basic diving equipment and barge were at hand for reuse, and much of the underwater installations — such as telephone booth, grid frames, and air lifts — had been left in place on the bottom at the end of the preceding season. Therefore, what had taken approximately 20 persons a month to prepare in

[1] Grateful acknowledgment is made to the Department of Antiquities of the Republic of Cyprus, with whose kind permission the second campaign of excavation on the Kyrenia shipwreck was undertaken in the summer of 1969. In addition to the sponsorship of the University Museum of the University of Pennsylvania, financial aid was received from the John Brown Cook Foundation, the National Geographic Society, the Ford Foundation, the National Endowment for the Humanities, Cyprus Mines Corporation, Oberlin College, and the Houghton-Carpenter Foundation. The Cyprus Mines Corporation continued to provide considerable on-site technical assistance, loan of equipment, and medical services. The Institute for Photogrammetry and Topography at the University of Karlsruhe, Germany, generously lent its Zeiss Stereotop for use in the excavation. Much gratitude also is extended to the expedition's personnel, many of whom voluntarily gave of their services and stayed weeks beyond their original commitments.

FIG. 1.   Excavation team at work within the hull. This view from the ship's stern shows ceiling planking still in place.

the initial year was accomplished by a crew of 7 in just 2 weeks. By the end of May the diving barge had been anchored over the wreck, and the site had been cleared of the sand and plastic sheets laid over it as winter protection at the conclusion of the 1968 excavation. By this time many of the students, archeologists, doctors, and photographers of the crew—eventually to number over 40—had assembled, and full diving operations began. We were fortunate that over half of the staff were members returning from the previous summer. Under their guidance the newcoming divers soon learned the skills of excavating and recording their finds under water, again reducing the time that had been spent in 1968 on basic training.

Several additions to the expedition's equipment provided not only greater efficiency on the bottom but also improved medical preparation against diving accidents. The previous season had seen a rather wide experimentation with excavation tools, ranging from a water jet and bubbling needle, which cleared the site of its thick blanket of eelgrass, to "suckers" used to deposit the overburden of sand just outside the excavation area. As we moved deeper into the cargo of amphoras and smaller finds, however, it became of prime importance for the divers to maintain clear visibility. The tools used previously, effective in removing the covering of grass and sand, now became inefficient in layers of silt, for they tended to cloud the site in the absence of a strong current. Thus, two air lifts capable of expelling sand and mud 60 to 100 feet distant from the wreck had been put into operation in 1968. For the second season we chose this tool exclusively, installing altogether seven different air lifts around the wreck, ranging in size from 6 inches in diameter to the "mini-lifts" of 2 inches. They provided each diver in the normal 4-man team with an excavation tool positioned for work in his particular grid area. Equipped with a valve for controlling the rate of suction and built of light-weight plastic tubing with ends of flexible rubber, the air lifts were easy to move across the wreck and suited themselves to heavy-duty suction as well as lifting the silt from the most fragile of the ship's wooden members.

To improve communications between the divers and their topside support on the barge, our electrician, Alfred Kann, installed an underwater loud speaker on the bottom by which individual divers could be called to come into the telephone booth to receive further instructions. It served also as a convenient means of alerting the entire team when it was time to ascend.

A 4-man recompression chamber for treating diving diseases was installed on the barge to replace the smaller chamber lent by the Canadian Government the previous year. For our large-scale diving operation this new chamber provided maximum safety insurance. Designed for oxygen treatment, it consisted of two compartments. Thus, two divers could be treated in the inner compartment while the expedition doctor was free to enter and leave during treatment. Or, in an extreme case, as many as four divers could be treated in the doctor's company, using both compartments at full pressure. Four doctors staffed the expedition over the 5-month season. During this time three of our expedition members were treated in the

FIG. 2.   Removing one of the last remaining amphoras.

chamber for cases of nausea or vertigo resulting from their dives. As these symptoms may be warning signals of the bends, the patients underwent chamber treatment in the company of a doctor. Fortunately, during treatment no further symptoms developed. The recompression chamber continues to be of use on Cyprus; the Cyprus Mines Corporation is maintaining it at its island hospital, and their company mechanics and staff doctors have received instruction in its use and upkeep. Now for the first time the many sport divers among the Cypriotes and United Nations forces, as well as professional salvage divers on the island, have access to recompression treatment. This expedition contribution fills a potentially tragic void in the island's medical facilities.

FIG. 3. Diver lifting grain millstone off wreck to a lifting basket.

The expedition divers followed the procedure of the previous season, diving in teams of two to six and spending 40 minutes' working time on the bottom each morning and 30 minutes in the afternoon. Over 2,000 individual dives were logged this summer, bringing the working hours on the wreck to better than 1,000. This represented a considerable increase over the working hours of the previous season.

Stereo-mapping continued throughout the excavation for recording the find positions of the remaining amphoras, grain mill blocks, and smaller cabin objects. As the ship's hull began to emerge, photogrammetrist Joachim Höhle joined the expedition, bringing with him stereo-plotting instruments on loan from his institution. In combination with photographer John Veltri, Höhle recorded and plotted to an accuracy of ±0.02 meter the wooden hull as it was revealed. The remaining portion exposed after his departure in late August was then plotted with a system of pointing rods. This manual system was capable of both planar and depth measurements and yielded an accuracy comparable to the stereo method. Though somewhat obstructive to an excavation site so heavily populated by working divers, this pointing system holds potential for small excavations subject to limited access of stereogrammetric instruments. It is hoped that publication of the method by its originators will prove useful to fellow excavators. The results of both the stereo and pointing measurements are being assembled into plans depicting the wood as the ship was constructed.

Bob Dunn, in cooperation with the National Geographic Society, again recorded the activities of the expedition with 16-millimeter film. The results were premiered by the Society in Washington's Constitution Hall in March 1970. This document was made available for educational lectures throughout the United States, providing a permanent record of this major event in maritime and archeological history.

The first phase of our 1969 diving season was the excavation of the entire circumference of the wreck site. During the previous summer we had cleared more than 300 amphoras from the upper levels, had come upon a cargo of stone grain mills beneath them, and had excavated a small trench to expose a tantalizing part of the ship's hull. We did not know, however, the extent to which the timbers were preserved or how far the ship's small objects of wood or pottery might have been thrown when the vessel jolted to its final resting place on the sea bottom. Thus, to determine the extent of the cargo and hull we began clearing a 3-meter-wide trench around the area excavated the year before. At the end of a month the outline of the preserved hull was uncovered and found to measure 4.8 by 11.4 meters.

FIG. 4.   Metal reference frame is leveled in preparation for stereo photography.

Recovered also was a considerable spillage of pottery from the fore and aft cabin areas of the ship, which indicated that the vessel had indeed impacted on the bottom with considerable force. A very extensive mass of concreted iron appeared in the stern area outside the preserved hull, and adjacent to it lay isolated wooden members, which we conjecture may be part of the ship's steering mechanism. The iron and associated wood fragments underwent continued excavation as the season progressed, but for the moment we were satisfied that the limits of the vessel and the full extent of its cargo had been defined.

In a pincer movement the excavation teams now proceeded inward to clear the remaining cargo within the wooden hull. In all, 96 amphoras whole and fragmentary were excavated, bringing the ship's total to 403 lifted in the two campaigns. Again some of the jars contained almonds, and clusters of almonds were found outside amphoras, resting in masses upon the interior of the hull. The more than 9,000 almonds recovered in this way would indicate that this commodity was also being transported aboard the ship in sacks of perishable material, such as burlap. The heavy grain millstones, mapped in 1968 and left in place to protect the wood beneath them, were ballooned

FIG. 5.   Diver measuring the exposed hull with pointing rod device.

to the surface in wire baskets. The 29 blocks cut from a volcanic stone bear a variety of mason's marks — single Greek letters chiseled into the short sides of the block. This may well be the largest excavated collection of milling stones of the hopper design. But the pairing of top with bottom stone has not yet been resolved, since not only is there an odd number of blocks, but also their disparity of size, variety of mason's marks, and different types of finish are sources of conflicting evidence. The fact that such a heavy commodity was being transported from a volcanic quarry some great distance from Cyprus is curious in itself. Indeed, the millstone cargo will form a most interesting segment in the final study of the merchant ship, bearing as it does both on ancient milling technology and trade patterns within the Classical world.

Forward and aft of the amphora and millstone cargoes the excavators began uncovering many more items from the ship's cabins. Three small black-glazed pitchers, two casserole lids, coarse-ware mixing bowls, fragments of a pottery sieve, a pitcher coated inside with a layer of bitumen, and a copper cauldron unfortunately crushed during the ship's settling, all provide new evidence of the culinary activity on board. Used for the crew's meals were 13 black-glazed echinus bowls, numerous flat plates again black glazed, and a fourth drinking cup, perhaps indicative of the number of crewmen on the last voyage. Adding weight to this supposition are three new oil jugs (gutti), combining with the single example from 1968 to total four, and four small echinus bowls or salt dishes. Parts of four wooden spoons and a lathe-turned wooden bowl in fragmentary condition complete the dining utensils found. Just forward of the bow cabin area lay two concentrations of lead weights once attached to fishing nets. Among the weights to the port side of the cabin were found a seal impression in lead depicting Athena Promachos and three bronze coins. A fourth bronze coin appeared amid the weights from the second net just forward the cabin. Although the coins are badly corroded, at least two can be identified. Both were struck some time after 316 B.C.

A single lamp fragment from the aft cabin area serves to validate the impression that the ancients limited their sailing principally to daylight hours. However, an unexpected refinement aboard the Kyrenia merchantman is an "inkwell" found adhering to the concretion of iron in the stern. This concretion, which weighed 1,400 pounds, was raised to the surface for restoration. Between the preserved hull in the stern and the concretion lay a marble columnar pedestal, its context on shipboard yet an enigma. Scattered throughout the stern area were almost a hundred flat lead rings, which probably served in guiding the brail lines used to reef the ship's sail. Amidships and resting directly on the hull were 10 double knobs, resembling yo-yos. That they served as toggles in the ship's rigging is a strong possibility. However, as with so many of the other objects from the vessel, their function will be definitely ascertained only after further study.

Once the ship had been completely cleared of its contents, it could be seen that it remained remarkably intact. The excavators moved their air lifts about the site with extreme caution as they uncovered and cleaned the hull for stereo-coverage. It was soon realized that in the course of its 2,200 years on the bottom the ship had split into two sections, the division occurring just to the starboard of the keel. A wooden pulley that had fallen into the separation may well have served in the raising and lowering of the ship's

Amphora from Samos

Bronze Cauldron

Belaying Pins

Lead Weights from
Fishing Nets

Lead Seal Impression
of Athena Promachos

Wooden Toggle,
Lathe-turned

Ring-handled Guttus

Wooden Pulley

Black-glazed Plate

FIG. 6.   Samples of artifacts found.

single square sail. The port side, which is the better preserved, contained some 12 unhewn tree limbs laden forward amidships. Beneath these and running aft under the rows of millstones the ship's ceiling planking was exposed. After labeling and stereo-recording, the planking was then systematically removed. Carved into the upper surfaces of these "flooring" planks were various graffitti. The frames, or ribs, of the vessel are so solidly preserved as to indicate both the curvature of the hull well above the bilge line and the counter curve where they slope to the keel. The outer strakes were joined one to another by mortise and tenon secured with wooden dowels. It is clear that the vessel was built in the "shell-first" manner, that is: the outer planking having been assembled and joined first, the ribs were later laid within it and fixed into position by copper nails driven in from the outside and clenched over the inner surface of the ribs. Interesting also is the regular alternation of ribs: one rib spans the keel and in a second piece presumably runs the full height to the gunwale, while its neighbor originates just short of the keel and terminates well above the bilge line. The entire outer surface of the preserved hull was found sheathed with lead affixed by regular rows of copper tacks. The construction of the ship's bow is unique. Here the outer planking is in two layers, separated by lead sheets and joined with thick square wooden dowels. Approximately one-third aft the bow, the intricately carved mast step was located. This piece, grooved as it is with numerous bracing slots and accompanied by two additional half-round bracing members forward, is testimony to the craft of Greek shipwrights, here demonstrated even in what must have been the most common type of vessel, the merchant ship.

Shortly before the last details of the ship's hull could be exposed, photogrammetrist Höhle had to return to his responsibilities at the University of Karlsruhe. Likewise, underwater photographer Veltri was called to an assignment elsewhere. It was decided that, no matter how small the remaining information to be recorded might be, a manual system must be devised to insure that no measurement available to us would go unrecorded. In early September, with the grid frames removed, Peter Leonard and Stephen Scheifele designed and installed on the bottom the pointing device capable of the $\pm$ 0.02-meter accuracy of the stereo method. With this they not only mapped the information newly uncovered but also made a spot check over the entire wreck to prove out the accuracy of their new instrument against the previous stereo record. As they worked, each member of the ship was being labeled in preparation for its eventual removal from the site.

It was clear by mid-August that the hull could be entirely exposed and prepared for lifting by mid-September. The choice was now before us

FIG. 7.   The intricately cut mast step with its two forward bracing members.

whether to bury the wood for the winter (as previously planned) or to raise it in the remaining weeks of calm weather. Twelve of the diving crew volunteered to stay on if we should decide on this latter course. Paramount in our considerations was concern for the optimum conservation of the wood. We had observed a noticeable softening over the summer of those timbers that had been earliest exposed, and we were certain the softening would continue through the winter on the sea bottom. Now that the original packing of mud had been removed, increasing amounts of oxygen were reaching the ancient hull. Covering the ship with silt would not be sufficient to arrest this totally or insure that marine life would not attack the wood again. The outer planks, for example, were even now so riddled by ancient teredo worms that a fresh assault would almost certainly weaken them to the point of disintegration. Lastly, the thought that over the winter clandestine sport divers might find the timbers tempting as relics or treasure made our decision incontestable: to undertake the hull raising immediately.

During the summer we had sought advice on raising the two sections of the ship to the surface intact and transporting them over the wall of Kyrenia Castle, which was to be the locus for preservation treatment and eventual display. Because of its downdraft, helicopter removal was considered too dangerous for the softened wood. No combination of lifting equipment could be found on the island to manage transfer of a 10-ton load from quayside up over the 80-foot castle wall. In short, nothing less than removing a section of the battlements would permit an intact transfer. Incidentally, this last was graciously offered by the Antiquities Department of Cyprus and most gratefully declined by the expedition. We concluded that the vessel would have to be cut up into convenient sizes for the lift and subsequent transfer through the castle doorways. The smaller eastern section would be the logical area in which to begin. Using a compressed-air-driven underwater saw, we separated this side into manageable pieces of approximately 1 by 2 meters. After cutting, a flexible sheet of galvanized iron was slid beneath each piece, and it was carefully moved into a rigid steel frame equipped with flexible bands that could adapt to the curvature of the hull. A diver would then attach a line from the barge and fill the lifting balloon. As the balloon carried the load upward, the diver followed, deflating the balloon gradually so that the frame would not rise too abruptly as it neared the surface. At the barge each basket was winched onto an awaiting boat. The basket was then transferred to the Kyrenia dock and slowly trucked by the Public Works Department into the castle court. There the wood was washed and placed in fresh-water tanks. No matter how cautiously it was handled throughout the lift and transfer, the wood was so soft and pliable that it settled within the trays, and the sections lost their original contours. It was clear that these sections would have to be dismantled after preservation for proper reconstruction. Thus, it was decided to dismantle the larger western side of the hull on the bottom and raise each piece separately. This we did, after an intensive labeling program was undertaken to insure correct reassemblage. First the ribs were removed and turned on their sides into new rigid lifting frames designed to suit their greatest length. Next the mast step complex and keel were lifted, and finally the outer planks were cut into manageable lengths and raised. Once inside the castle the timbers were washed of any remaining mud and catalogued, and each rib was traced on drafting film to record precisely its original curvature for later reconstruction. The wood then went into seven temporary fresh-water tanks and was then transferred into a large concrete tank built within a closed gallery of the castle.

Early in the summer the expedition storeroom within Kyrenia Castle was made ready for use by our conservator. Encircling the room are shelves holding the amphoras, grain mill blocks, and boxes of sherds and smaller finds. Work tables and sinks are in use by excavation conservator Frances Talbot. Miss Talbot, who joined the expedition from the Institute of Archaeology, University of London, completed restoration of the 1968 finds and began working on the considerable amount of material recovered in 1969. Built into the storeroom also are a booth for object photography and a

FIG. 8.   Detail of the west side partially excavated.

FIG. 9. Skeleton of the hull with plastic grids removed. A portion of the starboard side, not as extensively preserved, has been lifted, and another section resting on a galvanized plate awaits removal to a lifting tray.

cataloguing desk. In use over the 1969 season, these will continue to serve
in future summers as the cargo from the ship is studied.

A second goal projected for 1969 was achieved. During the previous
winter visitors to Kyrenia Castle, among them many Cypriotes, had expressed
interest in viewing the objects from the excavation. As the finds pointed to a
most interesting and rarely illustrated aspect of Mediterranean history, it
was felt that the public should not be denied some view of the material.
Toward this end the excavation opened its storeroom temporarily to groups
in the company of the castle custodian. However, it was clear that a more
permanent arrangement would have to be made. Therefore, the Department
of Antiquities made available and restored handsomely a small room adjacent to the storeroom to be used for exhibition purposes. By late September
an attractive display had been mounted by the expedition's architect Miss
Wylde and Miss Talbot. Arrangements were made by the Department of
Antiquities to open the temporary museum under adequate supervision. It
is hoped that in the future a more complete story of the excavation may be
assembled in these quarters to complement exhibition of the preserved ship
in its own gallery across the castle courtyard.

It is clear now that the conservation and restoration of the dismantled
Kyrenia ship for permanent display are the pressing and ultimate goal of the
excavation. If this can be accomplished, then the structure of the 4th-century
B.C. merchantman will be on view for maritime scholars and the public alike.
Toward this end the expedition sought for an experienced wood-preserva-
tion consultant to examine the timbers and provide expert advice on the
equipment and materiel required for treatment. In the meantime, the Department of Antiquities of Cyprus graciously undertook to restore one of
the vaulted galleries within Kyrenia Castle for housing the ship during
preservation and for eventual exhibition. The expedition has installed within this gallery a treatment tank with spray and circulation equipment for
polyethylene-glycol treatment, either by spray or immersion. A small crew
of expedition personnel, including the acting director, architect, draftsman,
and conservator, remained in Kyrenia over the winter tending the wood
against fungus growth, continuing to catalogue and measure the pieces, and
drawing in final form the plans and sections of the hull as it rested on the
bottom. Examination of samples of wood from different members of the
ship was begun by the Wood Chemistry Laboratory of the U. S. Department
of Agriculture's Forest Service. Through the analyses it is hoped not only to
identify the variety of wood species used in the building of the Kyrenia hull
but also to narrow geographically the point in the ancient Mediterranean
world where these timbers were cut and the ship constructed. To the carbon-

14 laboratory of the University of Pennsylvania Museum went samples from the hull and a collection of almonds. The date of the felling of the ship's lumber should be determined by the laboratory to an accuracy of at least ±50 years; but more important the differential dating between the hull and its cargo of almonds could provide an important clue to the age of the vessel when she sank.

The 1969 season, then, saw the goals of two summers realized in one. The excavation of the ship was completed. Yet the many unusual finds from the vessel, as well as her fascinating design, awaited interpretative study in the years ahead. There remained perhaps the greatest challenge of the undertaking — that of conserving the Kyrenia ship, the earliest ocean-going hull ever found, in order that it may be viewed and studied by generations to come.

REFERENCES

KATZEV, MICHAEL L.
  1970. Kyrenia 1969; A Greek ship is raised.   Expedition, vol. 12, no. 4, pp. 6-14, illus.
  1974. Cyprus underwater archeological search, 1967.   Nat. Geogr. Soc. Res. Rpts., 1967 Projects, pp. 177-184, illus.
  1976. Cyprus underwater archeological search, 1968.   Nat. Geogr. Soc. Res. Rpts., 1968 Projects, pp. 177-188, illus.
KATZEV, SUSAN WOMER
  1970. The riddle of the merchantman.   Swarthmore College Bull., October, 1970, pp. 16-22, illus.
  1971. Love affair: 54 people and a ship.   Oberlin Alumni Mag., vol. 67, no. 1, pp. 4-11, illus.
MORRIS, JOHN W.
  1971. The practical aspects of diving medicine.   Journ. Florida Med. Assoc., vol. 58, no. 3, pp. 24-27.

MICHAEL L. KATZEV

Archeological Research in Colima, Mexico

Principal Investigator: Isabel T. Kelly, Tepepan, D. F., Mexico.

Grant Nos. 842, 908:   In aid of continuing studies of western Mexico archeology.

The background — natural and cultural — for archeological field work in Colima, herein reported, has been outlined in the National Geographic Society Research Reports for 1968 (Kelly, 1976). The present summary begins where that of 1968 ended.

The 1970 season[1] started with efforts to disentangle problems that had been left dangling at the conclusion of the previous field work. Of these, the two most important were the need (1) to link east and southeast Colima with the ceramic series more or less satisfactorily established in the Armería basin and (2) to find material that would permit definition of a ceramic phase scarcely known but supposedly belonging to a time level equivalent to that of the Mesoamerican Preclassic and far earlier than anything previously recognized in Colima (Kelly, 1976).

The first part of the field season focused on the lower Coahuayana Valley, on the border of the states of Colima and Michoacán. Here a surface survey was completed and one important stratigraphic test was made at La Paranera, near San Vicente. Surface indications suggested a low mound, but our test cut into a deposit more than 4 meters deep; such depth is quite extraordinary for the Colima area, where remains seem consistently to be quite shallow. From this same test came our first really good sample of charcoal for dating. The resulting radiocarbon date — determined by courtesy of the University of Michigan radiocarbon laboratory — is 160 B.C. (sample M-2396) and applies to local ceramics that equate, in the Armería basin, with the Ortices phase.

Elsewhere the search for the supposedly much earlier material con-

---

[1] In 1970, as in 1968-1969, field investigation was supported by grants from the National Geographic Society and the Wenner-Gren Foundation for Anthropological Research.

FIG. 1.   Pottery of the Capacha phase, Colima: *a*, "Bule"; diameter at rim, 19.5-
20.0 centimeters. *b*, Stirrup pot; diameter at rim, 6.7-7.0 centimeters. *c*, "Bule";
diameter at rim, 23.0-23.7 centimeters. *d*, Small olla, wide mouth; rose slip; diameter at rim, 15.0 centimeters. (All specimens are property of the Instituto
Nacional de Antropología e Historia, on deposit in the Museo Nacional de
Antropología).

FIG. 2. Pottery of the Capacha phase, Colima: *a*, Compound vessel, considered a stirrup-pot variant; diameter at rim, 6.5-6.7 centimeters. *b*, Jar, with fluting above shoulder; diameter at rim, 14.2-14.5 centimeters. *c*, Effigy vessel; diameter at rim, 8.0-8.3 centimeters. *d*, Neckless jar *(tecomate);* diameter at rim, 9.0-9.2 centimeters. (All specimens are property of the Instituto Nacional de Antropología e Historia, on deposit in the Museo Nacional de Antropología).

tinued — gratifyingly, with considerable success. Several cemeteries were located, of which three were productive. Although a small one at La Capacha had been completely looted, purchased specimens attributed to it were so enlightening that the newly established phase was given the name Capacha.

Purchased specimens, in combination with those excavated under control, give a fairly good idea of the ceramic content of the Capacha phase. The cinctured vessel with wide mouth is especially characteristic (fig. 1, *a, c*). Certain of the vessel forms — particularly the stirrup pot (fig. 1, *b*) — suggest a time level earlier than had been anticipated. So also does the characteristic decoration in the form of broad incision and punctation. Indeed, these traits and others suggest that the Capacha phase aligns with the Preclassic or Formative cultures elsewhere in Mexico and in the Americas (Ford, 1969).

The one radiocarbon date available for Capacha reinforces this interpretation. Based directly on carbon recovered from potsherds, a date of 1450 B.C. (GX-1784) was obtained by a commercial laboratory. In the hope of confirmation, bone from several fragmentary burials was sacrificed but, lamentably, soil conditions were such that the material had been leached and did not provide sufficient carbon for processing.

However, indirect confirmation comes from a radiocarbon date of 1500 B.C., based on charcoal from a tomb at El Opeño, Michoacán (Oliveros, 1970, p. 135). Some of the Opeño tomb sherds resemble Capacha material very closely, and the two dates, almost synchronous, constitute welcome mutual support.

In summary, Capacha is the earliest phase known so far from Colima. Typologically, its pottery has some generic resemblances to even earlier ceramic material from coastal Ecuador (Meggers, Evans, and Estrada, 1965) and, indeed, may be largely derivative from early South American cultures. It has resemblances also in form and decoration to the well-known "Tlatilco style" of the central highlands, known particularly from the Basin of Mexico and the adjacent state of Morelos. In current reckoning, the "Tlatilco style" is considered some centuries more recent than Capacha. Although a radiocarbon date of 1450 B.C. places Capacha earlier than the first recognizable manifestation of the famous Olmec culture, there is no suggestion of ties with the latter.

REFERENCES

FORD, JAMES A.
  1969. A comparison of Formative cultures in the Americas: Diffusion or the psychic unity of man. Smithsonian Contr. Anthrop., no. 11, 211 pp., illus.
KELLY, ISABEL T.
  1976. Archeological research in Colima, Mexico. Nat. Geogr. Soc. Res. Rpts., 1968 Projects, pp. 189-197, illus.
MEGGERS, BETTY J.; EVANS, CLIFFORD; and ESTRADA, EMILIO
  1965. Early Formative period of coastal Ecuador: The Valdivia and Machalilla phases. Smithsonian Contr. Anthrop., no. 1, 234 pp., illus.
OLIVEROS, JOSÉ ARTURO
  [1970]. Excavación de dos tumbas en El Opeño, Michoacán. Tesis profesional ... para obtener el título de arqueólogo en la Escuela Nacional de Antropología e Historia, y al mismo tiempo el grade académico de maestro en ciencias antropológicas en la Universidad Nacional Autónoma de México.

ISABEL T. KELLY

Population Ecology of Key Deer

Principal Investigators: Willard D. Klimstra, James W. Hardin, and Nova J. Silvy, Southern Illinois University, Carbondale, Illinois.

Grant Nos. 750, 854, 959. For research on the ecology and population of the Key deer, Florida Keys.

During the past several years the population of the Key deer *(Odocoileus virginianus clavium)* has increased in numbers following a low level in the late 1940's and early 1950's. This response was the aftermath of protection from intense hunting and disturbance. The increase in numbers, however, appeared to have been much slower than that characteristic of other white-tailed-deer populations subjected to protection from hunting and afforded opportunity for increment. The reasons for this gradual increase, as well as questions regarding the physiology, subspecific status, and relationships of this deer to its unique island environment, precipitated the research to be reported. The objectives of this study, which was undertaken in December 1967, include investigation of movements and dispersal through the use of various marking devices including radio transmitters, study of social behavior and organization with emphasis on their effects on population dynamics, and examination of reproduction and survival. In addition, nutritional and population trend studies were made and miscellaneous data on life history and ecology were collected.

During January 1968 through mid-September 1968 and from December 1968 through December 1971, staff from the Cooperative Wildlife Research Laboratory, Southern Illinois University at Carbondale, were in continuous residence on Big Pine Key to collect data on the deer in its habitat. Subsequent periods of 2 weeks to 6 months were spent during 1972 and 1973, during which time specific emphasis was on capturing, marking, and monitoring pregnant does and newborn fawns, transplanting deer, and collecting vegetation samples. While field work was being conducted, personnel in residence at Southern Illinois University at Carbondale analyzed materials collected from mortalities and live deer.

Personnel associated with the study were: Dr. W. D. Klimstra, James W. Hardin, and Nova J. Silvy, principal investigators, Patricia Czapar, Allan L. Dooley, Todd Eberhardt, Bruce N. Jacobson, Katherine Jacobson, Jimmie

313

R. McCain, Douglas E. Morthland, Patricia Morthland, James L. Rachuy, John W. Schulte, Virginia A. Terpening, and Thomas Trudeau. The contributions of Jack C. Watson, Sr., manager, Key Deer National Wildlife Refuge, to this research cannot be adequately emphasized. Financial support was provided by the U. S. Department of Interior Bureau of Sport Fisheries and Wildlife, the National Geographic Society, the North American Wildlife Foundation, the National Wildlife Federation, and the Southern Illinois University at Carbondale.

Generally, Key deer proved difficult to capture as the more conventional methods (drugs and trail traps) either could not be used or were unproductive. During this study, of the numerous techniques employed, a 50-by-14-foot nylon net used in conjunction with hand captures was most productive (Silvy et al., 1975). A total of 364 deer were captured, including 131 recaptures. Of these, 227 were restrained in a 50-foot net; 21 were captured after they had jumped into dredged waterways; 90 were captured by hand; 17 were taken with the use of nicotine salicylate; 9 were taken with trail traps; and 2 were hand-caught while swimming between islands.

Various devices for marking deer for subsequent identification were employed, including plastic and aluminum numbered ear tags, colored ear streamers, permanent ear tattoos, small metal bells, and Boltaron collars bearing distinctive colored symbols made from Scotch-Lite reflective tape. Collars for small fawns were made of elastic strips on which small single-stage radios or discs of Boltaron bearing colored reflective tape were attached. This allowed for expansion as the fawns grew. Collars for yearlings and adult males also had strips of elastic attached to the Boltaron to allow for neck expansion.

Using radio telemetry, we monitored deer of various sex-age classes over a period of 2 years to determine ranges and movements as well as habitat utilization. Deer were also monitored closely in the field to determine behavior patterns, social organization, and aspects of their breeding biology.

Radios were powered with batteries sufficient for 300-600 days operation having a minimum range of 1 mile. Fawn radios weighing as little as 17 grams were powered for about 3-6 weeks and had a range of about 1/4 mile.

During 1969 through 1970, radio-tagged deer were located at least once each day at randomized hours; this permitted determination of movement patterns and range utilization. During this study 12,328 locations as determined by radio telemetry were recorded for 81 different deer. These represented 12 adult males, 21 adult females, 5 yearling males, 2 yearling females, 27 male fawns, and 14 female fawns (ages at time of first capture). In addition, data were available from over 10,000 sightings of the 223 marked deer.

By combining movement and range data for animals of various sex and age classes, various aspects of deer activities and life history were correlated. Movement indices for adult males were found to be largest during the rutting season (October through December) and lowest during July when there was maximum regrowth of antlers. During other periods of the year, movement indices were nearly the same except during April, when there was a substantial increase in size of the range. This corresponded with the reproductive season, at which time adult does with newborn fawns were actively running any other deer, including adult bucks, from the immediate area of the new fawn.

Indices suggested that beginning in September adult does utilized increasingly larger ranges, the peak being during November when the breeding season was at its highest level. Much of such movement was probably influenced through harassment by males. During the rest of the year, movement indices were quite similar except during the period just prior to the dropping of fawns, when adult does showed reduced movement and area utilized.

Yearling males showed an increase in size of area used at the commencement of the rut, reaching a peak during the height of the rut in November. These animals gradually exhibited reduced ranges up to the fawning season when size of area used declined sharply and leveled off for the summer months. Yearling males showed larger movement indices than any other sex or age group.

Yearling females tended to show rather stable ranges for the entire year; but two peaks could be identified — one at the end of the breeding season in December when a few animals were being harassed by bucks, the other in May when they were forced from normal ranges by their mother with the arrival of newborn fawns. It was during this latter period of the year that most yearling does first left their mothers; but most returned within 1 to 2 months after the adult doe fawned.

In general, movement indices for fawns of both sexes showed an increase as they grew older. During the first 2 weeks of life there was little movement except when "moved" by the doe. For the first month of life fawns stayed close to where the doe had left them; and size of area used reflected only the doe's placement of the fawn from day to day, which in turn was affected by the habitat of the doe's range. If the fawn and doe were undisturbed, the fawn was more likely to spend a greater period of time in a given area before it was moved to a new site. At 1½ or 2 months fawns were apt to wander alone in the area where left by the doe. As they became older there was some wandering back into old familiar areas without the doe. Fawns up to 2 months of age did not move at night, staying bedded. After 4-5 months of age, the area used by fawns tended to duplicate closely that of the adult female. During the rut, fawns became "lost" from their mothers, and at this time movement was the greatest. Following the rut, most female fawns returned to their mothers and movement indices of the two were similar; however, most male fawns did not return. Those that returned usually tended to break association with the doe before fawning the next year.

The longest movement from the point of original capture was 7 miles for both an adult and a yearling male. The longest move recorded for an adult doe was 5 miles and for a yearling doe 4 miles. Fawns usually did not make extended movements from their ranges; however, one male fawn was located over 1½ miles from its capture site. The longest daily movement was by a yearling male which moved over 4 miles during a period of 17¾ hours, an average of 1,190 feet per hour.

Observations and road mortalities of the 223 marked animals were used to determine dispersal of animals on and off Big Pine Key. Eight transplants of deer were utilized to gain further knowledge of deer dispersal. Only five marked deer were observed off Big Pine Key, all on No Name Key, a key adjacent to Big Pine. None of the 187 radio-tagged deer were ever located off Big Pine Key despite daily monitoring of their activities. Dispersal of deer from Big Pine Key was, therefore, considered to be very limited.

During this study deer or deer sign was observed on 22 different keys. It would appear that there has been considerable extension of the Key deer range since Dickson's (1955) study, much of which must be considered seasonal as well as temporary in time. Besides the 12 keys where Dickson (1955; p. 64) either had observed deer or deer sign, deer or deer sign was observed on Mayo, Porpoise, Water, Summerland, Sugarloaf, Toptree Hammock, Big Knockemdown, Big Munson, and Wahoo Keys and on an unnamed island southeast of Ramrod Key.

The social structure of Key deer was similar to that of the northern white-tailed deer in that adult bucks were generally solitary, forming only temporary feeding or breeding units, while other deer tended to form matriarchal family units, composed of the adult doe and her offspring of the current and occasionally of previous years (Hardin et al., 1976). While the bond between a doe and her young fawn was strong, bonds between most Key deer were generally looser than in the northern whitetails. While most young fawns were observed at some time with a doe, some 6-month-old fawns were never observed to be with a doe. All associations were variable, depending on the individual deer involved.

Frequencies of association between known related deer belonging to 12 family groups were determined. Based on observations of these 31 individuals, Key deer appeared to have lower associations than Illinois deer (Hawkins and Klimstra, 1970). Owing to the loose association of many deer, sightings of deer with fawns could not be used as an indication of reproductive success, as fawns were known to move with most any deer that passed. Generalizations or conclusions based on such observations must be arrived at with caution and after sufficient observations on a number of deer.

An adaptation of the Schumacher-Eschmeyer estimation procedure was applied to data collected from a once-weekly road census conducted over a predetermined 10-mile route within the Refuge on Big Pine Key. This census, conducted from June 1968 through June 1972, was begun at 2230 hours and completed in 1 hour depending on numbers of deer observed and attempts to capture deer. During January through December 1971, a 44-mile road census covering all major roads on Big Pine Key was established and run twice monthly beginning 1 hour before sunrise and then run again, commencing 1 hour before sunset. These censuses were conducted with the intention of establishing an estimate of the deer population for the Refuge and for all of Big Pine Key. Pellet transects and mortality (roadkill) data were also analyzed to determine population trends and to estimate deer numbers.

Annual population estimates for the area covered by the 10-mile census yielded a total of 61 deer in 1969, 83 in 1970, 120 in 1971, and 106 in 1972. Application of the Schumacher-Eschmeyer technique revealed a population of 177 animals for Big Pine Key when both the sunrise and sunset data were utilized. Individually, the sunrise census yielded a total of 213 animals in contrast to 165 animals for the sunset census. Data from pellet transects and road mortalities proved unacceptable for use in population estimates. Thick vegetation, uneven deer use, periodic shifts in centers of deer activity, porosity of the oolitic limestone, and deer use of tidal zones, as well as a variety of behavioral characteristics of the Key deer, seemed to eliminate the pellet transects as a useful technique at least on Big Pine Key. Uneven deer use, periodic shifts in centers of deer activity (especially during periods of drought), and the differing degree of automobile traffic using Big Pine from year to year added bias to mortality data, making such data unacceptable as an index to deer population trends.

Islands other than Big Pine Key were visited periodically to determine, by observation of animal sign, an estimate of the number of deer present. In addition to the estimated 200-250 deer on Big Pine Key, we estimate that 100-150 deer may utilize other islands.

The observed sex-age ratio of the Key deer herd varied throughout the year, primarily reflecting seasonal changes in behavior of the different sex-age classes. The ratio of females to males was greater than 2 to 1. During the 5 years, there was an apparent increase in the adult component of the herd with a decrease in the fawn component, suggesting a population with a low rate of increment. Several aspects of the deer's life history supported such a conclusion.

Male fetuses outnumbered females 1.75 to 1, while male newborn fawns outnumbered females 2 to 1. Older fawns were captured at a rate of 2.7 males to 1 female, possibly implying a greater loss of females or a difference in behavior making males more obvious and thus seen more readily. The ratio of males to females, which appeared to increase over the 5-year period, suggested a slowed rate of population increase.

Key deer have no natural predators; however, substantial mortality was recorded. During the 5 years of study, 304 mortalities of Key deer were recorded on 10 different islands. Highway mortalities, 87 percent of which occurred on Big Pine Key, accounted for 76 percent of all mortality. In later years there was an increase in the number of roadkills off Big Pine Key. Although this may suggest a reoccupation of its former range, land development and other human disturbances were extensive, causing changes in areas used by deer on these islands. During 1970 and the first half of 1971, severe drought resulted in scarcity of fresh water on the south end of Big Pine Key and on many outlying islands. During this time there was more mortality on the north end of Big Pine Key and an increase in the total number of deer killed. This may simply reflect either an increased movement by deer in search of fresh water or a movement of deer onto Big Pine from dry outer islands.

That drought may contribute to deer mortality was suggested by six deer skeletons found near dried water holes on outer islands following the drought. Other deer may have drowned while swimming between keys in the shark-infested channels, many of which had swift currents that could pose a hazard to deer.

Drowning in mosquito ditches accounted for most observed fawn mortality. Of 33 marked newborn fawns, 6 (18.2 percent) drowned in these ditches, as did 5 unmarked fawns. Some fawns were born in areas completely surrounded by these ditches. Big Pine Key alone has 100 miles of ditches, which connect basins of standing water to the salt water of Florida Bay. Since many of these flush daily with the tides, any fawns in the ditches would be carried into the channel.

Most Key deer behavior was similar to that reported for other white-tails. The earliest observation of breeding behavior involving bucks with polished antlers was on September 6. Breeding activities increased through September, peaking in early October and decreasing gradually through November and December. Some breeding occurred as late as February. Adult bucks with full racks were generally the earliest breeders, as those with lesser racks and yearling males were excluded by larger aggressive males. Male fawns did not appear to participate in breeding activities. The 3-5-year-old males bred most does and excluded other males when such encounters occurred. That such exclusion may have resulted in lowered numbers of females serviced, however, did not seem likely since those females that were not bred or which did not conceive recycled in 25-27 days, entering a second, third, or fourth estrus until successfully bred. This recycling and late breeding of yearlings or fawn does resulted in fawns being dropped over an extended period, thus contributing animals of varying sizes in the population.

Parturition began in mid-March, the peak drop occurring in April and tapering off through mid-May. Observations of "heavy" does and highway mortalities of pregnant does in midsummer indicated that fawns might be dropped throughout the summer months. One yearling female was known to have given birth in August. Gestation was around 204 days, similar to that of mainland whitetails.

Based on examination of 34 adult female mortalities during November through June, 31 (88.2 percent) were reproductively active, including 19 (55.9 percent) carrying single fawns and 7 (20.6 percent) with twins. Five (14.7 percent) were lactating, indicating they had produced at least 1 fawn. This resulted in a minimum count of 1.12 fawns per doe.

The structure of a population is determined by age, specific birth rate, sex ratio at birth, and mortality of each specific sex and age class. By using 110 marked deer of known fate, survivorship was determined. Both males and females had high mortality rates during the first 6 months of life, most mortality occurring the first few days after birth, chiefly through drowning in ditches. Fifty percent of the males survived to 1½ years, while females showed a 50 percent survival to around 2½ years.

It would appear that because of the relatively low reproductive rate, the high ratio of males to females in the younger segment of the population, and the relatively high mortality rate the population of Key deer was stable or increasing at a very slow rate. Such information may explain why this race of white-tailed deer had not overrun its habitat. The Key deer seem to have developed intrinsic mechanisms of control.

At birth fawns weighed 2.2 to 4.5 pounds, with a mean of 3.8 pounds for six fawns ranging up to 6 hours of age. Males attained 40.3 percent of the average maximum total weight during the first 12 months, while in the same period females attained 33.3 percent of the average maximum total weight. The average weight of bucks captured was 42.5 pounds at 1 year, 59.7 pounds at 2 years, and 79.8 pounds for all males over 2 years of age. All females captured had average weights of 37.0 pounds at 1 year, 54.9 pounds at 2 years, and 63.2 pounds for all over 2 years. The heaviest buck was road-killed on Little Torch Key in August 1971 and weighed 137 pounds. The heaviest doe weighed 90 pounds.

Color and size of the animals were variable. The coat color of Key deer varied from a deep reddish-brown to a grizzled, nearly gray color. Deer of various coloration were seen at all seasons. This variability may be a result of differential exposure to sunlight or salt for deer living in different habitat types, or it may be a reflection of genetic variability. Isolation between island complexes may serve to maintain such differences between deer living on different islands. Groups of deer on Big Pine in certain areas appeared smaller than other deer and most likely represented closely related animals. These differences may reflect a broad genetic front, possibly a result of breeding pockets of deer on the widely separated island complexes.

Key deer lost antlers during February and March, regrowth beginning almost immediately so that by June bucks with 2-inch stubs were seen. Growth was completed by August, and velvet was rubbed and kicked off in early September.

Male fawns produced buttons their first year, 1-2-inch spikes as yearlings, attained the first fork at the approximate age of 23 months, and produced the second fork at 2½ years. Bucks generally developed six points at 45 months and did not develop eight points until the age of 5 years. This slow rate of antler development may be a reflection of some aspect of the diet, since a captive buck produced a 6-point rack at 2 years and consistently produced large racks each year thereafter when kept on a diet of commercial food.

From a comparison of selected cranial measurements for *Odocoileus virginianus clavium* and *O. v. borealis,* it was found that *clavium* had a skull of shorter length without corresponding reduction in width. In all age and sex classes for which tooth-row lengths were compared between *clavium* and *borealis,* this was the most distinctive measurement, *clavium* being the shorter. Approximately 40 percent of adult skulls examined showed the loss of the first premolar on one or both jaws; milk teeth of fawns did not show this.

Tooth eruption and wear criteria as described by Severinghaus (1949) were used to estimate the age of Key deer; however, the validity of this technique as well as lens weight and dental cementum layering was questionable, at best. There was no assurance that the schedule of tooth eruption and replacement established for northern whitetails applied to Key deer. Some animals, obviously yearlings or less, showed heavy tartar deposition. Use of dental cementum layering exposed by tooth sectioning proved unproductive.

As part of the total effort to establish the precise identity of the Key deer race, analyses of blood serum were conducted using paper electrophoresis. Four similar proteins were found in deer from both the *clavium* and *borealis* races; however, the proportions of each protein varied so much that no significant differences were revealed between these two populations.

Parasitological studies revealed that in fecal samples there were three genera of nematodes, *Oesophagostomum, Neoascaris,* and *Gongylonema;* one trematode, *Dicrocoelium;* and a protozoan, *Eimeria* (Schulte et al., 1976). There was no indication that these intestinal parasites occurred in sufficient quantities to produce pathogenic effects. Only ticks, mosquitoes, and deer flies were found as external parasites.

REFERENCES

DICKSON, J. D., 3D
   1955. An ecological study of the Key deer.   Florida Game and Fresh Water Fish Comm. Techn. Bull., no. 3, 104 pp.
HARDIN, JAMES W.; SILVY, NOVA J.; and KLIMSTRA, WILLARD D.
   1976. Group size and composition of the Florida Key deer.   Journ. Wildl. Manag., vol. 40, no. 3, pp. 454-463.
HAWKINS, R. E., and KLIMSTRA, WILLARD D.
   1970. A preliminary study of the social organization of white-tailed deer. Journ. Wildl. Manag., vol. 34, no. 2, pp. 407-419.
SCHULTE, J. W.; KLIMSTRA, WILLARD D.; and DYER, W. G.
   1976. Protozoan and helminth parasites of Key deer.   Journ. Wildl. Manag., vol. 40, no. 3, pp. 579-581.
SEVERINGHAUS, CHARLES W.
   1949. Tooth development and wear as criteria of age in white-tailed deer. Journ. Wildl. Manag., vol. 13, no. 2, pp. 195-216.
SILVY, NOVA J.; HARDIN, JAMES W.; and KLIMSTRA, WILLARD D.
   1975. Use of a portable net to capture free-ranging deer.   Bull. Wildl. Soc., vol. 3, no. 1, pp. 27-29.

WILLIARD D. KLIMSTRA
JAMES W. HARDIN
NOVA J. SILVY

Reproductive Performance of Ospreys
(*Pandion haliaetus*) at Flathead Lake, Montana

Principal Investigator: James R. Koplin, Humboldt State College, Arcata, California.

Grant Nos. 771, 891:   In aid of a 5-year study of ospreys at Flathead Lake, Montana.

In 1966 my associate Donald L. MacCarter and I began studies on the nesting ecology of ospreys at Flathead Lake in Flathead and Lake Counties, Montana. Our initial efforts were stimulated by life-long interest in birds of prey, proximity of the University of Montana Biological Station — where we were student and instructor, respectively — to the nesting "colonies" of ospreys on the lake, and the disturbing report of Ames and Mersereau (1964) that ospreys in Connecticut were suffering reproductive impairment. Later, after we discovered that the Montana ospreys were reproducing at depressed rates, we narrowed our objectives to long-term measurements of reproductive performance of the ospreys to seek an explanation for the reproductive impairment. We were assisted in our latter endeavors by my second associate, Douglas S. MacCarter, Donald's twin brother, who joined us in 1968.

Flathead Lake, at an elevation of 2,893 feet, is 90 miles north of Missoula, is 28 miles long by 6 to 15 miles wide, has 121, 660 acres of surface area, is deep (more than three-fourths of the lake is in excess of 100 feet deep) and oligotrophic, and exhibits thermal stratification. The lake basin was produced by continental glaciation. Consequently the east and much of the west shores are quite precipitous; and shallow areas, required by ospreys for fishing sites, were produced by the deltas of the Flathead and Swan Rivers, principal tributaries, at the north end of the lake and by terminal and subterminal glacial moraines at the south end. The fish fauna is varied and includes 9 native and 9 exotic species (Weisel, 1955; Robbins and Worlund, 1966). The lake is sufficiently productive to support a moderate recreational fisheries.

Dominant vegetation along the relatively xeric west shore of Flathead Lake, composed now much as it was prior to settlement, is represented primarily by ponderosa pine *(Pinus ponderosa)* and Douglas fir *(Pseudotsuga menziesii)* on ridges and slopes, by black cottonwood *(Populus tricocarpa)* along streams, and by western larch *(Larix occidentalis)* in low-lying swampy areas. Prior to settlement, vegetation along the more mesic east shore was dominated by mixtures of ponderosa pine, Douglas fir, western hemlock *(Tsuga heterophylla)*, western arborvitae *(Thuja plicata)*, and grand fir *(Abies grandis)*. Most natural vegetation along the east shore has been replaced by cherry orchards; logging activity in the late 1800's and early 1900's altered the remaining natural vegetation. It now consists primarily of Douglas fir, ponderosa pine, and western larch.

Results

Academic commitments during our first summer of study prevented us from conducting more than a survey of the shoreline of the lake for nesting sites. We located 27 nests, at least 16 of which are known to have been used. We also found the nests were concentrated in three loose colonies: one on the north end of the lake at the mouth of the Flathead River, a second on the Bird Islands in the south-central region of the lake, and the third along the west shore and on small offshore islands in the south-central region of the lake. The majority of nests in these colonies were in the tops or upper branches of dead ponderosa pines or black cottonwoods; comparatively few were in live trees.

Three measurements of reproductive performance — clutch counts, hatching success, and fledging success — were obtained during the summers 1967 through 1970. A fourth measurement, nest use, was obtained during all five summers of study. Weather, predation, human disturbance, inadequate food resources, and chemical pollutants were considered as possible factors to account for reproductive impairment.

Reproductive performance. In all, 56 nesting sites were discovered during the study. Ospreys used only 35 of the 56 nesting sites, indicating a tendency for the birds, presumably the same pairs, to use a given nest or several alternate nests (nests used in alternate years) for a number of years in succession. Thus 16 pairs of ospreys used a total of 22 nests each year from the time the nests were discovered throughout the remainder of the study. Seven pairs used seven of the 27 nests discovered in 1966 throughout all five years of study. Four pairs used four of 14 nests discovered in 1967 during the remaining four years of study. Four pairs utilized one or the other of nine alternate nests available for all five years of the study. One pair used one or the other of two alternate nests during the remaining four years of study.

Of the remaining 13 sites used, one was used for four of the five summers available, one was used during two of the summers available, and nine were used for one summer only. It is possible that some of these 13 sites were alternates for one another. However, this point was not clarified.

Nest use was higher in 1970 than during any other year of the study. The increase resulted from the use of two previously unused nests and the construction and use of three new nests.

Ospreys used 49 to 60 percent of the sites available during each of the five summers of study. Of the sites used, 55 to 88 percent were active (contained eggs) and 40 to 71 percent were productive (contained one or more nestlings). Of the active nests, 64 to 81 percent were productive and 19 to 36 percent were unproductive (contained addled eggs only).

Twelve of 16 nests used in 1967 were active but only eight of these were productive; the remaining four were inactive (contained neither eggs nor nestlings). Eleven of 20 nests used in 1968 were active, eight of which were productive, and nine were inactive. Twenty-two of 24 nests used in 1970 were active, 17 productive, and two inactive. Thus, from a total of 79 nesting efforts, 42 (52 percent) were productive and 37 (48 percent) were unproductive or inactive.

The 79 nesting efforts produced at least 131 eggs — a conservative count, since nest contents were not checked prior to the first week in June when eggs began to hatch. (It is entirely possible that some eggs laid in late April or May disappeared prior to our arrival in June.) The 79 nesting efforts hatched 85 chicks, 77 of which fledged. Thus, the number of young fledged per breeding pair averaged 0.97.

If the breeding population of ospreys at Flathead Lake experienced the same mortality schedule as New York-New Jersey populations prior to 1948, then it was declining at an average annual rate of 3 to 4 percent (Henny and Ogden, 1970). An average of 1.22 fledglings per breeding pair must be produced to balance mortality and maintain stability in osprey populations subjected to these mortality schedules (Henny and Wight, 1969). However, on the basis of breeding-pair counts, it appeared as if the population at Flathead Lake may have been subject to a lower mortality schedule than New York-New Jersey populations. The Montana population apparently remained stable or increased slightly during the three summers since 1968 when essentially all nests within the study area were discovered. Nevertheless, the osprey population at Flathead Lake obviously was reproducing at a suboptimal rate as indicated by the annual patterns of reproductive performance of individual breeding pairs and by physical and chemical characteristics of addled eggs.

As indicated, 37 (48 percent) of the 79 nesting efforts were either inactive or unproductive and 42 (52 percent) were productive, indicating the tendency for birds to exhibit consistent patterns of reproductive performance. That is, birds tended to lay clutches of eggs that either all hatched or none hatched, or birds laid no eggs at all. These patterns were not consistent on a year-to-year basis for given nests or alternate nests.

Only two of the 11 nests used continuously were productive during all four years in which nest contents were checked. Two were inactive or unproductive every year. Three were unproductive in some years and productive in others. Three were inactive in some years and productive in others.

Only two of the 10 alternate nests used continuously were productive every year. Two were unproductive in one year and productive in the others. Two were inactive for three years and productive in the other. Two were inactive for one year and unproductive in the others. Two were inactive for two years, and productive or unproductive the others.

Thus, of the 15 pairs of ospreys for which we presumably have a four-year history of reproductive performance, only four were productive annually, three were inactive or unproductive annually, and the remaining eight were inactive, unproductive, or productive annually.

Careful examination and chemical analysis of 15 eggs failing to hatch revealed that the shells of five were chalky, flaking, or cracked. All contained well-developed but dead embryos. All were contaminated with sizable quantities of DDT residues, primarily DDE — up to 6 parts per million wet weight and to 135 parts per million in lipids.

Thus, reproductive impairment was related primarily to the failure of some birds to lay eggs and to the failure of others to hatch eggs laid. Eggs failing to hatch obviously were fertile.

Factors responsible for reproductive impairment. The characteristics of the reproductive impairment rule out weather, predation, and human disturbance as causative factors, although these factors could contribute to lowering over-all reproductive performance of ospreys.

In mid-July 1968, a storm with winds up to 60 miles per hour destroyed two nests. Both were occupied but fortunately inactive. Both were rebuilt. Four addled eggs disappeared from two other nests following a severe wind storm in late June 1969. These nests were intact at the time the losses were discovered, implying that the losses were not wind-caused. The nests were very actively defended by the parents even after the eggs disappeared, suggesting predators were not responsible for the losses. Reese (personal communication) reports similar findings at osprey nests in Chesapeake Bay.

It was impossible to account for the losses. Perhaps wind forced the parents from their nests, permitting predators to eat the eggs, or perhaps the rocking action of the wind caused the weight of the incubating parent to crush the eggs.

There is circumstantial evidence that magpies and ravens are predators of osprey eggs and that these or other birds or mammals are predators of nestlings. In 1967, a pair of ospreys on a nest containing two addled eggs became inattentive to the nest about five weeks after the normal period of incubation. During a visit to the nest at this time a magpie flushed from it; subsequent examination of the nest revealed that the addled eggs were missing. Two boiled chicken eggs were then placed in the nest to determine if they too would disappear. A raven flushed from the nest during a visit several days later; subsequent examination of the nest revealed that the boiled eggs were missing. Four nestlings disappeared from two nests in 1969. Contents of the two nests could be examined only by climbing adjacent trees and looking into the nests. Therefore, it is unlikely that other humans gained access to these nests. The disappearance of the nestlings may have been due to predators, although not necessarily to magpies or to ravens.

Most potential human disturbance was recreational activity, which did not begin until late June after the young hatched. Therefore, recreational activity was mainly a threat to the well-being of nestlings.

Short of shooting and nest destruction, the most severe human disturbance experienced by the ospreys was when their nesting trees were climbed and their nests examined by us. None of the nests examined were abandoned, but one normally developing egg was accidentally collected in 1968. There are no indications that our activities resulted in failure of the seven nestlings to fledge.

We knew of three shooting incidents involving the death of one osprey. In 1967, two boys were caught in the act of shooting at a fledgling osprey on the Flathead River about three-fourths mile south of Polson Bay. In 1968, a cabin owner reported a neighbor was using a nearby nesting tree for target practice. In 1969, another cabin owner reported the shooting death of an osprey near his cabin. The latter incident occurred late in August after the young fledged. We did not get to examine the bird. Therefore, it is impossible to state whether the bird killed was an adult or a fledgling. It is possible that the shooting of a parent was involved with the disappearance of three nestlings from one nest since only one parent was ever observed at the nest after the loss of the nestlings was discovered.

Inadequate food resources could account for or contribute to the large proportion of inactive and unproductive nesting efforts (Lack, 1966). The influence of food on reproductive performance of ospreys was assessed by measuring fishing success, relative rates of delivery of fish to nests differing in brood size, and relative rates of growth of chicks in nests differing in brood size. It was assumed that if food supply was not limiting the following postulates would be acceptable: (1) fishing success, measured by relative percentages of successful and unsuccessful fishing attempts, would be the same at Flathead Lake, an area with a relatively low biomass of fish, as in an area with a high biomass of fish; (2) the quantities of fish delivered to and consumed at nests would be the same per chick in broods of two and three as in broods of one; and (3) chicks in broods of two and three would grow at the same rate as chicks in broods of one.

The fishing success of ospreys at Flathead Lake was similar to that of ospreys at Eagle Lake, Lassen County, California, a mesotrophic lake with a comparatively high biomass of fish, suggesting that food was equally available in both areas. However, the providing parents at Flathead Lake were absent from their nesting territories for an average of approximately 70 minutes before returning with fish, whereas providing parents at Eagle Lake were absent for an average of only 30 minutes before returning with fish. These observations indicate that ospreys have a good chance of capturing prey once located, but that it is more difficult to locate prey in an oligotrophic lake than in a mesotrophic lake. Further indication of the greater difficulty of obtaining fish from Flathead Lake than from Eagle Lake was provided by the absence of prey remains at the bases of nesting sites at Flathead Lake and the usual presence of the remains of from one to three fish at the bases of nesting sites at Eagle Lake. Nevertheless, food supplies at Flathead were sufficiently abundant to enable the parents to provide an increasing quantity of fish as food requirements of the growing chicks increased. Thus, even though food resources may have been less readily available at Flathead Lake than at Eagle Lake, they were sufficiently available to meet the food requirements of growing chicks. Therefore, it is possible at least tentatively to accept the first hypothesis.

Quantities of fish delivered to nests with one, two, and three chicks per brood were recorded in 1969 and in 1970. Quantities delivered in 1969 averaged approximately the same per chick in a brood of one as in a brood of three, both of which received greater average quantities of fish per chick than in the brood of two. Quantities of fish delivered per chick in 1970 were highest for the brood of one and were the same in broods of two and three. These observations suggest that food supplies were adequate for the needs of each brood. But the brood of two may have been inadequately provided for in 1969, and the brood of one, reared in the same nest—presumably by the same parents—in which the brood of three was reared in 1969, may have been overly provided for in 1970. In any event, it is also possible tentatively to accept the second postulate.

During the first 25 days of life, prior to the time when altered by the influence of sex, growth rate of chicks was inversely related to brood size. This relationship apparently was not a function of available food resources. Quantities of fish delivered per chick during the first 25 days of life averaged the same in broods of two and three, but growth rate during the first 25 days of life was lowest in broods of three and highest in broods of one. The relationship apparently was not related to sex either. At the time of fledging the heaviest chick, presumably a female, was from a brood of three and the lightest chick, presumably a male, was from a brood of two. Thus, even though the third hypothesis is unacceptable in a strict sense, there is insufficient evidence to reject it on the basis of limited food resources.

The combination of inactive nests, thin eggshells, and DDT residues in egg contents are all indicative of reproductive impairment resulting from contamination by DDT metabolites, primarily DDE (Hickey and Anderson, 1968; Porter and Wiemeyer, 1969; Bitman et al., 1970; Peakall, 1970; Ratcliffe, 1970).

In North America, Hickey and Anderson (1968) found an inverse relationship between levels of DDE residues in contents and shell thickness of eggs of herring gulls *(Larus argentatus);* that decreases in eggshell thickness accompanied population declines of peregrine falcons *(Falco peregrinus),* bald eagles *(Haliaeetus leucocephalus),* and ospreys within the past 25 years; and that no changes in eggshell thickness occurred in stable populations of red-tailed hawks *(Buteo jamaicensis),* great horned owls *(Bubo virginianus),* and golden eagles *(Aquila chrysaetos)* within the past 25 years. Ratcliffe (1970) showed decreases in eggshell thickness in peregrine falcons, sparrow hawks *(Accipiter nisus),* golden eagles, kestrels *(Falco tinnunculus),* merlins *(Falco columbarius),* and hobbies *(Falco subbuteo),* but not in buzzards *(Buteo buteo),* within the past 20 to 25 years in Great Britain.

Porter and Wiemeyer (1969) fed diets containing DDT and dieldrin to captive breeding sparrow hawks *(Falco sparvarius)* which in comparison with control birds exhibited decreased eggshell thickness, increased egg disappearance, increased destruction of eggs, and decreased reproductive success.

Peakall (1970) and Bitman et al. (1970) demonstrated a direct relationship between eggshell thickness and carbonic anhydrase levels in the shell gland and that DDE reduced the activity of carbonic anhydrase. Thus, it appears as if the inhibiting influence of chlorinated hydrocarbons, in particular DDE, on the activity of carbonic anhydrase results in decreased deposition of calcium carbonate in the shell gland and is the causal mechanism of eggshell thinning in raptorial birds. Apparently the accumulation and concentration of chlorinated hydrocarbons are sufficient to affect primarily those birds at or near the tops of long food chains — bird-eating and fish-eating species — but insufficient to affect top carnivores of shorter food chains — mammal-eating and insect-eating species.

Eggshell thickness is influenced by several factors in addition to DDT metabolites. Diets deficient in calcium, manganese, and vitamin D can cause domestic chickens to lay thin-shelled eggs (Sturkie, 1965). It is extremely unlikely that either of the minerals or the vitamin was deficient; had one been, the deficiency would have manifested itself elsewhere in the lake ecosystem. Other researchers on Flathead Lake reported no indications of such deficiencies.

Well-developed but dead embryos in the majority of addled eggs seem to be unique to ospreys. Apparently the contents of cracked or broken eggs are readily consumed by other raptors, especially by peregrine falcons (Ratcliffe, 1970). There is no evidence that ospreys eat cracked or crushed eggs. In fact Garber (personal communication) reports that cracked or crushed osprey eggs at Eagle Lake, California, are either gradually broken up until the fragments become intermingled with nesting materials or are crowded from nests, indicating that ospreys actually avoid eating cracked or crushed eggs!

Addled but uncracked and embryonated eggs obviously are fertile and apparently contain sublethal levels of chlorinated hydrocarbon residues. Thus the cause of death of the embryos is puzzling. Perhaps they die from desiccation in eggs with shells too thin to retain adequate moisture.

Chemical analyses, on a wet-weight basis, of 76 samples of water, soil, lake sediments, plankton, and fish from Flathead Lake, and fish from osprey nests, revealed the presence of DDT residues, principally DDE, in varying concentrations in some components of the lake ecosystem. No residues were detected in 3 water samples or in 5 soil samples from the shore. Only 2 of 23 sediment samples contained trace levels (1 part per billion or less). Of 5 plankton samples 2 were contaminated: one with trace levels and the other contained 0.03 part per million (ppm) DDT metabolites. All but one of the 40 fish samples contained DDT metabolites, ranging from a low averaging 0.13 ppm in 9 whitefish (*Coregonus* sp.) to a high of 2.2 ppm in a lake trout (*Salvelinus namaycush*). Six fish recovered from osprey nests contained an average of 0.40 ppm DDT metabolites. The source of contamination is unknown but most likely originated from efforts to control fruit flies in cherry orchards and/or from efforts to control insect pests of crops of potatoes and corn in the Flathead Valley north of the lake. Thus, osprey eggs probably were contaminated by DDT residues in Flathead Lake. However, it is possible that at least some contamination may have originated in the wintering range, the locale of which is unknown, or on the spring migration, the route of which is unknown.

Conclusions

Weather, predation, and human disturbance may have exerted a depressing influence on reproductive performance of ospreys at Flathead Lake but were insufficiently influential to account for the extent of reproductive impairment documented. Food resources may have been sufficiently limiting to have contributed to the reproductive impairment of the ospreys, but considerations of food supply alone fail to account for thin-shelled eggs and the presence of dead embryos in intact eggs.

The only conceivable extrinsic factor which could result in embryonic death in intact eggs would be lethal chilling of eggs from prolonged absence of incubating parents from their nests. As previously indicated, those factors causing prolonged absence of incubating parents from their nests, namely, disturbance from human recreational activities, are unimportant until after the incubation period, suggesting that the observed mortality is related to intrinsic factors. The only intrinsic factor discovered was DDT residues in eggs. Thus, all evidence indicates that the primary factor responsible for the reproductive impairment of ospreys at Flathead Lake was contamination by DDT metabolites.

REFERENCES

AMES, PETER L., and MERSEREAU, GERALD S.
1964. Some factors in the decline of the osprey in Connecticut. Auk, vol. 81, pp. 173-185.
BITMAN, JOEL; CECIL, HELENE C.; and FRIES, GEORGE F.
1970. DDT-induced inhibition of avian shell gland carbonic anhydrase: A mechanism for thin eggshells. Science, vol. 168, pp. 594-596.
HENNY, CHARLES J., and OGDEN, JOHN C.
1970. Estimated status of ospreys in the United States. Journ. Wildl. Manag., vol. 34, pp. 214-217.
HENNY, CHARLES J., and WIGHT, HOWARD M.
1969. An endangered osprey population: Estimates of mortality and production. Auk, vol. 86, pp. 188-198.

HICKEY, JOSEPH J., and ANDERSON, DANIEL W.
    1968. Chlorinated hydrocarbons and eggshell changes in raptorial and fish-
        eating birds.   Science, vol. 162, pp. 271-273.
LACK, DAVID
    1966. Population studies of birds, 341 pp.   Oxford University Press.
PEAKALL, DAVID B.
    1970. p, p'-DDT: Effect on calcium metabolism and concentration of estradiol
        in the blood.   Science, vol. 168, pp. 592-594.
PORTER, RICHARD D., and WIEMEYER, STANLEY W.
    1969. Dieldrin and DDT: Effects on sparrow hawk eggshells and reproduction.
        Science, vol. 165, pp. 199-200.
RATCLIFFE, DEREK A.
    1970. Changes attributable to pesticides in egg breakage frequency and egg-
        shell thickness in some British birds.   Journ. Appl. Ecol., vol. 71, pp.
        67-115.
ROBBINS, OTIS, JR., and WORLUND, DONALD D.
    1966. Flathead Lake (Montana) fishery investigations, 1961-64.   U. S. Fish and
        Wildl. Serv. Techn. Paper no. 4, 45 pp.
STURKIE, DAVID PAUL
    1965. Avian physiology, 766 pp.   Cornell University Press.
WEISEL, GEORGE F.
    1955. Fish guide for intermountain Montana, 88 pp.   University of Montana
        Press.

JAMES R. KOPLIN

The Chicama-Moche Canal Project

Principal Investigator: James S. Kus, California State University, Fresno, California.

Grant No. 801:   In support of an archeogeographic investigation of La Cumbre Canal, Peru.

The Chicama-Moche Canal Project was a research study that analyzed specific geographical problems relating to the pre-Hispanic Chimu culture in northern coastal Peru. The focus of the project was a large irrigation canal that carried water from the Chicama Valley into the Moche Valley and thence to the area around the Chimu capital city, Chan Chan. This canal has been called La Cumbre Canal, although it is more correctly referred to as the Chicama-Moche Canal. The study of this canal was carried out in close coordination with the Peabody Museum's Chan Chan — Moche Valley project. Over-all archeological studies were made by the Peabody group at the same time that the canal project focused attention on some geographical implications of the use of water in the Chicama and Moche Valleys.

Research Methodology

The two most important questions dealt with in this study were: (1) What factors in the Moche Valley made the construction of the Chicama-Moche Canal necessary? and (2) What were the spatial effects of its construction? Stated specifically, the main hypothesis to be tested by the project was that the construction of the Chicama-Moche Canal was the result of a shortage of water at and around the site of Chan Chan and also that the removal of water from the Chicama Valley, by means of the intervalley canal, would have forced a subsequent movement of population from the Chicama Valley to the Moche Valley roughly proportional to the total percentage of water taken from the Chicama River. An important alternate hypothesis tested was that no population changes occurred during or after the construction of the canal because it removed an insignificant amount of water from the Chicama River. A study of Chimu field patterns and related irrigation systems was also planned as a part of this project.

A number of researchers have described irrigation systems in northern coastal Peru, although only one focused on the Chicama-Moche Canal to any great extent. Among others, Rafael Larco Hoyle (1945) and Hans Horkheimer (1961) mentioned the canal, and Paul Kosok (1965) described the canal in some detail and made a rough map of it. Kosok's field research, however, was carried out during the late 1940's; but inadequate cartographic and aerial photographic coverage of the intervalley region at that time precluded a detailed analysis of the canal system. Kosok was hindered also by lack of time, money, and transportation facilities; all these hindrances were not serious problems for the Chicama-Moche Canal project.

Field work for the study consisted of three distinct phases. First, about three months were spent in initial ground surveys along the intervalley canal route and in mapping the entire canal. These surveys located several areas suitable for further study and resulted in the production of a base map of the entire canal at a scale of 1:100,000. Second, three months were spent studying one area of irrigated fields in an attempt to define the Chimu irrigation types. This study involved the mapping of irrigated fields associated with the Quebrada del Oso site, located by the project, and the study of furrow patterns at the site. Third, three months were spent excavating cross sections along the canal. These cross sections were made with the hope that they would yield data on the manner of construction of the canal, the age of it, and also the size and slope of the canal. A crew of five workmen was utilized in the excavation project, and a total of 35 cross sections were made. Abundant material for dating the canal was uncovered, the manner of construction and the size of the canal were noted, and measurements of the canal's slope were made. On the whole the field work progressed very well, with few problems, although the project was concluded rapidly after a disastrous earthquake struck northern Peru on May 31, 1970.

Sufficient data were recovered during the period of field research, foreshortened though it was, to permit a detailed analysis of Chimu irrigation techniques.

Research Results

The results of this project may be broadly grouped into three categories: (1) Relating the canal to the Chimu culture; (2) describing the canal itself; and (3) commenting on the irrigation systems associated with the intervalley canal.

The Chicama-Moche Canal was probably very important in the over-all

FIG. 1.   Excavation of Chicama-Moche Canal aqueduct near Quebrada del Oso site.

use of the Chan Chan site, because the canal apparently supplied irrigation water to agricultural fields north and northeast of the city and also contributed to the ground-water supply under the city (Kus, 1971). Since most of the domestic water used within the city probably came from "walk-in-wells" located throughout Chan Chan, which were dependent upon constant recharge of the local water table (Day, 1974), water from the intervalley canal would have been extremely important to the city itself, regardless of its actual volume or of the amount of land actually irrigated. Also, there seems to be fairly good evidence to indicate that the canal was constructed about the same time as the first occupation of the Chan Chan site and that the construction of both the canal and the city may well have been carried out in an organized fashion by the Chimu rulers. It would seem likely that the city could not have reached its maximum size (estimated to have been no more than 50,000 persons) without the Chicama-Moche Canal having been in use. Finally, there is good reason to speculate that the abandonment of the Chan Chan site was caused by the destruction of Chimu canals, including the intervalley canal system. This probably occurred at the hands of Inca armies that conquered the Chimu some time during the seventh or eighth

FIG. 2. Typical Chimu field pattern, Quebrada del Oso site (half-meter stick for scale).

decade of the 15th century. The lack of water for the fields around Chan Chan may well have been important in the abandonment of the site, but equally serious was the lowering of the water table under the city, which apparently made the "walk-in-wells" unusable for domestic purposes.

Excavations along the Chicama-Moche Canal have led to a number of interesting observations. It seems likely that the sections of the canal near the city of Chan Chan, and possibly the entire length of the intervalley canal (about 74 kilometers in all), were constructed at one time. The canal was built some time between the years A.D. 800 and 1080, based on several radiocarbon samples (UCLA 1711G-H-I).

The Chimu culture is estimated to have been established (that is, the Chimu Period began) between A.D. 900 and 1000. Thus the probable time of construction for the canal overlaps the shift from outside (Huari-Tiahuanacoid Middle Horizon) influence in northern coastal Peru to local control postulated for the beginning of the Chimu Period.

The method of construction of the canal is also interesting (see fig. 1). Most parts of the intervalley canal are stone-lined, although where suitable stone was not located near the canal it was unlined. Average depth was slightly over 1 meter, and width varied from an average of 3 or 4 meters to a maximum of almost 10 meters. The manner of construction seems to have been rather crude, at least initially, with successive rebuilding of the canal leading to improvements in technique. This is especially true in terms of the slope of the canal. No leveling device of any sort is known to have been used during construction, and there is abundant evidence to indicate that much raising and lowering of sections of the canal bed was necessary to smooth the flow of water. In technical terms, the construction of the intervalley canal was probably a relatively simple task for the Chimu. The only new problem beyond those involved in other canals of the region was the determination of the level required to cross the divide between the two valleys, and this may well have been empirically determined. Evidence for this is seen in a number of unfinished dead-end canals found near the divide.

Prior to the Chicama-Moche Canal Project, the standard archeological description of pre-Hispanic irrigation systems in Peru, at least in terms of furrow techniques, was that they were rather simple. One very positive result of this study is that a number of different types of furrows were located, all within one field system definitely associated with the intervalley canal and therefore definitely dating to the Chimu period. This particular field system, at the Quebrada del Oso site, contained at least six different types of furrows (see fig. 2). The length, width, and slope of a number of different fields of each of the six types have been recorded, and a continuing analysis of this information may well prove useful in determining the various types of plants grown in these fields, their relative abundance, or at least the percentage of land devoted to various categories of crops.

One final comment may be made about the effect of the intervalley canal system upon the people of the Chicama and Moche Valleys, the study of which was, in reality, the basic aim of this research project. Sufficient water was supplied to the fields around Chan Chan to provide for an increased population in the urban area. This population increase is calculated to have been on the order of between 15 and 20 percent, based on an increase of agricultural land of about 18 percent around Chan Chan as a direct result of the use of the intervalley canal system. The effect on the population of the Chicama Valley may have been of lesser extent, simply because more water was available in the Chicama River and the movement of water through the intervalley canal would therefore have been of lesser effect on the total amount of water available to the Chicama Valley. During the early 20th century 12 large canals were in use in the Chicama Valley, removing almost all the water from the Chicama River. If the Chimu intervalley canal was about the same size as, or even slightly larger than, the average canal of the present century (which seems to have been the case), then no more than 10 percent of the water in the Chicama River would have been taken to the Moche Valley. The figure of less than 10 percent water extracted through the intervalley canal is substantiated when the area watered by it in the Moche Valley (less than 1,600 hectares) is compared to the area of Chimu irrigated agriculture in the Chicama Valley (more than 30,000 hectares). This is important because the loss of less than 10 percent of the water supply in the Chicama Valley would not have necessitated major population shifts, although some individuals undoubtedly did move to areas along the canal in order to maintain it and to carry out daily functions in the operation of it. Also, a few people may have migrated to the Chan Chan site to make use of the Chicama River water available in the fields north of the city. It must be noted, however, that there may have been one serious effect of the intervalley canal system, and that is that the Chicama-Moche Canal probably always carried its maximum capacity of water, regardless of the level of the Chicama River. When the flow of water in the river went down, the intervalley canal still probably drew its full complement of water, thus reducing the supply of water in the lower Chicama Valley by a more significant amount. The water supplied to Chan Chan might not have been a burden in normal times, but during the season of low water flow, and especially during periods of extended drought, this drain on the water supply of the Chicama Valley may well have been serious.

In summary, the Chicama-Moche Canal apparently was constructed during the early part of the Chimu period, some time between A.D. 800 and 1080. It was built to supply water to the area north of the Chan Chan site, and the reason for this seems to have been a desire either to enhance the value of the Chan Chan site or, perhaps somehow to demonstrate the power (political, economic, or military) available to the residents of Chan Chan. The canal was constructed using common local techniques, with only the determination of the level needed to achieve the intervalley divide not a technique common to the canals of the same or earlier periods. Finally, the construction of the Chicama-Moche Canal may have caused some population shifts, particularly in the Moche Valley where a relatively large area of irrigated fields north of Chan Chan came under cultivation after the completion of the canal.

REFERENCES

DAY, KENT C.
   1974. Walk-in wells and water management at Chan Chan, Peru. Pp. 182-194 *in* "The Rise and Fall of Civilizations: An Archaeological Reader." C. C. Lamberg-Karlovsky and Jeremy A. Sabloff, eds. Cummings Publishing Co., Menlo Park, California.
HORKHEIMER, HANS
   1961. La cultura Mochica. Las grandes civilizaciones del Antiguo Perú, vol. 1. Lima.
KOSOK, PAUL
   1965. Life, land and water in ancient Peru, 264 pp., illus. Long Island University Press, Brooklyn, New York.
KUS, JAMES S.
   1971. Chan Chan, Peru: Site characteristics. Paper read at 36th annual meeting, Society for American Archaeology.
   1972. Selected aspects of irrigated agriculture in the Chimu Heartland, Peru. Ph.D. dissertation, University of California at Los Angeles. University Microfilms, Ann Arbor, Michigan.
   1974a. Chimu techniques of canal construction and maintenance. Paper read at 14th annual meeting, Institute of Andean Studies, Berkeley, California.
   1974b. Irrigation and urbanization in pre-Hispanic Peru: The Moche Valley. Yearbook of the Association of Pacific Coast Geographers, vol. 36, pp. 45-56.
LARCO HOYLE, RAFAEL
   1945. Los Mochicas, 42 pp., illus. Sociedad Geográfica Americana, Buenos Aires.

JAMES S. KUS

Archeological and Paleontological Excavation at Olduvai Gorge, 1969

Principal Investigators: Louis S. B. Leakey[1] and Mary D. Leakey, National Centre for Prehistory and Paleontology, Nairobi, Kenya.

Grant Nos. 752, 808, 811.[2]   For continued support of Early Man studies in East Africa.

Field work was resumed at Olduvai Gorge at the end of 1968. During the first few months a systematic search for hominid fossils was carried out. Four years had elapsed since the deposits in the Gorge had last been searched in detail, and it was considered likely that further hominid remains would have become exposed by erosion during the interval. This in fact proved to be the case. The most complete skull of *Homo habilis* then known was found near the base of Bed I, in a level that has been reliably dated between 1.9 and 1.75 million years by the K-Ar isotopic method of dating. The skull was crushed and embedded in a block of limestone. After months of work in the laboratory it was mostly freed from the matrix and the face re-assembled.

Part of a human mandible was also found in Bed IV on a living site and associated with some magnificent Acheulean handaxes and other tools. The right half of another mandible, either from Bed III or Bed IV, as well as a number of isolated hominid teeth, was also discovered.

Detailed excavation of a number of sites in Bed IV continued after mid-June. Several different levels with artifacts and faunal material were uncovered. From the evidence now available it seems that in Bed IV as well as in Bed II a true Acheulean industry existed side by side with one that had evolved from the Oldowan.

So far, the occupational debris from living sites in Bed IV has been found only in riverine sands and shallow channels where it appears to have

---

[1] Dr. Leakey died on October 1, 1972.

[2] Grant No. 811 was for the purpose of subsidizing the publication of Volume 3 of the Olduvai Gorge series of reports. This was published by Cambridge University Press late in 1971.

been washed in by flood waters. It has, therefore, not been possible to determine any pattern of distribution or discover what forms of dwellings (if any) may have been in use.

Further work on the geology by Dr. R. L. Hay during this year showed that faulting previously thought to have been active only up to Bed IV times continued during Bed V times since this bed is faulted through in certain places. The deposits formerly known as Bed V have now been separated into two distinct units of different ages. No date has yet been obtained for the lower unit, but the upper, which contains a microlithic industry, has been dated by carbon 14 to 10,000 years B.P. (More recent dating of samples extends this date to 17,000 B.P.)

A few living sites in Bed I and Bed II were roofed over and the remains on the occupation floors preserved in place for the benefit of visitors. These exhibits have proved very popular, and it is hoped to display an Acheulean site similarly before long.

The number of visitors to the Gorge increases each year. During 1968 the total amounted to 10,000. This figure had already been reached by September 1969.

REFERENCE

LEAKEY, MARY D.
    1971. Olduvai Gorge, vol. 3: Excavations in Beds I and II, 1960-1963, 306 pp.,
        illus.   Cambridge University Press, London.

MARY D. LEAKEY

Reconnaissance and Paleontological Exploration East of Lake Turkana, 1968-1969

Principal Investigator: Richard E. Leakey, National Museums of Kenya, Nairobi.

Grant Nos. 694, 696, For paleontological and archeological investigation of
744, 822, 828. Plio-Pleistocene deposits to the east of Lake Rudolf, Kenya.

During 1968 I organized a preliminary reconnaissance of the area lying to the east of Lake Turkana (then known as Lake Rudolf), and this expedition was financed by a grant from the National Geographic Society. As a consequence of the 1968 survey, a further exploration was undertaken in 1969 under the umbrella of Kenya's National Museum but with further support from the Society. This report summarizes the outcome of those two expeditions.

Prior to 1968 there were no confirmed reports concerning vertebrate fossils or Plio-Pleistocene sediment outcrops in the area along the northeastern coast of Lake Turkana. Various geologic maps indicated volcanics and the underlying basement complex. Road access and communications were difficult and this may have accounted for the absence of any systematic program of investigation.

The areas in northern Kenya can be defined as semidesert, with the fauna and flora being typical of the Somali Arid type. One unusual feature of the region is the presence of a grassland fauna along the northeast coast of the lake, with large occurrences of zebra *(Equus burchelli)* and topi *(Damaliscus corrigum jimela)*. These animals are generally restricted to a very narrow zone of grassland that grows on the flood plain of the lake and must reflect a remnant population from an earlier time when conditions were wetter.

Geology

The geology of the region is complex, but at the conclusion of the 1969 season the following statement was possible:

343

"The northern portion of the East Rudolf Basin (Ileret) consists of four unconformable sedimentary units. The lowest unit consists of a series of fine-grained molluscan sandstones that grade upward into conglomeratic sandstones, siltstones, and claystones. The sediments are intercalated with four tuffs that serve as local markers. Interbedded tuffs and mudstones are predominant in the middle unit. The mudstones are preceded and followed by a coarse- to fine-grained sandstone sequence that exhibits high lateral variability. Algal stromatolites and *Etheria* banks are common. A gravelly sand caps the entire sequence.

"Three unconformable units are recognized in the southern portion (Koobi Fora). A series of laminated claystones, siltstones, and fine-grained sandstones is conformably overlain by lenticular conglomerates, fine-grained sandstones mudstones and two tuffs. The lower tuff (KBS Tuff) is a useful stratigraphic marker. Interbedded fine-grained, ripple-laminated sandstones and siltstones, thin beds of stromatolites, and molluscan sandstones with lenses of conglomeratic sandstones cap this sequence. The second unit consisting of gray, tuffaceous siltstones with an abundant molluscan fauna overlies the older sediments on a pronounced angular unconformity. A Holocene gravelly sand mantles the entire sequence.

"Correlation between the two areas was established by the use of two bentonites and the KBS Tuff. The Ileret sequence correlates with the upper half of the Koobi Fora sequence."

The mapping of the region was recognized as a primary goal, and, as a consequence, low-level aerial photography was arranged to provide a stereo-mosaic at a scale of 1:23,000.

Paleontology

Large numbers of vertebrate and invertebrate fossils were observed in the Ileret and Koobi Fora regions, and some attempt was made to collect representative samples of the more complete material. The state of preservation was quite excellent in many instances, and an impressive preliminary faunal list was compiled but will not be presented here because, in the light of more recent work, it is known to be incomplete.

Nevertheless, the vertebrate fossils permitted coarse correlation with other African localities such as Olduvai and the Omo Valley. Certain fossils indicated a Pliocene base to the succession, while the fossils from the uppermost levels presented a reasonable comparison with the middle part of Olduvai or Upper Bed II. The abundance of suids and bovids was indicative of a grassland ecology, and the relative rarity of primates and carnivore fossils was consistent with the picture that began to emerge from the geological and paleoecology interpretations. A preliminary statement on the lowest fossils zone was made by Vincent J. Maglio (1971):

"More than six hundred specimens of vertebrate fossils have been collected from the three major fossiliferous areas at East Rudolf: Kubi Algi, Koobi Fora, and Ileret. Preliminary identifications have been made on some of the material including the Primates (M. and R. Leakey), Suidae (H. B. S. Cooke), Bovidae (J. Harris) and Proboscidea (V. Maglio); but more detailed studies must await further collecting and geological analyses of the fossil-bearing horizons."

Two faunal units are represented. One is poorly known at present but is certainly Pliocene in age. The other, early Pleistocene in age, covers a fair time range within which definite evolutionary changes are apparent in several groups, but no distinct division of the unit is possible on faunal grounds. This faunal unit extends across the regional disconformity in the Koobi Fora area.

The earlier fauna is from a fluvial tongue within Koobi Fora I (now Kubi Algi Formation) in the Allia Bay area, near the mountain Kubi Algi. Fossil material derives from two sites that seem to have been contemporaneous on both paleontologic and geologic evidence. Two elephant species represent the earliest known occurrences of the *Loxodonta* and *Elephas* phyletic lineages. A fragmentary skull and a nearly complete mandible of *Loxodonta adaurora* are smaller and somewhat more primitive than those of the Kanapoi-Mursi Formation state, especially in the upper dentition. This would be expected from the earlier age of the Kubi Algi deposits. *Elephas ekorensis* is represented by a partial skull with complete upper third molars. It is less evolved than the Kanapoi-Ekora form, although it is similar in cranial morphology. A small fragment of a *Gomphotherium* molar adds further evidence for the antiquity of the fauna. This genus does not occur in East Africa later than late Pliocene, Kanapoi horizon.

Archeology

Very little attention was given to excavation in the preliminary exploration, but a number of artifact occurrences were noted in association with the KBS tuff. One of these was tested and yielded some material in situ. The low frequency of sites and the density of material are unlike the Olduvai Bed I evidence, and this might reflect a difference in habitat or else be related to the earlier age of the KBS level. Some samples of the KBS tuff were collected and these were sent to Cambridge, England, for age determinations.

Human Paleontology

The first two seasons resulted in the recovery of seven fossil fragments of early hominid material as listed below:

1968	KNM-ER	403	Right fragment mandible
1968	KNM-ER	405	Edentulous palate
1968	KNM-ER	404	Right fragment of mandible
1969	KNM-ER	406	Cranium, complete but lacking the dentition
1969	KNM-ER	407	Cranium with frontal region and face missing
1968	KNM-ER	417	Parietal fragment
1969	KNM-ER	164	Parietal fragment

The crania KNM-ER 406 and 407 were of particular interest in that they were both small-brained and yet the latter showed more gracile features. The 406 specimen is very like the skull from Olduvai, OH 5, that is recognized as *Australopithecus boisei.*

Speculation upon hominid taxonomy is continued every year and it is assumed that KNM-ER 407 represents a female of *Australopithecus boisei* rather than a second species. Both crania were recovered in a situation where their precise provenance could be documented.

REFERENCES

BEHRENSMEYER, A. K.
    1970. Preliminary geological interpretation of a new hominid site in the Lake Rudolf basin.   Nature, vol. 226, pp. 225-226, illus.
FITCH, F. J., and MILLER, J. A.
    1970. Radioisotopic age determinations of Lake Rudolf artefact site.   Nature, vol. 226, pp. 226-228.
LEAKEY, MARY D.
    1970. Early artefacts from the Koobi Fora area.   Nature, vol. 226, pp. 228-230, illus.
LEAKEY, RICHARD E.
    1970a. New hominid remains and early artefacts from northern Kenya.   Nature, vol. 226, pp. 223-224, illus.
    1970b. In search of man's past at Lake Rudolf.   Nat. Geogr. Mag., vol. 137, no. 5, pp. 712-732, illus.
MAGLIO, VINCENT J.
    1971. Vertebrate fauna from the Kubi Algi, Kubi Fora and Ileret areas, East Rudolph, Kenya.   Nature, vol. 231, pp. 248-249.

RICHARD E. LEAKEY

Geology, Petrology, and Isotopic and Trace-element Geochemistry of Basalts from the Snake River Basin, Southern Idaho

Principal Investigator: William P. Leeman, University of Oregon, Eugene, Oregon.

Grant No. 758:   For a study of the petrology and geochemistry of basalts from the Snake River Plain, Idaho.

Modern theories and speculations on the earth's origin commonly have been based on studies of chemical and mineralogical compositions of meteorites, terrestrial and, recently, lunar rocks, and electromagnetic radiations from celestial bodies including the sun. Inasmuch as these studies show that material of this solar system has undergone significant chemical fractionation, it is unlikely that we shall ever have a "representative" sample of the original (or primordial) matter that comprised the earth. We are forced to rely on indirect methods to infer the early beginnings and current physico-chemical state of our planet. Geophysical methods demonstrate that the earth is crudely layered with a thin surficial crust and thick mantle and core regions that increase in density and vary in composition with depth. The detailed composition and physical state of the earth's interior are matters of debate and subjects of considerable inquiry and great interest.

One of our most direct means of obtaining material derived from great depths is through sampling of volcanic rocks and the occasional accidental fragments of ultramafic rocks found in them. Because of their widespread occurrence, tectonic significance, and great depth of origin, basaltic lavas have been subjected to considerable study. Detailed petrogenetic studies of basaltic lavas conceivably can provide details concerning the mineralogy and composition of their mantle source regions and may shed light on the processes by which such melts are formed. The Snake River Plain, southern Idaho, is an excellent area for such a study because the crustal structure, geology, and to some degree stratigraphy are reasonably well known. I have attempted to understand the petrogeneses of the Snake River basalts through studies of their field relationships, chemical and isotopic compositions, and petrographic characteristics.

Geology and Geophysics

The Snake River Plain is a broad arcuate depression that extends about 500 kilometers across southern Idaho and geographically links the young caldera complexes of Yellowstone and Island Park on the east to the Columbia River basalt plateaus on the west (fig. 1). This depression contains a great thickness (locally greater than 1-2 kilometers) of basaltic lavas and inter-bedded fluvial-lacustrine sediments. The western portion of the Plain is bounded by northwest-trending normal faults (Malde, 1959), whereas the eastern portion apparently is not fault-bounded but is predominantly down-warped. Rocks exposed along margins of the Snake River Plain include Pliocene and Miocene silicic lavas and tuffs and pre-Tertiary intrusive and sedimentary rocks. Precambrian metamorphic rocks are exposed in the Albion Range, south-central Idaho (Armstrong and Hills, 1967). Strati-graphic control is good in the western Plain, where Malde and Powers (1962) subdivided post-Miocene rocks into three units: (a) lower and middle Pliocene Idavada Volcanics, (b) upper Pliocene to middle Pleistocene Idaho Group, and (c) upper Pleistocene to Holocene Snake River Group. The Idavada Volcanics consist mainly of silicic volcanic rocks whereas the Idaho and Snake River Groups consist of interbedded basalt and sediments. Most of the samples examined in my study belong to the latter two groups or their equivalents in the eastern Plain. Other details of late Cenozoic geology of the Snake River Plain are given by Stearns et al. (1938), Carr and Trimble (1963), and Malde (1965, 1971).

Gravity studies (Hill et al., 1961; Bonini, 1963; Hill, 1963) reveal large positive Bouguer anomalies in the western Snake River Plain. Seismic re-fraction studies (Hill and Pakiser, 1967) in the same area indicate an anom-alous crustal structure with a thin (8-10 kilometer) 5.2 km/sec layer under-lain by a thick (33-38 kilometer) 6.7 km/sec layer. Low Pn velocities (7.9 km/sec) in the underlying mantle suggest that the region is highly absorptive or that a low-velocity layer lies immediately beneath the Mohorovičic dis-continuity. The gravity and seismic data suggest that mafic material intrudes to a depth of 8-10 kilometers beneath the western Snake River Plain and is overlain by a layer of rocks having P-wave velocities similar to those in inter-bedded lavas and sediments on the island of Hawaii. Gravity studies in the eastern Snake River Plain (La Fehr and Pakiser, 1962; Bonini, 1963) reveal low-relief, northwest-trending linear anomalies. La Fehr and Pakiser (1962) suggest that less basalt accumulated in this region than in the western Plain and that the basalt filled troughs or valleys in an undulating subsurface basement. In short, the geophysical data suggest that the western Plain is under-lain by predominantly mafic crust whereas the eastern Plain is underlain by a more sialic crust.

K-Ar Radiometric Dating and Paleomagnetic Stratigraphy

One of the goals of the present study was a comparison of basalts from the eastern and western Snake River Plain because crustal structure seems to differ beneath the two areas. Unfortunately, no general stratigraphic framework exists for correlating the age of lavas in those areas. A program of K-Ar dating was undertaken with Dr. R. L. Armstrong to establish the absolute chronology of the Snake River basalts and the underlying silicic volcanics. Paleomagnetic polarities were measured in the dated samples to help define magnetic reversal horizons that could be used for correlation purposes. Work was initiated in the western Plain where stratigraphic rela-tions were known. It was found that some stratigraphic assignments made

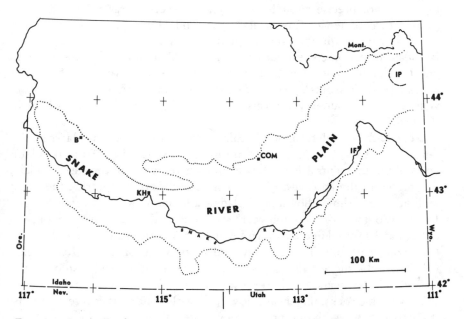

FIG. 1.   Generalized map showing location of the Snake River Plain in southern Idaho. The towns of Boise (B), King Hill (KH), and Idaho Falls (IF), Craters of the Moon National Monument (COM), and Island Park caldera complex (IP) are shown for reference.

by Malde and Powers (1962) were inconsistent with the K-Ar ages. In several cases geologic complexities led Malde and Powers to assign different basalt flows to the same stratigraphic unit. For example, their Banbury basalt included topographically high basalts along margins of the western Plain and topographically low basalts exposed in canyons of the Snake River drainage. K-Ar ages for the former basalts range from about 8 to 10 million years or older, whereas the latter (type) Banbury basalts have K-Ar ages of 5 to 4.5 million years and are bracketed stratigraphically by an Idavada vitrophyre (6.25 million years) and a younger (4.4 million years) basalt (Armstrong and Leeman, 1971; Armstrong et al., 1975).

The K-Ar dates indicate need for minor revisions of the Malde-Powers stratigraphy, but their main stratigraphic divisions are still useful in comparisons with sections elsewhere within the Snake River Plain. The magnetic polarity studies revealed that all the basalt flows above the Bruneau formation (upper part of the Idaho Group) in the western Plain have normal magnetization, whereas basalts of the Bruneau formation all have reversed magnetization. Below that formation absolute ages and details of the stratigraphy are not precise enough for magnetic reversal stratigraphy to be applied with confidence. Cox et al. (1965) and McDougall and Chamalaun (1966) have shown that the magnetic reversal we observe above the Bruneau formation corresponds to an age of 0.7 million years. Inasmuch as our date for the oldest basalt of the type Snake River Group is 0.50 ± 0.05 million years, it seems appropriate to use the magnetic reversal as a convenient lower boundary for this group and its equivalents elsewhere in the Plain.

The K-Ar ages determined in this study indicate that Idavada Volcanics range from 13 to 9 million years old in the western Plain, 10 to 8 million years old in the central Plain, 8 to 4 million years old in the eastern Plain, and merge in the east with silicic volcanic rocks erupted during the last 2 million years from Yellowstone, Island Park, and related volcanic centers. Basalts as old as 11-10 million years are found in the western Plain, but the oldest basalts found in the eastern Plain, near American Falls, are only about 6 million years old. The geology and chronology of Snake River Plain volcanic rocks suggest that a systematic facies relation has existed for the last 10 million years and is represented in an east-to-west order by: (a) silicic volcanic rocks, mostly ash flow tuffs, with minor basalt intercalations; (b) basalt flows with minor sediment intercalations and local siliceous domes; and (c) lacustrine and fluviatile sediments complexly interstratified with basalt flows. During the same time span these facies have shifted eastward across Idaho in a reasonably systematic manner at an average rate of about 4 cm/yr. Silver et al. (1974) have recently suggested that a similar rate is compatible with motions of the Pacific and North American lithospheric plates relative to a fixed melting spot in the upper mantle. They suggest that Snake River Plain volcanism is a response to moving the North American plate over such an anomalous melting zone. This model for the origin of the Snake River Plain can be examined for credibility in the light of petro-chemical, isotopic, and trace-element data.

Petrochemistry of Snake River Basalts

Ongoing petrologic and geochemical studies show that Snake River Plain basaltic lavas fall into two broad categories: (a) voluminous olivine tholeiites of relatively uniform composition and (b) evolved suites of small volume and local areal extent that range in composition from andesine-normative "basalts" to tholeiitic latites (these are herein designated as Craters of the Moon (COM)-type lavas for their occurrence at the national monument of that name). Analyses of some representative Snake River lavas are given in table 1 (see p. 360), with some other distinctive basalt types. The Snake River Plain has often been considered as an appendage to the larger Columbia River Plateaus. However, Powers (1960) first showed that lavas from the two provinces differ in important compositional respects. Comparison of the analyses in table 1 brings out the differences between Snake River basalts and those from the Columbia River Plateaus, while showing some similarities to basalts from Iceland. A more extensive survey of basalt chemistry on a world-wide basis has revealed few basalts that close-ly resemble those from the Snake River Plain. Compositional variations among the Snake River olivine tholeiites can be ascribed largely to fraction-ation of olivine and plagioclase, the only important phenocryst phases ob-served in these basalts. Other variations may have been caused by differing degrees of partial melting, which gave rise to individual magma batches. As shown below, trace-element compositions of some of the olivine tholeiites indicate that these magmas were formed by relatively large degrees of melt-ing, and in certain respects they appear to be as primitive as many midocean rise basalts.

The evolved COM-type lavas display compositional trends and petro-graphic features suggesting that they have experienced extensive fractiona-tion involving plagioclase, olivine, magnetite, apatite, and possibly clino-pyroxene in the later stages. They also appear to be contaminated by crustal material, as evidenced by the occurrence of partly resorbed xenocrysts and xenoliths of crustal origin. However, major and most trace-element data neither require nor are compatible with extensive *bulk* contamination by any known crustal rock types. The isotopic data suggest that contamination was selective (see below). The available data are consistent with a model involving entrapment of parental COM-type magmas in fault controlled chambers along margins of the Snake River Plain, because they invariably occur along the margins of the Plain (Leeman et al., 1976).

Isotopic Studies of Snake River Basalts

The isotopic compositions of Sr and Pb have been determined in selected lavas from the Snake River Plain to test hypotheses of their mantle origin or contamination by crustal material. Since Rb, U, and Th are significantly enriched in the continental crust relative to the upper mantle, their radiogenic daughters ^{87}Sr, ^{206}Pb, ^{207}Pb, and ^{208}Pb are also enriched in old crustal rocks to an extent dependent upon the Rb/Sr, U/Pb, and Th/Pb ratios in those rocks. Numerous studies have shown that basalts from oceanic ridges and islands, which are far removed from continental crust, have a narrow range in $^{87}Sr/^{86}Sr$ ratios (0.7025-0.704). These values have been accepted as representative of the oceanic mantle composition. Peterman and Hedge (1971) have shown that ratios as high as 0.706 may be observed in certain oceanic-island basalts, and they suggest that the oceanic mantle is heterogeneous with respect to Sr isotopic composition. Gast et al. (1964), Tatsumoto (1966 a, b), Oversby and Gast (1970), and others have demonstrated similar heterogeneities in the lead isotopic composition of oceanic volcanic rocks. However, these heterogeneities are relatively small when compared to variations in isotopic composition observed in continental volcanic rocks (Hedge and Walthall, 1963; Hedge, 1966; Doe, 1967). Differences in isotopic composition between continental and oceanic volcanic rocks often have been attributed to contamination by crustal rocks, although the means by which such contamination might occur are not at all clear. The Snake River Plain is an ideal area in which to test contamination hypotheses since the nature of the underlying crust varies significantly from one portion to the other.

Isotopic compositions were determined by solid-source mass spectrometry by the use of methods described by Leeman and Manton (1971) for Sr and Manton (1973) for Pb. All $^{87}Sr/^{86}Sr$ ratios are given relative to a value of 0.7080 for the Eimer and Amend $SrCO_3$ standard and are accurate to ± 0.0002 (2σ). Lead isotopic ratios are given as absolute ratios determined by

a double-spiking method (Compston and Oversby, 1969), which was calibrated against the NBS standard, SRM-981, and the ratios are accurate to
0.12 percent (2σ) or better.

$^{87}Sr/^{86}Sr$ ratios in the olivine tholeiites range from 0.7056 to 0.7076,
and average 0.7066 ± 0.0005 (2σ). In contrast, evolved lavas from two
localities, Craters of the Moon National Monument and near the town of
King Hill, have ranges in $^{87}Sr/^{86}Sr$ of 0.7081 to 0.7124 and 0.7103 to
0.7176, respectively. Furthermore there is a high correlation between $^{87}Sr/$
^{86}Sr and contents of SiO_2 K_2O, Rb/Sr, and other alkali metals and large-
ion lithophile trace elements (cf. Leeman and Manton, 1971, fig. 5). The
olivine tholeiites display no such correlations, and $^{87}Sr/^{86}Sr$ is inferred to
be independent of major- and trace-element composition. The hypothesis of
bulk contamination of the COM-type lavas to produce the observed correlations was tested using data for analyzed xenoliths found in some of those
lavas and for several metamorphic and igneous basement rocks and silicic
volcanic rocks from margins of the Snake River Plain. Bulk contamination
by these or similar rocks is ruled out because predicted compositional
trends do not agree with the observed trends. It is concluded that selective
contamination by ^{87}Sr must have occurred. It is concluded also that the
narrow range in $^{87}Sr/^{86}Sr$ for the olivine tholeiites cannot be explained by
contamination because (1) there is no correlation between this ratio and the
nature of the underlying crust through which the lavas erupted; (2) the
rocks show no textural evidence of contamination; (3) there is no correlation
between compositional parameters and isotopic composition; and (4) it
seems implausible that contamination could produce such large volumes of
isotopically similar lavas over a wide area and long time span. If the $^{87}Sr/$
^{86}Sr ratios in the olivine tholeiites are representative of the source region
for these basalts, then it is concluded that this region is isotopically distinguishable from that beneath oceanic ridges and most oceanic islands and
is probably characterized by higher Rb/Sr than is typical for oceanic mantle
regions.

$^{206}Pb/^{204}Pb$, $^{207}Pb/^{204}Pb$, and $^{208}Pb/^{204}Pb$ ratios in the Snake River
olivine tholeiites range from 17.84 to 18.84, 15.55 to 15.75, and 38.18 to
39.73, respectively (Leeman and Manton, 1972). The data define nearly
linear arrays when $^{206}Pb/^{204}Pb$ is plotted against the other ratios (fig. 2).
Since Oversby and Gast (1970) have discussed the lead isotope systematics
for these diagrams in some detail, the principles will not be repeated here.
The linear $^{206}Pb/^{204}Pb-^{207}Pb/^{204}Pb$ array has two possible interpretations.
The line may represent mixing of magmatic lead with that of a suitable

contaminant. The composition of any putative contaminant is necessarily restricted to lie along the mixing-line. A similar interpretation can be made for the ^{206}Pb/^{204}Pb–^{208}Pb/^{204}Pb line. The existence of a suitable contaminant cannot be ruled out, because we have very few lead isotopic data for crustal rocks from North America (see Doe, 1970), but it seems unlikely that any crustal contamination process could produce the large and system-

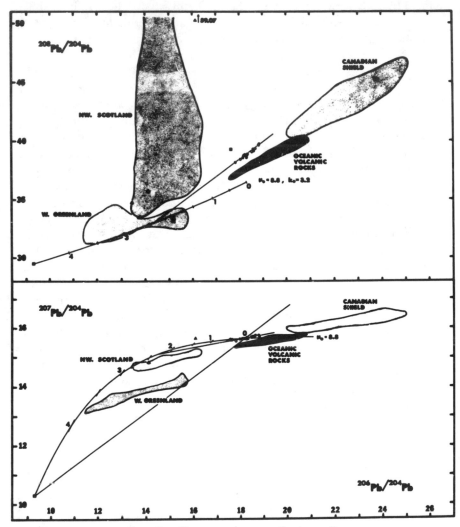

FIG. 2.   (See opposite page for legend).

atic heterogeneities seen in the olivine tholeiite lead isotopic compositions and yet maintain such a restricted range in strontium isotopic compositions. An alternate interpretation is that the linear arrays are secondary isochrons (Oversby and Gast, 1970; Doe, 1970). In the $^{206}Pb/^{204}Pb - ^{207}Pb/^{204}Pb$ diagram such a secondary isochron indicates a present-day $^{238}U/^{204}Pb$ (μ_0 ratio of about 8.8 in the basalt source region and infers that the lead isotopic composition in the source region was rehomogenized about 2.4×10^9 years ago. This putative age agrees well with ages of many basement rock complexes in Idaho, Wyoming, and Montana (e.g., Armstrong and Hills, 1967; Kistler et al., 1969; Reed and Zartman, 1973) and may represent the time of a major thermal perturbation in the region. The μ_0 value inferred for the source region coincides with that inferred for other igneous rocks in the region, including the Boulder Batholith (Doe et al., 1968) and the Absaroka and Yellowstone volcanic rocks (Peterman et al., 1970; Doe et al., 1970), but is significantly higher than that common to most oceanic volcanic rocks ($\mu_0=8.4$). It is interesting to note that the isotopic composition of lead shows no correlation with geographic location within the Snake

---

FIG. 2.   Lead isotopic systematics for Snake River olivine tholeiites (open circles). Ranges in composition are shown for oceanic basalts, modern lake sediments from the Canadian Shield (which represent samples of the Archean upper crustal leads), and Precambrian high-grade metamorphic rocks from northwest Scotland (ca. 2.7 billion years old) and west Greenland (ca. 3.7 billion years old). The latter samples represent leads of probable lower crustal type. Data are also shown for three crustal-derived xenoliths (▲) found in lavas from Craters of the Moon lava field and a monzonite plutonic rock (■) from the north margin of the Snake River Plain.

In the lower diagram the $^{207}Pb-^{206}Pb$ growth curve shown corresponds to $\mu_0 = 8.8$, the value inferred for the Snake River olivine tholeiites. A $t = 0$ chord passes through the compositions of primordial lead and the olivine tholeiite lead and shows the locus of present-day isotopic compositions expected as the result of single-stage evolution from the primordial composition (Tatsumoto et al., 1973). A linear regression line through the olivine tholeiite data intersects the $\mu_0 = 8.8$ growth curve at $t = 2.5$ billion years and is inferred to be a secondary isochron reflecting rehomogenization of lead isotopic composition in the basalt source region at that time.

In the upper diagram is shown a $^{208}Pb-^{206}Pb$ growth curve with parameters $\mu_0 = 8.8$ and Th/U (κ_0) = 3.2. These values were chosen to yield an intersection between the growth curve and a regression line through the olivine tholeiite data at a position corresponding to $t = 2.5$ billion years. If the linear array of olivine tholeiite data is indeed a secondary isochron, a Th/U ratio of 6.9 is implied for the basalt source region 2.5 billion years ago.

River Plain, but the data suggest that there may be a correlation with age, with the youngest olivine tholeiites having the least radiogenic leads. At present there are too few data to place much confidence in this correlation.

The evolved COM-type lavas also display wide variations in lead isotopic composition, but the data do not define linear arrays similar to those for the olivine tholeiites. The evolved lavas do display correlations between $^{87}Sr/^{86}Sr$ and both $^{206}Pb/^{204}Pb$ and $^{208}Pb/^{204}Pb$ that suggest contamination by crustal lead and strontium. Again the olivine tholeiites do not show such correlations. I conclude on the basis of these considerations that the olivine tholeiites represent uncontaminated magmas derived from source regions that have higher U/Pb and Th/Pb ratios than those inferred for oceanic mantle regions. If the above interpretations are correct, the source region for Snake River olivine tholeiites has behaved as an essentially closed system with respect to Rb/Sr, U/Pb, and Th/Pb for the past 2.5×10^9 years and is probably characterized by higher concentrations of large-ion lithophilic elements (Rb, U, Th, K, rare-earth elements, etc.) than those inferred for most suboceanic mantle regions.

Trace-Element Studies of Snake River Basalts

In the present study the abundances of about 20 trace elements (including Ni, Co, Sc, Cr, Ba, Sr, Rb, Cs, U, Th, Pb, Ta, Hf, Zr, and the rare earths La, Ce, Sm, Eu, Tb, Yb, and Lu) have been determined in more than 100 Snake River lavas. Detailed variations in concentrations of most of these elements were studied in a single lava flow, the McKinney Basalt (Malde, 1971). This study revealed that the observed variations in concentrations (up to 15-20 percent for some elements) are largely the result of the presence of differing amounts of olivine and plagioclase phenocrysts (Leeman and Vitaliano, 1976). The rare-earth elements are of particular interest in this case since they are geochemically quite similar to one another. An exception is Eu, which occurs predominantly in the divalent state, whereas the other rare earths are normally trivalent under terrestrial redox conditions (Weill and Drake, 1973). Chondrite-normalized rare-earth abundances in basaltic rocks, when plotted against atomic number (or ionic radius), define regular patterns that reflect either the nature of minerals that are removed or partial fusion processes giving rise to those rocks. Relative to the nearby rare earths (Sm, Tb) chondrite-normalized Eu abundances often appear to be anomalously high or low. This feature (the Eu anomaly), if present in the rare-earth pattern of a basaltic rock, strongly suggests that minerals such as plagioclase or clinopyroxene were involved in fractionations that led to the rock's formation because these minerals preferentially incorporated or reject divalent Eu relative to the trivalent rare earths (Philpotts and Schnetzler, 1968; Schnetzler and Philpotts, 1970; Grutzek et al., 1974).

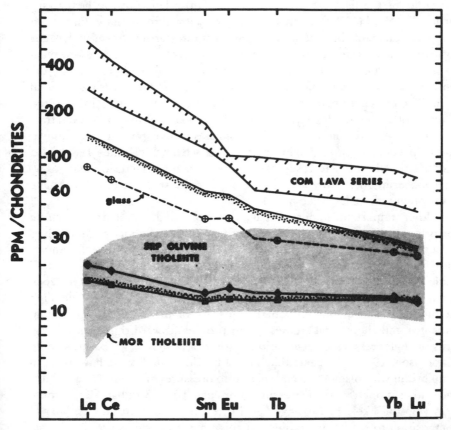

FIG. 3.   Chondrite-normalized rare-earth element abundances in Snake River Plain lavas plotted *vs.* atomic number. The range in values for midocean ridge basalts is shown for reference. Olivine tholeiites with the lowest rare-earth abundances (■,■) are inferred to have formed by more extensive melting than those with higher abundances. A pillow glass (●) with a positive Eu anomaly indicates that the original magma was formed by some process involving fusion of clinopyroxene. Most of the olivine tholeiite whole-rock samples also display slight positive Eu anomalies, which support an hypothesis of their origin by fusion of spinel or aluminous-clinopyroxene-bearing peridotite. Evolved COM-type lavas have high and fractionated rare-earth patterns which reflect extensive crystal fractionation.

Alternately, a Eu anomaly may result in liquids formed by melting of phases that preferentially incorporate or reject Eu.

The rare-earth patterns of most Snake River olivine tholeiites (fig. 3) are characterized by slight positive Eu anomalies and small to moderate enrichments of the light rare earths (La, Ce, Sm) relative to the heavy rare earths (Tb, Yb, Lu). A few samples have very low rare-earth (and large-ion lithophile) element abundances and nearly flat rare-earth patterns with slight positive Eu anomalies. These latter samples are thought to represent magmas that have undergone little crystal fractionation or were formed by extensive (ca. 30 percent) partial melting of clinopyroxene-bearing parental rocks. The rare-earth patterns of all the olivine tholeiites can be interpreted in terms of such a model with differing degrees of melting and crystal fractionation involved. The positive Eu anomalies cannot represent accumulation of plagioclase since plagioclase-free glass from McKinney Basalt also has a positive Eu anomaly. It seems inescapable that partial fusion of clinopyroxene-bearing rock is involved in the origin of most, if not all, of the Snake River olivine tholeiites (Leeman, 1976).

Other important minerals that are stable under anhydrous mantle conditions (olivine, orthopyroxene, spinel, garnet) cannot by themselves account for the light/heavy rare-earth fractionation and positive Eu anomalies found in the olivine tholeiites, based on existing data for crystal/liquid distribution coefficients (cf. Schnetzler and Philpotts, 1970; Grutzeck et al., 1974). There are at present insufficient data to establish the detailed melting and subsequent fractionation history of the Snake River olivine tholeiites, but theoretical studies are in progress toward this goal. On the basis of high-pressure crystallization studies of a McKinney Basalt sample (Thompson, 1972) it appears that such a basaltic liquid could have been in equilibrium with plagioclase and olivine to pressures of about 8 to 10 kbars, and with clinopyroxene at pressures between 10 to 26 kbars. Thus these would be the likely phases involved in fractionation of magmas similar in composition to the basalt studied. At this time it can be asserted only that some clinopyroxene fusion was involved in the formation of the olivine tholeiites. The most likely parental rock for the olivine tholeiite magmas is a spinel or aluminous clinopyroxene bearing peridotite (Leeman and Vitaliano, 1976). Partial melting probably took place at depths on the order of 50-60 kilometers, in which case a geothermal gradient of 20 26° C/km is required for anhydrous melting at about 1,300° C. If small amounts of water and/or CO_2 are present in the source region for the olivine tholeiites, melting could occur at lower temperatures. The geothermal gradient estimated for the anhydrous case is high but is no greater than gradients estimated for some midoceanic rises (e.g., Scheidegger, 1973) and is compatible with a mantle melting anomaly or plume hypothesis (Morgan, 1972; Shaw and Jackson, 1973; Silver et al., 1974).

Summary

This report describes portions of ongoing studies, and it is expected that further results will modify the interpretations made herein. With this qualification in mind, the following conclusions seem reasonable:

(1) The Snake River basalts are comprised of two main lava types — voluminous olivine tholeiites of rather uniform chemical composition and minor evolved (differentiated) lavas.

(2) The olivine tholeiites are derived from a mantle (?) source region, which has a narrow range in $^{87}Sr/^{86}Sr$ but systematically variable lead isotopic composition; these data infer that the source region has been undisturbed for about 2.5×10^9 years and has higher Rb/Sr, U/Pb, and Th/Pb ratios than do most suboceanic mantle regions.

(3) Rare-earth abundance patterns suggest that the olivine tholeiites were formed at depths shallower than about 60 kilometers where fusion of clinopyroxene-bearing rock occurred. Thus, a high geothermal gradient is implied for the Snake River Plain.

(4) Geologic evolution of the Snake River Plain can be considered in terms of facies, involving basaltic lavas, fluviatile-lacustrine sediments, and silicic volcanic rocks, which have migrated eastwardly at an average rate of about 4 cm/yr during the last 10 million years.

These studies provide further evidence that the earth's mantle is heterogeneous in detail and point out the need for similar studies in various geologic environments and geographic locations worldwide.

Acknowledgments

This study could not have been carried out without the generous support of many individuals and institutions. Drs. G. G. Goles and D. F. Weill at the University of Oregon and Dr. W. I. Manton at the University of Texas at Dallas provided inspiration, analytical facilities, and financial support for much of my research. Grants from the National Geographic Society and Geological Society of America provided funds for field work. I held a National Science Foundation graduate fellowship for part of the duration of this study. Dr. R. L. Armstrong, now at the University of British Columbia, made all the K-Ar age determinations. Finally, many of my colleagues at the University of Oregon, University of Texas at Dallas, and the U. S. Geological Survey have contributed through discussion and example. I particularly wish to thank Dr. H. E. Malde of the U. S. Geological Survey for providing unpublished field maps and access to numerous unpublished chemical analyses of Snake River lavas.

TABLE 1. SNAKE RIVER PLAIN AND COMPARATIVE LAVAS

	72-24	Avg. SRP	McK. GL	PG-HMg	PG-LMg	Roza	Ice-land	69-22	72-27	69-20
SiO_2	47.74	46.90	47.99	50.14	51.19	50.23	48.01	44.42	46.68	62.07
TiO_2	1.07	2.69	4.15	1.55	1.78	3.12	1.87	4.03	3.27	.77
Al_2O_3	16.31	15.06	12.92	15.47	15.31	13.84	14.09	13.28	13.62	14.75
FeO^*	10.15	13.47	15.63	11.43	12.67	14.47	12.48	17.12	16.30	9.28
MnO	.18	.20	.17	.20	.23	.23	.21	.30	.30	.23
MgO	9.66	7.63	5.18	6.65	4.83	4.44	8.29	4.90	3.97	.41
CaO	12.28	10.03	9.81	10.62	9.40	8.88	11.77	8.53	7.56	3.20
Na_2O	2.98	2.53	2.47	2.94	3.27	2.80	2.17	3.34	3.39	4.55
K_2O	.17	.61	.97	.57	.74	1.29	.29	1.59	2.08	4.50
P_2O_5	.11	.58	.72	.22	.33	.59	.19	2.48	2.41	.25

72-24	primitive SRP olivine tholeiite
Avg. SRP	average of 78 SRP olivine tholeiites
McK.-GL	pillow lava glass, McKinney Basalt
PG.HMg	Columbia River Group, high-Mg Picture Gorge basalt
PG-LMg	Columbia River Group, low-Mg Picture Gorge basalt
Roza	Columbia River Group, Yakima-type Roza flow
Iceland	Reykjanes olivine tholeiites
69-22	mafic COM basalt
72-27	apatite-andesine COM lava
69-20	COM ferro-latite

Columbia River Group analyses from Wright et al. (1973)
Reykjanes analyses from Jakobsson (1972)

REFERENCES

ARMSTRONG, RICHARD L., and HILLS, F. ALLAN
  1967. Rb-Sr and K-Ar geochronologic studies of mantled gneiss domes, Albion Range, southern Idaho, USA.   Earth Plan. Sci. Lett., vol. 3, p. 114.
ARMSTRONG, RICHARD L., and LEEMAN, WILLIAM P.
  1971. K-Ar chronology of Snake River Plain, Idaho.   Abstr. Rocky Mt. Sec. Geol. Soc. America, 1971, p. 366.
ARMSTRONG, RICHARD L.; LEEMAN, WILLIAM P.; and MALDE, HAROLD E.
  1975. K-Ar dating, Quaternary and Neogene volcanic rocks of the Snake River Plain, Idaho.   Amer. Journ. Sci., vol. 275, pp. 225-251.
BONINI, W. E.
  1963. Gravity anomalies in Idaho.   Idaho Bur. Mines Pamphl. 132, 13 pp.
CARR, W. J., and TRIMBLE, D. E.
  1963. Geology of the American Falls quadrangle, Idaho.   U. S. Geol. Surv. Bull. 1121-G, 44 pp.
COMPSTON, W. W., and OVERSBY, V. M.
  1969. Lead isotope analysis using a double spike.   Journ. Geophys. Res., vol. 74, pp. 4338-4348.
COX, A.; DOELL, RICHARD R.; and DALRYMPLE, G. BRENT
  1965. Quaternary paleomagnetic stratigraphy.   Pp. 817-830 *in* "The Quaternary of the United States," H. E. Wright, Jr., and D. G. Frey, eds.
DOE, B. R.
  1967. The bearing of lead isotopes on the source of granite magma.   Journ. Petr., vol. 8, pp. 51-83.
  1970. Lead isotopes, 137 pp.   Springer-Verlag.
DOE, B. R.; CHRISTIANSEN, R. L.; and HEDGE, CARL E.
  1970. Radiogenic tracers and the basalt-rhyolite association, Yellowstone National Park and vicinity.   Abstr. Ann. Meeting Geol. Soc. America, 1970, pp. 538-539.
DOE, B. R.; TILLING, ROBERT I.; HEDGE, CARL E.; and KLEPPER, M. R.
  1968. Lead and strontium isotope studies of the Boulder Batholith, southwestern Montana.   Econ. Geol., vol. 63, pp. 884-906.
GAST, PAUL W.; TILTON, GEORGE R.; and HEDGE, CARL E.
  1964. Isotopic composition of lead and strontium from Ascension and Gough Islands.   Science, vol. 145, pp. 1181-1185.
GRUTZECK, M. W.; KRIDELBAUGH, S. J.; and WEILL, DANIEL F.
  1974. The distribution of Sr and REE between diopside and silicate liquid.   Geophys. Res. Lett., vol. 1, pp. 273-275.
HEDGE, CARL E.
  1966. Variations in radiogenic strontium found in volcanic rocks.   Journ. Geophys. Res., vol. 71, pp. 6119-6126.
HEDGE, CARL E., and WALTHALL, F. G.
  1963. Radiogenic strontium-87 as an index of geologic processes.   Science, vol. 140, pp. 1214-1217.

HILL, DAVID P.
   1963. Gravity and crustal structures in the western Snake River Plain, Idaho. Journ. Geophys. Res., vol. 68, p. 5807.
HILL, DAVID P.; BALDWIN, H. L., JR.; and PAKISER, LOUIS C.
   1961. Gravity volcanism, and crustal deformation in the Snake River Plain, Idaho.   U. S. Geol. Surv. Prof. Pap. 424-B, pp. 248-250.
HILL, DAVID P., and PAKISER, LOUIS C.
   1967. Seismic-refraction study of crustal structure between Nevada Test Site and Boise, Idaho.   Geol. Soc. America Bull. 78, p. 685.
JACOBSSON, S. P.
   1972. Chemistry and distribution pattern of Recent basaltic rocks in Iceland. Lithos, vol. 5, pp. 365-386.
KISTLER, RONALD W.; OBRADOVICH, JOHN D.; and JACKSON, E. DALE
   1969. Isotopic ages of rocks and minerals from the Stillwater Complex, Montana.   Journ. Geophys. Res., vol. 74, pp. 3226-3237.
LA FEHR, THOMAS R., and PAKISER, LOUIS C.
   1962. Gravity, volcanism, and crustal deformation in the eastern Snake River Plain, Idaho.   U. S. Geol. Surv. Prof. Pap. 450-D, pp. 76-78.
LEEMAN, WILLIAM P.
   1976. Petrogenesis of McKinney (Snake River) olivine tholeiite in light of rare-earth element and Cr/Ni distributions.   Geol. Soc. Amer. Bull., vol. 87, pp. 1582-1586.
LEEMAN, WILLIAM P., and MANTON, W. I.
   1971. Strontium isotopic composition of basaltic lavas from the Snake River Plain, southern Idaho.   Earth Plan. Sci. Lett., vol. 11, pp. 420-434.
   1972. Lead isotopic composition of Snake River basalts, Idaho.   EOS, vol. 53, p. 277.
LEEMAN, WILLIAM P., and VITALIANO, CHARLES J.
   1976. Petrology and origin of McKinney Basalt, Snake River Plain, Idaho. Geol. Soc. Amer. Bull., vol. 87, pp. 1777-1792.
LEEMAN, WILLIAM P.; VITALIANO, CHARLES J.; and PRINZ, M.
   1976. Evolved lavas from the Snake River Plain: Craters of the Moon National Monument, Idaho.   Contrib. Mineral. Petrol., vol. 56, pp. 35-60.
MALDE, HAROLD E.
   1959. Fault zone along northern boundary of western Snake River Plain, Idaho.   Science, vol. 130, p. 272
   1965. Snake River Plain.   P. 255 *in* "The Quaternary of the United States," H. E. Wright, Jr., and D. G. Frey, eds.
   1971. History of Snake River Canyon indicated by revised stratigraphy of Snake River Group near Hagerman and King Hill, Idaho.   U. S. Geol. Surv. Prof. Pap. 644-F, 21 pp.
MALDE, HAROLD E., and POWERS, HOWARD A.
   1962. Upper Cenozoic stratigraphy of western Snake River Plain, Idaho.   Geol. Soc. America Bull. 73, pp. 1197-1219.
MANTON, W. I.
   1973. Whole rock Th-Pb age for the Masuke and Dembe-Divula complexes, Rhodesia.   Earth Plan. Sci. Lett., vol. 19, pp. 83-89.

McDougall, Ian, and Chamalaun, F. H.
  1966. Geomagnetic polarity scale of time. Nature, vol. 212, pp. 1415-1418.
Morgan, William J.
  1972. Plate motions and deep mantle convection. Geol. Soc. America Mem.
    132, pp. 7-22.
Oversby, V. M., and Gast, Paul W.
  1970. Isotopic composition of lead from oceanic islands. Journ. Geophys.
    Res., vol. 75, pp. 2097-2114.
Peterman, Zell E.; Doe, B. R.; and Prostka, H. J.
  1970. Lead and strontium isotopes in rocks of the Absaroka volcanic field,
    Wyoming. Contr. Min. Petr., vol. 27, pp. 121-130.
Peterman, Zell E., and Hedge, Carl E.
  1971. Related strontium isotopic and chemical variations in oceanic basalts.
    Geol. Soc. America Bull. 82, pp. 493-500.
Philpotts, John A., and Schnetzler, Charles C.
  1968. Europium anomalies and the genesis of basalt. Chem. Geol., vol. 3,
    pp. 5-13.
Powers, Howard A.
  1960. A distinctive chemical characteristic of Snake River basalts of Idaho.
    U. S. Geol. Surv. Prof. Pap. 400-B, p. 298.
Reed, John C., Jr., and Zartman, Robert E.
  1973. Geochronology of Precambrian rocks of the Teton Range, Wyoming.
    Geol. Soc. America Bull. 84, pp. 561-582.
Scheidegger, K. F.
  1973. Temperatures and compositions of magmas ascending along mid-ocean
    ridges. Journ. Geophys. Res., vol. 78, pp. 3340-3355.
Schnetzler, Charles C., and Philpotts, John A.
  1970. Partition coefficients of rare-earth elements between igneous matrix
    material and rock-forming mineral phenocrysts, II. Geochim. Cos-
    moschim. Acta, vol. 34, pp. 331-340.
Shaw, Herbert R., and Jackson, E. Dale
  1973. Linear island chains in the Pacific: Result of thermal plumes or gravi-
    tational anchors? Journ. Geophys. Res., vol. 78, pp. 8634-8652.
Silver, E. A.; von Huene, Roland; and Crouch, J. K.
  1974. Tectonic significance of the Kodiak-Bowie Seamount Chain, north-
    eastern Pacific. Geology, vol. 2, pp. 147-150.
Stearns, Harold T.; Crandall, Lynn; and Steward, W. G.
  1938. Geology and ground-water resources of the Snake River Plain in south-
    eastern Idaho. U. S. Geol. Surv. Water Supply Pap. 774, 268 pp.
Tatsumoto, Mitsunobu
  1966a. Isotopic composition of lead in volcanic rocks from Hawaii, Iwo Jima,
    and Japan. Journ. Geophys. Res., vol. 71, pp. 1721-1733.
  1966b. Genetic relations of oceanic basalts as indicated by lead isotopes. Sci-
    ence, vol. 153, pp. 1094-1101.
Tatsumoto, Mitsunobu; Knight, Roy J.; and Allegre, Claude J.
  1973. Time differences in the formation of meteorites as determined from
    ratio of lead-207 to lead-206. Science, vol. 180, pp. 1279-1283.

THOMPSON, R. N.
   1972. Melting behavior of two Snake River lavas at pressures up to 35 kb. Carnegie Inst. Washington Yearb. 71, pp. 405-410.
WEILL, DANIEL F., and DRAKE, MICHAEL J.
   1973. Europium anomaly in plagioclase feldspar: Experimental results and semiquantitative model. Science, vol. 180, pp. 1059-1060.
WRIGHT, THOMAS L.; GROLIER, M. J.; and SWANSON, DONALD A.
   1973. Chemical variation related to stratigraphy of the Columbia River basalt. Bull. Geol. Soc. Amer. 85, pp. 371-386.

WILLIAM P. LEEMAN

Mediterranean "Knee-line" Studies

Principal Investigators: Olivier Leenhardt, Institut für Geophysik der Universität Kiel, Germany, and Harold E. Edgerton, Massachusetts Institute of Technology, Cambridge, Massachusetts.

Grant No. 766: To explore with seismic equipment "knee-line" depths and positions in the Mediterranean Sea.

When testing a modification of the continuous seismic profiling device "boomer" in 1965, off Monaco, we obtained a record showing an unexpected structure that we called the "knee line." Figure 1 shows the section. Its position is mapped in figure 2.

The continental shelf of Monaco is an almost plane surface, about 1 mile wide, which ends southeastward at a depth of 130 meters; then follows the continental slope with an average slope of 10°. At the border of the plateau a prominent formation, like a knee, is superimposed on the slope. Its shape looks like a triangle, its height is about 40 meters, and its horizontal landward length is less than 500 meters. The reflections to be observed in it have a greater slope than those underlying ones. The resulting conclusions are (1) that the continental shelf off Monaco is a marine abrasion surface formed after tectonic construction of the slope and (2) that the knee line is a more recent sedimentological feature without any tectonic relation to shape and formation.

The Monaco knee-line study is developed in two papers — Edgerton and Leenhardt (1966) and Edgerton, Giermann, and Leenhardt (1967). In two other papers (Leenhardt et al., 1969; Froget and Leenhardt, 1968) the Monaco records are utilized.

Various questions immediately arose:

Is the *knee line* restricted in one place or is it a general observable phenomenon?

At what depths is the knee line to be observed?

Is the knee line similar to progradation?

What was the water level during formation of the knee line?

Is the knee line a morphological or a stratigraphic feature?

365

Program

With these problems in mind we applied to the National Geographic Society for a grant to support the study. The grant was made with the condition that a larger program could be undertaken, with the participation of other research institutions. Various problems have delayed the beginning of the larger study, but the following institutions have so far taken part in this research: Musée Océanographique de Monaco (1969-1973), Centre de Recherches de Géologie Marine de l'Université de Perpignan (1969), Massachusetts Institute of Technology (1969), and Institut für Geophysik der Universität Kiel (1973). We had also the support of the Centre National de la Recherche Scientifique, the Campagnes Océanographiques Françaises, the Centre National pour l'Exploitation des Océans, and the Deutsche Forschungsgemeinschaft, to all of whom we extend our thanks. We planned first to undertake a specific search for the knee line, to collect all the available data from previous cruises, and to collect as much new data as possible when profiling for other major purposes. Co-workers in the research were Mrs. G. Alla Dumaine (formerly Monaco), Dr. H. Got (Perpignan), and Dr. Theilen (Kiel).

Methods and Materials

The prime requisites for obtaining a good picture of the knee line appeared to be: (1) Enough penetration to reach down 100 meters into the sea bed, below some 100 to 300 meters of water; i.e., a certain level of output energy; and (2) a very high resolution, in order to get the most detailed picture possible of the inner stratification of the knee line. Table 1 summarizes the materials required for such a purpose.

Various ways of reconaissance have been used. In the case of specific knee-line work we used a small (about 60-foot) boat, the *Espadon,* from the COF, or the *Winnaretta Singer,* from the Musée, convenient for quick turns and small profiles. Positioning has been obtained with radar or, better, by using two hydrographic circles (sextant). Profiling using a precision boomer is the best tool for that purpose (figure 3 shows the original one).

We intended first to cover an area where the chances were best for finding a knee line. The chances were estimated by studying the morphology of Calvi Bay as described by S. Pierrot (see Alinat et al.) and discussed by G. Giermann. The latter showed an accumulation platform forming a kind of outcrop above the "normal morphology." But we found that there are

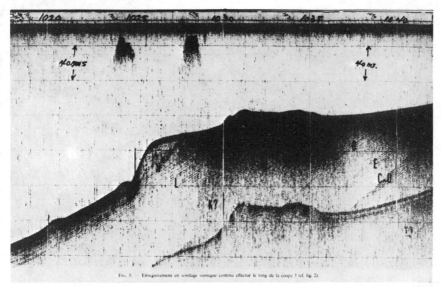

FIG. 1.   Typical section showing knee line as recorded off Monaco in 1965 (see map, fig. 2).

very few cases where the bathymetrical map is good enough to help such a search, and so we tried to explore systematically the French Mediterranean shelf. Many profiles, undertaken for other purposes (structure of the shelf, for example), have, therefore, been projected to the end of the plateau. In many cases (Golfe du Lion), we used a very precise positioning system. In other instances, we used mainly radar.

Search for Knee Line off Corsica and Côte d'Azur

Various sites in this area, representing different tectonic conditions, have been surveyed (fig. 4).

Tyrrhenian Sea—Bastia:

The northern part of the Tyrrhenian Sea shows the same subsidence phenomenon as the whole Tyrrhenian, but just as marginal; 9,000-Joule sparker records (Leenhardt) have demonstrated this. The bathymetrical charts do not show a real continental shelf, but rather a continuously deepening sea floor; it was important to check this out. Some profiles have been surveyed around Bastia. A significant one is presented on figure 5, from which it is clear that—

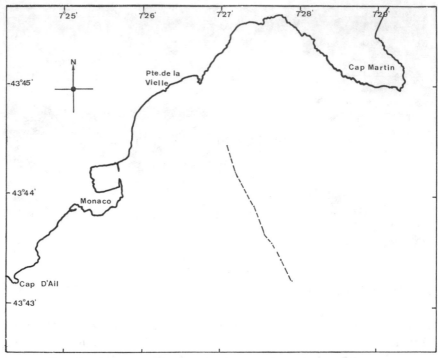

FIG. 2.   Map showing position of section in figure 1, off Monaco.

- There is a shelf, with slope beginning about 120 meters deep;
- on the upper part of the shelf (to the left side of the record) beach deposits are observable;
- on the shelf the normal stratification is almost horizontal, with some erosion (or regression) features;
- the outer part of the shelf has been, twice, deeply eroded through a kind of canyon, and then buried by more recent sediments (using oil seismic records, we know that this phenomenon occurred within the Quaternary).

The sedimentation stage (before the regression noted on the shelf) has covered a large part of the burying sediments. A "fossil" knee line just below the actual one was observed. The terminal stage of erosion presents the characteristics of the knee line, at a distance of about 300 meters and a depth between 120 and 150 meters. Then, off Bastia, the knee line appears as the sedimentation feature, but the presence of a "fossil" knee line raises the question of a "morphological phenomenon."

FIG. 3.   The original 300 J precision boomer.

FIG. 4.   Map showing sites surveyed off Corsica and the Côte d'Azur.

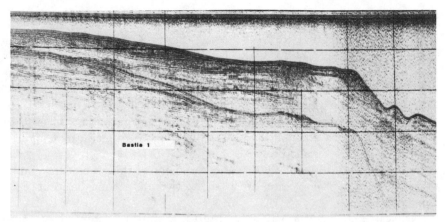

FIG. 5.   Section Bastia 1, off Corsica (see fig. 4). Scale (distance between lines): vertical—100 meters, horizontal—about 500 meters.

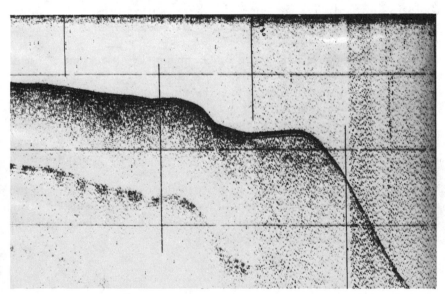

FIG. 6.   Section Île Rousse 2 (scale as in fig. 5); no knee line is present.

Sites Near Calvi:

The sites near Calvi are Île Rousse 2 (fig. 6), Calvi 3 (fig. 7), Calvi 4 (fig. 8), Calvi 5 (fig. 9), and Calvi 6 (fig. 10).

This area has been formed by the subsidence of a previous large massif or by the counterclockwise rotation of the Corsican block. The shelf is always divided into 2 parts: (1) A normal shelf, from shore to a depth of 120 meters, and (2) an intermediate step at a depth varying between 140 and 180 meters. This step is not indicated on the bathymetrical maps; its length is usually less than 1 kilometer.

The seismic profiles show that the basement of this step corresponds to the deepening prolongation of the shelf, covered by a more recent sedimentation.

Typical knee-line formation is observable only on site Calvi 6. See especially figure 7 (Calvi 3).

Numerous reflections show curvatures with their concavity downward. These actually interfere with others with a smaller reflectivity, of opposite concavity (upward). The first ones are diffraction patterns (reflection hyperbolae) caused by some inhomogenities on the sea floor. The second ones represent the true reflectors.

The morphological units given by Giermann (1969) become clarified:
• Crystalline basement, subsiding seaward with an erosional terrace.
• Short sedimentation stage before the subsidence of the basement.
• Large sedimentation after the subsidence.

The patterns of this accumulation are prograding (Dietz and Fairbridge), which means that the sedimentation was mainly a Delta-type during a time when the sea level was lower than today. There was not enough material to cover completely the ancient shelf.

In conclusion, the real knee line is exceptionally represented in the Calvi region. This seems to be due to the fact that the deposit (with concavity upward) results from shore-line processes. The knee line will result from submerged sedimentation processes.

Sites on the Côte d'Azur

The sites Antibes 8, Cannes 9, and Cannes 10 (figs. 11, 12, 13) belong to the northern part of the Ligurian basin, as opposed to the Calvi sites. Only one (Cannes 10) is located on the metamorphic basement; in Cannes 9 and in Antibes 8, eastward, the bedrock is limestone from various Mesozoic ages. The continental shelf does not exist, or almost not, in its usual concept, and the slope is always sharper than in Corsica. At Cannes 10 (fig. 13) the

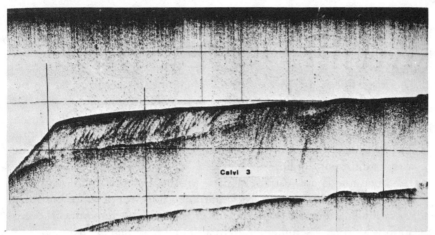

FIG. 7.   Section Calvi 3 (scale as in fig 5).

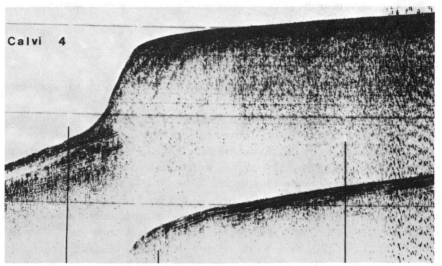

FIG. 8.   Section Calvi 4 (scale as in fig. 5).

very narrow shelf shows the significant feature of a knee line between 90 and 140 meters. At Cannes 9, the same feature is observable but between depths of 60 to 90 meters. At Antibes 8, the slope is covered by sediments paralleled to its surface. It could be formed as a knee line if the slope was not, as it seems to be, almost straight downward.

Conclusions

We can advance these provisional conclusions, which must be checked at other sites:

1. The knee line is a widely extended phenomenon occurring at various depths (between 50 and 200 meters in the Mediterranean). It seems to be related to ancient sea levels, possibly Ice Age or Holocene.
2. Progradation phenomenon and knee line are distinct in their repetition. As progradation is known as a "near sea level" process, the knee line, with its different dipping, appears as a "below sea level" process.
3. The knee line is not a stratigraphical process but a morphological one.

If these conclusions are correct, the knee line would represent a secondary sedimentation in a predominant erosional environment as the progradation is a primary sedimentation in a sedimentational environment. Existence of knee line or of progradation would, thus, signify the latest mode of sedimentation near the coast before the surrounding waters become deep enough to stop any of these processes.

Other Results in the Knee-line Study

Pictures in various publications show knee line, but, up to now, few authors have used the concept.

At the Oceanographic Museum in Monaco, in cooperation with the sedimentological centers of the Universities at Perpignan and Kiel, we obtained various results on Golfe du Lion and off the Catalan coastline. Part of the results are of lesser interest, as they were collected with a 3,000 J Sparker, which does not give the suitable resolution (that is also the case for the data discussed by Froget and Leenhardt, 1968, and Leenhardt et al., 1969, on the Planier Plateau, south of Marseille, where the problem was to decide if "calcarenites" reefs, observed with a good descent with the Cousteau diving Saucer SP 300, were to be related with small descent reflections observed on the shallower layers of the plateau). In fact, we can now say that these seismic reflections do not correspond to the definition of the knee line; they are not situated at the beginning of the continental slope. They seem to be related to another sedimentological process.

Along the French coast, westward, the private society Scop Océanographique mentioned in its reports a knee line in La Napoule and in Bormes les Mimosas (30 kilometers east from Toulon); no results have been obtained by the Monaco team between Toulon and La Ciotat, during a search for sand.

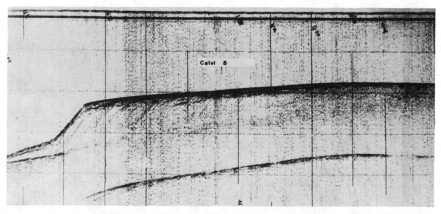

FIG. 9.   Section Calvi 5 (scale as in fig. 5).

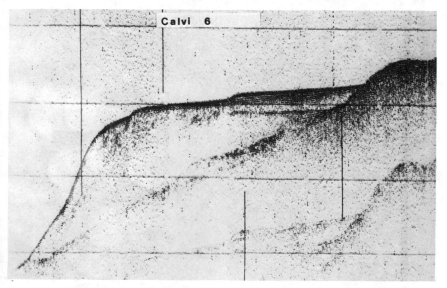

FIG. 10.   Section Calvi 6 (scale as in fig. 5). To the south this type of formation disappears.

Along the Golfe du Lion, most of the work has been conducted with a 3000 J Sparker, but near the Pyrenees Mountains we again found good examples of knee lines. Toward Spain, the search will be continued during the two next years through international cooperation, under a French government contract.

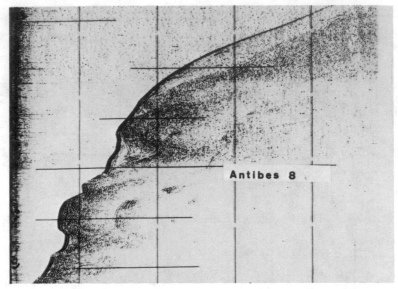

FIG. 11.   Section Antibes 8 (scale as in fig. 5) shows almost no knee line.

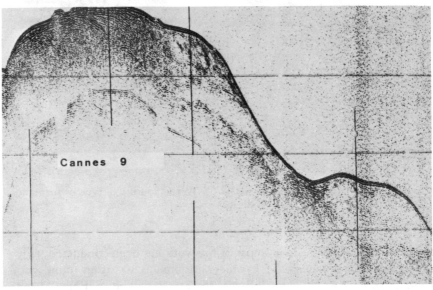

FIG. 12.   Section Cannes 9 (scale as in fig. 5) shows some evidence of knee line.

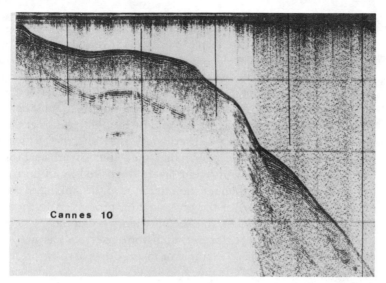

FIG. 13. Section Cannes 10 (scale as in fig. 5). Knee line is more pronounced than in figure 12.

A 1973 publication by another group of French and Italian workers (Fierro et al.) presented pictures of the Italian Ligurian Shelf to Genova. The knee line is apparent on most of the profiles cutting the slope. But the authors ignored the concept of knee line.

We come to the following conclusions:

- So far as we are able to foresee, we will find knee lines when operating with suitable devices (high resolution boomer or very small sparker).
- The knee line can be expected to be a general morphological feature around the Mediterranean Sea.
- The main problem in the interpretation of the knee line remains the distinction between knee line and progradation.
- Our search must take into account any publication dealing with progradation, and we must try to consult the original documents.
- A further difficulty relates to the somewhat "religious" concept that scientists have concerning the formation of the actual deep basin of the Mediterranean. For many American scientists (Hsü et al.) the development of the basin results from plate tectonics action, in this case from a rotation of the Corsica-Sardinian microplate some time in

the Oligocene or early Miocene. The Messinian Salt, in this theory, deposited in a deep basin, which means that every dipping reflector in the Pliocene (see fig. 1) is a progradation reflector along a still existing slope of the bedrock. Other scientists argue (Burollet and Byramjee; Stanley, Got, et al.) that the basin's salt deposits were shallow at one time; that the development of the basement must have occurred much more recently, at the end of the Pliocene or at the beginning of the Quaternary; consequently the reflectors, which are, stratigraphically speaking, below the knee line, as in the Monaco example (fig. 1), would represent layers deposited in an horizontal position, and then tilted under the influence of the sinking of the sea floor — hence, not a part of the progradation process. A further geomorphological argument for this second theory is that the classical distinction between topset, foreset, and bottomset beds is not to be recognized in the Monaco example or in any other of those presented up to now.

A recent result has been given by Kremer. He got a core from the knee line of Monaco (43°44', 3 N.-07°31', 4 E.) on the 370-centimeter long core:

TABLE 1. USABLE MATERIALS

Type of Material [1]	Instrument	Frequency	Power	Penetration on the Shelf (m)	Resolution (m)	Observations
1. Mud penetrator	E.G. & G.	12 kHz	600 W	2-5	0.05	used for K.L.[2]
2. Pingerprobe	E.G. & G.	5 kHz	600 W	5-15	0.15	
3. Sondeur de sediments	S.Oc.	3-12 kHz	1 kW	5-20	0.15	used for K.L. (French)
4. Subbottom profiler	ORE	2-7 kHz	10 kW	5-30	0.25	
5. Subbottom sounder	EDO	3,5 kHz	3 kW	5-25	0.30	
6. Etinceleur	I.F.P.		100-1,000 J	50-200	5	(French)
7. Sparker	S.I.G.	600	18-144 J	10-150	2	(French)
8. Precision boomer	E.G. & G.	—	300-500 J	50-150	2	used for K.L. (see figs. 1-3)
9. Uniboom	E.G. & G.	2,000 Hz	300 J	50-150	2	
10. Sparker (3,000 J)	E.G. & G.	200 Hz	3,000 J	200-500	15	used for K.L.
11. Bottom profiler	Huntec	?	?	50-150 ?	2 ?	

[1] The first five items operate as any echo sounder: i.e., the transducer acts as emitter as well as receiver for acoustical waves in the water; the frequency is lower than in a conventional echo sounder; and the recorder is tuned for a fine reception of the signals. The other six items use a special sound source — for items 6, 7, and 10 that is the noise produced by an electrical spark (1 electrode for no. 6, 3 for no. 10, and between 100 and 300 for no. 7), or by the acoustical pulse of the movement of a thin aluminum plate under the effect of Eddy currents produced by a flat coil (items 8, 9, 11), the fixation of the coil to the plate varying with the type considered, but always the electrical impulse is formed by the discharge of a capacitor (between 1 Mfd and 160 Mfd) load under a high voltage (between 1,000 and 10,000 volts depending on the items). The resolution obtained with the boomer system (nos. 8, 9, 11) is always twice better than that with the sparker, owing to the absence of bubble after the spark (fig 3).

[2] K.L.=Knee Line.

    0-95 cm = fine size homogeneous mud
    95-155 cm = shells clean washed
    155-245 cm = another mud layer
    245-370 cm = shells with a very little silt content.

Both C^{14} and paleontological datings give an age of about 10,000 years for the two shelly layers.

Such a deposit needs quite rapid variations of the sea level. When the water is shallow enough, the eroded material is transported by wave action out on the shelf. At the knee line, a few meters deeper than the shelf itself, the shells remain, stopped because the force of the current is not strong enough; when the water-depth increases, only silt sedimentation remains.

This, and our observations, allow us, finally, to conclude that the knee line is a morphological process, related to the end of the slope and the depth of the water. It is not to be confused with the progradation process.

REFERENCES

ALINAT, JEAN; COUSTEAU, JACQUES-YVES; GIERMANN, GÜNTER; LEENHARDT, OLIVIER; PERRIAN, CHRISTIAN; and PIERROT, SERGE
    1969. Lever de la carte bathemétrique de la mer Ligure. Bull. Inst. Océanogr. Monaco, vol. 68, no. 1395, 12 pp., illus.

BUROLLET, P. F., and BYRAMJEE, R.
    1974. Evolution géodynamique de la Méditerranée occidentale. Compt. Rend. Acad. Sci. Paris, ser. D, vol. 278, no. 10, pp. 1321-1328.

DIETZ, R. S., and FAIRBRIDGE, R. W.
    1968. Wave base. Pp. 1224-1228 *in* "The Encyclopedia of Geomorphology." Reinhold Book Co., New York.

EDGERTON, HAROLD E., and LEENHARDT, OLIVIER
    1966. Monaco: The shallow continental shelf. Science, vol. 152, no. 3725, pp. 1106-1107, illus.

EDGERTON, HAROLD E.; GIERMANN, GÜNTER; and LEENHARDT, OLIVIER
    1967. Etude structurale de la baie de Monaco en sondage sismique continu. Bull. Inst. Océanogr. Monaco, vol. 67, no. 1377, 6 pp.

FIERRO, G.; GENNESSEAUX, M.; and REHAULT, J. P.
    1973. Caractères structuraux et sédimentaires du plateau continental de Nice à Gènes. Bull. Bur. Recherches Géol. et Min., vol. 4, no. 4, pp. 193-208.

FROGET, C., and LEENHARDT, OLIVIER
    1968. Précisions sur les calcarenites pleistocènes submergées au large de Marseille. Compt. Rend. Soc. Géol. France, vol. 4, pp. 113-114.

GIERMANN, GÜNTER
    1969. Morphologie et tectonique du plateau continental entre le cap Cavallo et Saint-Florent (Corse). Bull. Inst. Océanogr. Monaco, vol. 69, no. 1397, 6 pp., illus.

Hsü, K. J.; Cita, M. B.; and Ryan, W. B. F.
    1973. The origin of the Mediterranean evaporits. Initial Reports of the
        Deep Sea Drilling Project, vol. 13, pp. 1303-1331. National Science
        Foundation.
Kremer, Y.
    1974. Littoral et précontinent de Menton (A.M.): Morphologie, sedimentologie
        et structure. Thèse 3e cycl. Nice, 160 pp.
Leenhardt, Olivier
    1970. Sondages sismiques continus en Méditerranée occidentale. Anal. Inst.
        Océanogr. Monaco, vol. 1, 120 pp.
Leenhardt, Olivier; Pierrot, Serge; Rebuffatti, Andre; and Sabatier,
    Réné
    1969. Étude sismique de la zone de Planier (Bouches-du-Rhone). Rev. Inst.
        Française Pétrole, vol. 24, no. 2, pp. 1261-1287.
Stanley, Daniel J.; Got, H.; Leenhardt, Olivier; and Weller, Y.
    1974. Subsidence of the Western Mediterranean Basin in Pliocene-Quaternary
        time: Further evidence. Geology, vol. 2, pp. 345-350.

OLIVIER LEENHARDT

The Phytogeography of the Pteridophytes
of the Departamento del Chocó, Colombia

Principal Investigator: David B. Lellinger, U. S. National Herbarium, Smithsonian Institution, Washington, D. C.

Associate Investigator: Elías R. de la Sota, Museo de La Plata, La Plata, Argentina.

Grant No. 770:   In support of a phytogeographic study of the pteridophytes of the Departamento del Chocó, Colombia.

Many parts of the New World tropics are little known biologically. The Departamento del Chocó is one of these, for reasons of having a disagreeable climate and a scarcity of roads and other transportation routes. And yet such areas often are of great importance to science. For instance, floristic works, which account for the species of plants of a given area, are more rationally and efficiently written when they cover a natural phytogeographic region, rather than a political region like a single country. It is important to know the phytogeographic affinities of the various floras of the world, for without this information it is difficult to delimit the phytogeographic boundaries for floristic work. In order to assess the phytogeographical affinities of any flora it is necessary to have a reasonably good idea of the species that the flora contains. The purpose of our field work and the research based on the field work was to inventory the pteridophytes (ferns and fern-allies) and to determine the phytogeographic affinities of the pteridophyte flora of the Departamento del Chocó, which is the northwesternmost department of Colombia.

The principal investigator has been working on a Pteridophyte Flora for Costa Rica and Panama since 1967 (see Wagner et al., 1967). A natural phytogeographic boundary for this work lies at the Lago de Nicaragua and the Río San Juan, which form or are near the boundary between Nicaragua and Costa Rica. But it has not been known whether a similar boundary existed between Panama and Colombia or whether the Chocó should be included with Costa Rica and Panama as part of that phytogeographic region, principally because the botanical explorations of the Chocó have been too few to amass the necessary specimens and information.

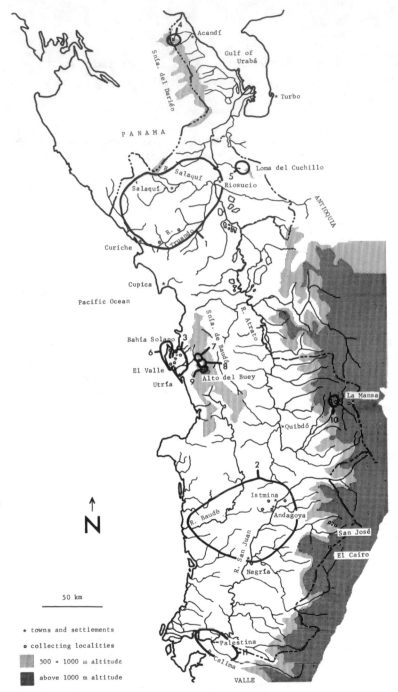

FIG. 1.   Map of the Departamento del Chocó with 11 lowland areas marked. The
5 upland areas lie near San José del Palmar and La Mansa.

In the course of our field work (see Lellinger and de la Sota, 1972), from January 15 to April 15, 1971, we collected 961 numbers of plant specimens, aiming for five duplicates of each number, which resulted in a total collection of about 5,000 sheets. Most of these are ferns and fern-allies; occasionally we collected flowering plants, for we realized that many years might pass before other botanists would again collect plants in the area. During the field work and in the herbarium study that preceded and followed it, we found about 15 new (i.e., undescribed) species and varieties of pteridophytes in the Chocó, all of which will be described and published. There are now about 334 species of pteridophytes known from the Chocó, about a quarter of them as a result of our collections.

Intra-Chocó Phytogeographical Relationships. In order to understand the phytogeographic affinities of the Chocó pteridophyte flora, it was necessary to define this flora and to separate it from adjacent floras. We did this by studying the distribution of species found in several scattered areas lying at various altitudes within the Departamento del Chocó. For purposes of analyzing the variation and of making the floristic separation, we grouped our collecting localities and those of other botanists into 16 areas, 11 from the lowlands below 1,000 meters altitude and 5 from the Andean slopes of the Chocó lying above 1,000 meters altitude. Figure 1 shows the 11 lowland areas. The 5 upland areas are from near San José del Palmar and La Mansa.

The name of each pteridophyte taxon (species, subspecies, variety, or form) known from the Departmento was written on an edge-notched card, and the 16 areas were each assigned a position along the margin. These were punched out for each area in which we knew the taxon occurred, either as a herbarium specimen collected by another person, as one of our own collections, or as a sight record made by us.

We then compared these presence data of the taxa for the various areas for each pair of areas, using a familiar coefficient of association: $(++)/(+-) + (-+)$, which is the number of taxa present in both areas divided by the number found in one or the other of the areas, but not both areas. We found that the average of all the correlation coefficients linking the 11 localities lying below 1,000 meters altitude was $r = 0.156$. Also, the average of all the correlation coefficients linking the five localities lying above 1,000 meters altitude on the Andean slopes of the Departamento del Chocó was $r = 0.060$. But the average of all the correlation coefficients linking the lowland Chocó localities with the upland Andean ones was only $r = 0.040$. This indicates strongly that the lowland pteridophyte flora is distinct from the upland pteridophyte flora; the lower can be called Chocó and the upper Andean.

We suspected this floristic division while we were in the field, and so we

FIG. 2. Map showing percentages of Chocó pteridophytes known also from other countries or Antillean island groups in the New World.

made observations of the ferns along the road near San José del Palmar. We found that the species of *Nephrolepis* and *Cnemidaria* found typically along the roadside at and below 500 meters altitude were not found much above 1,000 meters altitude. Also, the collections we made behind the cemetery at San José del Palmar (at an altitude of 1,100 meters) correlate slightly more with the Andean localities than with the lowland Chocó ones. We confirmed these roadside observations along the road from Ciudad Bolívar to Quibdó, and again we found that 1,000 meters altitude was the approximate boundary between the two fern floras.

As one would expect in an area some 475 kilometers long, the Chocó pteridophyte flora is not entirely uniform. A study of the matrix of correlation coefficients for the 11 lowland Chocó areas revealed some interesting facts. The mossy forest on the upper slopes (1,450 to 1,750 meters altitude) of Alto del Buey, the highest peak of the coastal Serranía del Baudó, correlates most closely with the lower Andean slopes at 750 meters altitude, more so than with the pteridophyte flora of the slopes at the base of Alto del Buey. Thus, the pteridophyte flora is definitely Chocó, even though it is above the 1,000-meter Chocó-Andean pteridophyte flora boundary. The Serranía del Baudó, being surrounded by steamy, lowland Chocó, is probably warmer for its altitude than the Andes, which rise much higher. The lower Río San Juan area, the southernmost locality in the Chocó, is also least related to the other Chocó localities, probably because some species typical of the Pacific Coast slopes farther south in Colombia and in Ecuador occur there, but not farther north. The ferns and fern-allies of the Pacific coastal strip very close to the ocean are divergent from most of the other localities in the central and northern parts of the Northern Chocó. The coastal strip is much drier than the inland areas, and this presumably accounts for the difference. Also fairly distinct in this regard was Loma del Cuchillo, which is isolated from the other areas by many miles of lower Río Atrato swamps; this area has some affinity with the adjacent lowlands of the Departamento de Antioquia. Additional details may be found in de la Sota (1972) and Lellinger (1975).

Extra-Chocó Phytogeographic Relationships. The evidence concerning the phytogeographic relationships of the lowland Chocó pteridophytes with the pteridophytes of other areas is substantial but not completely conclusive. The data on extra-Chocó distributions are almost all taken from the U. S. National Herbarium collections, with some additions from the literature for the species of a few genera. To study the affinities of the Chocó pteridophyte flora, the New World was divided into 27 areas — countries or (in the Antilles) island groups. Each Chocó taxon card was notched for each country or group in which it was found. Figure 2 shows the results rounded off to the nearest percent. Note the dropoff in the percentage of affinity from Costa Rica to Nicaragua, from Guatemala to Mexico, from Venezuela to the Guianas, from Colombia to Brazil, and from Peru to southern South America. The highest percentages of pteridophyte taxa corresponding between the Chocó and the other areas are found in Colombia, Costa Rica, Panama, and Peru.

Although we have no numerical data, from the Chocó collections that we made we estimate that at least 85 percent of the Chocó pteridophytes are known from elsewhere in Colombia, mostly from the adjacent provinces of Antioquia and El Valle, both of which have some areas similar in climate and topography to the lowland Chocó. Note that this figure is a little higher than the one recorded from Costa Rica and Panama. This does not mean, however, that the Chocó pteridophyte flora is more closely related to the Colombian pteridophyte flora as a whole than it is to the Costa Rican-Panamanian pteridophyte flora. We have seen that the affinity of the Chocó pteridophyte flora is not primarily with the Andean pteridophyte flora. The affinity is even less likely to be with other inland continental or Caribbean floras of Colombia; they are all in areas of different climate (drier or colder) and some are distant geographically. Rather, the affinities are most likely to be with the Pacific Coastal phytogeographic areas, which also are adjacent to the Chocó geographically and are more like it in climate. If we take the percentages found in Colombia (estimated at 85 percent), Ecuador, and Peru and average them, we arrive at a value of 66 percent. The 79 percent for Costa Rica and Panama is somewhat, but not greatly, higher. We believe this represents the true affinity of the Chocó pteridophyte flora—primarily with that of Costa Rica and Panama and secondarily with the Pacific coastal and submontane slopes from Colombia to Peru.

We conclude, therefore, that the pteridophyte flora that is bounded on the north roughly by the Nicaragua-Costa Rica border extends in the south through the Departamento del Chocó to an elevation of 1,000 meters in the Andes and to the ridge of the Serranía Los Chancos, just beyond the southern border of the Departamento del Chocó.

REFERENCES

LELLINGER, DAVID B.
1972. A phytogeographic analysis of Chocó pteridophytes. Fern Gaz., vol. 11, pts. 2, 3, pp. 105-114.
1977. Nomenclatural and taxonomic notes on the pteridophytes of Costa Rica, Panama, and Colombia, I. Proc. Biol. Soc. Washington, vol. 89. no. 61, pp. 703-732, illus.

LELLINGER, DAVID B., and SOTA, ELÍAS R. DE LA
1972. Collecting ferns in the Chocó, Colombia. Amer. Fern Journ., vol. 62, pp. 1-8, illus.

SOTA, ELÍAS R. DE LA
1972. Las pteridofitas y el epifitismo en el Departamento del Chocó (Colombia). Anal. Soc. Cient. Argentina, vol. 194, pp. 245-278, illus.

WAGNER, W.H., JR.; MICKEL, J. T.; LELLINGER, D. B.; and EVANS, A. M.
1967. Pteridophytes of Costa Rica: Preliminary checklist of species known to be or probably occurring in Costa Rica. (Mimeographed, limited edition, prepared for the Organization for Tropical Sudies, San José, Costa Rica.)

DAVID B. LELLINGER
ELÍAS R. DE LA SOTA

Archeological Work in the Grand Gulch Region, Southeastern Utah, 1969

Principal Investigator: William D. Lipe, Washington State University, Pullman, Washington.

Grant No. 787:   For study of the prehistoric Basketmaker occupation of upper Grand Gulch, Utah.

Archeological survey and excavation were carried out in the upper Grand Gulch region between June 15 and September 10, 1969, by a crew of eight students under my direction. The work was supported by a research grant from the National Geographic Society and by the State University of New York at Binghamton with which I was then associated in the Department of Anthropology.

Before proceding to an account of the findings of the 1969 season, a brief summary of the background of this project is in order. In the late 19th century, literally tons of archeological materials were taken from the dry caves of Grand Gulch, Utah (fig. 1), much of it by Richard Wetherill of Mancos, Colorado. Wetherill's Grand Gulch collections were deposited in the American Museum of Natural History in New York, where they remain. Wetherill himself developed the concept of a Basketmaker stage of what is now called the San Juan Anasazi culture largely on the basis of his work in Grand Gulch (McNitt, 1957); this conception gained currency in the anthropological literature through the publications of Pepper (1902a, b) on the Wetherill collections in the American Museum.

Wetherill's inferences about the character and temporal priority of the Basketmaker stage were abundantly confirmed in the early 20th century by Kidder, Guernsey, Morss, and Morris, working in northeastern Arizona and southeastern Colorado (Kidder and Guernsey, 1919; Guernsey and Kidder, 1921; Guernsey, 1931; Morss, 1927; Morris, 1925; Morris and Burgh, 1954). No controlled stratigraphic excavation of the sort done by the workers listed here was ever carried out in Grand Gulch, however. Whereas it was once the best-known area of Basketmaker sites in the San Juan drainage, the advance of archeology has been such that today it is perhaps the least known.

In order to remedy this situation, I began in 1969 a program of research in the Grand Gulch region. The objectives were not only to place the older collections in some kind of substantiated scientific context but also to add

FIG. 1.   View into Grand Gulch from the rim.

entirely new knowledge about the San Juan Basketmaker culture. For example, the early workers listed above concentrated almost entirely on dry cave sites, where well-preserved burials and artifacts of ordinarily perishable materials could be found. This produced data on only certain aspects of Basketmaker culture. My research is emphasizing problems and kinds of data neglected by the earlier workers, such as open sites, house sites, pictographs, settlement patterns, collection of pollen and soil samples, and application of modern dating techniques. My goals include obtaining data on past ecological conditions and on the Basketmakers' adaptations to these conditions, so that we may better understand how the Anasazi evolved from a hunting and gathering society to one dependent on farming.

The Archeological Survey

The efforts of the archeological survey were concentrated in an area about 6 miles in maximum diameter located in the upper part of the Grand Gulch drainage between Kane Gulch and Bullet Canyon. The floors of the Gulch and its tributaries were explored, but the bulk of the survey time was spent on various sections of the plateau surface east of Grand Gulch proper. On the plateau surface the survey procedure emphasized intensive sampling of large plots. In carrying out the search for sites, survey teams of 3 or 4 men formed a line of march with each man about 50 to 75 feet from his nearest companion. When sites were located, some members of the team made notes and photographs of the surface manifestations, while others made surface collections. Attempts were made at most of the plateau surface sites (fig. 2) to collect intensively from plots of standard size, generally bounded by 20-foot-diameter circles, so that comparable samples of artifacts and flanking debris could be obtained from a number of sites.

In the canyons less attention was paid to making collections, because most of the sites had already been disturbed, and most had been occupied by Puebloans. The emphasis in surveying the canyon sites was on locating sites previously dug by Wetherill, on attempting to determine whether Basketmaker components existed at the sites, and on assessing the potential value of the sites for excavation directed toward investigating Basketmaker occupation. (Author's note: Although the bulk of the survey data reported below was gathered in 1969, sites recorded in 1970 in the same area have been added for purposes of completeness.)

The survey resulted in the location and study of a total of 165 sites in the upper Grand Gulch area. Of these, 143 were located on the plateau and

FIG. 2.   Survey crew members making intensive surface collection from standard
20-foot diameter sampling plot at GG69-58, one of the plateau-surface sites discovered near the rim of Grand Gulch.

22 in Grand Gulch or its entrenched east-bank tributaries. Of the plateau
sites, 86 were nonceramic, and 57 yielded ceramic materials. A number of
the latter were adjudged to probably contain a nonceramic component. On
the other hand, many of the nonceramic sites yielded very little artifactual
material. It is possible that some of these sites may not in fact be preceramic,
but may, instead, reflect special activities of ceramics-using people. Further
study and analysis of the artifacts and site characteristics of both the ceramic
and nonceramic sites should help reduce this area of uncertainty.

In the canyons, ceramic components were more abundant. Of the 22
sites, only 4 were nonceramic. Of the remaining 18 ceramic-bearing sites,
10 were adjudged probably to have preceramic components.

Several tentative inferences about Basketmaker II settlement patterns
and adaptation can be proposed on the basis of the 1969 survey. These are
summarized below:

1. Nonceramic open sites probably assignable to the Basketmaker II

FIG. 3. Excavations in progress at GG69-20, one of the larger plateau-surface sites encountered. The site is approximately 600 x 200 feet in extent, and displays a number of "activity loci," where artifacts, hearths, and occasionally the remains of other structures are clustered. Here, the workers are clearing what was probably the entrance to a shallow pithouse. This structure was badly eroded and incomplete. The trench leads away from the structure through an old occupation surface that had become buried by sand.

period are very common on the mesa-top areas immediately surrounding Grand Gulch. In one intensively sampled strip of about 3/4 x 3½ miles, extending due east from the rim of Grand Gulch, approximately 108 sites were located, of which approximately 60 percent were nonceramic. Although a number of these were too small for definite identification at least half can probably be assigned with reasonable assurance to the Basketmaker II period. A few similar open sites were discovered in Grand Gulch proper, although they were not as common as on the surrounding mesa tops. Cave sites with evidence of Basketmaker (and generally also Pueblo) occupation were fairly common in the canyon. Unfortunately, virtually all these have been extensively dug over. My inference from these site distributions is that the Basketmakers were using both the canyon bottom and canyon rim environments. I suspect that this use had a seasonal pattern, with perhaps the canyons being used in the summer for corn-growing, and the mesa tops in the other seasons for hunting and gathering.

2. On the mesa tops, the Basketmaker open sites tend to be more numerous and larger in the dissected, rather barren juniper-pinyon covered areas close to the rim of Grand Gulch than in the less-dissected and less barren areas back from the rim. Pueblo sites, on the other hand, decrease in size and number as one approaches the rim. The Pueblo sites seem to be associated with large sage flats having deep soils in the middle and upper segments of shallow washes tributary to Grand Gulch; the Basketmaker sites do not seem to be as strongly associated with these flats. My inference from this is that the Puebloans were more dependent on large bodies of deep soil suitable for farming than were the Basketmakers.

3. There is considerable heterogeneity among the Basketmaker sites recorded. The open sites range from isolated fireplaces with a surrounding scatter of chips to large areas with numerous concentrations of chips, hearths, and other structures. Several of the open sites had definite shallow pithouses, most had slab-lined fireplaces, some had large unwalled fire areas, some had great quantities of workshop debris, some did not, some had high frequencies of hammerstones, choppers, and other heavy tools, others did not, etc. The cave sites were harder to diagnose, owing to Pueblo reoccupation and to extensive digging, but it did appear that some were primarily burial places and some primarily storage places. None were identified that had substantial amounts of Basketmaker habitation debris, but this observation should not be given much weight, considering the problems mentioned above. Pictographs of probable Basketmaker origin were found in several caves. I believe that a substantial amount of the heterogeneity observed amongst these Basketmaker sites is due to the differing activities carried out at these sites.

Finally, the survey resulted in the location of most of the sites that Richard Wetherill collected from in 1896-97. Wetherill's field notes and field catalog, copies of which were obtained at the American Museum, are surprisingly good, considering the time that they were done. I feel reasonably confident that I located 11 of the 12 principal sites that he worked in those years. I also feel that I was able, in most cases, to make a reasonably good estimate of whether or not these sites were multiple component (most of them were). This information will be helpful in evaluating Wetherill's provenience assignments in possible future studies of the Wetherill collections in the American Museum of Natural History.

FIG. 4. Pithouse structure at site GG69-18, fully excavated. Note slab-walled entryway (facing south), central fire hearth with deflector, slab wing-walls or partitions between fire hearth and exterior wall of house pit, and storage pit just to the left of the entryway.

The Excavations

Excavations were carried out in four sites during the 1969 season. All were open sites located on the plateau surface (fig. 3).

Since analysis of the materials recovered from these excavations has only just begun, no very detailed statement of findings can be made. The main contribution of the excavations so far would seem to be the demonstration of the existence of a distinctive house style for the Basketmaker II occupation of this region. Because of the early emphasis on cave sites, it was thought for many years that the Basketmaker II people did not build houses. More recent work (e.g., Morris and Burgh, 1954) has shown that this is not the case, but there has still been very little work done on Basketmaker II housing. During the summer of 1975 we excavated three pithouses (fig. 4) completely or partially. They were about 20 to 25 feet in diameter, were less than 2 feet deep, were circular in plan, had a slab-lined entryway facing

south, and had a central fire hearth. They did not appear to cluster, but occurred one to a site. They resemble in detail a house excavated by the University of Utah Glen Canyon project in the Clay Hills Pass area about 40
miles west of the 1969 field area (Sharrock et al., 1963, pp. 151-161), but
differed in detail from Basketmaker II houses reported from the Durango
area (Morris and Burgh, 1954), the Navajo reservoir area (Eddy, 1961), and
the Little Colorado Valley in Arizona (Gumerman, 1966). A number of tree-
ring and carbon-14 dates have been obtained from the pithouses we excavated; the dates consistently fall in the period A.D. 200-400.

Author's Note: The research reported here developed, after 1969, into a long-
term study of Anasazi settlement patterns of the Cedar Mesa region. Cedar Mesa is
the highland into which Grand Gulch and several other canyon systems are cut. This
project has expanded from the initial concern with the Basketmaker II period to
take in all periods of Anasazi occupation of the area through its abandonment in late
Pueblo III times, at about A.D. 1270. Cedar Mesa Project research has not yet been
fully reported, but several papers have appeared (e.g., Lipe and Matson, 1971, 1975,
and Matson and Lipe, 1975) and several other works are in preparation.

REFERENCES

EDDY, FRANK W.
    1961. Excavations at Los Pinos phase sites in the Navajo Reservoir district.
        Mus. New Mexico Pap. Anthrop., no. 4, 107 pp., illus.
GUERNSEY, SAMUEL J.
    1931. Explorations in northeastern Arizona.   Pap. Peabody Mus. Amer. Arch-
        aeol. and Ethnol., Harvard Univ., vol. 12, no 1, 123 pp., illus.
GUERNSEY, SAMUEL J., and KIDDER, ALFRED V.
    1921. Basket-maker caves of northeastern Arizona.   Pap. Peabody Mus. Amer.
        Archaeol. and Ethnol., Harvard Univ., vol. 8, no. 2, 121 pp., illus.
GUMERMAN, GEORGE J.
    1966. Two Basketmaker II pithouse villages in eastern Arizona: A preliminary
        report.   Plateau, vol. 39, pp. 80-87.
KIDDER, ALFRED V., and GUERNSEY, SAMUEL J.
    1919. Archeological explorations in northeastern Arizona.   Bur. Amer. Ethnol.
        Bull. 65, 228 pp., illus.
LIPE, WILLIAM D., and MATSON, R. G.
    1971. Human settlement and resources in the Cedar Mesa area, southeastern
        Utah.   Pp. 125-151 *in* "The Distribution of Prehistoric Population
        Aggregates," George J. Gumerman, ed. Prescott College Anthrop.
        Rpts., no. 1. Prescott, Arizona.
    1975. Archaeology and alluvium in the Grand Gulch-Cedar Mesa area, south-
        eastern Utah.   Four Corners Geological Society Guidebook, 8th an-
        nual conference, Canyonlands, 1975, pp. 67-71. Farmington, New
        Mexico.

MATSON, R. G., and LIPE, WILLIAM D.
   1975. Regional sampling: A case study from Cedar Mesa, southeastern Utah.
      Pp. 124-143 *in* "Sampling in Archaeology," James Mueller, ed. Univer-
      sity of Arizona Press, Tucson, Arizona.
MCNITT, FRANK
   1957. Richard Wetherill: Anasazi, 362 pp., illus.   University of New Mexico
      Press, Albuquerque, New Mexico.
MORRIS, EARL H.
   1925. Exploring in the canyon of death.   Nat. Geogr. Mag., vol. 48, pp. 263-
      300, illus.
MORRIS, EARL H., and BURGH, ROBERT F.
   1954. Basket Maker II sites near Durango, Colorado.   Carnegie Inst. Wash-
      ington Publ. no. 604, 135 pp., illus.
MORSS, NOEL
   1927. Archaeological explorations on the middle Chinlee.   Amer. Antrhop.
      Assoc. Mem. no. 34, 41 pp., illus.
PEPPER, GEORGE H.
   1902a. Ancient basket makers of southern Utah.   Amer. Mus. Journ., vol. 2.
      no. 4, Suppl., Guide Leaflet no. 6, 26 pp., illus.
   1902b. The throwing-stick of a prehistoric people of the Southwest.   Proc.
      13th Int. Congr. Americanists, pp. 107-130.
SHARROCK, FLOYD W.; DAY, KENT C.; and DIBBLE, DAVID S.
   1963. 1961 excavations, Glen Canyon area.   Univ. Utah Anthrop. Pap., no.
      63, 376 pp., illus.

WILLIAM D. LIPE

Studies of the Natural History of the American Bison

Principal Investigator: Dale F. Lott, University of California, Davis, California.

Grant Nos. 769,   In aid of the continuation of grantee's studies of the social
880, 993.   behavior of the American bison.

This report concerns several studies of behavioral aspects of the natural history of the American bison. The studies were undertaken with two goals: First, to take advantage of the potential of this species to advance our understanding of animal behavior as a discipline; second, to learn some of the behavioral adaptations of bison that made them perhaps the most numerous large mammal in the history of the earth and that bear upon their survival and prosperity today.

The research was conducted on two study sites—the National Bison Range in Moiese, Montana, and Catalina Island, off the coast of California. Each study area supports a population of about 400 bison (which varies from season to season and year to year). In both areas the bison are an esthetic resource, and regular visits by tourists have adapted them to the presence of humans, especially those in motor vehicles, making them ideally suited for observation of their undisturbed behavior.

Social Relationships among Mature Males

Mature male American bison have a great deal of presence. They are large, noisy, and altogether unforgettable. But although they have been a national symbol of conservation and the beauty of the North American nature for generations, only a modest body of scientific knowledge of their behavior exists.

The first goal in this study program was to describe relationships between mature bulls. The first step was to create a reasonably complete description of the pattern of communication by which relations between individuals are expressed. Since the most salient and apparently the most important relationship between males has to do with their aggressive competition, the description of their communicatory behavior emphasizes aggression. In my 1972 *Natural History* article (Lott, 1972a) I summarized this communication as follows:

The threat that operates at the greatest distance is vocalization. On a still day the bellow, or roar, of a bull carries several miles. If you can't see the bull or don't recognize the sound, you're likely to think that a thunderstorm is brewing.

If the competition presses, the bellowing becomes louder, and a quality that is hard to define but somehow easy to recognize — a quality of fury — begins to grow in it. Often one or both bulls will interrupt their bellowing to paw the ground or wallow.

If the challenge does not end in the wallowing or bellowing stage, the bulls draw closer to each other and special postures come into play. There seem to be two distinct threat postures. In the "head-on threat," which is simply the posture and movement that precedes a charge, the bull moves toward his opponent with his head held slightly to one side. The more slowly the challengers are moving, the farther to the side their heads are held. When they approach nearly straight-on, either one bull submits by turning away or they bang heads. But when they approach slowly with their heads well to one side, they often stop close to, but not quite touching, each other and enter into a pattern I have named "nod threat."

Nod-threatening bulls stand close enough to reach one another; their bodies may form a single, straight line or an angle of up to ninety degrees, but in either case their heads are held well to one side. From this position they can attack suddenly by hooking a horn into the opponent's head. The hook always starts when the head is close to the ground, the muzzle tucked back toward the feet.

But in the threat, the head-low, muzzle-back position is only a brief interruption of a head-high stance: the bulls' heads drop in a matched movement, then swing back up again, still to one side. A hooking attack may start at the bottom of any one of the down swings, but the opponent never seems to be caught off guard. After a series of such nods one animal may suddenly submit, ending the clash.

Nod-threatening takes place most often between bulls that are not tending cows. In this respect, it resembles another important threat, the "broadside threat." A bull in this posture keeps himself broadside to his opponent with his head held a little higher than normal. Usually his back is arched and he is bellowing. If he moves, he does so slowly; in short, stiff steps that keep him broadside to his opponent. Often two bulls will threaten by standing parallel to each other with only a few feet separating them. Only rarely does this threat lead to a fight. The encounter may be long as threats go, as much as a minute or more, but one of the animals almost always submits...

All bison submission signals are variations on a theme; the submitting bull turns away. Sometimes it is a 180-degree turn followed by a galloping retreat. Other times it is an abbreviated swing of the head and neck to one side. When it involves a 90-degree turn, the submitting animal ends up in the same general position as one who is threatening broadside. It is easy to tell the difference, however. In submission the bull's head is usually low, muzzle extended as if to graze (and sometimes he does graze), and the bull is silent. Whatever form the submission signal takes, it almost always stops the threat or attack immediately. [For a more detailed description see Lott, 1974a, 1974b.]

The existence of this description of the communicatory patterns made it possible to take the next step, that of following the behavioral interchange among males and describing their social relationships and so their social organization.

It was already clear that the basic form of organization is a dominance system. For two breeding seasons, my son Terence and I studied the dominance relationships in herds with a minimum of 22 mature bulls. We found that there are dominance relationships between individuals and that they can fairly be said to compose an organization. In comparison to many dominance organizations, however, that of bison bulls is not very consistent. About 20 percent of the outcomes of the conflicts between males do not correspond to a dominance hierarchy; that is, about 20 percent of the time a male dominates one that dominated him before, or a bull yields to another who is dominated by one of the first bull's subordinates (i.e., there is a triangle). But that means that some 80 percent of the outcomes are correctly predicted by a dominance hierarchy. The social status of bulls has considerable, though not complete, consistency from moment to moment.

The bulls pay a high price for their status. Perhaps one bull in 40 dies as a result of the injuries incurred in status fights in an average year, and all the bulls lose a great deal of weight during the breeding season. Such costly behavior would be eliminated by natural selection if it did not confer some considerable benefit. One benefit that could justify all this cost would be a gain in reproductive rate as a result of greater breeding opportunities accruing to high-status bulls. We evaluated this possibility by recording all the breedings we could in one season (we saw half the cows bred) and comparing individual breeding rates for the bulls with dominance status. The highest status one-third of the bulls did two-thirds of the breeding. That is a very handsome payoff indeed: The animals that run the risk and pay the price for status will be the fathers of the next generation of bulls.

The Social Context of Breeding

Breeding in bison takes place in a one-to-one relationship called tending. A mature bull stays with a mature cow and alternates his activity between preventing the approach of other males and trying to mount the cow. The relationship is normally terminated when the bull is displaced by another bull or leaves voluntarily. Very rarely the cow ends it by escaping the herding efforts of the bull.

When one surveys a breeding population of bison it is clear that only about one cow in 15 is attractive to bulls at any one time. Since cows are in estrus only about 24 hours, and since the breeding season lasts only about three weeks, it seems only reasonable that the cows that are attractive at any one time are those that are in estrus that day.

Much as this conclusion appeals to our common sense, it should be tested by identifying particular cows, then determining whether they are in fact tended only or even primarily during those periods when they are in estrus. In practice this means that some individually recognized cows must be located several times a day, every day during the breeding season, and their social companions, if any, recorded. If it is possible to determine the day that they breed, then the relationship between tending and estrus can be described. This was done for two consecutive seasons, and the full cycle of behavior of eight cows was determined. The results were rather surprising. Only half the cows were tended by mature bulls only on the day that they were bred. The others were tended for longer periods, in one case five days, before they came into estrus.

It seems mysterious that some cows should be attractive to bulls when they are not in estrus, and others not be attractive until they are in estrus. I have no information so far on how they could be attractive though not in estrus, or what advantage or disadvantage there might be in that. It is clear, however, that where superficial observation suggested that a simple and sensible system was in operation, closer observation has revealed it complex and difficult to interpret, but potentially a very interesting pattern.

Mother-Infant Relations

Even mammals that are solitary for most of their lives will have at least one important social bond: that between the infant and its mother. Among ungulates, two basic patterns of mother-infant behavior can be recognized. There are those mothers whose young follow them from birth and those whose young are hidden for long periods with the mother only occasionally returning to nurse and perhaps move them. A bison calf follows its mother from birth. Since the calves can stand within a few minutes and run within a few hours of their birth, it is essential that there be some mechanism that quickly establishes the mutual attraction and recognition of the mother and the young. In fact, this is not perfectly achieved in bison, and at least occasionally a mother adopts another young in addition to her own (Englehard, 1970). This is important because the occasional mother that adopts another young in addition to her own reduces the supply of precious milk for her own calf, and thus her own reproductive fitness. These confusions seem to be rare, however, and so it is clear that bison cows have some means of increasing the likelihood that they will get to know their own calf and restrict their attention to it.

Goats have a special capacity to learn to identify their young in as little as five minutes. This "maternal imprinting" mechanism is likely to be available to a number of ungulate species with precocial young. Since the mother will adopt any young she is exposed to during this period, the value of maternal imprinting is enhanced by a behavioral mechanism that puts the female alone with her offspring during the time that she is imprintable. In some species this is accomplished by a female leaving her social group when she is about to have her calf.

To learn how bison solve this problem, the behavior of parturient females was observed during two calving seasons on the National Bison Range in Montana. It turns out that there is no one solution. About half the cows left the herd for a distance of at least half a mile and stayed away for several hours. The other half had their calves within 50 yards of the herd, some of them not bothering to leave at all. The newborn calves displayed a strong tendency to press themselves against the nearest animal, wherever they were born, and this no doubt helped to reduce the potential risk of mix-ups. Mix-ups were, however, clearly possible. It may be that this behavioral polymorphism provides two possible solutions to the two challenges of reproduction: (1) reducing the risk of adopting the wrong calf by leaving the herd to give birth and (2) avoiding the increased risk of predation by staying in the herd. As in so many behavioral adjustments, both solutions would be compromises.

Age and Sex Class Differences in Habitat Use

Field studies of behavior often concentrate on reproductive activities because it is during the time of these activities that the animals are most social and because it is then that some extremely important competitive events take place, e.g., the aggressive competition between mature male bison.

In bison, this is the only season when bulls and cows are together consistently. In fact, they are together so little at other times of the year that they seem to be subject to the operation of some mechanism that keeps them apart. The population of approximately 400 on Catalina Island offers an excellent opportunity to begin the study of this question. The animals have access to a very large area that is not crowded and permits a good deal of choice of location by individuals.

Bison regularly use about 50 square miles of this island, and if they are regarded as simply biomass they are rather evenly distributed over this area. But the subparts of the population are not all equally distributed. When the location of bison on the island is described by age and sex class, day after day and season after season, it is clear that except for the breeding season there are parts of the island that are used almost exclusively by mature bulls, and other parts that are used by cow herds (which include bulls up to about the age of 4 years). This difference is consistent year after year with the only exception in memory coming when the drought conditions were very severe and cows entered some bull areas for the first time.

The one consistent difference between the bull and cow areas is that in general the bulls are in much steeper terrain, and on Catalina Island the steeper terrain is very steep indeed. This does not mean, however, that the bulls are voluntarily withdrawing from a better food source in favor of the cows and calves. A survey of the areas of use indicates that the same forage species are present in both areas and are, if anything, more abundant and less heavily utilized in the bull areas.

This would be circumstantial evidence that the bulls are keeping the other members of the population out of the best areas, but in thousands of hours of observation I have never seen one bison exclude another from any area. It is something that they simply do not do.

What we have then is a very marked and consistent difference in the distribution of the animals in this population; but the reason is as yet quite obscure. Certainly it is a question that will reward further study.

REFERENCES

ENGLEHARD, J. G.
    [1970]. Behavior patterns of American bison calves at the National Bison Range, Moiese, Montana, 150 pp.   Unpublished master's thesis, Central Michigan University.

LOTT, DALE F.
    1972a. Bison would rather breed than fight.   Nat. Hist., vol. 81, no. 7 (Aug.-Sept.), pp. 40-45, illus.
    1972b. The way of the bison: Fighting to dominate.   Pp. 320-332 *in* "The Marvels of Animal Behavior," 422 pp., illus. National Geographic Society, Washington, D. C.
    1974a. Aggressive behavior in mature male American bison.   Motion picture released by Pennsylvania State University Psychological Cinema Register, 12 minutes, sound, color.
    1974b. Sexual and aggressive behavior of adult male American bison *(Bison bison)*.   Pp. 382-394 *in* "The Behaviour of Ungulates and Its Relation to Management." IUCN Publ., new ser., no. 24. Morges, Switzerland.
    1974c. Behavioral aspects of the rut in American bison.   Nat. Geogr. Soc. Res. Rpts., 1967 Projects, pp. 193-195.

DALE F. LOTT

Underwater Research in *Sublimnos*

Principal Investigators: Joseph B. MacInnis, MacInnis Foundation, Toronto, Canada; and Alan R. Emery, Royal Ontario Museum, Toronto, Canada.

Grant Nos. 784, 876: In support of the development and emplacement of *Sublimnos* and of a preliminary assessment of its potential.

Since 1962 several countries have conducted extensive research and development projects utilizing manned underwater research platforms, popularly called "habitats." *Sublimnos I* was conceived by Dr. J. B. MacInnis, a veteran Canadian diver and hyperbaric physician, to accomplish several aims: To create public awareness of research and exploration of the lake and sea floors of Canada; to develop new and inexpensive concepts for underwater technology, thus allowing consideration of the potential of the concept of habitation underwater for interested scientists; and finally to give scientists the opportunity to utilize an underwater habitat for direct observation of, and in situ experimentation with, the underwater environment and biota.

The design and fabrication of *Sublimnos* were completed in early 1969. In May of the same year she arrived in Canada to be displayed at the Royal Ontario Museum, while site surveys and emplacement arrangements were completed. True to the inexpensive approach conceived to be important in its design, on June 24, 1969, *Sublimnos* was launched, towed to the final resting site, and submerged, a small launch and only three divers being used. Lowered in two sections, each of which was first air-filled, members of the construction team (which included Dr. MacInnis) agreed that the concept was not a difficult one to operate.

The *Sublimnos* habitat is located in 30 feet of clear fresh water in Little Dunk's Bay, which is near Tobermory, Ontario, at the tip of the Bruce Peninsula, which separates Lake Huron from Georgian Bay. Tobermory is about 200 miles northwest of Toronto.

Almost as soon as the habitat was in place, members of the Canada Centre for Inland Waters (CCIW) began a series of experiments and observations utilizing *Sublimnos*. A survey of bottom-living chironomids, supplemented by direct observation of their behavior at night, was closely linked to a geological investigation of the rate of sediment transport in the areas of ripple marks on the lake floor. The diver observation and photography of the efficiency and operation of shipboard remote dredges allowed evaluation of the quantitative effectiveness of the apparatus. (CCIW's use of the habitat was so soon following installation that they suffered, with us, some of the early mechanical problems.) In early August 1969, Dr. Lee R. Somers, of the University of Michigan, began a short series of experiments. Utilizing a 15-by-15-foot sampling grid on a framework designed to minimize diver disturbance, the researchers collected 36 triplicated samples in 12 quadrants. Primary productivity of the benthic algae was determined by the use of plexiglass chambers with C^{14} solutions injected into the chambers. One of the most unusual experiments utilized 1,000-gallon plastic bags into which nutrients had been introduced, in an attempt to measure the effect of accelerated eutrophication on natural lake waters in natural conditions. These bags were affectionately referred to as "pollution balloons." The researchers also evaluated techniques of making bathymetric surveys of great detail, using divers. The detail used allowed measurement of sediment movement.

Among other things Dr. Somers concluded that the "Volkswagen approach" may make underwater habitation acceptable for widespread scientific work. In his words, "Economic feasibility is the password. . . . A university can afford to own and operate this type of habitat. The shallow-water '*Sublimnos*' type habitat has a definite place in basic research in the Great Lakes and throughout the world."

Shortly after this, an artificial reef constructed of concrete blocks was installed within viewing range of *Sublimnos*. Built in a complex of rows and columns, it was designed to provide a fixed number of hole sizes and fixed amount of cover. No cement was used, but the blocks seemed to be quite stable. Immediately on completion we started a series of watches, and within 24 hours concentrations of animals had begun to build up in the reef. The buildup continued for about a month, with maxima at night. Somewhat surprisingly, immediately after reaching a peak of concentration the numbers began to diminish. We have now determined that there are seasonal highs and lows that correspond to times of migration. Some diverse groups are present all year (such as sculpins and crayfishes), but even these exhibit migration patterns and thus seasonally variable peaks of abundance. Other species, such as the rock bass *(Ambloplites rupestris)*, are present only in the fall and spring, during periods of travel to hibernation sites.

One of the most important ecological areas is that of the open-water column. Planktonic plants and animals are at the mercy of horizontal cur-

FIG. 1. *Sublimnos* habitat and underwater work area as it was in December 1969.

rents, but only if these are of some strength. A hydrodynamic boundary layer of slow-moving water is to be found just above the lake floor. Yet this area has been very poorly sampled, because nets are normally towed from boats. To be sure of retrieving the net, some distance is left between the net and the bottom. We found when sampling this stratum using a diver-towed sampling device that concentrations of plankton were at a maximum in the near-bottom layer at depths between 6 and 15 meters.

Observations of fish behavior were being made over a 24-hour period on August 14, 1969, near *Sublimnos* when an internal seiche occurred, drastically altering the environmental conditions. Temperatures were recorded in situ with hand-held thermometers. Observations were recorded on plastic slates under water and dictated to shore from *Sublimnos*. Fish behavior distant from *Sublimnos* was observed by divers swimming slowly and intermittently turning on a flashlight. By chance, a survey of fish distribution was made between 9:15 and 9:50 p.m., just before the incursion of cold water. This survey extended from beyond *Sublimnos* nearly to the shoreline (depth 11-2 meters). Observations from *Sublimnos* on the behavior of fishes in a fixed, vertically directed beam of light were made for comparison to "natural" conditions.

Water transparency was measured under water. A diver noted the

horizontal distance from which a Secchi disc could be seen. At night, measurement was similarly conducted, except that the disc was lighted from a
distance of 1 meter with a flashlight beam.

Temperatures in the water column varied from 21.1° C. at the surface to
18.7° C. at the bottom (10 meters) at noon. These conditions prevailed until
10:00 p.m., when much cooler water (8.5° C.) was noted in the bottom 1.5
meters. Within 1 hour the cooler water was present in the bottom 6 meters
of the water column. Water temperature at the bottom (6 meters below the
new thermocline) was 7.0° C. This cold-water mass remained in the lower
6 meters of the water column for about 2 hours, after which it began to
recede. By 2:00 a.m. the cold water had retreated. The temperature of the
water column was uniformly 18.3° C. at this time. Water transparency was
increased to 12-15 meters. Thus the duration of the seiche was about 4
hours. Water transparency in both daylight and darkness was 10 meters horizontally. The transparency of the cooler water, however, was reduced to approximately 2 meters. At the peak of the cold-water influx, a strong flashlight shining directly up from the bottom was barely discernible at the
surface.

As cold water moved into the area, many species began to move shore-
ward and those near the fixed light also began to leave, until at peak ingress
most of the suckers, smelt, perch, and sticklebacks were found close to the
bouldery and steep-sloping shoreline in the shallow, warmer (20.2° C.) water. Whitefish and alewife moved upward, dipping only rarely into the
murky, cold water.

Only the trout-perch seemed unaffected by the colder water mass and
continued moving and feeding slowly just above the bottom. (Trout-perch
were observed in the area only at night.) Darters, present before the seiche,
were seen neither in the cold-water mass nor in the warm water returning
after it had left.

The behavior of slow-moving benthic species such as sculpins and crayfishes was most affected by the cold-water influx. These species ceased feeding and in the cold water often swam erratically. Of particular importance
was the observation that numbers of both sculpins and crayfishes were dead
after the cold water retreated. Thirteen sculpins and 14 crayfishes were
picked up dead in the same area in which observations on the distribution
of fish were made.

The only apparent reason for the deaths observed in crayfishes and
sculpins was the rapid change in temperature. For these animals, restricted
to slow movement and bottom life, the change in temperature from 20° to
7° C., would have occurred in seconds. After a period of hours in cold water,

a sudden return to warm conditions occurred. Changes of this magnitude normally occur over a much greater time. In the case of an animal swimming through a thermocline, the rapidity of temperature change is controlled by the speed of swimming. Both sculpins and crayfishes can withstand the observed temperature extremes, and seasonal variation in temperature is greater. Environmental factors other than temperature and transparency were not measured. However, oxygen content in these waters is quite high. Thus it is unlikely that oxygen was a metabolic problem. Water of the observed temperatures must have come from depths of approximately 30-45 meters, and the vertical movement of cold water therefore was about 20-40 meters.

The cold-water transparency was much reduced. Occasionally, suspended solids (usually the result of storms) cause respiratory distress in fishes. Assuming solids accounted for this change, a visibility of 2 meters remained, and it is thus unlikely that the concentration of solids was sufficient to cause stress. However, plankton concentrations were much higher in this water mass and may have accounted for most, if not all, of the decrease in transparency.

Thus it is most probable that the deaths were a result of thermal stress. The fact that epilimnion transparency increased after the seiche remains unexplained.

Internal seiches involving the thermocline are common in stratified bodies of water but are ephemeral and thus often go undetected. The ecological effects of breaking internal waves are not well known. That their influence could be severe enough to cause mortalities indicated the need for more thorough investigation. We have, therefore, been monitoring the area for similar disturbances.

Research slowed in the fall of 1969 to allow proper installation of winter equipment. A series of storms were both destructive and instructive. Although the artificial reef was placed at a depth of 35 feet, storm waves tossed the concrete blocks around, placing it in complete disarray. In late December, ice cover began to form and we rebuilt the reef. Increasing numbers of gizzard shad (*Dorosoma cepedianum*) were attracted to the area but were dying nearby. By monitoring the occurrence of these deaths, we have determined that these may represent a significant biomass input. In fact, surveys of nearby areas in the spring indicated massive die-offs of shad.

Our winter operations were very successful mechanically, and we felt that a baseline of knowledge was established for ecological studies. Our knowledge of under-ice events in the winter is, of course, very limited and several observations were very confusing. At about this time Larry Bell, from Guelph University (who later became our resident biologist), began tagging crayfishes to monitor population dynamics. But they gradually diminished in numbers with no real evidence of them migrating away. We noticed what appeared to be an increased growth of benthic algae under the ice, both on the artificial reef and near shore. Surprisingly, even the plastic pollution balloons became covered with a massive colony of diatoms.

In the spring of 1970 plans and arrangements were settled for the employment of three students to act as project managers and resident scientists to help with the data collection for the coming season.

REFERENCES

EMERY, ALAN R.
  1970a. Fish and crayfish mortalities due to an internal seiche in Georgian Bay, Lake Huron.   Journ. Fish. Res. Board Canada, vol. 27, no. 6, pp. 1165-1168.
  1970b. *Sublimnos:* "Volkswagen" of underwater habitats.   Science, vol. 168, p. 62. (Letter to the editor.)
  [1971a.] Proposal for an underwater park at Tobermory, Ontario.   Report to Ontario Government (unpublished).
  1971b. *Sublimnos* researchers go underwater.   Rotunda (Toronto), vol. 4, pp. 20-27, illus.
  1971c. Underwater research from *Sublimnos.*   Science Affairs (Toronto), vol. 5, pp. 5-6, illus.
  1971d. *Sublimnos.*   Ontario Fish and Wildl. Rev., vol. 10, nos. 3-4, pp. 2-10, illus.
  1973a. Preliminary comparisons of day and night habits of fish in Ontario lakes.   Journ. Fish. Res. Board Canada, vol. 30, pp. 761-774.
  1973b. Sediments of deep Canadian shield lakes: Observations of gross structure and biological significance.   Science, vol. 181, pp. 655-657, illus.
MACINNIS, JOSEPH B.
  1969. First underwater habitat in the Great Lakes: *Sublimnos.*   Limnos, vol. 2, no. 2, pp. 22-23.
  1970a. *Sublimnos:* The Volkswagen approach to underwater habitats.   Mar. Techn. Soc. Journ., vol. 4, no. 6, pp. 29-32.
  1970b. A letter from the deep frontier.   Bull. Fed. Ontario Nat., March, pp. 16-17.
SOMERS, LEE R.
  1969. *Sublimnos:* Sinking to new depths for the benefit of us all.   Limnos, vol. 2, no. 3, pp. 20-25.
  1970. Underwater habitats and science.   Undercurrents, January, pp. 17-21.

JOSEPH B. MACINNIS
ALAN R. EMERY

Archeological Reconnaissance of East Baffin Island
between Narpaing Fiord and Canso Channel

Principal Investigator: Lorna McKenzie-Pollock, California Department of Parks and Recreation, Sacramento, California.

Grant No. 792:   For an archeological survey in East Baffin Island, Northwest Territories, Canada.

In July 1969 I undertook an archeological survey of some 60 miles of the east coast of Baffin Island, Northwest Territories, Canada, in the vicinity of Broughton Island. The first objective of my research was to evaluate the validity of the apparent relationship between the location of Arctic archeological sites and sea-level elevation. This had been the subject of a paper I had written during the previous academic year for Dr. John T. Andrews, associate professor of geology at the Institute of Arctic and Alpine Research of the University of Colorado (a revised version of this paper subsequently appeared in *Arctic* in 1971). At the time I found a good correlation between the two but was greatly hampered by lack of elevation data on archeological sites in the eastern Arctic.

My second objective was to construct an archeological sequence for the region and to correlate this with other regional sequences in the Arctic. The region is of particular interest because, although the areas to the east (Greenland), west, and south are known archeologically, no work had been done in this area. It is of interest also because it was visited in 1883-84 by Franz Boas, whose account, *The Central Eskimo* (1888, 1964), is at once one of the first major contributions to modern American anthropology and one of the first scientific monographs on the Eskimo (Collins, 1964). There is, therefore, detailed ethnographic information on the inhabitants of the area some 90 years ago to supplement the archeological record.

Logistics and Procedures

On July 8 I flew into Frobisher Bay, Baffin Island, on the first stage of my journey. I had planned to arrive the day before the departure of the

411

weekly DC-3 flight to Broughton Island, on which I held a reservation. However, on arrival I was informed that it had left a day early. This was my first lesson in the unpredictability of life above the 60th parallel! After four days of delays because of bad weather over Broughton Island, we took off, but engine trouble forced us to turn back and make an emergency landing. Finally, late in the fifth day, after flying over some magnificent scenery on the Cumberland Peninsula, we landed on Broughton Island. I was met there by the D.I.A.N.D. agent, John Scullion, who graciously offered me accommodations in his office.

Broughton Island is some 11 miles long by 8 wide at its maximum and is only a mile away from the main land mass of Baffin Island. The settlement consists of about 300 people, most of them Eskimo. The Eskimos travel up and down the coast for up to 20 miles on regular hunting trips, using canoe and Peterhead whaleboat in summer and sled and skidoo in winter. During spring and early summer, however, while the sea ice is breaking up, travel becomes impossible, for it is too soft to support a sled, but too plentiful to allow passage of a boat. I had planned to arrive in July when the sea ice has generally dispersed, but in 1969 the ice had been exceptionally slow to break up, and travel was not yet feasible.

I therefore began my research by interviewing Eskimos in the settlement about the location of archeological sites. I secured as my interpreter a young man by the name of Levi Ilingayook, who spoke good English and quickly learned what was required. We visited a number of older people who knew the coastline well. We would first explain what we needed and then show them my topographic map and explain what it was. All my informants were quick to grasp the concept of a map, even though they had never seen one before. This did not surprise me, as Boas (1888) had included a number of quite accurate maps drawn by Eskimos.

Of the 24 sites I recorded that summer, 7 were located on the map by the Eskimos. Altogether, 17 site locations were given to me by Eskimos. Because of sea ice and transportation problems I was able to field check only 10 of these, of which 7 proved to be accurate, while either 3 were mislocated or Levi and I had failed to communicate adequately what we wanted.

By July 19 the ice had broken up enough to enable me to travel over to the mainland directly across from Broughton Island. However, as the Eskimos had warned me, there did not appear to be any sites in that area. So on July 25 I returned to Broughton Island to continue interviewing Eskimos about site locations and to survey the coastline for sites. By the end of July the ice had dispersed sufficiently to enable me to start traveling south look-

FIG. 1.   Canso Channel 2: Tent ring.

ing for sites, and I made several day trips by canoe with hunting parties of Eskimos.

Dr. John T. Andrews arrived on August 2, and on August 5 I traveled with him in a Peterhead boat to the Canso Channel area, where I recorded a number of sites. By August 10 the ice was sufficiently clear to the north to enable us to travel up to the Kivitoo area, my original destination, where I spent the remainder of the summer surveying this area. At this time I camped both with John Andrews and Ken Duffield, a Canadian schoolteacher who accompanied him; and with David Pheasant and Gifford Miller, two geology students from the University of Colorado who had been in the area since May. I traveled on foot and in the small boat that David Pheasant and Gifford Miller had brought.

We had arranged that on August 22 a party of Eskimos would arrive in the Peterhead boat to help us break camp and return to the settlement. However, on August 20 the sea ice moved back in, and the Eskimos were unable to reach us. They were unable to travel down the coast for over a week, during which time it snowed and we began to run low on food. Though we were only some 30 miles or less from the settlement as the crow flies, the rugged and deeply indented nature of the coastline meant that attempting to return on foot by land would have involved a rugged hike of probably well over a hundred miles.

At the end of August several canoes finally appeared instead of the Peterhead boat. We loaded our gear on these, and with considerable difficulty and delay caused by the sea ice, we finally reached Broughton Island. By this time heavy snow was falling and we were told that it might be some time before a plane could come and get us. After I had spent eight days in the settlement, a small charter plane came through and I arranged with the pilot to ride to Frobisher Bay, where regularly scheduled commercial flights were available. As there was room for only one on the plane, I had to abandon the geologists with whom I had worked during the latter part of the summer. I arrived back in Frobisher Bay on September 8.

The Sites

The sites are briefly described below (see also table 1, pp. 426-427).

Canso Channel 1 (MhBx-1), located on the south shore of an island at the mouth of north Pangnirtung Fiord, is situated in a grassy area on two hillsides overlooking the ocean. The easternmost hillside contains four semisubterranean winter houses of typical Thule form (Collins, 1955; Jenness, 1925). The houses are half buried in sod, but the stone walls and long entrance tunnel can still be seen. Each house has a large depression, probably a storage anteroom, to the left of the entrance.

The hillside to the west contains five house remains of a similar type. In none of these houses is there evidence of the whalebone or wooden rafters characteristic of Thule winter houses. Also on the second hillside is a large tent ring with a sleeping platform outlined in stones. The only artifact associated with the site was part of a kayak frame near the tent ring.

Canso Channel 2 (MhBx-2), located on the mainland directly across Canso Channel from MhBx-1, is on a terrace overlooking the sea at about 300 feet above sea level. The site consists of three large (14-by-13-foot) subrectangular tent rings in excellent condition. All have raised sleeping platforms and work areas on each side of the entrance outlined with stones (see fig. 1). Two fireplaces containing patches of hard black consolidated seal oil are associated with the tent rings; one is 125 feet west of tent ring 1, overlooking the sea. The second is 15 feet south of tent ring 1.

Tent ring 1 is the southernmost of the three. Found there were a bone harpoon head, of an unusual form (see fig. 7), on the surface of the sleeping platform area, and a caribou antler object, 10 inches long, with two drilled

FIG. 2. Cape Broughton: Stone house remains.

holes. The function of the latter is problematical, but it appears similar in form to the sirmijaung, or scraper, for a kayak illustrated by Boas (1964, p. 80). Also found on the sleeping platform was a crude pipe, hand carved from a piece of driftwood. In the work area to the right of the entrance were found several dozen tiny Italian glass trade beads, a small piece of lead, and about a dozen unmodified quartz crystals. In the area to the left of the entrance were found a quantity of mica slabs, about a dozen tiny Italian glass trade beads, 8 unmodified quartz crystals, and 6 quartz flakes. Also in the area were some small metal objects, including the remains of a rusted needle and a small (0.5-inch) metal heart. A dark stained area in the soil here appears to be burnt consolidated seal oil, probably from cooking.

In tent ring 2, located north of 1, large quantities of quartz crystals, mostly unmodified, were found as well as 16 flakes, 4 of which show retouch.

In tent ring 3, a wooden plug, similar to wound plugs used in seal hunting, described by Boas (1964, p. 71), was found in the area to the left of the entrance.

This site is a summer encampment, and appears to date from early contact times. Stone and bone tools were still in use, as indicated by the bone harpoon, the caribou antler object, and the quartz flakes, but contact with

Europeans is indicated by the trade beads, metal objects, and wooden pipe. Whalers began to come to this area in the mid 1800's (Boas, p. 17); so the site presumably dates from this period or perhaps slightly later.

Canso Channel 3 (MhBx-3), located about three-quarters of a mile south of Canso Channel 2, also on the east bank of the inlet, consists of a circular semisubterranean stone house and a very small rectangular stone structure, 5 feet long and 4½ feet wide. Both structures were heavily covered with large specimens of *Umbilicaria* lichen, indicating considerable antiquity (Andrews and Webber, 1964). The larger of the two structures was more densely covered, probably indicating that it is somewhat older.

Eskimos on Broughton Island settlement reported that structures similar to the small one recorded here used to be built for women to occupy during childbirth. This is also reported by Boas, who noted in addition that small huts such as this were sometimes built to house the sick and dying.

Cape Broughton (MjBx-1), located on the first point southeast of Cape Broughton, consists of two house remains in a rocky area overlooking the sea. The houses are circular and appear to have been built entirely above ground (see fig. 2). They consist of one room with no entrance passage or interior features in evidence. The walls consist of massive rectangular stones, but no roofing material is present. It seems likely, therefore, that the roof consisted of either skins or snow. Boas (1964, p. 142) described a similar house at Anarniting and notes that the entrances to such houses were made of snow. The houses appear to have been disturbed, as a test excavation of the shallow soil layer on the floor uncovered no artifacts. Boas (p. 110) illustrates a Thule ulu from a stone circle in this location. It seems likely that it came from one of these house remains, as these were the only two structures I observed in the area.

Broughton Island (MjDa-1), located on a small point 7 miles south of Broughton settlement in a low-lying grassy area, consists of about 6 large, solidly built circular semisubterranean stone house remains of Thule winter-house type, with massive entrance passages. No artifacts were found that could be associated with the houses, but the area is scattered with whale, caribou, and seal remains. There are large quantities of modern debris, and a number of modern tent rings in the area.

Maktak Fiord 1 (MhDa-1), located on a grassy hillside in the southwest corner of an island at the mouth of Maktak Fiord, consists of 6 large circular semisubterranean stone houses with massive entrance tunnels built into the side of the hill. They are of typical Thule winter-house type. A number of large stone cairns are also located in the area. The houses are all covered with turf and appear to be undisturbed. Abundant walrus and seal bones are scattered on the surface, but no surface artifacts were found.

Maktak Fiord 2 (MiDc-1), located at the head of Maktak Fiord on the river delta, consists of a very small stone house similar to the possible birth (or death) house at Canso Channel 2. It was recorded by J. T. Andrews.

Kangeeak Point (MlDc-1), located on Kangeeak Point on a terrace about 200 yards back from the sea, consists of a series of stone structures, tent rings, and caches, running roughly north-south along the terrace parallel to the ocean, all heavily covered with lichen. Seven of the structures consist of a rectangular or subrectangular scatter of stones ranging in size from 12 by 13 to 13 by 14½ feet. The number and large size of the stones outlining them indicate something more substantial than a tent ring, yet there is no depression in the ground to indicate a house pit and the soil in the area appears to be too shallow to hide such a feature; hence they appear to represent aboveground structures. The lack of evidence of roofing stones indicates that they may have consisted of stone walls roofed with skins or snow. Each of these structures has a pile of large stones on one side, at the end of the long axis, and one has what appears to be a second room adjacent to the first, with the large pile of stones connecting the two.

An additional deteriorated structure may be similar to those described above. In addition, a semicircular wall built of stones more substantial than those generally associated with a tent ring, may be the remains of a circular stone house. There is also an oval tent ring, a circular stone cairn (probably a cache), and a long narrow cairn of large rocks that appears similar in form to a grave. A few caribou bones were scattered in the vicinity, but no artifacts were recovered from the surface.

Kivitoo 1 (MlDc-2), located in the Kivitoo area, south of Kangeeak point, consists of one circular tent ring and one rectangular tent ring. A weathered and possibly worked piece of bone was found on the surface of the circular tent ring.

Kivitoo 2 (MlDc-3) consists of two large oval meat caches and two large tent rings nearly 20 feet in diameter and heavily covered with lichen. In a rocky area about 50 yards southwest of the tent rings was a large Thule-type circular semisubterranean stone house. There was scattered bone in the area.

Kivitoo 3 (MlDc-4) consists of a number of tent rings, four of which appear to be quite old. Abundant small shells were associated with these.

Kivitoo 4 (MlDc-5) includes two substantial tent rings with raised sleeping platforms and work areas on each side. Large quantities of whale, polar

Fig. 3. Clear quartz artifacts from Kivitoo 5.

bear, and walrus bones are scattered on the surface, and near the tent rings are what appear to be the remains of a semisubterranean stone house; however, extensive turf cover makes the original form uncertain.

Kivitoo 5 (MlDc-6), located on the south side of the inlet just south of the old settlement of Kivitoo, is on a low-lying grassy area on a point. The site has been extensively looted. The turf has been stripped off in patches over a 200- by 300-foot area, revealing a stony layer with soil underneath. Artifactual material is found in the stony layer just below the turf. The end blades from this site were collected by Manusee Ilingayook (Levi's brother) and were given to me by his mother, Mary. The remainder of the material, which I collected from the stony layer, was spread over a wide area and the limits of the site probably extend beyond the looted area.

From MlDc-6 12 artifacts were recovered, plus a number of waste flakes (see fig. 3). The artifacts consist of 5 end blades, of which 1 is triangular concave based, 1 is eared, and the remaining 2 are stemmed. They vary between 1.5 and 2 centimeters in length. Three show evidence of "tip fluting" (Maxwell, 1973, p. 310), a technique in which tiny spalls are pressed off the tip of the point to thin and sharpen it. This trait, says Maxwell "becomes very common in the Dorset assemblages of 700 B.C. and later." The artifacts also include 1 end scraper, 4 microblades, and 2 utilized flakes. All lithic material from this site (with the exception of one coarse-grained milky-quartz waste flake), is of clear glassy quartz.

The assemblage seems to be quite typically Dorset (Maxwell, 1962, 1973; Lowther, 1960; Collins, 1955-56; Taylor, 1968) on the basis of the end blade forms. However, with such a small collection it is difficult to date the site with certainty, particularly since, as Maxwell (1973, p. 159) has pointed out, "there is very little individual typological difference between the artifacts of the earliest sites in the locality, and those from sites dating from the beginning of the Christian Era. In fact it is often difficult to determine whether a given stone artifact belongs to a late Dorset or early Pre-Dorset horizon."

Kivitoo 6 (MlDc-7), located on the point marked Kivitoo on the topographic map of the area, consists of 8 long narrow stone cairns heavily covered with large growths of *Umbilicaria* lichen. All are probably graves, in one of which human bones are exposed.

Kivitoo 7 (MlDc-8), located about 200 yards south of Kivitoo 6 in a rocky area just above the beach (see fig. 4), consists of two extremely large circular stone houses quite distinct from any which I had up to that time recorded, set 30 feet apart and each about 20 feet in diameter. The southern

FIG. 4.   Kivitoo 7: Possible qaggi, or singing house.

structure is the most clearly defined. The remains of an entrance tunnel about 12 feet long can still be discerned, and a large cairn formed of massive boulders is located northeast of it. The northern structure also has a large pile of stones located northeast of the house. In this latter structure the remains of an entrance passage cannot clearly be defined. In both structures massive piles of stones which formed the walls are still in evidence. However, no roofing material is present.

These structures in size and form are similar to qaggi, or winter singing houses, described by Boas (1964, pp. 192-3), as follows: "In summer feasts are celebrated in the open air, but in winter a house, called qaggi, or, as we may call it, singing house, is built for that purpose. . . . It is a large snow dome about fifteen feet in height and 20 feet in diameter, without any lining. In the center there is a snow pillar five feet high, on which the lamp stands. . . . Among the stone foundations of Niutang, in Kingnait (Cumberland Sound), there is a qaggi built on the same plan as the snow structure. Probably it was covered with a snow roof when in use."

Kivitoo 8 (MlDc-9), located about 250 yards south of the possible qaggi on the south side of the point, consists of 4 circular semisubterranean house remains of Thule type. Two have well-defined entrance passageways with lintel stones still in evidence. Walrus, whale, and caribou bones are scattered in the area, but no surface artifacts were found.

Kivitoo 9 (MkDd-1), recorded by John Andrews and located near the mouth of the first fiord north of Quajon, on a point on the southern shore of the fiord, consists of two stone winter houses, one partly covered by the present sea level, the second at 100 feet above sea level. Both used natural overhangs as part of the construction and both were fairly heavily covered with lichen.

Idjuniving Island 1 (MlDc-10) is located in a bay in the southeast portion of Idjuniving Island, Kivitoo area. Erosion of a cliff face above the beach has exposed a layer of rich peat soil between 6 and 8 inches below the surface containing a heavy concentration of chipped stone. The material is concentrated in one 6-foot-long area, although the peat layer continues for at least 8 feet in one direction and 20 feet in the other.

From the peat layer at the cliff edge were collected (see fig. 5): a narrow side-notched clear-quartz end blade, a basal fragment of a triangular smoky-quartz end blade, a broken tip of a clear-quartz end blade, a basal fragment of an eared end blade made of coarse-grained milky quartz, and a number of lamellar flakes, one containing a burin. A chert scraper, which looks as though it may have been fashioned from the broken base of a stemmed end blade, was also found, as well as a chert knife tip. A clear-quartz lamellar flake fragment with unifacial retouch on both edges was also found. In addition, a number of flakes were recovered, of which only three were of chert, the rest being of clear quartz. Artifacts found at this site resemble those found at both Dorset and Pre-Dorset sites reported in other locations in the eastern Arctic. The small number of artifacts recovered makes it impossible to determine which of the two cultures is represented.

A carbon-14 sample taken from the dark peat layer was submitted to Geochron Laboratories, Cambridge, Massachusetts. Unfortunately, the sample appears to have been contaminated by a combination of humic acid and nuclear fallout, as it yielded a date later than modern. This was extremely disappointing as the site may well be the earliest reported so far in the area.

The site is presently being destroyed by erosion. It is uncertain how much of it had already been lost by the time I discovered it, which was, unfortunately, at the end of the field season, when I did not have time to sink a test pit to determine how far back from the cliff edge the deposit extends. The site contains a rich concentration of stone tools and because of the erosion warrants further investigation as soon as possible.

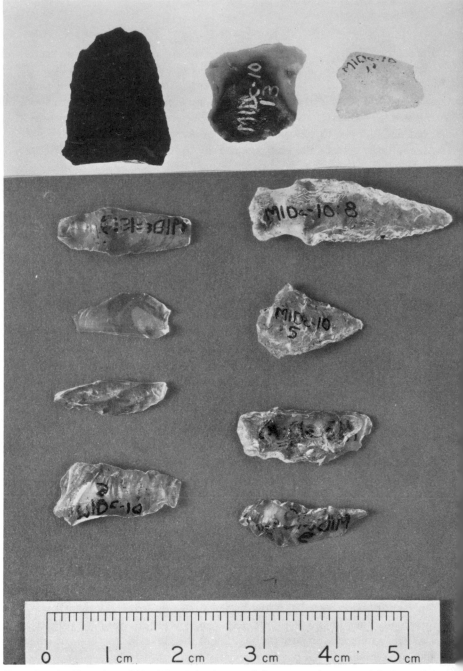

FIG. 5. Artifacts from Idjuniving Island 1: top left two are chert, top right is smoky quartz, remainder are clear quartz.

Idjuniving Island 2A (MlDc-11), located in a bay in the southern part of Idjuniving Island, adjacent to Kekerturnak Island, consists of a series of tent rings partially covered with turf. They have been extensively looted, the turf having been stripped off in several of the tent rings, and the soil disturbed. South of this is an area of stones almost completely covered with turf. Structures may be buried here, but their form is obscured by the turf cover. Southeast of this site is a mounded area which probably contains three buried stone semisubterranean houses that are probably rectangular but this cannot be determined without excavation. The dimensions of one house appear to be roughly 14 by 10 feet. This area has been disturbed in places but not extensively so. Bone can be seen in one of the disturbed areas, and two quartz flakes were recovered from another.

Idjuniving Island 2B (MlDc-12), located in an extremely rocky area directly behind MlDc-11, consists of 8 houses, 3 possible houses, 13 stone caches, and 10 possible burial cairns. All structures are heavily covered with large specimens of *Umbilicaria* lichen, indicating considerable antiquity. One of the houses has a well-preserved outline. Rectangular and semisubterranean, it is built of large stones, and has a long entrance passage. The width of the house is 8½ feet, and the length of the house and the entrance together is 18 feet, the entrance passage itself being 7 feet long and 4½ feet wide (fig. 6). These houses appear to be quite distinct from the deep round Thule winter houses. I believe them to be Dorset houses, but no artifacts were found to support this conclusion.

The possible burials, long narrow stone cairns, are readily distinguishable from the meat caches, which tend to be roughly circular. Some of the cairns in the possible burial group consist of two large rectangular stones placed parallel to one another about a foot apart. A number of smaller stones are piled over the two large rectangular stones. These cairns, all of which occur in one area of the site, are similar in form to the cairn containing human skeletal remains recorded at Kivitoo 6.

Idjuniving Island 2C (M1Dc-13), located 200 yards northeast of the previous two sites, consists of a series of tent rings with stones outlining the sleeping platform and entrance way. One is extremely small and looks like something constructed by children. A bone object with four drilled holes was recovered from the surface of one of the tent rings.

Narpaing 1 (MlDe-1), located on the south side and near the mouth of Narpaing Fiord, consists of a large number of tent rings heavily covered with lichen. The site was recorded by Ken Duffield, who found a clay pipestem and a stone weight bound with a thong within one of the tent rings.

FIG. 6.   Idjuniving Island 2B: Possible Dorset winter house.

Narpaing 2 (MlDd-1), located on the south side of outer Narpaing Fiord, consists of a stone house, covered very heavily with lichen, with an entrance passage and an annex off to one side. The structure, roughly rectangular, measures 12 feet by 14 feet, with an 8-foot-long entrance way. It seems likely that this is another Dorset house. It was recorded by John Andrews and Ken Duffield.

Narpaing 3 (MlDe-2), located on the south shore of a small island in the mouth of Narpaing Fiord opposite the entrance to Okoa Bay, consists of 5 well-preserved Thule winter houses with the lintel stones over the entrance ways still standing. A Thule open-socket harpoon head and a bone snow beater were found on the surface. The site was recorded by John Andrews.

Three additional Thule artifacts from the Home Bay area, the exact provenience of which is unknown, were given to me by an Eskimo woman in Broughton Island settlement (fig. 7). They consist of a harpoon finger rest (cf. Collins, 1951, plate 14), made from a polar-bear tooth; a bone toggle; and a pointed bone object 18 centimeters in length with a concave end, a hole drilled 2.5 centimeters from this end, and 5 notches incised near the pointed end.

FIG. 7. Artifacts of bone, tooth, and wood: *a,* Bone object (Idjuniving Island 1); *b,* bone tool of unknown function (Home Bay area); *c,* pipe of driftwood (Canso Channel 2); *d,* bone harpoon (Canso Channel 2); *e,* Thule open-socket harpoon head (Narpaing 3); *f,* bone toggle (Home Bay area); *g,* possible harpoon finger rest (Home Bay area); *h,* wooden wound plug (Canso Channel 2).

TABLE 1—NUMBER AND TYPE OF STRUCTURES

Site	Site Type	Stone Winter Houses	Tent Ring	Other	Artifacts	Associated Features
MhBx-1 Canso Ch. 1	Thule	9	1		kayak frame	
MhBx-2 Canso Ch. 2	Early Contact		3		bone, stone, metal	2 fire-places
MhBx-3 Canso Ch. 3	unknown	1		1 (birth house)		
MjBx-1 C. Broughton	Dorset	2				
MhDa-1 Maktak Fiord 1	Thule	6				stone caches
MiDc-1 Maktak Fiord 2	unknown			1 (birth house)		
MjDa-1 Broughton Is.	Thule	6				
MkDd-1 Kivitoo 9	unknown	2				
MlDc-1 Kangeeak Pt.	unknown		1	8 (Quar-mat) 1 (cir-cular)		2 caches 1 grave
MlDc-2 Kivitoo 1	unknown		2			
MlDc-3 Kivitoo 2	Thule & unknown	1	2		possible worked bone & thong	2 caches
MlDc-4 Kivitoo 3	unknown		6+			
MlDc-5 Kivitoo 4	unknown	1	2			

TABLE 1 – CONTINUED

Site	Site Type	Stone Winter Houses	Tent Ring	Other	Artifacts	Associated Features
MlDc-6 Kivitoo 5	Dorset				micro-liths	
MlDc-7 Kivitoo 6						8 burials
MlDc-8 Kivitoo 7	unknown			2 (qaggi)		2 caches
MlDc-9 Kivitoo 8	Thule	4				
M1Dc-10 Idjuniving Is. I	Dorset or Pre-Dorset				stone micro-liths	
MlDc-11 Idjuniving Is. 2A	unknown	3	5			
MlDc-12 Idjuniving Is. 2B	Dorset	8-11				13 caches 10 burials
MlDc-13 Idjuniving Is. 2C	unknown	(ca.) 4		1 (child's tent ring)		
MlDd-1 N 2	possible Dorset	1				
MlDe-1 N 1	post contact	(ca.) 6			clay pipestem, stone bound w. thong	
MlDc-2 N 3	Thule	5				

Summary (see table 1): Of the 24 sites located, 22 were habitation sites with architectural remains still in evidence. Almost all these were characterized by a remarkable lack of artifactual material on the surface. In some this is probably due to extensive looting; in others, the covering of sod may have made surface collecting an inadequate means of obtaining a sample. Of the 49-52 stone winter houses, 31 were Thule, 10-13 were Dorset, and 7 were of unknown origin. The tent rings totaled 32 and the other structures, 14. The artifacts recovered, together with a map of site locations, are on file at the National Museum of Canada, Ottawa 4, Canada.

Conclusions

The 95 to 98 structures recorded show a great deal of variability. They may, however, be divided into six categories:
1. Deep massive circular semisubterranean stone houses.
2. Shallower rectangular semisubterranean stone houses.
3. Rectangular surface structures with no evidence of roofing material.
4. Substantial tent rings with interior divisions.
5. Tent rings without interior divisions.
6. Miscellaneous specialized structures.

The majority of the structures recorded had no artifacts associated with them; it is therefore impossible to make inferences with a high degree of reliability about either their temporal placement or their place in the seasonal cycle. On the basis of information from other sites in the eastern Arctic, however, the following may be postulated as a series of hypotheses to be tested by further research:

- That the first type represents Thule winter houses on the basis of their similarity to sites recorded elsewhere (e.g., Maxwell, 1973; Collins, 1955; Jenness, 1925). One feature that appears to be different is that none of the Thule-type winter houses had whalebone roof supports. It it possible that some had been removed (I was told that old whalebone was much prized for carving and was being taken from sites). However, some of the sites recorded appeared to be undisturbed, and it seems unlikely that no traces would be left of this feature. It seems possible, therefore, that Thule houses in this area did not use whalebone as roof supports.
- That the second type represents Dorset houses, based both on comparison with other sites, and on the fact that the sites of this type found here had a lichen covering indicating considerable age.

- That the third type of structure represents what Boas has called a qar-mat, a house with stone walls roofed with skin. McGhee (1972) has suggested that such structures date from what he has termed the "Intermediate interval," which falls between the Thule and historic periods in the Victoria Island area. He suggests (p. 103) that they are "probably an adaptation of the Thule winter house to a shorter season of occupation during which a skin roof would provide sufficient protection against autumn weather." The assumption is that during this time period snow houses on the sea ice came into use as winter dwellings. It seems possible that a similar situation exists in this area.
- That the fourth type of structure dates from the historic period. This is indicated by the Canso Channel 2 site. Mathiassen (1928) also notes sites of this type as occurring in historic times in the Igloolik area.
- That the fifth type of structure, which varied in shape from rectangular to circular, probably dated from all different time periods and all could be assumed to be summer dwellings.
- That the sixth type, again, could not be assigned to a cultural period; their postulated functions include a qaggi or singing house, a house to be occupied during childbirth or by the sick or dying, and a miniature tent ring presumably built for or by a child.

The prehistoric inhabitants of the area showed a marked preference for relatively flat grassy areas close to the ocean. No sites were recorded more than about 600 yards from the ocean. It is possible, however, that the sites recorded in this survey do not represent the total settlement system of the prehistoric inhabitants. Several biases are built into the methods used in this survey. First: the possibility that some of the sites are now underwater, and that others are closer to the shore now than they were at the time of occupation. One of my interests in doing this study was to correlate the location of archeological sites with ancient shorelines. However, the geologists informed me soon after our arrival that this area was exceptional, as it was one where almost no isostatic recovery had occurred (Andrews, McGhee, and McKenzie-Pollock, 1971). Instead of the expected sequence of ancient raised shorelines, therefore, the marine limit (or highest point to which the sea reached) was in most cases the present shoreline. Second: the fact that I used present-day informants to help locate sites. This meant that they would tend to know only about sites located in the areas presently utilized by them. This could cause me to overlook, for example, inland caribou hunting sites, as caribou are no longer a significant source of subsistence for the present-day inhabitants, now almost entirely dependent on hunting the ringed seal.

This preliminary survey has shown the area of East Baffin Island between Narpaing Fiord to the north and Canso Channel to the south to be rich in archeological sites. It has provided evidence that the area may have been occupied for as long as 4,000 years and was certainly occupied by shortly after the beginning of the Christian Era. A number of sites located merit further investigation. A research project that would add a great deal to our knowledge of the archeology of the eastern Canadian Arctic would be an excavation of a sample of each of the six types of structures to test my hypothesized functions and period of occupation. Since it is common in the eastern Arctic to find structures with few or no associated artifacts, a typology of house forms would be extremely useful.

REFERENCES

ANDREWS, JOHN T.; MCGHEE, ROBERT; and MCKENZIE-POLLOCK, LORNA
    1971. Comparison of elevations of archaeological sites and calculated sea levels in Arctic Canada.   Arctic, vol. 24, no. 3, pp. 211-228.
ANDREWS, JOHN T., and WEBBER, P. J.
    1964. A lichenometrical study of the northwestern margin of the Barnes Ice Cap: A geomorphological technique.   Canada Dept. Mines and Techn. Surv., Geogr. Branch, Geogr. Bull. 22, pp. 80-104, illus.
BOAS, FRANZ
    1964. The central Eskimo.   Pp. 399-669, illus., *in* Sixth Ann. Rep. of Bur. of Ethnol. to the Sec. Smithsonian Inst., 1888 [1889], Bison Book ed., University of Nebraska Press, Lincoln, 1964.
COLLINS, HENRY B.
    1951. Excavations at Thule culture sites near Resolute Bay, Cornwallis Island, N.W.T.   Bull. 123, Ann. Rpt. Nat. Mus. Canada for 1949-1950, pp. 49-71, illus.
    1955. Excavations of Thule and Dorset culture sites at Resolute, Cornwallis Island, N.W.T.   Bull. 136, Ann. Rpt. Nat. Mus. Canada for 1953-1954, pp. 22-35, illus.
    1955-56. Archaeological investigations of Southampton and Walrus Islands, Northwest Territories.   Bull. 147, Ann. Rpt. Nat. Mus. Canada for 1955-56, pp. 22-61, illus.
    1964. Introduction.   Pp. v-xi *in* "The Central Eskimo," by Franz Boas. Bison Book ed., University of Nebraska Press, Lincoln.
JENNESS, DIAMOND
    1925. A new Eskimo culture in Hudson Bay.   Geogr. Rev., vol. 15, no. 3, pp. 428-437, illus.
LOWTHER, G. R.
    1960. An account of an archaeological site on Cape Sparbo, Devon Island.   Nat. Mus. Canada Contr. Anthr. Bull. 180, pp. 1-55.

MATHIASSEN, THERKEL
    1927. Archaeology of the central Eskimo.   Report of the Fifth Thule Expedition, 1921-24, pt. 1, 327 pp., pt. 2, 208 pp., illus. Copenhagen.

MAXWELL, MOREAU
    1962. Pre-Dorset and Dorset sites in the vicinity of Lake Harbour, Baffin Island, N.W.T.   Nat. Mus. Canada Contr. Anthr. Bull. 180, pp. 20-55.
    1973. Archaeology of the Lake Harbour District, Baffin Island.   Archaeol. Surv. Canada, Paper 6, 362 pp., Mercury Series.

McGHEE, ROBERT
    1972. Copper Eskimo prehistory.   Nat. Mus. Canada Publ. Archaeol. no. 2, 141 pp., illus.

TAYLOR, WILLIAM E., JR.
    1968. The Arnapik and Tyara sites: An archaeological study of Dorset culture origins.   Mem. Soc. Amer. Archaeol. no. 22, 129 pp., illus.

LORNA MCKENZIE-POLLOCK

Eruption of Arenal Volcano, Costa Rica, 1968-1973

Principal Investigator: William G. Melson, National Museum of Natural History, Smithsonian Institution, Washington, D. C.

Grant No. 756:   In support of studies of Arenal Volcano, Costa Rica.

Arenal Volcano, Costa Rica, began its first historic eruption with a violent explosion on July 29, 1968. Periodic intense explosions continued until July 31, 1968. During this initial phase, approximately 80 persons were killed and 12 square kilometers were devastated by hot avalanches and ejected blocks. The eruption quickly passed into quiet effusive activity with the emission of a thick andesitic flow on September 19, 1968.

Arenal Volcano had not been studied prior to the current eruption. Publications deal with its initial explosive phases (Melson and Saenz, 1968), the chronology of events prior to and during the explosive phases (Simkin, 1968), and the significance of the ejecta velocity on magma chamber pressure (Fudali and Melson, 1972). There is also a brief unpublished account of the early phases (Waldron, 1968). Matumoto studied the seismology of the eruption but its results have not been published. Stoiber and Rose (1970) have analyzed condensates from the fumaroles on the rim of the new explosion crater on March 29, 1969, and compared them with other Central American condensates (Taylor and Stoiber, 1973). Chavez and Saenz (1970) and Minakami and Utibori (1969) have also discussed the current eruption. This report is summarized from a technical article in the Bulletin of Volcanology (Melson and Saenz, 1973).

Arenal Volcano (lat. 10°27.8' N., long. 84°42.3' W.) is a nearly perfectly symmetrical, small stratovolcano which rises to 1,633 meters in central Costa Rica (figs. 1, 2). The volume of Arenal above the 500-meter contour is about 6 cubic kilometers. Cerro Chato, a truncated, probably extinct, volcano is about 3 kilometers south and contains a small, lake-filled caldera, Laguna Cerro Chato. The increasing age of these two volcanoes toward the west, and the opening of the current new craters and some prehistoric craters on Arenal's west side, show migration of vents to the west and northwest through time. Arenal is about midway between the active groups of Costa Rican volcanoes and, prior to its current eruption, was not listed among the active volcanoes of the world. Like Mount Lamington, New Guinea (Taylor, 1958), Arenal Volcano emphasizes the difficulty of distinguishing active volcanoes with long periods of repose from truly extinct ones.

Arenal is one of seven active and one of numerous presumably extinct Quaternary and Pliocene volcanoes of the northwest-trending continental divide of Costa Rica. It is about midway between a northwestern group — the Guanacaste Cordillera — and a southeastern group, which is part of the Cordillera Central (fig. 3). Arenal is one of the smaller but more perfect volcanic cones of the active volcanoes of Costa Rica. Most others are higher and larger and have irregular forms that have been deeply incised by erosion. Their elevations range from 1,487 meters at Orosi to 3,433 meters at Irazú.

The ongoing block flow at Arenal is the first lava flow in Costa Rica's history. All other historic eruptions of Costa Rican volcanoes have yielded tephra only.

The eruption can be divided into six phases, with mainly gradational boundaries. Maximum human fatalities and property damage occurred during the first explosive phase. After 10 hours of intense seismic activity, the first of a series of large explosions began at 7:30 a.m. on July 29, 1968. Most fatalities occurred in this and the shortly following explosions. The last fatalities occurred around 1:10 p.m. on July 31, 1968, when the last major explosion occurred. At least three new explosion craters formed during the initial three days of explosions. All are aligned along a roughly east-west zone (fig. 2). Eyewitness accounts indicate that all three probably opened simultaneously during the first major explosion of 7:30 a.m., July 29, 1968.

On September 14, 1968, renewed but much smaller explosions occurred in the lower crater. Ejecta this time were essential, scoriaceous bombs. These explosions produced only a small amount of ejecta, and, on September 19, 1968, the lower crater began to be filled by viscous lava, which eventually spilled over the west, or outer, rim. This flow, a thick block flow (fig. 4) first advanced down Quebrada Tabacón but has since sent tongues far to the southwest, and other tongues now have overridden earlier ones. All these lava tongues originate from a vent at the end of a well-developed notch eroded through the lava that initially filled the lower crater. The lava descends a strikingly developed chute before branching into the individual lobes. The lava flow has completely filled the valley of Quebrada Tabacón and buried most of the devastated zone.

Nuees ardentes were an important part of the explosive phase of Arenal

FIG. 1. Arenal Volcano viewed from the ruins of Tabacón on August 13, 1968. New explosion craters opened at A (see fig. 2), the largest and source of most pyroclastic flows, impact ejecta, and air-fall ash, and at B and C. The summit crater (D) remained in fumarolic activity only.

and caused many fatalities. Observations of nuees ardentes and their effects at Mayon Volcano, Philippines (1968: Moore and Melson, 1969), Ulawun Volcano, New Britain (1970: Melson et al., 1972), and at Arenal (Melson and Saenz, 1968) show the dominant role of gravity in accounting for their high mobility. In all three cases, fallback of explosively ejected materials created hot avalanches which coalesced and descended major drainage channels reaching about 3 kilometers from the lower crater before coming to rest. Composition and gas emission from the avalanching tephra, which range from basalt (Ulawun) to basaltic andesite (Mayon and Arenal), appear to play minor roles in accounting for the high mobility of these small avalanches. The nuees ardentes — used here to designate the hot avalanche and its envelope of fine tephra and hot gases — leveled trees at their margins at the three volcanoes and produced other effects that may be viewed as a result of "directed blast," where ash and gas velocities are attributed to accelerations imparted at the vent. Gravity flow alone, though, accounts for the accelerations of the avalanches of these three eruptions. The hot

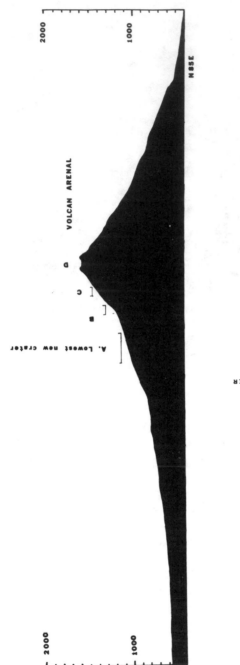

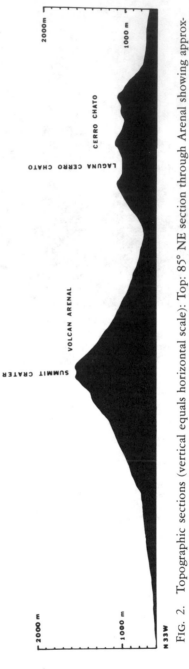

FIG. 2. Topographic sections (vertical equals horizontal scale): Top: 85° NE section through Arenal showing approximate locations of new craters; bottom: N33W section including Cerro Chato.

avalanches are analogous in some of their properties, especially their high mobility, to major landslides and snow avalanches, where entrapped air, in only partly permeable, poorly sorted debris, tends to provide "air-layer lubrication" and hence high mobility (Shreve, 1968). McTaggart (1960) noted that in experiments heated sand traveled farther from an incline than did sand at room temperature, indicating that thermal expansion of entrapped air may contribute to the increased mobility of hot avalanches.

The impact crater field produced by ejecta roof rocks from the lower explosion crater covered over 5 square kilometers and is one of the most remarkable features of the explosions (fig. 5). Large blocks reached up to 5 kilometers from the lower crater, and some areas were 100 percent cratered, as near Tabacon (Melson and Saenz, 1968). This maximum distance of 5 kilometers from the crater, considering effects of atmospheric drag on ejected blocks, we used to calculate ejection velocities of up to 600 meters per second (Fudali and Melson, 1972). From this velocity, Bernoulli's equation was used to calculate an overpressure of 4,700 bars in the magma chamber just prior to ejection of such blocks.

Most material from the 1968-73 eruption has flowed during the current quiet effusive phase. Estimated volume, as of September 1971, is about 0.06 $\pm$ 0.02 cubic kilometer and the surface area, about 2.74 square kilometers. The large uncertainty in the volume results from the highly variable and poorly known flow thickness, ranging from 10 to probably in excess of 150 meters where it has filled Quebrada Tabacón. The average rate of emission is about $8.3 \pm 2.5 \times 10^4 \mathrm{m}^3$ per day from September 19, 1968, to September 11, 1970. The emission rate of the block flow does not appear to be constant. The rate of advance and flow front thickness range greatly. New additions to the flow front ranged from 4,000 to 100,000 m^3 per day averaged weekly for the period July 7 to September 11, 1970. Flow thickness appears to correlate inversely with rate of low movement. With slow emission rates, the flow cools considerably as it moves downslope, greatly increasing in viscosity and hence greatly thickening. Under such conditions, the flow front may exceed 40 meters. Such a great thickness was observed in November 1968, during the waning of the first major pulse of lava emission. During times of rapid advance, the flow front is typically 10 to 15 meters high.

About $0.03 \pm .02$ cubic kilometer of tephra (corrected for pore space) was emitted in about 3 days (July 29-31, 1968) during the explosive phase. This gives an average rate of 1×10^7 m^3 per day, or nearly 10^3 times the average rate of emission of the lava flow. The rate during an individual

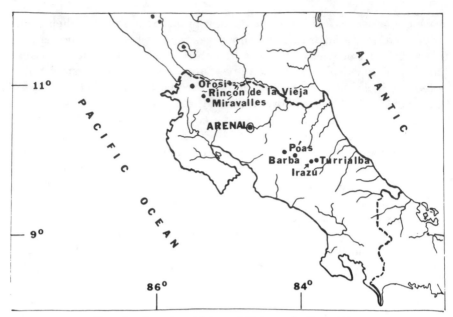

FIG. 3.   Location of Arenal Volcano in Costa Rica.

explosion is probably still greater by three to four orders of magnitude. The combined volume of all the new explosion craters, estimated at an upper limit of $7 \pm 2 \times 10^6 m^3$, is considerably less than the $3 \times 10^7 m^3$ ejected during this phase. Evidently about 25×10^6 m^3 rapidly rose up in the conduit beneath the craters during or immediately after the explosions. Any void left must have been immediately infilled by collapse of the conduit walls. Since this collapse could be no more than about 20 percent of the total volume of ejecta, a rapid rise of magma must have occurred simultaneously with, and probably caused, the explosions.

In the grossly oversimplified assumption of a 350-meter cylindrical conduit beneath the lower crater, the volume of erupted material extended approximately 300 meters below the original surface, and was replaced by the rising magma column. For the total volume of eruptives, such a column would extend to a depth of 1 kilometer.

The approximate equations of Hedervari (1963) relating volumes of essential eruptive rocks to thermal energy released on cooling can be used to calculate the approximate energies of Arenal's last two eruptions. The probable energy of the July 29-31 explosions was estimated at $2.4 \pm 1.2 \times$

10^{21} ergs, based on the estimated volume of the lower explosion crater, and mean ejection velocities inferred from impact crater distributions (Fudali and Melson, 1972). New measurements show that the lower crater is larger ($7 \pm 2 \times 10^6 m^3$) than these early estimates ($2 \pm 1 \times 10^6 m^3$). Also new measurements of the probable volume of explosively ejected materials give volumes of $2.4 \pm 1.6 \times 10^7 m^3$.

Assuming the same mean ejection velocities (300 meters per second), the total kinetic energy is 2.8×10^{22} ergs, which is about 10 times greater than the early estimate of 2.4×10^{21} ergs. This kinetic energy is about 10 percent of the total thermal energy available from the volume of explosive ejecta, assuming all ejecta was essential. If all energy were supplied by heating phreatic water prior to the explosions, magma temperature drops on the order of 100° C, perhaps from 1,100° C. to 1,000° C., assuming optimal exchange of magmatic heat to ground water prior to the explosion, would provide adequate kinetic energy for the explosions.

The total thermal energy released from the 1968-1973 and ca. A.D. 1500 eruptions is about $7.8 \pm 4 \times 10^{23}$ and $1.8 \pm 1 \times 10^{24}$ ergs, respectively, based on the volume of ejecta, and assuming most ejecta are essential.

The thermal energy involved in the formation of the rocks of the total cone of Arenal, from 1,663 to 500 meters, is about 6.6×10^{25} ergs. The total eruptives, most of which were deposited downwind from the volcano, would possibly increase this energy estimate by more than an order of magnitude, perhaps to about 10^{27} ergs.

These calculations show that the energy of Arenal's eruptions are small compared to a number of historic eruptions, given below (energy in ergs/ 10^{23}).

Santorini	ca. 1400 B.C.	45,000
Tambora	1815	8,400
Kilauea	1952	18
Arenal	1968-70	8
Arenal	ca. 1500	18
Arenal	Total cone and surrounding tephra	700

The estimated energy from the formation of the total cone and surrounding tephra is less by 10 than the single 1815 eruption of Tambora, and less by nearly two orders of magnitude than Santorini's ca. 1400 B.C. eruption. On the other hand, the energy of Arenal's 1968-70 eruptions (not allowing for energy increments from the new lava of 1970-73) is larger than the number of recent explosive eruptions, including Mayon (1968, 4×10^{22} ergs) and Ulawun (1970, 6.3×10^{22} ergs).

The current eruption consists in simplest terms of three successive events: (1) large explosions separated by periods of quiet, (2) continuous tephra emission, and (3) a lava flow. Studies of the tephra deposits faithfully record these first two phases. Typically, a layer of coarse tephra grades sharply into a zone of fine tephra. Individual grade beds are recognizable within the coarse tephra zones. The ratio of fine to coarse tephra ranges from about 0.10 at the margin of the ash apron to 0.50 in the middle. Excavations reveal at least three prehistoric eruptions with the same cyclicity, but all of greater total thickness than the tephra from the 1968 eruption. Typically, paleosoils are poorly to well developed in the uppermost fine tephra units, probably reflecting long periods of repose between major eruptions.

This last prehistoric major eruption followed a similar cycle, but the volumes of each phase differ from those of the current eruption. It has been possible to date this last eruption by radiocarbon and archeological means. A major prehistoric lava flow is underlain by a blocky ash flow near the road crossing of Quebrada Tabacón. Two wood samples from carbonized tree trunks buried by this flow have been dated by R. Stuckenrath of the Smithsonian's Radiocarbon Laboratory, giving analytically indistinguishable ages A.D. 1525 ± 20. The dated bark and wood are of *Pitnecellobium racemiflorium* (identified by B. F. Kukachka, U. S. Department of Agriculture). The low density of the wood, revealed by thin walls of the wood fibers, suggests fast growth and hence minimal postsample growth errors. Indian ceramic objects were excavated from airfall ash from this eruption by George Metcalf, Smithsonian archeologist. Mr. Metcalf and Dr. Clifford Evans infer a cultural age of between A.D. 1200 and 1400 for the excavated ceramics, an interval earlier than the radiocarbon dates.

A measured excavated section at 84°46.00′ W., 10°27.10′ N., about 7 kilometers south-southwest of Arenal's summit, shows a particularly well-developed sequence of the 1968 and ca. A.D. 1500 eruptions. The 1968 eruption deposits are an upper 12 centimeters of fine and a lower 25 centimeters of coarse tephra. Beneath these, there are 100 centimeters of fine and 75 centimeters of coarse tephra, including a 10-centimeter diameter pumiceous bomb. Assuming comparable wind directions and intensity during these two eruptions, the ca. A.D. 1500 eruption was about 5 times more voluminous during its explosive phase. Other sections show a similar ratio between the ca. A.D. 1500 and 1968 tephra deposits. The ca. A.D. 1500 lava flow, the largest exposed prehistoric flow, on the other hand, covers

FIG. 4. Block lava flows as of September 9, 1971, issuing from lower explosion crater. Width of field is about 2 kilometers. Photo courtesy Costa Rican Instituto Geográfico.

only about 1 km² compared to about 3 km² for the 1968-73 flow (and is thinner on the average). The probable volume of the ca. A.D. 1500 eruption is about twice that of the current one, or 0.17 km³: tephra composes about 90 percent of the total eruptives versus 30 percent of the 1968-73 eruption.

In a given eruptive cycle of Arenal Volcano, the essential eruptive rocks become successively less differentiated through time. Since initial work (Melson and Saenz, 1968), seven new analyses have revealed this trend. The first three analyses are of essential eruptive rocks in chronological order from oldest to most recent, spanning the 5-year period of September 1968 to August 1973. Small but significant decreases in Na_2O, and K_2O and increases in total Fe, MgO, and TiO_2 are evident. The ejecta and lava of the previous, ca. A.D. 1500 eruption show even stronger fractionation, with SiO_2 ranging from 59.27 percent (pumiceous bomb, analysis 7) to 53.61 percent (lava flow).

The following is put forth as one qualitative model which is consistent with the observations on the eruption. Arenal's eruption began with renewed upsurges of andesitic magma after about 470 years of repose. Three major surges occurred, all part of a single pulsating rise of magma which eventually cleared conduits, became degassed, and yielded, finally, the most voluminous emission of new lava — the present ca. 0.06 km³ lava flows.

Initially, a new surge of magma moved upward along a roughly east-west trending tension fracture on Arenal's west side. This zone parallels an older fault zone just to the south of Arenal. The new magma rose rapidly through or pushed upward from below the cooling magma of Arenal's A.D. 1500 eruption, capped by at least 125 meters of crust formed by about 450 years of cooling (calculated from equations of Jaeger, 1968). Explosions resulted from explosive degassing of the uppermost part of magma oversaturated with volatiles. The successive explosions reflect degassing of successive zones of magma, as each neared the surface, until, finally, magma undersaturated with volatiles was erupted, forming the block flow. The magma column was zoned not only in regard to volatile content, but in major and minor elements as well, with successively lower volatile contents correlating with lower SiO_2 and alkali contents.

Alternatively, the explosions were produced by movement of low-volatile magma in low-temperature, water-saturated rocks, mainly volcanic ash interlayered with massive flows. The rapid mingling of magma and water-saturated ash could create overpressures in excess of 4,000 bars, resulting in the explosive opening of three craters simultaneously along the east-west fracture. The lowermost crater, closest to the site of maximum pressures, became the largest, and most gas and fragmented cap rocks were blasted from it. The stratified ash and lava flows over the rising column were leaky, and may not have failed explosively in the way of a slowly rising magma column.

The gas and ash at the base of the explosion clouds near the vent were in excess of 300° C., igniting vegetation. A mean temperature of 800° C. is not unreasonable for the supercritical water-rich vapor. At such a temperature, 4,000 bars is generated in water of initial density 1.0 gm/cc if expansion is not allowed to exceed 20 percent by the rock permeability and rate of heating of the water (Kennedy, 1950). The energy of the initial explosion, supplied by the expansion of the heated supercritical vapor, was on the order of 10^{21} ergs. Release of vapor pressure led to a brief period of quiet, but continued explosions occurred for the next two days with upward new surges of magma. The ejecta of these phases consisted largely of heated country rocks, until, on September 14, 1968, the top of the magma column broke through to the surface, with minor explosions of mainly essential, degassed, scoriaceous to pumiceous bombs of andesite. Emission of lava then became quiet and continuous but with varying rates of emission, until lava welled out into the lower crater, eventually spilling over the rim, and in two years covering 2.7 square kilometers.

During the major two explosions (the initial and final ones) much

FIG. 5.   Impact crater field near Tabacón; and (bottom) house destroyed by impacting block near Tabacón during explosions of July 29, 1968 (photo courtesy R. E. Carillo).

TABLE 1.—VOLUME OF ERUPTIVE ROCKS, 1968-1970,
ARENAL VOLCANO, COSTA RICA

Material	Dates	Volume (km³, including pore space)
Explosive Phase		
1. Airfall apron from 4 to 20 kilometers west.	July 29-August 10, 1968	0.04 ± 0.02
2. Airfall apron from 0 to 4 kilometers west.	July 29-August 10, 1968	0.003 ± 0.001
3. Airfall apron, greater than 20 kilometers west.	July 29-August 10, 1968	?
4. Blocky ash flows.	July 29-July 31, 1968	0.00.8 ± 0.0005
Quiet Effusive Phase		
5. Lava flow.	September 19, 1973 (no flow movement, October 1973)	0.06 ± 0.02
Total Volume (Including pore space)	July 29, 1968 — September 11, 1970	0.11 ± 0.03
Total Volume (Excluding estimated pore space; 3% for lava flow; 30% for tephra)	July 29, 1968 — September 11, 1970	0.09 ± 0.03

debris fell back from the explosion cloud mainly on the steep headwaters of drainage basins adjacent to the lower crater. This fall-back stripped and ignited vegetation and, cascading into drainage channels, generated high velocity hot avalanches, of which the blocky ash flows are the remains. Entrapped air and gases emitted from the ejecta provided air-layer lubrication and increased the mobility of the hot avalanches (Shreve, 1968; McTaggart, 1960). These heated, largely trapped gases moved outward from the avalanches at high speed, leveling trees, and causing most fatalities. The high velocities of the ash-laden winds and the mobility of the blocky ash flows were impelled entirely by gravity flow. No "directed blast" from the crater was involved.

Volatile oversaturated magma could be produced by either partial crystallization or anhydrous phases (mainly plagioclase and pyroxene) since the A.D. 1500 eruption, or by displacement of deep-seated volatile saturated magma to near the surface. A volatile saturated magma intially at depths between 4 and 15 kilometers if it were to be displaced isothermally to near the surface, would, with complete retention of volatiles, be able to generate about 1 to 5 kilobars overpressure on release of volatiles.

The average total volume of ejecta from the 1968 and A.D. 1500 eruptions is about 0.13 cubic kilometer. If all of Arenal's eruptions average about this volume, and have the same period of repose, and if 10 percent of the total volume is added to the cone, Arenal would develop in about 500 such eruptions, or about 200,000 years. However, these assumptions are probably unlikely. The relative thickness of tephra layers indicates that Arenal's early eruptions were on the average more voluminous than the current one, perhaps from 5 to 10 times more voluminous, lowering its calculated age to as low as 20,000 years.

Acknowledgments

Numerous people have contributed substantially to the work reported here. Especially important contributors to this study of Arenal include Rodrigo Saenz, Tom Simkin, Richard Berg, Brian Kanes, Robert Read, and Helen Wolanin. George Metcalf and Dr. Clifford Evans assisted with archeological excavations at Arenal and provided cultural ages of excavated objects. The Smithsonian Research Foundation, the National Geographic Society, and Educational Expeditions International have supported field work at Arenal.

REFERENCES

CHAVEZ, R., and SAENZ, R.
  1970. Efectos de las erupciones recientes del Volcán Arenal. Informe Semestral Enero-Junio 1970: San José, Costa Rica, Min. de Transportes, Inst. Geogr. Nac., p. 23.
FUDALI, R. F., and MELSON, W. G.
  1972. Ejecta velocities, magma chamber pressure, and kinetic energy associated with the 1968 eruption of Arenal Volcano. Bull. Volcanol., vol. 35, no. 2, pp. 383-401.
GORSHKOV, G. S.
  1959. Gigantic eruption of the volcano Bezymianny. Bull. Volcanol., vol. 20, pp. 77-109.
HEDERVARI, P.
  1963. On the energy and magnitude of volcanic eruptions. Bull. Volcanol., vol. 25, pp. 373-390.

JAEGER, J. C.
1968. Cooling and solidification of igneous rocks. Pp. 503-536 *in* "Basalts," H. H. Hess and A. Poldervaart, eds. John Wiley & Sons, New York.

KENNEDY, G. C.
1950. Pressure-volume-temperature relations in water at elevated temperatures and pressures. Amer. Journ. Sci., vol. 248, pp. 540-564.

MCTAGGART, K. C.
1960. The mobility of nuees ardentes. Amer. Journ. Sci., vol. 258, pp. 369-382.

MELSON, W. G.; JAROSEWICH, E.; SWITZER, G.; and THOMPSON, G.
1972. Basaltic nuees ardentes of the 1970 eruption of Ulawun Volcano, New Britain. Smithsonian Contr. Earth Sci., no. 9, pp. 15-32.

MELSON, W. G., and SAENZ, R.
1968. The 1968 eruption of Volcan Arenal: preliminary summary of field and laboratory studies. Smithsonian Center for Short-Lived Phenomena, Report 7/1968, p. 35.
1973. Volume, energy, and cyclicity of eruptions of Arenal Volcano, Costa Rica. Bull. Volcanol., vol. 37, no. 3, pp. 416-437.

MINAKAMI, T.
1950. On explosive activities of andesitic volcanoes and their forerunning phenomena. Bull. Volcanol., vol. 10, pp. 59-87.

MINAKAMI, T., and UTIBORI, S.
1969. The 1968 eruption of Volcano Arenal, Costa Rica. Earthquake Res. Inst. Bull., vol. 47, p. 789.

MOORE, J. G., and MELSON, W. G.
1969. Nuees ardentes of the 1968 eruption of Mayon Volcano, Philippines. Bull. Volcanol., vol. 33, no. 2, pp. 600-620.

RICHARDS, A. F.
1965. Linear relationship between energy and pressure of volcanic explosions. Nature, vol. 207, no. 5004, pp. 1382-1383.

SHREVE, R. L.
1968. Leakage and fluidization in air-layer lubricated avalanches. Bull. Geol. Soc. Amer., no. 79, pp. 653-658.

SIMKIN, T.
1968. Mt. Arenal volcanic eruption, Costa Rica, 29 July — 3 August, 1968: Event chronology. Smithsonian Center for Short-Lived Phenomena.

STOIBER, R. E., and ROSE, W. I., JR.
1970. The geochemistry of central American gas condensates. Bull. Geol. Soc. Amer., no. 81, p. 2891-2912.

TAYLOR, G. A.
1958. The 1951 eruption of Mt. Lamington, Papua. Australian Bureau of Min. Res., Geol. and Geophys., Bull. 38, 117 pp.

TAYLOR, P. S., and STOIBER, R. E.
1973. Soluble material on ash from active central American volcanos. Bull. Geol. Soc. Amer. no. 84, pp. 1031-1042.

WALDRON, H.
1968. The 1968 eruption of Arenal Volcano, Costa Rica. 5 pp. Unpublished report, U. S. Geological Survey, American Embassy, San José.

WILLIAM G. MELSON

Studies of the Outer Solar Corona at the Eclipse of March 7, 1970

Principal Investigators: Donald H. Menzel,[1] Harvard College Observatory and Smithsonian Astrophysical Observatory, and Jay M. Pasachoff, Hopkins Observatory of Williams College, Hale Observatories, and Harvard College Observatory.

Grant No. 812:   In support of a joint expedition of the Harvard College Observatory, the Smithsonian Astrophysical Observatory, and the National Geographic Society to observe the total solar eclipse of March 7, 1970, from a site in Miahuatlán, Oaxaca, Mexico, in order to study the solar corona.

The occasional total solar eclipses that we can observe afford us a few minutes to study regions of the solar atmosphere that are not normally visible. Fortuitously, the moon almost exactly covers the bright solar photosphere, the shining everyday disc of the sun, and the faint corona becomes visible for a few minutes. The shadow of the moon traces out a path thousands of miles long and only a hundred or so miles wide, so that one must travel to reach the zone of totality. In the eclipse of March 7, 1970, weather forecasts and astronomical circumstances led most professional astronomers, including our group, to set up instruments in the State of Oaxaca in southern Mexico.

During totality, a pearly-white halo around the sun, called the corona, becomes visible surrounding the dark lunar disc. The light we see as the corona actually comes from several sources. The major contributor is basically photospheric light scattered by electrons of the solar corona, located within a few million miles of the solar surface. Scattering of sunlight by dust particles in interplanetary space and by the earth's atmosphere augments this illumination and is especially important in the outer corona. We wished to assess the relative importance of these components in order to study the structure of the outer solar atmosphere. The emission lines from highly ionized elements that are important for studies of coronal temperatures and

---

[1] Dr. Menzel died on December 14, 1976.

FIG. 1. Photographs of the solar corona at the eclipse of March 7, 1970, in polarized light. The angle of the Polaroids changes by 90° between the two pictures (see arrows), and one can readily see the difference in the direction in which the corona appears to extend the farthest. Computer analysis of the difference between the photographs gives the coronal electron density.

FIG. 2. We built this "house" around our coronal spectrograph to protect it from dust and temperature changes. The first days of the expedition were devoted to such construction, building bases for our telescopes out of concrete and brick, and aligning the axes of rotation of our telescope drives. The field trip began one month prior to eclipse day.

densities contribute an insignificant amount to the total light.

One can distinguish the coronal constituents by studying their spectra and their polarizations. Light scattered by the solar electrons is polarized. The electrons, rapidly moving because of the million-degree temperature, wash out the Fraunhofer absorption lines of the normal solar spectrum. On the other hand, scattering by dust or atmospheric molecules polarizes light only very slightly and does not transform the Fraunhofer spectrum.

We brought a variety of equipment to Mexico to observe the outer solar corona in many ways. All together, our instruments weighed over 2 tons. Our larger device was a spectrograph designed by Dr. James G. Baker. Its unique feature was a wide-angle capability, which allowed us to use a slit

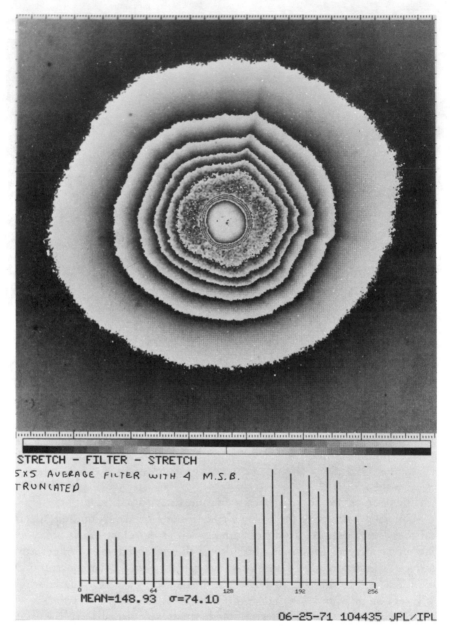

STRETCH – FILTER – STRETCH

5×5 AVERAGE FILTER WITH 4 M.S.B. TRUNCATED

MEAN=148.93   σ=74.10

06-25-71 104435 JPL/IPL

FIG. 3. Isophotal equal-intensity contours of the solar corona, measured from our eclipse negatives using the scanning microphotometer at the Jet Propulsion Laboratory. The edge of the field is 8 solar radii from the disc center, and streamers are visible at least that far as sharp deviations in the contours. The 8 solar radii are equivalent to over 4,000,000 kilometers (2,500,000 miles).

covering 10° centered on the sun. With this instrument we could simultaneously observe the corona and use light from the center of the lunar disc for calibration. Since the dark center of the moon is illuminated only by earthshine, most of the radiation detected in the direction of the moon must be attributed to multiple scattering in the earth's atmosphere and can be subtracted from the total measured for the corona. Our spectrograph included a 4-by-6-inch original ruled diffraction grating and a Schmidt camera system with a 16-inch camera mirror. Light was reflected into the instrument, which was so large that it was mounted horizontally, by a tracking 16-inch coelostat mirror. With the spectrograph we photographed the solar spectrum from 3,500 to 6,500 Å. at a dispersion of 18.6 Å/mm.

We also used a 5-centimeter f/20 apochromatic eclipse telescope to photograph the white-light polarization of the corona at four different angles. A variety of auxiliary apparatus included cameras to take direct photographs of the corona with lenses of various focal lengths, with black-and-white films for scientific reduction and with color films for display. We also made a time-lapse 16-millimeter color motion picture. All films were calibrated so that they could be reduced to an intensity scale, with film sensitivity effects removed, for scientific analysis.

Conditions were perfect for totality, and the sky was exceptionally clear. Consequently, our observations of the outer corona were of a quality not usually attainable from the ground. Totality lasted for 3 minutes 23 seconds; pinkish prominences radiating chiefly hydrogen light appeared at the solar limb at the beginning and end of totality, and Mercury and Venus shined. Our spectra show emission lines on both limbs, with the dark moon in between. Our polarization photographs show the expected strong dependence of coronal streamers on polarization angle.

Our photographs of the outer corona show streamers extending beyond 8 solar radii, a distance normally not visible from the ground during eclipses because of sky brightness. We are still continuing our data reduction. For example, we have measured isophotal equal-intensity contours with the digitizing microphotometer of the Jet Propulsion Laboratory of the California Institute of Technology.

Most coronal models regard the Fraunhofer corona, the part caused by scattering from interplanetary dust, as dominating beyond a few solar radii. Our observations, however, clearly show that coronal streamers define the structure of the corona even at large distances above the solar limb. As a result, we conclude that most of the coronal illumination to perhaps 8 to 10 solar diameters can arise from electron scattering in an atmosphere containing intense radially oriented streamers.

REFERENCES

MENZEL, DONALD H., and PASACHOFF, JAY M.

1968a. On the obliteration of strong Fraunhofer lines by electron scattering in the solar corona. Publ. Astron. Soc. Pacific, vol. 80, pp. 458-461.

1968b. Polarization of the corona at the eclipse of 22 September 1968. Sky and Telescope, vol. 36, pp. 380-381.

1970a. The outer solar corona at the eclipse of 7 March 1970. Nature, vol. 226, pp. 1143-1144.

1970b. Eclipse instrumentation for the solar corona. Applied Optics, vol. 9, pp. 2626-2630.

1970c. Spectrographic and photographic coronal studies. National Science Foundation Solar Eclipse 1970 Bull. F, pp. 141-142.

1970d. Solar eclipse: Nature's super spectacular. Nat. Geogr. Mag., vol. 138, no. 2, pp. 222-233, illus.

JAY M. PASACHOFF

Long-tailed Fowl of Japan

Principal Investigator: Frank X. Ogasawara, Department of Avian Science, University of California, Davis, California.

Grant No. 817:   For a study of the long-tailed fowl of Japan.

Breeders in southern Japan have been raising the long-tailed fowl for some three centuries. Evolved in the 1600's from a domestic chicken, probably the Shokoku, the tail of which may have been three feet long, they are called Onagadori *(O — tail, naga — long, dori — fowl).* Of these there are three principal varieties: the black-and-white Shirafuji, the red-and-black Akazasa-onaga, and the white Shiro-onaga.

My trip to Japan in 1970 in search of specimens for experimental breeding took me to Kochi, on Shikoku Island, where a principal breeder is Masashi Kubota, who raises all three of the varieties named above and who gave me 30 eggs to take back for this purpose to the United States. My illustrated story of this undertaking appeared in the December 1970 issue of the *National Geographic* (vol. 138, no. 6, pp. 844-855).

Although the transit time for this small number of eggs acquired in Japan from Mr. Kubota was short, we were able to hatch only 15 chicks in the laboratory of my university department at Davis, California. Their livability was surprisingly good, however, as the facilities of the department for brooding and rearing chicken stock are excellent. We have since expanded this original hatching to a constant number of some 20 females and 20 males, which are kept in one of the department's animal rooms. The requests for eggs or chicks have been constant — apparently a result of the article in the *Geographic,* and these demands have compelled me to write a form letter wherein I state that since research with the bird is in progress, I am not desirous of dispersing the gene material. Unfortunately, because of my involvement with other assignments having higher priority, this research has proceeded intermittently.

We are attempting to minimize the amount of inbreeding in the chickens that will naturally occur from such a small population. About three years ago I crossed some of the males with Leghorn stock (a Mediterranean breed) to instill some hybrid vigor into the cross and because the Leghorn hens are prolific egg producers in contrast to that of the long-tail hens.

However, in order to recover most of the original genes lost by crossing I would have needed to backcross many generations of the progeny with the original males, a costly process. The department at that time was in a budgetary crisis, and so I was forced to abandon this phase of the project.

More recently a graduate student has been in charge of the limited program to control inbreeding. She helps with the artificial insemination of the breeding stock, does the incubation and rearing of the chicks, and cleans the cages and special boxes, called tomebakos (these are illustrated in the *Geographic* article), in which we now have placed two selected males so that their tails can grow to the lengths expected.

We propose to do a variety of experiments with the present population. We hope to measure thyroxine (thyroid hormone) levels in the males since this is a key hormone in molting (tail feather loss) in chickens. And we will do some histology of the feather follicles of the tail region, since this tissue type apparently is in constant growth, an uncommon occurrence in the feather follicles of the chicken.

A major project with the long-tailed fowl will be the freezing of the semen from the males and its retention for periods of five years or more to demonstrate that we can preserve the genes of the male lines with this technique. We have developed a method of artificial insemination of frozen fowl semen which after insemination produces progeny, so that we are confident that our proposed project will be successful. One benefit from these experiments, because chicken males as they grow older become less productive in volume of semen, is that we are hoping to insure ourselves of a large supply of male gametes to produce future generations of the fowl. Furthermore, if we are able to find an extremely valuable male, his gene pool will then not be lost. I would not care to make a prediction, but I feel that chicken spermatozoa can be frozen and kept in liquid nitrogen for 10 years without an appreciable loss in fertilizing capacity.

Many questions remain. How do the special cells in the feather follicles of Onagadori respond to the hormones circulating in the chicken's blood? What would happen to these cells if they were transplanted in the embryo stage to tissues of the tail in the normal embryo of a barnyard hen or rooster? The whole molting process — the periodic shedding of feathers — still poses a major physiological riddle.

Hippocrates in the fifth century B.C. launched the science of human embryology by certain deductions he made in a study of chicken embryos. Berthold's transplants of rooster testes in 1849 started the complicated field of endocrinology, and Peyton Rous's experiments with chickens in 1911 first demonstrated the role of a virus in tumors. One day the long-tailed fowl may well make its own special contribution to science.

FRANK X. OGASAWARA

Excavation of the Phoenician and Roman Cities at Sarepta (Modern Sarafand, Lebanon)

Principal Investigator: James B. Pritchard, University Museum of the University of Pennsylvania, Philadelphia, Pennsylvania.

Grants Nos. 741, 827, 938, 1062. To find, excavate, and record the remains of the urban settlements at the coastal site of Sarafand, Lebanon, 8 miles south of Sidon.

During the summers of 1969, 1970, 1971, and 1972 the University Museum of the University of Pennsylvania, with the support of the National Geographic Society and certain foundations, discovered the remains of a port of the Roman-Byzantine period and a succession of cities dating from Phoenician times on the coast at Sarafand, Lebanon.

The seasons of excavation were as follows: June 2 to July 25, 1969; April 1 to June 5, 1970; April 19 to June 24, 1971; and April 17 to June 29, 1972. In addition to the grants by the National Geographic Society financial aid was supplied by an anonymous foundation; the Trans-Arabian Pipeline Co. provided living accommodations for the staff; the American University of Beirut made space available for the storage and study of artifacts; the Ford Foundation, through its grant to the University Museum for a trainee program in archeology, made it possible for graduate students to participate in the excavations; the Service des Antiquités, under the direction of M. Maurice Chehab, assisted greatly in obtaining a presidential decree for a concession to excavate at Sarafand for a period of 6 years.

The core staff throughout the four seasons consisted of James B. Pritchard, director; John E. Huesman, assistant director; Thomas McClellan and Leila Badre, supervisors; Martha Joukowsky, pottery analyst; and Pierre Bikai, architect. In 1969 there were, in addition, Leila Khalidy, cataloguer, and Magnus Ottosson, supervisor. The core staff was augmented in the 1970 season by Leila Khalidy, cataloguer, and Magnus Ottosson, Pierre Proulx, Patricia Cecil, and William Anderson, supervisors. In 1971 there were, in addition to those who had worked on both of the two previous seasons, Patricia Cecil, Ellen Herscher, and Adrianna Hopper, who served as cataloguers and pottery recorders; Pierre Proulx, Susan Long, Sigurdur

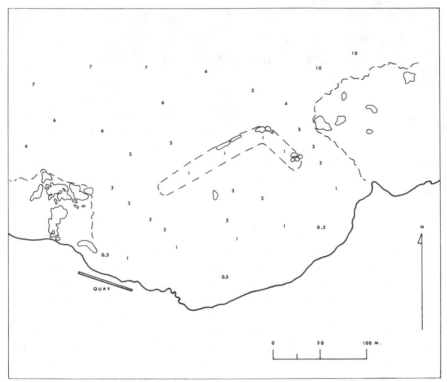

FIG. 1.   Sketch map of the harbor at Sarepta in use during the Roman and Byzantine periods. Figures indicate present depth of water in meters.

Orn Steingrimsson, and Gioacchino Falsone were supervisors; and William Anderson was architectural recorder and draftsman. In 1972 Homer Athanassion, Julia Costello, Marian Laaf, and Holly Hartquist joined the staff. During the 1969 season the average number of laborers employed was 51; in 1970, 80; in 1971, 90, in 1972, 75. All the labor was recruited from Sarafand and the surrounding villages.

   The site of Sarafand consists of plots of land, now under cultivation, that extend along the seashore for more than a kilometer in the vicinity of Râs esh-Shîq (map reference 1704.1084 on Carte du Liban, 1/20,000). Evidence of ancient occupation has long been observed as architectural fragments, and pieces of pottery have appeared on the surface of the cultivated fields. Yet no systematic excavations for ancient remains had been undertaken until we began in the summer of 1969.

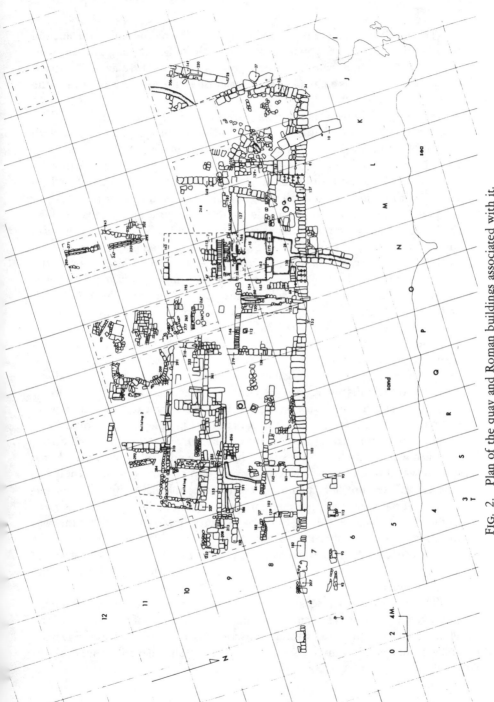

Fig. 2. Plan of the quay and Roman buildings associated with it.

The modern Sarafand has long been judged to be the site of the ancient Sarepta that figures in Egyptian, Assyrian, Biblical, Greek, and Latin sources. According to ancient references Sarepta lay between Tyre and Sidon; and Sarafand has been taken as an Arabic variation of the Greek Sarepta and the Hebrew Zarephath.

The earliest-known mention of Sarepta is in an alphabetic text of the 14th century B.C. found at Ras Shamra in Syria. The city is bracketed with Byblos, Beirut, Sidon, and Tyre as an important city of Phoenicia in an Egyptian papyrus dating to the 13th century B.C. It is more widely known as the city to which the prophet Elijah repaired in time of famine to find hospitality with a widow of Zarephath. There, according to the story in I Kings 17:8-24, he performed two miracles, the multiplication of meal and oil throughout the famine, and the raising of the widow's son from the dead. More than a score of references to Sarepta by Christian pilgrims, beginning in the 4th century A.D., attest its importance as a holy place through the Byzantine period, the Crusades, and down to comparatively modern times. These references in an extensive literature, along with those found in Greek and Roman sources, provide a sketch of the city's existence through more than 3,000 years (Pritchard, 1972).

The purpose of the excavations at Sarafand was to discover and document the archeological history of the site. Up until 1969 no stratified urban remains for the period of Phoenician colonization of the western Mediterranean had been discovered on the coast of Lebanon. Thus, for a picture of Phoenician culture the historian was dependent to a great extent upon what evidence there was for this important historical people in the colonies they founded in North Africa (particularly Carthage), Sicily, Sardinia, and Spain. The discovery of a Phoenician site in the homeland of Phoenicia would provide, it was thought, direct evidence for such important aspects of their culture as architecture, city planning, commerce, and daily life. The ancient remains at Sarafand were not encumbered with the buildings of modern life as they are at Byblos, Beirut, Sidon, and Tyre. It was obvious that this was the one major site of a Phoenician city that provided an opportunity to sample the little-known remains of a period of commercial and colonial activity that played a role in the diffusion of the Semitic alphabet to the western world.

The results of four seasons of excavations have justified our expectations. Not only have we located and charted the history of occupation of the Phoenician city, but also we have discovered the Roman-Byzantine port and a number of buildings associated with it. We shall describe the results in

FIG. 3.   The Roman quay as seen from the sea side with mooring ring in the center.

the two major areas of excavation, Area I, the Roman-Byzantine harbor, and Area II, the site of the Phoenician city.

Area I. The harbor of the Roman and Byzantine periods is a moon-shaped bay lying to the east of Râs esh-Shîq (fig. 1). An L-shaped natural reef, the top of which lies only a meter below the surface of the water, about 100 meters offshore, provides a shelter from the open sea. Access from the sea to the harbor is by two channels, one 20 meters wide and 3 meters deep at the east end of the submerged reef, and the other slightly wider and of the same depth at the west end. These two openings to the harbor not only served to provide channels for the entry of ships but also allowed a circulation of water that prevented the harbor from being clogged with silt.

The quay of the port runs east-west in a straight line along the shore of the bay for a distance of 59 meters (see fig. 2, plan, and fig. 3, photograph). The long stretch of wall had been built in two periods. Only a 12.70-meter segment of it belonged to the first period of construction (segment in L/N-5 on the grid of fig. 2). This portion of the sea wall is the north end of a rectangular quay that was surrounded by water on three sides. The north wall

FIG. 4.   A mooring ring built into the east wall of the docking area.

of this rectangular docking area, as well as the east and west walls, was built of well-cut sandstone blocks set firmly on bedrock and frequently clamped together, to judge from the notches cut for iron clamps, all of which had been robbed. The stones of this early structure were generally marginally drafted on the exterior surface. Set firmly into the east wall of the docking area is a mooring-ring by which a line from a ship could be secured (fig. 4).

An integral part of the quay of the earliest port is a series of four connected basins hewn from the native rock (see fig. 5, plan and section, and fig. 6 photograph of Basin 1). The north wall of each of the four basins has an opening through which water could be conducted from basin to basin and from Basin 1 to the sea. A notch on the side of each of these doorways provided the seats for sluice gates, which controlled the flow of water. The most plausible explanation for this construction, at the present stage of our study, is that the four basins constitute a system for filtering by sedimentation and storing fresh water at the port where it would be available to be taken aboard ships sailing from the harbor. Water from the hills to the south would have been conducted into Basin 4, where the first settling would have taken place. The clearer water from the basin would then have been allowed

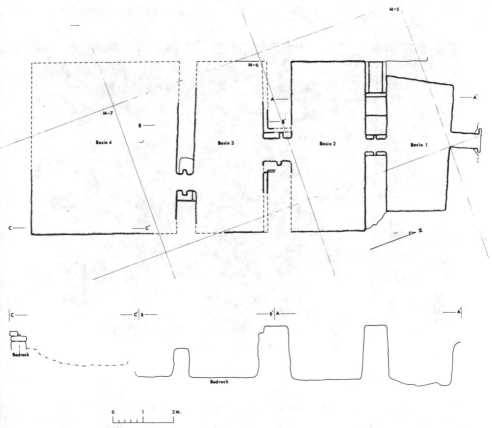

FIG. 5. Plan and section of the four connected basins hewn from the natural rock.

to flow over the top of the sluice gate, which served as a spillway, into Basin 3. The same process of sedimentation would have taken place in Basins 3 and 2 in a process of further cleaning until the purified and potable water was caught in Basin 1, from which it was easily accessible to ships within the harbor. The levels of the spillways could have been lowered periodically by the partial removal of the upper sections of the sluice gates. The sediment that accumulated in the bottoms of the basins could have been flushed out to sea by the complete removal of all the sluice gates. One additional feature in the plan of Basin 1 supports the hypothesis sketched above for the use of the water system. It is a dipping basin cut into the north wall of the basin nearest to the sea. Three steps led down to it from the quay to the east and the rock wall that separated the dipping basin from Basin 1 was pierced with a hole to allow the water to flow freely into it. Within the debris that filled the dipping basin there were found the upper parts of four amphorae,

FIG. 6.   A view of Basin 1, looking eastward.

which may well have been broken at the time of the last use of this device.

Two buildings in the complex seem to have been contemporaneous with the early quay. Building 1 (fig. 2) has a north wall built of marginally drafted stones well fitted together in the same style as masonry of the early quay. To the southwest of it Building 2, although built of large ashlar blocks set header-and-stretcher, seems because of its orientation to belong to the same period of use. Two coins dating from the 1st century A.D. found in the vicinity of these two large buildings suggest that the earliest use of the area is to be dated from the 1st century. A coin from the 2d century A.D., found within the debris of Basin 1, provided evidence for the continued use of the water system in that period.

The quay of the early period was eventually enlarged. The sea walls to the east and to the west along the two estuaries were abandoned and the north sea wall was enlarged by additions at each end. Maintaining the line of the sea wall of the original quay, an addition was built for a distance of 9.50 meters to the west. The eastern extension of the original quay was traced for a distance of 34.70 meters. Two features distinguish the additions from the original construction: the stones are considerably larger and many of them exhibit previous architectural use. Obviously some important building had been dismantled and looted of its stones for the enlargement of the port facility.

Midway along the line of this enlarged quay a large header projects some 0.33 meter beyond the sea wall. The projection has a circular opening 0.21 meter in diameter, that served as a mooring-ring for ships (fig. 3). The edges of the circular hole are worn smooth by the action of lines from ships offshore.

The foundation walls of several buildings are bonded into the eastern extension of the quay and must belong to what were once warehouses or other buildings connected with the activity of the port. Unfortunately looting and rebuilding in the area have made it impossible to trace the outline of a coherent plan for this period of the use of the port area. As yet the dating of this subsequent use of the port is not firmly worked out. Of the 98 identifiable coins found scattered about Area I, 49 percent were minted in the 4th century A.D., while only one coin of the 3d century was found. Thus it would seem that the 4th century represented the major period of use of the area as a port and the expanded facilities represented by the long quay with its adjacent buildings should probably date to that century.

Area II. When it became apparent that there were no remains earlier than the 1st century A.D. in Area I we picked a new site with the hope that it might be productive of remains from the Phoenician period of occupation. The place chosen for a sounding was a hill that rises approximately 12 meters above sea level at Râs el-Qantara, the promontory that shelters the modern fishing harbor to the east. The site, called Area II, lies about 400 meters to the northeast of the Roman-Byzantine port. Although no fragments of pottery earlier than the Hellenistic period could be found on the surface, there was the possibility that this low hill could have been the accumulation of earlier urban settlements at Sarafand and have been able to record the sequence of occupation from about 1300 B.C., when this site was first settled, down through early Byzantine times, when it was finally abandoned.

In the 1970 season we were able to chart the stratigraphy of the site in an area of 100 square meters, where there appeared nine architectural levels, each with its distinctive plan of buildings. The earliest evidence on the bedrock, 5 meters below the surface, consisted of a distinctive type of pottery (white shipware) that had been imported from Cyprus somewhere about the beginning of the 13th century B.C. Above this level was a series of buildings that extended without interruption down to the Roman period. During the 1971 season we enlarged this original sounding to an area of

FIG. 7. The remains of the firing chamber of a circular pottery kiln of the Phoenician period discovered in Area II.

FIG. 8.   An installation for pressing olives: A large crushing basin (right), a press
(left), and a basin for collecting the oil (between the two).

600 square meters in an attempt to recover larger sections of the city plans
for each of the levels discovered in the smaller soundings of the preceding
season. Four major strata were excavated and correlated with the material
found at these levels in the 1970 season.

The section of the ancient city we had selected had, throughout a period
of about a thousand years, been given over to industrial purposes, the manufacture of pottery and the pressing of olives for their oil. The evidence for
potterymaking came from levels that belong to the cities of the Iron Age;
while that for the pressing of olives is to be dated to the Hellenistic and
Roman periods.

Two fairly complete pottery kilns were discovered, and fragmentary
evidence for four more was found. The largest and best preserved consists
of a circular structure of stone lined with clay (fig. 7) that measures 3 meters
in diameter on the inside. On one side there is a well-formed doorway, 0.30
meter wide, from which the kiln, when filled with vessels, was fired. Opposite the doorway on the other side of the circular structure there is a projecting wall extending slightly more than halfway into the circular chamber.

This wall probably served as a support for the domed roof of the kiln, built of clay and equipped with flues to allow the smoke from the fire to escape. Since there was no evidence for a platform within the kiln to separate the firing chamber from the vessels to be fired, it may be conjectured that the vessels were stacked on the floor. The heat from the firing chamber would then have been conducted through the stacked vessels in the direction of the flues at the top of the structure. When the firing process was complete the temporary dome would have been destroyed and the vessels removed from the kiln. The walls of the kiln evidenced successive replastering with layers of clay, about 1 centimeter thick, which had been burned red in the process of firing.

Ten meters distant from this kiln appeared another example similar in plan but smaller. Its diameter measured 2.10 meters on the inside. Beside the latter kiln there was found a plastered tank, measuring 4.60 by 5 meters, partly filled with well-levigated yellow clay, which had apparently been prepared for turning into vessels. Further evidence for the use of this area for the manufacture of pottery appeared in the form of heaps of sherds from vessels that had been blistered, cracked, or warped in the firing process. From these heaps of discards, sometimes over 1.50 meters high, we were able to document the pottery styles for the periods to which they belonged. During the 1971 season alone more than 2,500 samples of stratified pottery were counted, classified, and recorded. When these data on about a quarter of a million sherds are processed we should have a useful qualitative and quantitative analysis of the pottery of the Iron Age in Phoenicia.

A well-preserved installation is that of the olive press, which appears to have been in use during the Hellenistic and Early Roman periods. It consisted of three principal elements, each hewn from a large block of stone (fig. 8): (1) The circular crushing basin, 1.50 meters in diameter, had been hollowed out to provide a track or groove for the crushing stone that was rolled around the basin. In the center of the basin a raised portion had been left in the center as a support for an upright post to which the axle for the crushing stone was pivoted. The ripe olives were first crushed by this device; the pits and pulp were then dipped from the crushing basin and placed in the pressing basin, the second element of the installation. (2) About a meter to the east there is a pressing basin, 1.10 meters in diameter, with a shallow rim pierced with a channel by which oil could be drained off into the adjacent basin. Although no pressing weight was found it is reasonably certain from other examples of olive presses that a heavy stone was attached to a cantilevered bar over a fulcrum and weighted on the other end. By this means a single operator could bring the heavy stone down with sufficient pressure to extract the oil from the crushed olive pulp. (3) The stone basin provided to catch the pressed oil from the press measured 0.80 meter in diameter at the rim and has a capacity of 37.5 U. S. gallons. All of these elements are known from the well-preserved Hellenistic olive press found at Umm el'Amed, 19 kilometers south of Tyre (Dunand and Duru, 1962, pp. 81-84, figs. 18, 19).

What is unique in this installation is a secondary press consisting of two elements. The first is a column of stone, 0.95 high and 0.69 meter in diameter, which had been cut on the top to provide a setting for a block of wood

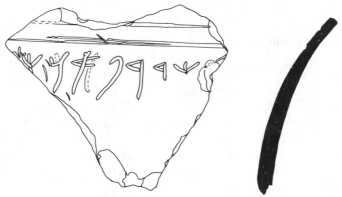

FIG. 9.   A dedication to the Phoenician god Shadrapa on a fragment of a storage jar.

FIG. 10.   Potsherd inscribed with six letters of the Phoenician alphabet in order (upper line) and the dedication "A lamb for our lord Ger Melqar[t]" (second line).

to which a horizontal level could be attached for turning the column. The stone is mounted on a smooth stone base that sloped slightly toward an adjacent wall. When the circular stone was turned by means of the attached lever a quarter to a half turn it would be thrown against the wall beside it by this eccentric mounting. The second element consisted of a well-worn curved backing to a wall that provided the stationary part of the press. It would appear that the remains from the first pressing of the olives were given a second pressing (probably confined in a bag of porous material) to extract the remaining oil. The installation also had a tank of well-built stones cemented together to contain oil or a byproduct of the pressing.

Evidence for writing in the Phoenician script was found on a dozen potsherds. One shoulder of a jar bore a dedication in a 6th-century B.C. script to the Phoenician god Shadrapa, a deity known from Leptis Magna, Carthage, and elsewhere (fig. 9). The longest inscription consisted of two lines of writing (fig. 10). The lower can be read as 'm r l' d n n g r m l q r [t]. "A lamb for our lord Ger-Melqar [t]." The upper line is a portion of an abecedary containing the six letters of the Phoenician alphabet ḥ w z ḥ ṭ y This first example of an abecedary in the Phoenician script makes it clear that the order of at least six of the letters is the same as that of the Ugaritic alphabet, documented on a tablet of the 14th century B.C., and of the Hebrew alphabet as it is known from the acrostic Psalm 119. Our text is to be dated to the 5th-4th centuries B.C.

The most important inscription found thus far in the excavations is a stone stamp seal, 1.9 centimeters in length and pierced longitudinally, possibly for a cord for suspension around the neck (fig. 11). There are three lines of writing. The top line gives a name, 'm. . . , the last letter of which is broken away. The second line is complete with the place name ṣ r p t, Sarepta, or Zarephath, as it appears in I Kings 17:9. The third line is the number 32, or the abbreviation of a personal name ', followed by the numeral 12. The appearance of the place name of Sarepta on a personal seal from about 400 B.C. is a confirmation of the earlier guesses that the site of the ancient Sarepta is at Sarafand.

In addition to the objects mentioned above, hundreds of artifacts were found and catalogued — clay vessels, beads, copper and iron implements, glass, figurines, clay masks, etc. The interpretation of this mass of evidence will require further study and analysis before a clear picture emerges of the daily life of the Phoenicians and their contacts. For the present it is safe to say that we have here in this first stratified urban settlement yet to be discovered in the homeland of the Phoenicians a rich and unique record of a significant people and their culture.

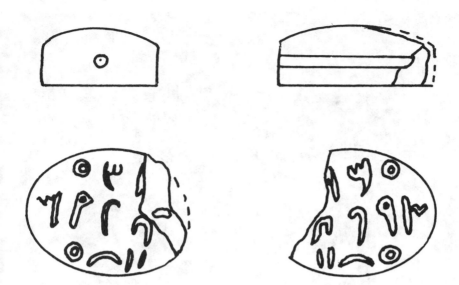

FIG. 11. Drawing of stamp seal with the name "Sarepta" on second line. Seal (top and left); impression (right).

The principal discovery of the 1972 season (fig. 12) was a shrine, a rectangular structure of one room, measuring 2 by 6.10 meters (fig. 13). Its walls were built of well-cut sandstone blocks set in the familiar Phoenician pattern of header (short side out) and stretcher (long face outside) (Pritchard, 1975). The floor is a single cement slab, about 10-13 centimeters thick. It appears that the temple was in use during the 7th and 6th centuries B.C.

At the west end of the room there is a stone altar, 0.94 by 1 meter, with a single step before it. The altar had been faced with slabs of white chalkstone, traces of which remain on the front side. A short distance before the step of the altar there had stood a stone betyl, or standing stone characteristic of Phoenician temples as they have been known from designs on coins and in descriptions in classical writings. A clear impression of the base of the sacred pillar, 40 by 40 centimeters, remains in the cement floor, but this important cultic object had been looted when the temple was destroyed. Benches of stone overlaid with plaster lined the four walls of the room; they had once served as tables on which offerings were presented to the gods.

The objects strewn about the floor, principally in the area of the altar, provide clues for reconstructing Phoenician religious practices and beliefs. More than 180 different objects of terracotta, faience, alabaster, glass, carnelian, and ivory were found and recorded.

FIG. 12.   General view of the excavation of 1972.

Beads were numerous, as were small amulets pierced for suspension. Faience pendants of Egyptian deities were found, such as Ptah, Thoth, the lion-headed Sekhmet, the cat-headed Bastet, and Bes. A half dozen plaques, also pierced for suspension around the neck, have the representation of the well-known Egyptian charm, the "Eye of Horus." These apotropaic or good-luck charms were probably brought from Egypt by Phoenician sailors who are known to have traded throughout the Mediterranean.

More direct evidence for the practices of the cult was provided by a collection of fertility figurines generally associated with Astarte, the Phoenician goddess of love. Altogether, fragments from 13 different figurines in terracotta can be identified. Among them are two examples of a seated woman playing a tambourine and a figure seated on a throne supported by two sphinxes. Many of the figurines are lavishly decorated with red and black paint.

FIG. 13. Shrine with offering table (at top).

The best preserved of the small figures are faience statuettes. One is of the Egyptian god Horus as a child with a sidelock of hair, and another is that of the god Thoth represented as a seated baboon.

Evidence for the rites performed in the temple is provided by other cultic objects. Parts of a terracotta mask appeared with holes around the edges for the cords or thongs which may once have held it over the face of a functionary of the shrine. A part of an incense stand and the side of a box-like cultic house were remnants of the furniture with which the temple had been provided.

Three pieces of carved ivory were found. The most artistic is that of a woman wearing a heavy wig and a crown of the Egyptian uraeus, or sacred cobra. The ivory carver had succeeded in portraying the woman's face with a faint smile. Another ivory figure of a female, originally in full figure but now broken into six pieces, can eventually be reconstructed.

Other articles of value in the cache found on the temple floor served utilitarian rather than purely religious or magical purposes. A delicately cut alabaster container for eye-paint was found partly filled with kohl. A faience top to a cosmetic jar was among the discarded objects. Twelve small circular disks of pottery are of a kind known to have been used as playing pieces for a chesslike game.

REFERENCES

PRITCHARD, JAMES B.
>
> 1971a. The Phoenician city of Sarepta.   Archaeology, vol. 24, no. 1, pp. 61-63, illus.
>
> 1971b. The Phoenicians in their homeland.   Expedition, vol. 14, no. 1, pp. 14-23, illus.
>
> 1972. Sarepta in history and tradition.   Pp. 99-114 *in* "Understanding the Sacred Text," John Reumann, ed. Judson Press, Valley Forge, Pennsylvania.
>
> 1975. Sarepta: A preliminary report on the Iron Age, 114 pp.   Museum Monographs, University Museum, Philadelphia.

DUNAND, M., and DURU, R.
>
> 1962. Oumm el-'Amed, une ville de l'époque hellénistique aux échelles de Tyr, pp. 81-84, illus. Paris.

JAMES B. PRITCHARD

Marine Biological and Archeological Expedition
to Southeast Oceania

Principal Investigator: John E. Randall, Bernice P. Bishop Museum, Honolulu, Hawaii.

Grant No. 821:   To study and collect fishes and marine invertebrates and to make a preliminary archeological reconnaissance of Pitcairn, Rapa, Cook Islands, and other Pacific islands from the schooner *Westward.*

A grant from the National Geographic Society to the Bishop Museum, Honolulu, Hawaii, provided for a marine biological-archeological expedition to 28 different islands of southeast Oceania on the sailing vessel *Westward,* then owned by the Oceanic Foundation of Hawaii. The Foundation donated half of the cost of vessel operation. The *Westward* is a 99-foot Marconi-staysail schooner rigged with square sail and raffee on the foremast. Steel-hulled, she was built in Germany in 1961.

In addition to myself as ichthyologist there were three other scientists on the cruise: Dr. Dennis M. Devaney, invertebrate marine biologist, and Dr. Yosihiko Sinoto, anthropologist, both of the Bishop Museum, and Dr. Harald A. Rehder, malacologist of the Smithsonian Institution. Two students of the University of Hawaii, Rich Costello and Aki Sinoto, were members of the crew. Rich and another crew member, David Bryant, conducted research on cetaceans (principally dolphins) during the trip, and Aki assisted his father in archeological excavation of ancient Polynesian sites. Dr. Guy S. Haywood, a neurosurgeon from Maui, was the ship's doctor and occasional fisherman; his son Jim was one of the crew. The able Captain was Roger Gray, and his wife, Frances, served us well as cook. Dennis Hewett was engineer and generally a great help to us all in many capacities. Others of the crew were Dean B. Cannoy and Rhett McNair, both experienced divers. Rhett was especially pleased to participate in the cruise, for it gave him an opportunity to test a new type of powerhead (an explosive device for killing sharks underwater), which he had invented.

Westward left Oahu in October 1970 for Tahiti. The only scientist aboard for this leg of the trip was Dr. Rehder. Drs. Devaney, Sinoto, and I flew to join the vessel in Papeete. On December 2 we left Tahiti and headed southeast for Mangareva. French authorities in Tahiti were worried about

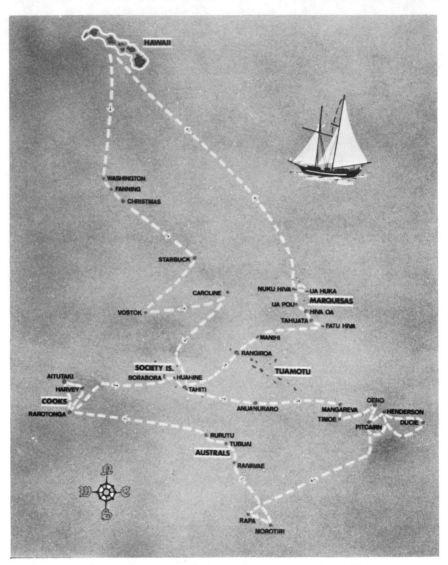

FIG. 1.   The route of the *Westward* in southeast Oceania. (Prepared by Department of Anthropology, Bernice P. Bishop Museum.)

our passing near Muruoa, the island where they set off nuclear test explosions, and so they requested that we take a French scientist with us as far as Mangareva. This was marine biologist Jean Pierre Bablet. Young and enthusiastic, he assisted us in diving operations at Mangareva.

FIG. 2. The schooner *Westward* at anchor off Rikitea, Mangareva, Tuamotu Archipelago, in December 1970. (Photo by John E. Randall.)

The first three days out of Tahiti we were thankful for the vessel's big diesel engine for we had strong head winds and rough seas.

On December 6 we made a brief stop at the uninhabited atoll of Anua-nuraro, diving in both the lagoon and outer reef. We arrived at Mangareva on December 9 in the rain, threading our way through a maze of coral reefs to drop anchor off the principal settlement of Rikitea.

Mangareva consists of a group of high islands enclosed by a barrier reef at the southeastern end of the Tuamotu Archipelago at 23° S. The name applies also to the largest of the islands (about 1 by 4 miles) on which Riki-tea is located. The total population is about 1,600.

We spent a productive week on Mangareva, running four rotenone stations for fishes and spearing several important species. At one place outside the barrier reef we scouted a promising location for the use of the fish poison at 100 feet. As I was about to mix the rotenone, divers McNair and Cannoy suddenly emerged from the water with the announcement that we should perhaps consider some other site. They had just sighted a mako shark that seemed as large as a 10½-footer they had caught a month earlier from *Westward* off Caroline Atoll about 500 miles north of Tahiti. The mako is a swift, sharp-nosed, streamlined shark of the open ocean rarely seen inshore. A porpoise had been found in pieces in the stomach of the mako from Caroline. This had come as a surprise to me, for the mako has slender, protruding, raptorial teeth, which are admirably suited for seizing small slippery prey such as fishes but which would seem ill-adapted to bite pieces from an adult porpoise. Nevertheless, the teeth had obviously functioned well on the porpoise. We motored our boat a considerable distance before we entered the sea again at Mangareva.

We had been approached in Tahiti by Len and Thelma Brown of Pitcairn who wanted us to transport them and two of their children back to Pitcairn. They had gone on a yacht to Papeete for medical reasons. They joined the vessel at Mangareva just before our departure.

At Yosi Sinoto's request we stopped at the uninhabited atoll of Temoe 25 miles southeast of Mangareva. He wanted to examine the marae (burial structures) at the island. The marae of Mangareva had been destroyed by the priest Pierre Laval between 1834 and 1871 in building the largest church in French Polynesia. While Yosi investigated the marae of Temoe several of us made a small but very valuable fish collection at 100 feet outside the reef in incredibly clear water.

Two days out of Temoe we reached the atoll of Oeno in the Pitcairn group. I had once seen this from the air on a flight from Easter Island to

FIG. 3. A school of small barracudas *(Sphyraena helleri)* off Oeno, Pitcairn group. (Photo by John E. Randall.)

Tahiti. It was like a glittering emerald narrowly wreathed in white set in cobalt. Although uninhabited, it is visited on rare occasions by Pitcairn islanders. Len Brown had been there and was helpful in showing us a place where we could take a small boat over the reef to the sheltered lagoon, but we had to wait for a period of lower surf to make the dash across the reef.

In spite of rain most of the day, we ran successful rotenone stations in the lagoon and outside the reef where the *Westward* had anchored in about 50 feet. While the lagoon station was in progress, Dr. Haywood and others fished with hook and line from the vessel and caught 78 fishes, including two dogtooth tunas to 49 pounds, five red snappers to 36 pounds, 9 black jacks *(Caranx lugubris)* to 13 pounds, 17 groupers *(Epinephelus fasciatus)*, and 35 lethrinids of the species *Gnathodentex aureolineatus*.

Just before darkness on the second day, Dean Cannoy powerheaded a large moray of the species *Gymnothorax javanicus*. It was 6 feet 3 inches long and weighed 54 pounds. Later at Pitcairn, Rhett McNair took a 45-pounder (5 feet 4 inches long) that had an 8-inch porcupinefish *(Diodon)* in its stomach.

We motored overnight the 80 miles to Pitcairn, arriving at 8:30 a.m. on

December 20, with the Browns waving wildly to their friends on shore. We anchored in 12 fathoms off Bounty Bay, and soon the ship was swarming with people from Pitcairn who came out in their two 37-foot longboats. Formerly equipped only with oars, these boats are now diesel-powered. The islanders are all expert seamen and experienced with the treacherous waves of Bounty Bay. Customarily they take their boats out to ships that stop at the island rather than wait for visitors to try to enter the bay.

Pitcairn is a small island (1 by 2 miles) of volcanic origin lying about 1,350 miles east-southeast of Tahiti. It is rugged in topography, the highest point nearly 1,000 feet above sea level. Along most shores, cliffs of reddish brown or black lava rock plunge almost vertically into the sea. There are no sand beaches. Most of the island is thickly verdant, reflecting the abundant rainfall (about 80 inches annually), but there are no permanent streams.

When we arrived, Pitcairn had 93 inhabitants, although before we left the number rose to 94. Dr. Haywood delivered the daughter of Tom and Betty Christian. Tom, the island's radio operator, is the great-great-great grandson of Fletcher Christian who led the mutineers of H.M.S. *Bounty* to Pitcairn.

Pitcairn was discovered by H.M.S. *Swallow* in 1767, but landing was impossible because of the surf which "broke upon it with great violence." Christian and nine other mutineers arrived in 1790, bringing with them 12 Tahitian women and six Tahitian men. They ran the *Bounty* ashore and burned her at the edge of Bounty Bay. We had wanted to dive on the site, though all we would have seen would have been ballast stones in about 15 feet of water, but the surf was so heavy during our stay that we did not attempt this.

When Europeans first came to the islands of the Pitcairn group, none was inhabited. But there is ample evidence from marae, petroglyphs, a tiki, and adzes that Pitcairn had been occupied by Polynesians at an earlier date. Some archeological work had been carried out at the island, but more excavations were needed.

The islanders who came aboard seemed mainly Caucasian in appearance, but a number of them clearly showed their Tahitian ancestry. One was Pervis Young, a descendant of Midshipman Young, the second in command of the mutineers. Pervis is the chief magistrate of the island. He invited Sinoto and me to stay ashore at his house. Everyone on our vessel was more or less adopted by a Pitcairn family and encouraged to spend as much time ashore with them as possible.

The opportunity for a base ashore was most welcome to me, for I require a more stable area for fish photography than *Westward,* which rolled heavily off Pitcairn. Also, the island's 220-volt current would be available to me (until the generator was turned off at 11 p.m.). Living ashore was a great advantage to Sinoto too for his excavations.

In contrast to Mangareva and Oeno, which have well-developed littoral coral reefs, the inshore environment of Pitcairn consists mainly of large basalt boulders with a thick covering of brown algae *(Sargassum,* etc.). Coral is rare in shallow water except in a few sheltered deep tidepools. Undoubtedly the consistently heavy surf is the major factor in the paucity of coral. There is relatively little sand inshore, but at depths of about 50 feet or more the bottom is mostly sand; what rock there is has a low profile.

Advice from island fishermen led us, however, to some well-developed coral reefs in deeper water. One off Adamstown occurs at 70 to 100 feet (here we found two crown-of-thorns starfish), and another called "The Bear" off Gannet Ridge rises 30 feet above a sand bottom at 145 feet. Our most successful rotenone stations were either in tidepools or at these deep reefs. The most noteworthy was the one at "The Bear" where three teams of two divers went down. Among the fishes we took were a new butterflyfish, a large and undescribed angelfish of the genus *Genicanthus,* two new wrasses *(Pseudocheilinus* and *Halichoeres,* though I had collected both previously in the Marshall Islands), a new soldierfish *(Myripristis randalli* Greenfield), and two apparently new squirrelfishes *(Adioryx).*

The local names for fishes are an interesting combination of English, Polynesian, and local "Pitcairnese." Some of the English names have been applied to very different fishes from those of European waters. The "cod," for example, is the grouper *Epinephelus tauvina,* and the "goatfish" is a triggerfish *(Sufflamen bursa* and other balistids). The names of Polynesian origin have made the transfer from Tahiti more successfully. A few examples are "hue" for puffers *(Arothron),* "moi" for a species of threadfin *(Polydactylus sexfilis),* "po' ou" for the wrasse *Thalassoma purpureum,* and "buhi" for moray eels (from the Tahitian "puhi"). Some of the local Pitcairn fish names are quaintly unique, such as "jackass" for the dogtooth tuna, "pic pic" for the bait-stealing triggerfish *Xanthichthys,* "mummy" for the damselfish *Abudefduf sordidus,* "archie" for the abundant *Pseudolabrus inscriptus,* "Auntie-and-Ann" *(Cephalopholis urodelus),* "whistling daughter" *(Thalassoma lutescens),* and "Elwyns' trousers" *(Coris)* — these last three appeared on stamps issued in 1970.

The fish fauna of Pitcairn is mainly tropical Indo-Pacific in origin. It is somewhat impoverished; the total number of species we took at the islands of the Pitcairn group is about 250. In addition to those mentioned above from the deep reef station, we collected other apparently undescribed species including a new high-finned parrotfish *(Scarus)*, an undescribed half-black, half-yellow butterflyfish *(Chaetodon)*, and an unidentified species of *Paracaesio*. The next to last day at Pitcairn we finally captured some sand lances, which had on several occasions led us on a merry chase as they dived in and out of the sand. These represent the first species of the family Ammodytidae from the South Seas.

We have perhaps 30 undescribed species of fishes from the Pitcairn group, but most of them have been taken previously or were collected later during the cruise at other islands. Thus the level of native species of fishes at Pitcairn is low. The studies of our collections have not progressed to the point where we can state the level of endemism with confidence, but 2 percent seems to be a reasonable estimate at this time.

As predicted, there proved to be a link between Easter Island and Pitcairn. Several fishes thought to be unique to Easter turned up in our collections at Pitcairn; thus the level of endemism of Easter Island is considerably lower than first believed.

The success of the marine biological part of the expedition was to be equaled by Dr. Sinoto's archeological research. For his digging he enlisted the aid of Pitcairn men. The payment of $5 per day seems modest by our standards but is very good at Pitcairn, and many of the island's men wanted to work for Sinoto. As a result, he rotated his field crews from day to day.

His most exciting discovery was an ancient round-ended pit house, which was built before A.D. 1350 (radiocarbon dating). This dwelling was used by adz-makers who brought stones there from a quarry site. Thousands of stone flakes were found, but only a few unfinished adzes.

Knowing the islanders' dependence on miro wood *(Thespesia populnea)* for their carvings, we offered to take some of them to Henderson Island to cut miro timber, which has been depleted on Pitcairn (though they have begun to cultivate it there). Nothing could have pleased them more. Their woodcarving is second only to the sale of postage stamps as a source of income. It is easy to see why it is hard for the people of Pitcairn to get money. Their contact with the outside world is limited to just an occasional passing ship.

The rest of us wanted to visit Henderson too, especially Sinoto who had been told of a cave in which ancient adzes had been found. We started the 105-mile run to that island the evening of January 10 with 14 Pitcairn men aboard, towing their 28-foot open boat, the *Dumpy*. We arrived shortly after noon the next day.

FIG. 4. The slate-pencil urchin *(Heterocentrotus)* at Henderson Island, Pitcairn group, is a lovely orange-red in life. (Photo by John E. Randall.)

Henderson is an elevated coral island about 3 miles wide and over 5 miles long; it is 100 feet at its highest point. Cliffs of about 50 feet drop directly into the sea around most of the island. There are many caves in the cliffs both above and below the sea. The interior of the island is deeply dissected by crevices with jagged sides and so heavily overgrown with trees and other plants that traversing it by foot is both hard and hazardous.

Sinoto and his son and 12 of the islanders disembarked off the north shore where there is an attractive sandy beach and a stand of tall coconut palms planted years before by Pitcairn people. Two of the younger men of Pitcairn, Steve Christian and Noggie Young, stayed with the ship, for they wanted to accompany us to Ducie, the fourth island of the Pitcairn group, which lies 190 miles to the east of Henderson. Before leaving Henderson, we spent the rest of the day diving at several localities along the northwest and western shores. Several fishes were speared, among them a specimen of the wrasse *Bodianus bilunulatus* in 110 feet. This is the first record for Oceania, except for Hawaii.

Reaching Ducie at noon of January 13, we first circled the atoll, which is only 1.3 miles at its widest point. I went aloft on the foremast to get a good view of the outer reef area. As we sailed around the island, we caught five yellowtail *(Seriola lalandi)* and one yellowfin tuna on a trolling line. While bringing in one of the smaller yellowtail, I could see it being pursued futilely by three large yellowfin tuna and two frigatebirds.

Though Ducie is one of the least visited islands on this earth, it has the distinction of being among the first to be found in the Pacific. The discovery is attributed to Captain Edwards of H.M.S. *Pandora* on his mission in 1791 to search for the *Bounty* mutineers; however, Dr. Rehder and I have ascertained that the first European to sight it was Queirós in 1606, who first named it Luna-Puesta (later he changed the name to La Encarnación).

The atoll was reported to be without a passage to the lagoon; however, we noted what seemed to be a navigable shallow channel at the southwest corner, off which we anchored *Westward* in 6 fathoms. With a small boat we were able to enter the lagoon, but when coming out at low tide we had to walk the boat through a maze of small coral heads.

Within minutes of setting the anchor, we caught a 7-foot Galápagos shark from the *Westward.* Two more of about the same size were soon boated, as was a smaller gray reef shark. With such a start on fishing, we thought we would fill the vessel with sharks before morning but caught only one small gray during the night.

When we dived outside the reef we were amazed at the fearless approach of the black jacks and the large yellowtail. One large jack grabbed the tip of my small multiprong spear; another misjudged a turn as it approached and slammed into my leg with its tail. Jim Haywood discovered that he could feed the jacks by hand with pieces of octopus within a few minutes after entering the sea.

The most striking thing about the marine realm of the atoll was the evidence that an extensive coral kill had taken place in the past — both in the lagoon and in outer reef zones. Judged from the overgrowth by coralline red algae, the corals had been dead for well over a year. Occasional small heads of coral were still alive here and there, but in all the places where we dived or over which we were towed the majority of the corals were dead. In spite of intensive searching we found only one crown-of-thorns starfish.

In spite of the ease with which we caught a few species of fishes by handline, the over-all biomass of fishes at the atoll was low. This was especially true of the lagoon. The number of species of fishes was also low. We collected a total of 111 species and sighted another 27. While it is true that 2½ days are hardly enough to collect and observe the entire fish fauna of an island, it was obvious from our recent diving at other islands of the Pitcairn group that Ducie had much the poorest fauna.

We wisely refrained from eating any of the large jacks we caught, for these are prone to cause a type of fish poisoning known as ciguatera (as are other large piscivorous species such as barracuda, morays, and certain groupers and snappers). Irving Johnson of the 96-foot brigantine *Yankee* visited Ducie for only 3 hours in 1937. A black jack was caught and served as a birthday dinner to one of the crew. The result was ciguatera. Irving wrote, "We were all incredibly sick. Luckily my wife for the first time in her life made herself throw up and, while she still had some of the symptoms, she was able to take the wheel the entire night and part of the day while the rest of us couldn't even crawl without fainting. Some symptoms last as much as seven weeks."

Since we were scheduled to pick up the Sinotos and Pitcairn islanders at Henderson on January 17, we had to leave Ducie sooner than we wished. We found Sinoto jubilant, for his cave digging had been most productive. In the deeper part of his excavation he had found basalt adzes, fragments of pearl shell hooks, and *Porites* coral files; the carbon dating was later established as A.D. 1160. The style of these artifacts suggested that the Polynesian owners had come from the Marquesas. Certainly the basalt adzes could not have been made at Henderson, for it is a limestone island without any basalt. And we saw no blacklip pearl oysters in the sea. It was interesting to note that the overlying strata showed a gradual change in culture, whereby the inhabitants had to adopt locally available resources for their tools. Their adzes were made from fossilized *Tridacna* shells and their fishhooks from the shell of a smaller species of oyster.

It required nearly a day to load all the miro wood and gear aboard *Westward,* and so the divers made good use of the time collecting fishes, etc. After one rotenone station gray sharks appeared and one had to be power-headed. A huge jack (*Caranx ignobilis*) was also attracted to the area and was taken the same way; it weighed 84 pounds.

Rising winds and increasing heavy surf made loading the wood and equipment at Henderson hard work. On the voyage back to Pitcairn the seas were very rough, and the *Dumpy* that we were towing began to break up in the night and had to be cut free. The men explained that it was an old boat; they have since constructed a new one.

We stayed only two more days at Pitcairn. I was in the water every minute frantically trying to spear the last few fishes I had often sighted but had not been able to collect. However, there were still 18 species left on my "wanted" list when we had to assemble our gear and head for the ship.

One of the Pitcairn boats, filled with islanders, came out to see us off. They sang two farewell songs in perfect harmony that deeply touched all of us on the *Westward*. We sailed away at sunset, filled with regret, for we all knew there was little chance we could see the fair isle of Pitcairn again. Our next stop would be Rapa, 800 miles to the west.

The 800-mile run from Pitcairn to Rapa was a glorious five days of "downhill" sailing for which the *Westward* was well designed. This was the first time since we had left Tahiti that she had been able to run with the wind.

We sighted Rapa on January 26 as a tiny jagged irregularity on the horizon. Captain Gray altered our course slightly, realizing at our present speed that we would arrive at the island during the night. Landfall after dark had to be avoided, as there are no lights to aid navigation, and the entrance to the principal anchorage is a maze of treacherous coral reefs.

Rapa, at lat. 27° 35′ S., is the southernmost island of French Polynesia. Although sometimes grouped with the Austral Islands to the northwest, it is sufficiently remote to be regarded as a distinct geographic entity.

Early the next day we cautiously approached the entrance to Rapa's Ha'urei Bay, and I noticed the water change from deep blue to gray. This was the same uninviting hue I had seen two years before when we visited Palmyra on *Westward*. The reason for this color in both areas was the same —heavy rainfall. Both islands get over 100 inches of rain in a year, hence much runoff from the land. Nearing the outlying coral reefs, we were thankful to see a skiff approaching with two Frenchmen who had come to pilot us into the bay.

Rapa's rugged topography, which had been apparent so far at sea, was breathtaking at anchor in magnificent Ha'urei Bay. The bay, which is reputed to be the crater of a long-extinct volcano, dissects into the center of the island. The mountains that rise around it are green to their summits, and during periods of rain, such as the time of our arrival, waterfalls cascade down the cliffs at many sites.

The first European contact with Rapa was made by George Vancouver of the English ship *Discovery* on December 22, 1791. Missionaries arrived in 1826, at which time the population was estimated at 2,000. A scant eight years later the population had dropped to about 300. In 1867 there were only 120 inhabitants on the island. The population loss was mainly the result of the ravages of Western diseases for which the Polynesians had little resistance. Other problems as a result of contact with Caucasians also contributed to the disastrous decline. Rapa thus followed the tragic pattern of so many South Seas islands.

In the 1971 census the population of Rapa was 411. The people live in two villages, the largest of Ha'urei on the south side of the bay and 'Area diagonally across on the northern shore.

Rapa is best known for its ancient mountaintop forts. Apparently at one time tribal warfare was common, probably as a result of overpopulation and limited lowland areas for taro production. From our anchorage we could see several of the forts. Though overgrown, the sites can easily be spotted by the terracing and central tower. By the time of Vancouver's arrival, one chief had gained ascendency over all the tribes, and the forts were not in use.

For food the Rapans rely heavily on taro, which they cultivate in low wet terraced fields (particularly toward the head of Ha'urei Bay), and on fish. The taro is rendered into sticky poi by boiling the tubers, pounding them with rocks, and ultimately by mixing by hand. The women of Rapa today use only squarish pieces of basalt to crush the taro, whereas their ancestors fashioned handsome stone poi-pounders with cylindrical handles which expanded to a broad convexly curved basal portion. Disconcerting also to the Western eye expecting Polynesian accoutrement for native activities are the modern gaudily colored plastic buckets and other containers that have permeated virtually every Rapan household.

Similarly, one sees few outrigger canoes in Rapa today. Nearly all the fishing is carried out from locally built boats 18 to 20 feet long and only 3 to 4 feet wide; native materials are used, however, except for imported planking, and the craftsmanship is exceptional. Most of the boats are powered by outboard motors. Rapans employ many types of fishing methods, including hook and line, trolling, spearfishing, gillnetting, and harpooning at night with a pressure gas lantern as a light source.

Dr. Sinoto and I recorded the Rapan native names of fishes by interviewing fishermen. We showed them fishes or illustrations of fishes from books, and they supplied the names. Sinoto, who is fluent in Tahitian, found that he could converse easily with the people of Rapa, whose native dialect has been largely supplanted by Tahitian. This language loss began with the arrival of the missionaries, many of whom were Tahitians and taught in church schools. One of the reasons for recording fish names was to obtain a linguistic link with the past. Under such circumstances animal and plant names would seem less likely to change than the common words of day-to-day conversation. Analyses of language similarities and differences are a useful adjunct in plotting migration routes of a mobile people such as the Polynesians. Another reason for documenting fish names was to gain insight into species that occur at Rapa which we might not see during our short stay.

Our first dives at Rapa were on the patch reefs at the entrance to the bay. We were surprised by the rich coral growth, including *Acropora* (Rapa must be near the southern limit for *Acropora* and some of the other reef-building corals). We could not fully enjoy the corals, however, because of the turbidity of the water. Also, the sea temperature was a cool 24° C. (considering that we were in Rapa during the warmest time of the year).

Within a few days the marine faunal picture of Rapa began to emerge. The majority of the fishes and other marine animals are well-known tropical Indo-Pacific species. In addition, there is a noteworthy segment of species that might be termed southern subtropical — species that were common either to Norfolk and Lord Howe to the west or to Pitcairn and even Easter to the east (and in some cases common to both east and west). We found only a few new species of fishes that are known only from Rapa (which is not saying these may not turn up elsewhere). In spite of its relatively isolated location, Rapa is evidently near enough to other islands not to have engendered an endemic marine biota.

Among our more spectacular new species of fishes were a half-yellow, half-black butterflyfish of the genus *Chaetodon* (described as *C. smithi* by Randall, 1974), which was more abundant at Rapa than Pitcairn; a new soldierfish *(Myripristis tiki)*, first taken at Easter and later at Pitcairn (Greenfield, 1974); a red cardinalfish *(Apogon),* which is blackish posteriorly (we had collected it previously at Pitcairn in the same inshore habitat); a new parrotfish of the genus *Scarus,* also first taken at Pitcairn and later discovered in the southern part of the Great Barrier Reef (Randall and Choat, MS.); a yellow damselfish *Glyphidodontops galbus* Allen and Randall (1974; see also Randall, 1973, p. 14); a slender bluish *Chromis* with dark median fins and a large black spot at the pectoral base (this damselfish, which occurs in large zooplankton-feeding aggregations, was collected earlier at Mangareva and Pitcairn); and a snapper of the genus *Pristipomoides* caught by hook and line in deeper water by Rapan fishermen (Kami, 1973). The colorful sharpnose puffer *Canthigaster epilamprus* was captured in deep dives; it is different enough at Rapa to warrant recognition as a new subspecies (Allen and Randall, in press).

The most abundant fishes at Rapa seen by divers are *Pseudolabrus fuentesi* (this wrasse is also the most common fish at Easter and Pitcairn); another wrasse, *Thalassoma lutescens;* the surgeonfish *Acanthurus leucopareius* (an antitropical insular species common at Easter, Hawaii, and Marcus); the drab damselfish *Stegastes fasciolatus;* and the above-mentioned yellow damselfish and *Chromis.* The jack most frequently seen was *Caranx cheilio;*

occasional groups would appear suddenly, circle a diver closely a few times, and move on. The most common grouper is *Epinephelus fasciatus,* except in the bay environment where *E. merra* predominates. Abundant on staghorn coral fringing reefs in Ha'urei Bay are the damselfishes *Dascyllus aruanus* and *Chromis atripectoralis.* In the shallow muddy inner reaches of the bay, the mullet *Mugil cephalus* is often sought by the Rapans with gill nets.

The only shark we saw while diving at Rapa was the Galápagos; we caught several up to 8 feet 2 inches in length. We took one other species, the tiger shark *(Galeocerdo cuvier).* A 10-footer, which weighed 385 pounds, had a partially digested seabird in its stomach and pieces of another tiger shark even larger than itself (probably it had been caught on another hook of the set line). Other species of sharks undoubtedly occur at Rapa. The fishermen instantly recognized an illustration of a hammerhead shark *(Sphyrna),* which they said is occasionally seen at Rapa. Another species they call "ma'o afata" might be the lemon shark *(Negaprion).*

Toward the end of our stay we were confident we had collected specimens of the majority of the species of inshore fishes at Rapa. Much effort was being expended to obtain the 16 species we had seen but not yet captured. We also turned to some deeper fishing with hook and line. Yosi Sinoto and Jim Haywood went out with two Rapans one day to fish in 70 fathoms. They returned with four fishes we had not yet collected: the previously mentioned *Pristipomoides,* the grouper *Epinephelus tuamotuensis* (recently described by Fourmanoir; very closely related to *morrhua),* the deep red bigeye *Cookeolus boops,* and the soapfish *Aulacocephalus temmincki,* which has never been recorded from any locality in Oceania. It is bright blue with a yellow band along the back. The Rapan fishermen professed never to have seen it. Later we obtained a new centrolophid fish of the genus *Schedophilus* (McAllister and Randall, 1975), which Rapan fishermen caught by deep handlining.

Yosi was very discouraged with his cave excavations at Rapa, which had resulted in almost no artifacts. All the caves he investigated are apparently subjected to enough moisture to cause the deterioration of most man-made objects. Even pearl shellfish hooks probably decompose in time in such an environment.

He was understandably very interested to hear of an ancient Polynesian canoe that had been found by Rapan people some years ago in a cave at Îlots de Bass (Polynesian name, Marotiri), a group of ten rocky islets that lie 45 nautical miles southeast of Rapa. He wanted to visit these islets, as did the marine biologists, and so on short notice, with the weather only marginal for such a venture, we left for Îlots de Bass on February 19. We sailed overnight in order to arrive early in the morning. As there was no protected anchorage, we dropped anchor in 150 feet off the largest islet (which had the cave). Since the skipper did not want to leave the ship in such an exposed location at night, we had only the daylight hours of the 20th for all we wanted to accomplish at Îlots de Bass. Yosi immediately went in the whaler with two Rapan guides and circled the islet looking for a place to land. It seemed impossible, with surge rising and falling nearly 20 feet at times on the clifflike shore, and so he came back very dejected. Later Aki, Rich, and the two Rapans managed to get ashore (though Rich once fell unhurt back into the sea). The cave was hastily explored; only one thing was found, the barbed end of a large wooden fishhook. Yosi said it looked like a Maori type from New Zealand. Some interesting stone structures high on the islet were investigated and photographed.

Aboard ship Rhett McNair and Jim Haywood began fishing for the highly prized yellowtail *(Seriola lalandi)* and other jacks for food. At many islands of the Pacific such fishes as these can cause ciguatera, but Rapa and Îlots de Bass seem to be too far south for the still-unknown reef organism that produces ciguatoxin. Along with the yellowtail, 21 Galápagos sharks were boated.

Although somewhat deterred by the obvious abundance of sharks, Dennis Devaney and I were still anxious to make some collections underwater. It seemed likely that we would be the first persons to dive at this remote, rarely visited place. We decided to go more inshore and ultimately selected a crevice at a depth of about 40 feet, which harbored a large aggregation of rudderfishes *(Kyphosus fuscus),* some in bright-yellow color phase. Dean and I ran a small station with rotenone just inshore of the gorge, Dennis collected mainly ophiuroids and crinoids, and Rhett guarded the three of us with his powerhead. A few sharks ventured near but retreated when Rhett approached with his weapon. Dean and I obtained some valuable fishes, though none we had not taken at Rapa. Back at the ship Dean's powerhead was flipped over the side by a rubber fender in the surge and sank to the bottom in 150 feet (though it hardly seemed that deep as the water was so clear). Four of us dived together to retrieve it, with six sharks circling. We were surprised to see the bottom almost completely covered with live coral (mostly *Acropora*).

After Rapa and Îlots de Bass our destination was Raivavae, Tubuai, and Rurutu in the Austral Islands. Although the marine life at these islands has not been well collected, there was no reason from their proximity to other islands of Polynesia to expect much in the way of endemic forms. Therefore we spent only three days there, beginning with Raivavae in February 25. Some valuable collection of fishes were made nevertheless, particularly at Rurutu where rotenone was set in 190 feet. I ran out of air rather suddenly at this depth and barely made the surface. Double vision and other symptoms of anoxia were experienced as a result.

We left Rurutu on February 28 for the 480-mile passage to Rarotonga in the Cook Islands. Winds were light, and we had to motor most of the way, arriving in the middle of the night of March 2. We laid offshore until dawn, then motored into the harbor of Avarua.

Rarotonga presented an interesting contrast to the sleepy Austral Islands. Though only 7 miles long, it has a population of about 13,000. It is a bustling little center of commerce, with a new jet airport, a paved road that encircles the island, and already too many vehicles. Agriculture is important, the principal crops being citrus, pineapples, bananas, and tomatoes. Most produce is shipped to New Zealand.

We had heard reports of numerous crown-of-thorns starfishes *(Acanthaster planci)* in the Cook Islands, and as time was short Dean and I took one of the small boats and remained to survey Rarotonga for the starfish as well as collect some fishes while the *Westward* went on a side trip to Aitutaki where Devaney and others checked on starfish population there.

Taking advantage of an unusually calm day, we made our first survey at Rarotonga off Avaavaroa Pass on the south shore. The Agriculture Officer, Walter Hambuechen, joined us in this. I was towed behind the boat in a zigzag course outside the reef over the coral-rich bottom to the south of the pass. I could see well to 70 feet and observed none of the usual signs of starfish activity — white patches on the coral indicating recent feeding. We decided to use aqualung tanks to investigate the reef deeper than we could see from the surface. In the zone of 80 to 125 feet we found ample evidence of *Acanthaster planci,* especially below 100 feet where 90 percent of the coral was dead. One starfish brought to our skiff was 15.7 inches in diameter and weighed nearly 3 pounds. Evidently the usual heavy swell from the south caused the starfishes to confine their activity to the deeper sectors of the reef.

On the north side of the island off the harbor area, where the wave action is generally less, we found numerous starfishes and heavy damage to the coral below depths of about 40 feet. In a roughly square area 60 feet on a side I counted 38 adult starfishes in a period of 30 minutes, 18 of which were actively feeding on coral. The coral of this area was 85 percent dead;

most of the surviving coral was *Porites,* a type the starfish generally avoid until the polyps of most of the other corals such as *Acropora* and *Pocillopora* have been eaten.

In order to determine if the starfishes were feeding, I detached each from the coral. If their stomach was everted onto the coral, I took a sample of the coral. When detached, a crown-of-thorns starfish folds its arms orally, thus forming a nearly complete spinous ball that tends to roll to and fro in channels when there is surge. On this day there were strong waves. One detached starfish rolled back with the surge and struck my hand as I was pulling another starfish free from the coral. I sustained a deep spine wound on one finger and seven punctures in my wrist. The pain was excruciating. Though some have contested the existence of a venom associated with the spines of *Acanthaster,* anyone injured by the spines does not question the presence of venom. The discomfort was confined mainly to the wrist and hand, but some pain radiated up my arm. The next day the pain had somewhat subsided in the limb but an over-all illness prevailed that necessitated bed rest.

Devaney found an area of coral knolls in the Aitutaki lagoon in which up to 90 percent of the branching corals were dead. Each of these knolls had several adult *Acanthaster* on it. He concluded from his survey that a single relatively small population of starfish moving in a southerly direction in the lagoon between the wreck of the *Alexander* and Tikoutu Point has been responsible for the coral damage he observed.

At only two of the islands we visited, Tahiti and Rarotonga, did we find heavy infestations of *Acanthaster planci.* I don't think it is any coincidence that these are much the most populous of the islands we investigated. They have the heaviest agriculture and the greatest use of pesticides. Aitutaki does not have a large human population but there has been extensive use of pesticides there too. The cause of the outbreaks of the crown-of-thorns starfish may therefore be chemical pollution by man (Randall, 1972, *Biotropica* 4(3):132-144). It is suggested that the pollutants — perhaps chlorinated hydrocarbon insecticides — reduce the population of one or more of the predators of the larval starfish in the plankton, thus resulting in a high survival of the young starfish. A comparable explanation might be given for the population explosion of sea urchins in the sea off southern California.

Westward left Rarotonga on March 13 for the return trip of 680 miles to Tahiti. We made a one-day stop at Bora Bora and spent the daylight hours of the next day at Huahine. Successful deep rotenone stations were carried out off each of these islands. We took specimens of a new deep-bodied

FIG. 5. John Randall aboard the *Westward* in the Marquesas. Photo by Helen Randall.

species of *Chromis* that I had collected previously only at Palau; a slender new moray of the genus *Uropterygius,* which was chestnut-brown with white markings on the head; the first scorpionfish of the subgenus *Hypomacrus* from the Society Islands; and the wrasse *Pseudojuloides cerasinus,* previously reported only from Hawaii. The rare trunkfish *Ostracion whitleyi* was observed at Huahine and later collected at Tahiti.

Back in Papeete on March 20 preparations soon began for the cruise back to Hawaii, which was to feature a month of collecting fishes in the Marquesas Islands. Since Harald, Dennis, and Yosi had all spent much time in the Marquesas, they left the *Westward* in Papeete. I had been to the Marquesas too, but only briefly in my own small ketch in 1957. I had done just enough diving to realize that these islands possessed a unique fish fauna that was begging to be explored. Now, after nearly 14 years, I was about to return, this time fully prepared to collect the fishes. My wife, Helen, joined me in this last leg of the cruise.

From March 28 to April 4 fish collections were made at Tahiti. As I had spent nearly two years of my life in research on fishes in the Society Islands, I concentrated my efforts on the deeper zones—some dives to 250 feet. Several valuable fishes were taken, including the angelfish *Centropyge multifasciatus,* a first record from Tahiti.

We stopped briefly at three atolls in the Tuamotus, Rangiroa, Manihi, and Takaroa, before reaching the Marquesas. At Rangiroa we were joined by Dr. Pierre Fourmanoir, a French ichthyologist, and assisted him in making fish collections there.

Since *Westward* could not enter the lagoon of Manihi because the pass is too shallow, we anchored outside in 70 feet. The vessel swung over a depth of 350 feet. Jim Haywood then began fishing and came up with a new species of triggerfish of the genus *Xanthichthys.* I went ashore to the village to photograph the fish. Manihi is famous for captive nurse sharks in a pool that children ride for sport. We wanted to film this action but encountered reluctance. We found out why when one boy displayed a recent wound from a bite on his thigh by one of the sharks. Nevertheless, one brave lad volunteered to ride a shark for our benefit and was rewarded with a bag of candy.

At Takaroa we tied *Westward* to the concrete quay in the pass. Our most valuable fishes from this atoll came from a rotenone station at the edge of the pass under the vessel at slack tide.

We arrived at Fatu Hiva, the southernmost island of the Marquesas, at 1 a.m. on April 18. We drifted about 1½ miles off Matahumu Point until daylight. We engaged in shark fishing while drifting and landed a 6½-foot oceanic whitetip *(Carcharhinus maou—longimanus* of most authors). It had squid beaks and porpoise flesh in its stomach. Our anchorage at Fatu Hiva was Omoa Bay. We used some of the whitetip for bait on our shark line and soon caught a 12-foot 3-inch tiger shark. I noticed there wasn't much swimming around *Westward* after that.

We stayed four days in Omoa Bay. These were the most exciting and productive of the entire cruise. Many specimens of fishes were taken by various methods. I photographed 42 species on shore in the home of the late chief Tetuanui. At least 12 of these are new, including a butterflyfish closely allied to *Chaetodon tinkeri* of the Hawaiian Islands (described as *C. decliois* by Randall, 1975); a parrotfish *(Scarus),* a wrasse *(Coris)* I had first collected in the Marquesas in 1957, a new damselfish of the genus *Chromis,* and a new and surprisingly abundant anthiine seabass of the subgenus *Mirolabrichthys.* Also we took the first specimens of *Chromis leucurus* and the squirrelfish *Flammeo sythrops* outside Hawaii, and the third record of the wrasse *Anampses melanurus.* Some well-known wide-ranging Indo-Pacific species were colored differently. The damselfish *Plectroglyphidodon*

FIG. 6. An undescribed species of moray eel *(Gymnothorax)* being "cleaned" by a juvenile wrasse *(Labroides dimidiatus)* at Nuku Hiva, Marquesas. (Photo by John E. Randall.)

imparipennis, for example, has broad brown bars on the body, whereas the fiery red angelfish *Centropyge loriculus* has lost its dark bars on the side of the body.

We spent only one day at the next island, Tahuata, but it was a memorable one, for here on a vertical wall of Vaitahu Bay I found a lovely new deep-red shrimp with white antennae to which Devaney had alerted me, and I managed to collect it. It was often associated with a dark-brown moray with a black area on the head covering the eye like a mask. I knew this eel to be undescribed from a specimen taken previously in the Line Islands, from *Westward* in 1968. I observed the shrimp on the body of the eel, and so it is evidently a cleaner. I also watched the moray being cleaned by the wrasse *Labroides dimidiatus,* the shrimp *Hippolysmata grabhami,* and a white *Stenopus* with a red spot on the side. I didn't collect the latter shrimp until we reached Nuku Hiva. It proved to be new (now being described by Drs. Bruce, Devaney, and the author).

The next stop was Hiva Oa, the largest and most populous of the southern group of Marquesas Islands. We spent four days in sheltered Tahauku

Bay. I set up for photography at the infirmary in the principal town of Atuona. Christian Rauzy, the medical technician there, was most helpful.

We collected fishes at a number of different habitats including a stream and a rocky shore of a muddy bay. Again several apparently new species resulted.

At the island of Ua Pou we made a prearranged rendezvous with Henri Lavondes, a French anthropologist who was then director of O.R.S.T.O.M. in Papeete. Henri and I then began our long-planned collaboration on a manuscript on the Marquesan names of fishes.

Henri sailed with us to Nuku Hiva. We anchored in murky Taiohae Bay on Helen's birthday, April 30, for which occasion we brought champagne from Tahiti. Except for a brief trip to Ua Huka on May 7 all our remaining time was spent collecting and photographing at Nuku Hiva, the seat of the government of the Marquesas. I set up for photography on the back porch of the home of one of the administrators.

Among the more significant discoveries at Nuku Hiva were the first record of the soldierfish *Myripristis vittatus* from the Pacific, a new sharpnose puffer *(Canthigaster)* (Allen and Randall, in press), a new goby *(Cryptocentrus)* living symbiotically with a red-barred snapping shrimp *(Alpheus,* n. sp.) (Randall and Banner, MS.), and a new yellow, blue-striped goatfish of the genus *Mulloidichthys,* which swims with and mimics the snapper *Lutjanus kasmira* (Randall and Guézé, MS.).

The two University of Hawaii students, Aki Sinoto and Rich Costello, who were receiving some academic credit for their participation as combined crew members and naturalists on the expedition, did their most significant scientific work in the Marquesas. Aki collected fishes off archeological sites that his father had excavated and from which he had numerous unidentified fish bones. Later in Hawaii Aki prepared skeletons from the fishes he collected, thus providing for the identification of the disarticulated bones and fragments in the Bishop Museum ethnological collections. Rich, with the aid of Dave Bryant, collected three species of porpoises, one of which may be a new *Stenella* (under study by Rich and Kenneth Norris).

Westward left Nuku Hiva on May 18 for Hawaii, while Helen and I remained behind for several precious additional days of shore collecting. We flew home via Papeete from the air strip on Ua Huka.

The collections of fishes made during the expedition on *Westward* are now fully curated at the Bishop Museum. The number of species from the Marquesas represented in the museum totals about 350. Approximately 10 percent are native to the islands. Only the Hawaiian Islands and Easter

Island in the tropical and subtropical Pacific have a higher percentage of endemism among the reef and shore fishes.

REFERENCES

ALLEN, GERALD R., and RANDALL, JOHN E.

    1974. Five new species and a new genus of damselfishes (family Pomacentridae) from the South Pacific Ocean. Trop. Fish. Hobbyist, vol. 21, no. 9, pp. 36-46, 48-49, illus.

GREENFIELD, DAVID W.

    1974. A revision of the squirrelfish genus *Myripristis* Cuvier (Pisces: Holocentridae). Nat. Hist. Mus. Los Angeles County Sci. Bull. no. 19, illus.

KAMI, HARRY T.

    1973. A new subgenus and species of *Pristipomoides* (family Lutjanidae) from Easter Island and Rapa. Copeia, 1973, no. 3, pp. 557-559, illus.

MCALLISTER, DON E., and RANDALL, JOHN E.

    1975. A new species of centrolophid fish from Easter Island and Rapa Iti Island in the South Pacific. Nat. Mus. Canada Publ. Biol. Oceanogr., no. 8; ix + 7 pp., illus.

RANDALL, JOHN E.

    1973. Expedition to Pitcairn. Oceans, vol. 6, no. 2, pp. 12-21, illus.

    1974. Rapa and beyond. Oceans, vol. 7, no. 6, pp. 24-31, illus.

    1975. Three new butterflyfishes (Chaetodontidae) from southeast Oceania. Uo (Japan), vol. 25, pp. 12-22, illus.

REHDER, HARALD, and RANDALL, JOHN E.

    1975. Ducie Atoll: its history, physiography and biota. Atoll Res. Bull. no. 183, 40 pp., illus.

JOHN E. RANDALL

The Ecology, Behavior, and Conservation of the Galápagos Tortoises

Principal Investigators: William G. Reeder and Craig G. MacFarland, University of Wisconsin, Madison, Wisconsin.

Grant No. 764: To study the distribution, ecology, and behavior of Galápagos tortoises.

From August 1969 to November 1971 a detailed study of the ecology and behavior of the Galápagos giant tortoises *(Geochelone elephantopus)* was carried out under the present grant. The primary goals of the investigation were threefold.

Firstly, we wished to conduct a long-term field study of the ecology and social behavior of the largest living terrestrial reptile. We proposed to include a consideration of population dynamics, seasonal migrations and daily movements, feeding ecology and habitat relations, and association of the tortoises with other animal species. The literature and unpublished research reports appearing before 1969 consisted almost entirely of anecdotal observations and affirmed that no detailed field studies had been conducted to that time.

Secondly, it was desired to determine the prospects for survival of all the extant subspecies and to provide basic information for the design of conservation-management programs by determining, for each race where possible, the present geographic distribution, population size and structure, reproductive cycle and reproductive potential, natural mortality rate, and the mortality rate and other negative effects caused by introduced mammalian predators and competitors.

Thirdly, and as an outgrowth of objectives one and two, it was proposed to collaborate extensively with the Galápagos National Park Service (part of the Ecuadorian Forestry Service) and the Charles Darwin Research Station in the design and execution of conservation-management programs for all the endangered subspecies. Through the decade of the 1960's, the Darwin Station, and later the Park Service, carried out surveys of the geographic distribution of some of the subspecies populations and made rough estimates of population sizes. Also, they began, for two subspecies, management programs that included nest protection to increase survival and the artificial incubation and raising of young for restocking on their respective native islands.

The following report covers those portions of the investigation supported by the National Geographic Society during the period 1969-1971. Results of part of the study have been published (see References); the remainder are presently in preparation. The studies and the conservation practices developed are being continued by the Galápagos National Park Service and one of us (MacFarland) in his present official capacity as director of the Charles Darwin Research Station, Santa Cruz, Galápagos.

Geographic Distribution and Population Biology

Numerous visits to and extensive surveys of the tortoise populations and their habitats resulted in accurate determination of which subspecies survive, detailed distributions of the populations on the various islands, and the population sizes and size class structures of almost all the subspecies. The permanent marking of tortoises for individual identification (by notching the marginal scutes in various combinations) was continued to the point that large percentages of the tortoises of the seven smallest, most endangered subspecies populations had been marked. The marking is required primarily for the continuing study of population dynamics, seasonal migrations, daily movements, reproductive biology, and growth and development, but it also allows some control of poaching and possible interisland transfers.

It is now known that 11 of the 15 tortoise subspecies originally described definitely survive (fig. 1); two became extinct in the latter part of the last century, and one probably never existed (the only individual ever seen and collected probably having been an artificial introduction). The fifteenth, that from Fernandina, is an enigmatic case. One individual was seen and collected there in 1906. In 1964, unmistakable large tortoise scats were found by Dr. John Hendrickson in a small meadow at 1,100 feet altitude on the west slope of the island. In full agreement with a request from the National Geographic Society, we made a special search of the best potential tortoise habitats on Fernandina (those lying on the western and southwestern slopes) including an extensive search of the same meadow and surrounding areas examined by Hendrickson. However, no tortoises or their sign were found in any of the areas, even though some would be excellent tortoise habitat. Since 1971 virtually all the remaining smaller vegetated areas on Fernandina

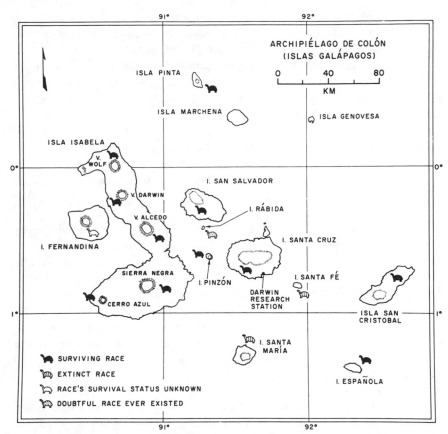

FIG. 1. Distribution of the 15 subspecies of Galápagos tortoises *(Geochelone elephantopus)* as originally recognized.

have been searched by the Park Service, but no tortoise sign has been located. Thus it is very probable that the 1906 and 1964 discoveries were of some of the very few remaining Fernandina tortoises. Perhaps the subspecies is now extinct. If so, it has probably been due largely to gradual reduction of available habitat on the island through volcanic activity, since no introduced mammals occur on Fernandina and man has never had notable influence there. The surface of Fernandina now consists of approximately 90 percent harsh, barren lava; only a few scattered strips of vegetation remain within which tortoises could survive. Further searches, especially in a few tiny vegetated areas not previously explored, are planned.

Population distributions are now known for each of the 11 surviving subspecies (fig. 2). For most of the populations these range limits represent considerable reduction from former times, either due directly to the activities of man or indirectly through predators and competitors that were introduced to the archipelago. Also, in two cases, the populations have been split into two or three units by the effects of colonization, which have eliminated tortoises in the intervening areas.

Population sizes have been estimated with considerable accuracy by means of the marking and repeated observation program for 9 of the 11 subspecies (table 1). Only for the two subspecies populations of Darwin and Wolf volcanoes of northern Isabela Island are the estimates somewhat doubtful; those given are conservative, and recent evidence indicates that these populations may be larger by 20 to 40 percent.

Size class structures were determined from samples of all individuals of curved carapace length of 10 centimeters or larger that were encountered in each of 10 populations during periods of one year or less (fig. 3). The eleventh subspecies is represented at present by only a single male survivor. These samples demonstrate strikingly that, in at least six of the subspecies, size class distributions are strongly skewed; they consist largely or completely of adults and contain very few or no tortoises of smaller size classes. Although samples of equivalent completeness are not available, surveys of the other two populations of the Volcán Sierra Negra subspecies suggest them to be similarly characterized. Thus, in seven of the populations, adequate recruitment is not occurring.

The same samples show that the sex ratios of adult tortoises are not unusual in these populations, with the notable exception of the Española Island subspecies.

Conservation: Status of the Populations and Management Program

A detailed analysis of the status of the giant-tortoise populations and an evaluation of the management program being conducted by the Park Service and the Darwin Station have been published (MacFarland, Villa, and Toro, 1974a; 1974b). In brief, the majority of the subspecies are definitely threatened, principally because of predation and/or competition by one or more species of introduced mammals. The most damaging of these exotic species are feral pigs, goats, dogs, cats, and the black or wharf rat. The tortoise subspecies and various populations can be divided into five groups based on their status (fig. 3; table 1).

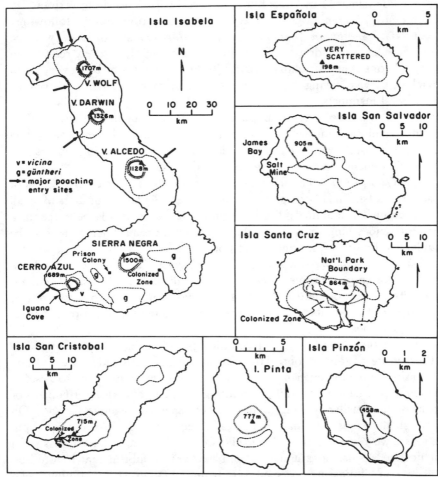

FIG. 2. Distributional limits (dotted lines) on individual islands and volcanoes of the 11 surviving subspecies of Galápagos tortoises.

(1) *Geochelone elephantopus hoodensis* and *G. e. abingdoni.* — These populations are extremely small. The density of the *hoodensis* population is so low and the sex ratio so skewed that the few adults still existing rarely, if ever, encounter one another and no reproduction occurs. The single Pinta Island male was discovered in November 1971 after several extensive searches indicated no sign of living tortoises. Thus there is still hope of finding a few additional individuals there. The vegetation of both islands had

been badly damaged by goats but is now recovering slowly in response to a successful program of goat control and extermination (see the following).

(2) *G. e. ephippium, chathamensis, darwini, vicina,* and *güntheri* (western and southern populations). — These populations are all severely reduced in size and consist almost entirely of adults, but no young, or but a very small number, survive, owing to predation on the nests and/or young by one or more feral mammals.

(3) *G. e. güntheri* (eastern population). — This population consists mainly of small- and medium-sized tortoises, most of the adults having been killed by settlers in past years. The population may be self-replacing, but its survival will depend upon continued patrolling.

(4) *G. e. porteri.* — The main population, on the southwestern slopes of Santa Cruz Island, is large and contains moderately large numbers of small and medium-sized animals. Predators, however, destroy a large percentage of nests and young; it is likely that recruitment is insufficient to replace adults lost by natural mortality and poaching.

(5) *G. e. vandenburghi, microphyes,* and *becki.* — These moderate to large populations contain sizable percentages of small- and medium-sized animals. Recruitment may be sufficient to replace losses by mortality, but not enough is known of the possible effects of the feral cats and black rats present on all three volcanoes.

Given these conditions, conservation programs have been initiated to (1) eradicate or at least control the introduced mammals and (2) raise young tortoises from the seven most threatened subspecies in order to restock endemic populations. Systematic hunting has been effective for control of goats on the smaller, less elevated, and more sparsely vegetated islands. On three small islands goats have been eradicated by this method and pig populations have been greatly reduced. However, systematic hunting has been ineffective against dogs and cats, and it is very doubtful that it could be effective in eliminating goats and pigs from the larger islands of higher elevation with a diversity of vegetation zones. Alternative control or extermination methods are being sought and tested for these feral mammals as well as the black rat. Broad ecological studies of the latter species and feral goats are now under way.

In the interim, while new control methods are being investigated, management programs aimed at increasing the reproductive success of the populations and restocking of the endemic tortoise populations have been instituted. To increase yearly recruitment of hatchlings, lava corrals have been constructed around nests on several islands. This technique has resulted in almost total success in preventing nest destruction by pigs. During the past 9 years an extensive program of hatching and raising the young of endangered subspecies in captivity has been developed. Improved and highly successful techniques were developed for (1) establishment of breeding colonies and construction of artificial nesting sites in captivity, (2) transport of eggs from wild nests, (3) incubation of eggs, and (4) raising of young in captivity. Over 420 young tortoises of six subspecies are now being raised. In all, 122 captive-raised tortoises, 4.5 to 6.5 years old, were released on Pinzón Island between 1970 and 1973. They are now in good condition and growing rapidly and are large enough to be threatened no longer by the introduced black rats present in numbers on Pinzón.

These management programs are now so successful that 10 of the 11 extant subspecies will definitely survive if the control of introduced mammals and the raising and restocking program are continued.

Reproductive Biology, Reproductive Potential, and Mortality

Reproductive biology and potential and natural mortality were studied intensively in two subspecies: *G. e. porteri* of Santa Cruz Island, one of the largest and most dome-shaped races, and *G. e. ephippium* of Pinzón Island, one of the smallest and saddle-backed subspecies. Since Santa Cruz is an island of large size and high altitude, with vegetational diversity and relatively wet highlands, and Pinzón is one of the smaller, drier islands, these two situations approximate the range of conditions found among present tortoise populations and habitats. Similar but less complete information was obtained for eight of the remaining nine subspecies; these studies are being continued.

Although tortoises were seen mating during every month of the year, most of the activity occurs from December to June, the peak mating season being February to April. The nesting season extends from late June into mid-December. Females migrate from highland feeding zones to lower altitudes where they nest, then return to the highland zones one to three weeks later. When individual females nest sequentially in a single season, this same pattern occurs between nestings.

Based on estimated population sizes (table 1), censuses (fig. 3), and the known minimum size of females which nest, it was estimated that the Santa Cruz population contains 300-450 nesting females and that on Pinzón 99 to 132 nesting females. The Santa Cruz females lay one or two clutches each per year. The range of clutch number for Pinzón females has not been

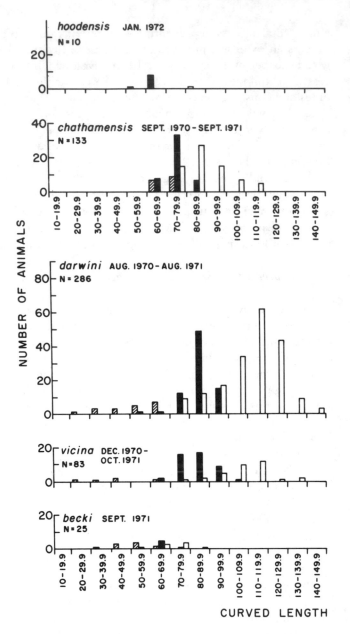

FIG. 3. Size class distributions of all tortoises encountered in the vari◄

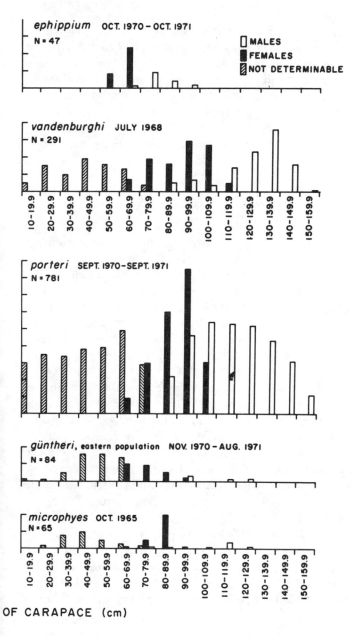

OF CARAPACE (cm)

lations during sampling periods of one year or less.

determined precisely, but limited observation plus records from captives of a similar subspecies, *G. e. hoodensis,* suggest a range from 2 to 4. Studies of nests in the wild during two seasons (1969-70 and 1970-71) provide accurate values for both the mean and range of clutch size for *porteri* and *ephippium* (table 2). By using these combined results, the potential reproductive output of each population can be calculated as follows:

(No. nesting ♀♀) × (Avg. no. clutches/♂/yr.) × (Avg. clutch size) = Total no. young per year.
Thus, for *G. e. porteri:*
    maximum value: (450) (2) (9.45) = 8,505 young per year
    minimum value: (300) (1) (9.45) = 2,835 young per year
For *G. e. ephippium:*
    maximum value: (132) (4) (5.1) = 2,693 young per year
    minimum value: (99) (2) (5.1) = 1,010 young per year

It has not yet been possible accurately to determine the age at maturity, longevity, and length of reproductive life for any of the tortoise subspecies. However, composite growth curves from wild tortoises plus records from captive animals indicate that females probably reach maturity at 20 to 35 years of age and remain reproductively active thereafter throughout life, and that longevity probably ranges from 100 to 150 years. There is some evidence that the smaller-sized subspecies, such as *ephippium,* mature at a younger age (and thus, smaller size) and have a shorter life span than the larger-sized subspecies such as *porteri.*

Mortality before emergence of young tortoises from the nest reduces the reproductive potential of the populations. The mortality factors include (1) breakage of eggs during laying or due to nest interference (e.g., two females nesting in the same site); (2) infertility; (3) developmental failure or anomaly during incubation or hatching; and (4) failure to escape from the nest (entombment of hatchlings). Of these factors the greatest reductions in reproductive potential are due to infertility and failure to escape from the nest. None of the factors is responsible alone for a large mortality rate, and the total mortality due to all these factors is not notably high. Based on the wild nests studied in 1969-70 and 1970-71, 66 percent of the *porteri* eggs and 72 percent of the *ephippium* eggs resulted in live hatchlings which emerged from the nests (tables 2, 3). The potential recruitment of hatchlings for each population can be calculated by multiplying the previously calculated values for reproductive potential by these percentages as follows:

$$\left(\genfrac{}{}{0pt}{}{\text{Potential no. young/yr.}}{\text{i.e., total no. eggs}}\right) \times \left(\frac{\text{No. hatchlings escaped}}{\text{No. eggs}}\right) =$$

Total no. hatchlings recruited per year.

Thus, for *G. e. porteri:*

maximum value: (8,505) x (0.66) = 5,613 hatchlings per year

minimum value: (2,835) x (0.66) = 1,871 hatchlings per year

For *G. e. ephippium:*

maximum value: (2,693) x (0.72) = 1,950 hatchlings per year

minimum value: (1,010) x (0.72) =   731 hatchlings per year

Post-emergence mortality has not been studied sufficiently to provide accurate survivorship curves. However, studies of marked hatchlings on Santa Cruz introduced in a predator-free area and censuses and general observations of mortality in most of the subspecies populations allow a few tentative conclusions. Very high percentages of hatchlings die from starvation during the first two to three years of life. At least three out of every four years are very dry, resulting in little available vegetation in the lower altitudes, where the nesting zones lie. The young do not migrate to higher altitudes, where more lush vegetation occurs throughout the year, until they reach 8 to 12 years of age. Being incapable of storing large amounts of water or fats as can older tortoises, the very young succumb easily to starvation. On some islands, there is apparently heavy predation on hatchlings by the Galápagos hawk, the only known natural predator of the tortoise.

The mortality rate for tortoises older than three to four years appears to be extremely low, deriving primarily from accidents (*e.g.,* falling into crevices, being crushed by falling rocks) and from thermal stress. Occasional deaths may be caused by a respiratory disease.

Thus the tortoise populations almost certainly display a Type III survivorship curve in the natural state: high loss in early life, followed by a long period of much lower and relatively constant loss. But most populations are now affected adversely by exotic predators and/or competitors that have introduced artificial effects to the natural situation. This interference could easily lead to the extinction of any or all tortoise populations that did not evolve on the archipelago with such mammalian predators and competitors and therefore are not adapted to the new and suddenly changed conditions.

Seasonal and Daily Movements

Analyses of data on seasonal migrations, daily movements, and home range size in relation to habitat quality and social behavior are now being completed for the Santa Cruz population. A few general conclusions can be made.

During most of the year the great majority of adult and subadult tortoises are concentrated in the higher, more moist, and densely vegetated areas from 450 to 1,000 feet in elevation on the southwestern slope of the island. In contrast, the juveniles are distributed mainly at elevations between 200 and 450 feet in drier transitional zone vegetation, and the youngest animals (up to 10-15 years of age) are confined throughout the year to the arid lowland nesting areas between the coast and about 200 feet elevation. Despite this general distributional pattern, juveniles can be found in other zones extending all the way from the coast up to 550 or 600 feet and adults and subadults in all zones from the coast to 1,400 or 1,500 feet in elevation.

Two periods of more concentrated migratory movement are observed. (1) Between June and December the very large-sized females move to the nesting areas. (2) On the average, in three out of four years, a large percentage of adults and subadults move to the arid lowlands (coast to 200 feet elevation) during the later two to three months of the hot season (January to May). This is apparently due to the fact that little or no rainfall occurs during the period, vegetation at the higher altitudes dries severely, and the tortoises move to lowland *Opuntia* forests for food.

During the *garúa* season (misty rain; from June to December, when the vegetation is relatively lush and standing water is normally available above 300 feet altitude) and during rainy hot seasons (about one out of every four), the daily movements and home range size of all tortoises are more limited (based on observations of one to two weeks of individual tortoises). The home-range size is generally positively correlated with tortoise size, ranging from 200 to 400 square meters for small juveniles of 25 to 35 centimeters curved carapace length to 1,000 to 1,500 square meters for large adult males and females. During those hot seasons with little or no rain, when the vegetation dries and standing water becomes unavailable, home-range size increases dramatically for all size classes, becoming 5 to 10 times the area of activity during the wetter seasons.

Social Behavior

Detailed quantitative as well as descriptive data were gathered on mating and agonistic behavior patterns by direct observation and still and motion-picture photography. This information is still to be analyzed and will be published later. A few general conclusions follow.

(1) Adult males have a definite rut period, whereas adult females never display any period of special receptiveness. The females attempt to avoid copulation throughout the year.

(2) "Courtship" is relatively simple; the males appear to select adult females by visual and/or olfactory inspection. Most of the male-female interaction consists of male behavior patterns designed to threaten the female to passivity and acceptance of copulation.

(3) The tortoises are definitely not territorial. However, specific feeding sites, resting sites in areas with limited shade, and mud or water wallowing sites are defended for short periods (a few hours up to one to three days) by all size classes. The larger of two tortoises in such encounters almost invariably dominates in the interaction. Similar aggressive fights occur between adult males over access to adult females during the mating season.

(4) Although not enough data yet exist to make an unequivocal statement, dominance hierarchies appear not to exist in the tortoise populations. Rather, the largest individuals almost always are dominant in any given interaction. There is no evidence for the occurrence of individual recognition and some against it.

Association with Other Species

A number of associations with other animal species were studied. The most thoroughly investigated, both descriptively and quantitatively, is that of a cleaning symbiosis in which the small ground finch removes ticks from the tortoise subspecies of Volcán Alcedo and Pinzón and Santa Cruz Islands. The finches initiate a cleaning sequence by approaching and sometimes performing a presentation display to the tortoise. After perceiving either or both the approach and display, the tortoise responds by assuming a motionless, fully raised posture with the legs and neck fully extended. The posture appears to serve at least two functions: (1) It increases to a maximum the exposure of skin surface area, especially those portions that are mostly unavailable when the tortoise is in a resting or inactive posture; (2) it minimizes flightiness of the finches and the danger that they will be injured. Both the ticks eaten (*Amblyomma*) and the cleaning activity are most concentrated on those skin areas that are least exposed—the leg and neck pockets and the basal area of the neck. The finches only rarely cleaned or initiated the approach display with inactive tortoises, and the latter were

TABLE 1. POPULATION SIZE ESTIMATES AND NUMBER OF MARKED TORTOISES FOR SUBSPECIES OF *GEOCHELONE ELEPHANTOPUS*

Race	Location	Marking period	Total No.	Adults ♂	Adults ♀	Medium sized ♂	Medium sized ♀	Medium sized Non-sexed	Small sized	Estimated population size
Geochelone elephantus										
hoodensis	Española	8/63-6/72	13	2	11	0	0	0	0	20-30
abingdoni	Pinta	11/71-6/72	1	1	0	0	0	0	0	very small
ephippium	Pinzón	4/63-3/69	100	35	63	1	1	0	0	150-200
chathamensis	San Cristóbal (northeastern part)	12/65-9/71	213	94	63	54	2	0	0	500-700
darwini	San Salvador	6/65-10/71	389	224	97	27	6	27	8	500-700
vicina	Cerro Azul	4/66-10/71	196	77	85	11	12	9	2	400-600
güntheri	Sierra Negra:									
	east	7/66-7/71	178	7	19	4	26	21	101	200-300
	south and west	7/66-8/71	41	14	20	3	1	0	3	100-200
vandenburghi	Volcán Alcedo	5/65 and 7/68	402	135	117	13	26	39	72	3,000-5,000
microphyes	Volcán Darwin	10/65	65	6	26	2	1	8	22	500-1,000?
becki	Volcán Wolf	–	0	–	–	–	–	–	–	1,000-2,000?
porteri	Santa Cruz:									
	southwest	4/62-10/71	1,368	284	245	150	98	161	430	2,000-3,000
	east	5/62-11/71	92	17	18	25	9	7	16	50-100

unlikely to respond to such attempts. Most initiation attempts occurred with active tortoises, which almost always responded. The results suggest that feeding efficiency has determined the finches' preference for active tortoises. Quantitative details of the symbiosis and related factors have been published elsewhere (MacFarland and Reeder, 1974).

A number of other associations were noted, as follow:

(1) The vermillion flycatcher, the endemic Galápagos flycatcher, and the Galápagos hawk all use the tortoise as a "beater," capturing insects that the tortoise stirs up while walking.

(2) The yellow warbler, lava lizards, and geckoes all capture small insects that fly very near to and land on the tortoises.

(3) The Galápagos dove, the Galápagos mockingbirds, and several

TABLE 2. FERTILITY AND HATCHING RESULTS FROM NESTS IN THE WILD

Race and nesting season	No. nests	No. eggs	Clutch size Average	Range	Percent definitely fertile (No.)	Percent hatched (No.)	Percent dead embryos (No.)	Percent addled* (No.)	Percent broken† (No.)
Geochelone elephantopus porteri									
1969/70	10	91	9.1	6-11	85.7	84.6	1.1	12.1	2.2
					(78)	(77)	(1)	(11)	(2)
1970/71	45	429	9.5	3-16	77.9	73.2	4.7	21.0	1.1
					(334)	(314)	(20)	(90)	(5)
Geochelone e. ephippium									
1969/70	13	65	5.0	2-7	78.5	75.4	3.1	20.0	1.5
					(51)	(49)	(2)	(13)	(1)
1970/71	13	68	5.2	4-8	82.4	79.4	2.9	7.4	10.3
					(56)	(54)	(2)	(5)	(7)

*A liquefied egg, i.e., infertile or the embryo having died before attaining sufficient size to be detected.
†Broken during laying or due to nesting interference, i.e., two females nesting at same time.

TABLE 3. ESCAPE OF HATCHLINGS FROM COMPLETELY UNDISTURBED NESTS IN THE WILD

Race and nesting season	No. nests	No. hatched	Percent hatchlings escaped (No.)	No. hatchlings escaped / No. eggs
Geochelone elephantopus porteri				
1969/70	10	77	80.5 (62)	0.681
1970/71	39	272	89.9 (249)	0.665
Geochelone e. ephippium				
1969/70	12	46	95.7 (44)	0.721
1970/71	11	46	87.0 (40)	0.727

species of Darwin's finches were seen to search or pick through tortoise scats for food (seeds, insects, or snails living within the scats).

(4) The tortoises on almost all islands were found to have ticks of at least one, in some cases two, species. Careful collections of these ectoparasites were made from tortoises of most subspecies. These specimens and data have provided the major source of information for reports on the taxonomy of the ticks and their co-distribution with the tortoises (Hoogstraal,

Clifford, and Keirans, 1973; Keirans, Hoogstraal, and Clifford, 1973).

(5) Tortoises of almost all subspecies were found commonly to have algae, fungi, and lichens growing on the carapace. The lichens are particularly interesting, for it appears that at least six or seven species, commonly found on rocks in the Galápagos, grow also on those carapace surfaces that are protected from abrasion. Such relationships are extremely rare, the only other known case being that of lichens apparently growing on the elytra of certain beetles in New Guinea.

These relationships will be described at greater length in a series of short publications.

Environment of the Tortoise Reserve, Santa Cruz

A preliminary quantitative study of the vegetation was made along a transect from the sea to the upper boundary of the Tortoise Reserve (ca. 200 meters elevation; Santa Cruz Island) along a gradually ascending distance of 12,900 meters. The purpose of the separate study was (1) to establish suitable methods by which the herb and shrub cover, of importance to tortoises as shade and food, could be quantitatively described, and (2) to study the character of vegetation change along such a gradual ascent. This transect passes from the upper margin of the Mangrove or Littoral Zone through the *Cryptocarpus,* Arid, and Transition Zones.

Stand organization, comments on species replacement, and several methods of data analysis are discussed in the paper of Reeder and Riechert (1975).

At the same time, using the vegetation sampling areas along the same transect, we made initial quantitative collections of arthropods. The long-term intent is to relate in detail arthropod and vegetational distributions, with the view of studying their interdependencies.

Thus it has been that not only is the tortoise program, established under National Geographic Society sponsorship, continuing to the present, but also other ecological studies have been undertaken as logical extensions and have themselves become full-fledged research programs.

REFERENCES

HOOGSTRAAL, HARRY; CLIFFORD, CARLETON M.; and KEIRANS, JAMES
  1973. *Argas (Microargas) transversus* (Ixodoidea: Argasidae) of the Galápagos tortoises: Description of the female and nymph. Ann. Ent. Soc. America, vol. 66, no. 4, pp. 727-732, illus.
KEIRANS, JAMES; HOOGSTRAAL, HARRY; and CLIFFORD, CARLETON M.
  1973. The *Amblyomma* (Acarina: Ixodidae) parasitic on giant tortoises (Reptilia: Testudinidae) of the Galápagos Islands. Ann. Ent. Soc. America, vol. 66, no. 3, pp. 673-688, illus.
MACFARLAND, CRAIG G.
  1972. Goliaths of the Galápagos. Nat. Geogr. Mag., vol. 142, no. 5, pp. 632-649, illus.
MACFARLAND, CRAIG G., and BLACK, JUAN
  1971. The law & the Galápagos. Journ. Int. Turtle and Tortoise Soc., vol. 5, no. 4, pp. 36-37.
MACFARLAND, CRAIG G., and REEDER, WILLIAM G.
  1974. Cleaning symbiosis involving Galápagos tortoises and two species of Darwin's finches. Zeitschr. für Tierpsychol., vol. 34, pp. 464-483, illus.
  1975. Breeding, raising, and restocking of giant tortoises *(Geochelone elephantopus)* in the Galápagos Islands. Pp. 13-37 *in* "Breeding Endangered Species in Captivity," R. D. Martin, ed., illus.
MACFARLAND, CRAIG G.; VILLA, JOSÉ; and TORO, BASILIO
  1974a. The Galápagos giant tortoises *(Geochelone elephantopus),* pt. 1: Status of the surviving populations. Biol. Cons., vol. 6, no. 2, pp. 118-133, illus.
  1974b. The Galápagos giant tortoises *(Geochelone elephantopus),* pt. 2: Conservation methods. Biol. Cons., vol. 6, no. 3, pp. 198-212, illus.
REEDER, WILLIAM G., and RIECHERT, SUSAN E.
  1975. Vegetation change along an altitudinal gradient, Santa Cruz Island, Galápagos. Biotropica, vol. 7, no. 3, pp. 162-175.

WILLIAM G. REEDER
CRAIG G. MACFARLAND

A Malacological Expedition to the Moluccas

Principal Investigators: Joseph Rosewater, Smithsonian Institution, Washington, D. C., and Barry R. Wilson, Western Australian Museum, Perth, Australia.

Grant No. 813: In aid of a biogeographic and historical study of marine mollusks of the Moluccas Islands.

No place on earth has a greater abundance and diversity of marine life than the shallow seas surrounding the islands of the Indo-Malay Archipelago lying between the Southeast Asian and Australasian continents and between the Indian and Pacific Oceans. In this area exist all the factors known to produce a rich marine fauna. There are warm tropical waters, vast expanses of seabed at depths less than 100 fathoms, and a rich source of sediments and nutrients from the large and mountainous islands. Also, the area has had a complex orogenic history that has produced high mountain chains (the islands) and deep ocean trenches. The latter, together with ocean currents, break up the shallow shelf areas and isolate the marine faunas of adjacent areas within the region, thus giving spur to the processes of speciation and faunistic change. This region is the home of many marine species not found elsewhere. It is also the barrier between or the meeting place of closely related Indian and Pacific Ocean species and subspecies.

For such reasons the waters of the Indo-Malay Archipelago have special interest for marine taxonomists and zoogeographers. If there is ever to be an "ultimate" classification of marine life, the fauna of the Indo-Malay Archipelago region must first be properly described, for it comprises a large percentage of living marine species. At present it is far from properly described. There have been several important marine collecting expeditions to the region during this century and a great quantity of specimens from very shallow waters of some areas have found their way into museums and other research institutions. Yet the amount of material from deeper water available for study is minimal, and even the shallow-water fauna of certain inaccessible areas within the region has been neglected almost entirely. One such neglected area is the Moluccas group of islands, though they hold particular interest for several reasons.

The Moluccas Province of eastern Indonesia comprises a number of islands that, geologically speaking, are of diverse character and origin. The high and mountainous islands of the northern Moluccas (e.g., Halmahera, Obi, Ceram, Buru, Ambon) lie on orogenic ridges between deep trenches that separate the wide continental shelf of southeastern Asia from that of Australasia. The southeastern islands comprising the Aru complex are low-lying, relatively recent structures located on the fringe of the Australasian shelf itself, while the Kai and Tanimbar groups are situated on orogenic ridges close to the Australasian shelf and separated from it by narrow but moderately deep trenches.

Thus, the Moluccas form the eastern part of a series of transitional steps between the continental shelf areas of southeastern Asia and the continental shelf of Australasia. It has long been known that the deeps separating these two continental regions have been a major factor in the separation and evolution of the distinctive terrestrial faunas and floras of Asia and the isolated Australasian continent. The classical faunal demarcation "lines" of Weber and Wallace run through the transitional zone today occupied by Sulawesi, Lesser Sunda Islands, and the Moluccas.

There is some evidence to suppose that the deeps of this transitional zone may also form an isolation barrier for many marine shelf and shore animals and that this may be responsible for many of the differences. However, the limits of generic and species distribution in the critical transition zone are not well documented. For this reason intensive sampling of the marine fauna across the transition zone was seen to offer a great deal to our understanding of the biogeographical history of the central Indo-West Pacific region. Of particular value would be the material obtained from moderate depths by dredging.

Recognizing this, Dr. Joseph Rosewater, of the Smithsonian Institution's Division of Mollusks, and I resolved to undertake a mollusk-collecting expedition to these islands, primarily to obtain specimens by dredging in depths from a few fathoms to the edge of the continental shelf.

We approached the late Mary Eleanor King of Honolulu for assistance (see also Rehder, 1974) and it was agreed that her research vessel *Pele* would be available for the expedition. The National Geographic Society made a grant to cover costs, and this was supplemented by contributions from several private donors. While these financial matters were being considered, Mrs. King was taken suddenly ill, and she died on September 11, 1969.

Subsequently it was revealed that Mrs. King had willed the *Pele* to the Bernice P. Bishop Museum, in Honolulu, and the director and trustees of

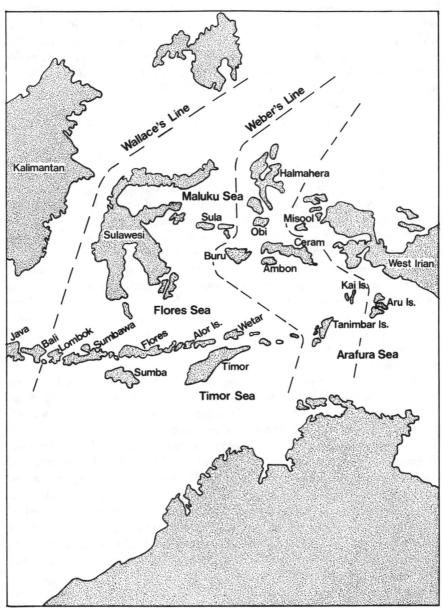

FIG. 1.   Eastern end of Indo-Malaysian Archipelago, showing the faunal change
   lines of Wallace and Weber. Position of Australasian continental shelf indicated
   by unlabeled dashed line.

that institution generously agreed to allow the vessel to be used for the expedition as originally planned. Furthermore, Mrs. King's mother, Grace King, agreed to contribute the remaining funds necessary to operate the expedition, which was named the Mariel King Memorial Moluccas Expedition in recognition of her great service to natural science (see Wilson, 1971; Rosewater, 1972; and Rehder and Wilson, 1975).

After many delays the expedition began work in the northern part of the Moluccas Province of Indonesia on May 19, 1970. During the following six weeks the expedition collected and studied marine specimens throughout the province, terminating at Darwin, Northern Territory, Australia, on July 1. Like most expeditions the original program was not fully achieved because of loss of time and vagaries of weather and equipment. Nevertheless, we are confident that the specimens and information collected are more than sufficient to satisfy the aims of the expedition. These were: (1) To obtain fresh and well-preserved specimens of marine invertebrate animals, especially mollusks, from the Moluccas region, and to make these available through museum collections to specialists for taxonomic and anatomical studies; (2) in particular to re-collect as many as possible of the mollusks described and illustrated by the early Dutch naturalist Rumphius (1705) from the seas around Ambon; and (3) to study and make comparisons of the invertebrate faunas, especially mollusks, of the islands in the transitional zone between the Southeast Asian and the Australasian continental shelves.

The *Pele* sailed from Honolulu via the American Pacific Trust Territory Islands to Davao, in the southern Philippines, and thence to Manado, Sulawesi (Celebes), where she made her official entry into Indonesian waters. The scientific personnel boarded at Davao and Manado.

From Manado *Pele* sailed eastward to the west coast of Halmahera near Ternate, where work began. The expedition then worked southward to Ambon, where repairs were made to the hull and fuel, water, and stores were obtained. Several days were then spent among the islands to the east of Ambon and in the vicinity of Piru Bay in southern Ceram. After another brief visit to Ambon to refuel, *Pele* sailed southeastward to the islands of the Tajandu, Kai, Aru, and Tanimbar groups. The work of the expedition was completed in the Tanimbar Islands, from which passage was made direct to Darwin.

More than a week was lost because of generator problems before *Pele* reached Davao. Also, while sailing in the night toward Ambon the vessel struck a large floating log, which severely damaged the hull. This caused a

FIG. 2. *Pele* captain supervises raising of giant clam *(Tridacna gigas)* from the sea-bed off Gomumu Island in the Northern Moluccas Province. The specimen is now displayed in the Western Australian Museum, Perth.

further loss of several days while the damage was repaired in the Ambon dry dock. Because of this loss of time some parts of the original program had to be deleted. The expedition did not visit the northern end of Halmahera or the small islands off the southeastern end of Ceram, and little work was done at Ambon itself.

The Collections

Specimens were collected at a total of 80 stations, of which 38 were dredging stations and 42 were shore-collecting and skin-diving stations. Altogether 187 dredge-hauls were made.

Prior to the start of the expedition, agreement was reached with the director of the Indonesian national museum, Dr. Soemarwoto, concerning the division of the collections made by the expedition among the National Biological Institute of Indonesia, the Smithsonian Institution, and the Western Australian Museum. It was agreed that all holotypes, and the first and second and the ninth and tenth specimens of each species taken, should be lodged eventually at the National Biological Institute. Remaining specimens would be divided between the other institutions.

It was agreed also that the entire collections would be taken initially to the Western Australian Museum, where the preliminary sorting and analysis have been done prior to the final division of the material. In some cases where scientists have made special requests to examine certain specimens collected by the expedition, these have been made available subject to the terms of the agreement with the Indonesian authorities.

Most of the preliminary work on the collections has now been completed and they have been divided and distributed among the three participating institutions. More than 1,000 species of mollusks are represented. A provisional list of the mollusks is being prepared by Western Australian Museum staff, but many species remain unidentified. Some are certain to be new to science. In general no immediate attempt will be made to describe these; new species are better described by specialists within major taxonomic revisions. The crustacean collection also is very substantial. Some parts of the echinoderm collection have already been roughly sorted and the better-known asteroid species (starfishes) have been identified by Mrs. L. M. Marsh of the Western Australian Museum. Approximately 60 species of starfishes are represented, as well as a lesser number of each of the other classes, constituting a substantial contribution to knowledge of the echinoderm fauna of the central Indo-West Pacific region. It is hoped that provisional lists of the whole collection will be published with a zoogeographic analysis of the results.

Some Preliminary Zoogeographic Impressions

Although a final zoogeographic analysis of the results has not been made so far some preliminary impressions seem warranted. Two main factors deserve comment.

The marine fauna of the northern and central Moluccas. It has become almost a fable that the seas around Ambon in the central Moluccas abound with an unparalleled profusion of marine life, and shells in particular. Speaking of Ambon Bay in his classic work "The Malay Archipelago," Alfred Russel Wallace (1886) stated: "The bottom was absolutely hidden by a continuous series of corals, sponges, actiniae, and other marine productions, of magnificent dimensions, varied forms, and brilliant colours.... It was a sight to gaze at for hours, and no description can do justice to its surpassing beauty and interest. For once, the reality exceeded the most glowing accounts I had ever read of the wonders of a coral sea. There is perhaps no spot in the world richer in marine productions, corals, shells and fishes, than the harbour of Amboyna."

It was a disappointment then to members of the expedition to find that collecting in Ambon Bay was not as productive as expected. The reason for this seems to be related to the rapid drop off, or "steep to" nature, of the shores around these islands.

The islands of the northern and central Moluccas are sedimentary and volcanic and lie on upthrust ridges in the deep channels separating the continental shelves of Southeast Asia and Australasia. They are surrounded by seas more than 4,000 meters deep, and they have so little fringing shelf around their shores that it is often very difficult for vessels to find anchorage. In Ambon Bay itself, for example, the depth exceeds 200 meters everywhere except at the head of the bay and along a narrow shoreline fringe only a few yards wide on either side. Along the south coast of Ceram the shore drops off into depths of more than 4,000 meters within a few kilometers. It was very difficult to locate dredgeable ground for *Pele.* Off the open coasts the bottom was usually either too deep, too steeply sloping, or too rocky for the dredge to operate safely and effectively. Inside the few shallow bays, on the other hand, the bottom consisted of sterile terrestrial mud. However, several ridges were located where the tops were sandy and wide enough and shallow enough and dredging was immensely successful.

Shore collecting was less successful among these northern and central Moluccas islands. Most of the reefs and sand flats were very narrow with little habitat diversity. Species diversity seemed correspondingly low compared to that of other islands in the Indo-Malay area which are surrounded by broader areas of shallows.

Affinities of the southeastern Moluccas marine fauna with that of northern Australia and New Guinea. In our application to the National Geographic Society for financial assistance we hypothesized that the deep trenches of the transition zone between the continental shelf areas of Southeast Asia and Australasia may have operated as dispersal barriers influencing the evolution of distinctive marine faunas in the two areas. This would be most effective in those marine animals lacking the planktonic larval (dispersal) stage capable of being carried across the deeps by surface water currents. If this were the case we should expect to find many typically northern Australian marine animals in the shallow seas around the Indonesian island of Aru, for this island is situated on the northwestern edge of the Australasian shelf. Conversely, we should not expect to find there Asian species that have direct development (i.e., lacking a pelagic larval stage). Also, we might expect to find some Australian elements in the marine faunas of the Kai and Tanimbar Islands which are separated from the Australasian shelf by relatively short distances and shallow trenches (less than 500 meters), but the proportion should be less than at Aru.

A well-studied family of neogastropods, the Volutidae, may serve best to illustrate this. The family is especially well represented in Australia (with about 67 living species). In northern Australia there are several genera that are generally considered to be endemic there, e.g., *Volutoconus* and *Amoria,* and some that are also represented by species in the Southeast Asian region, e.g., *Melo* and *Aulicina.*

The expedition dredged one species of *Volutoconus (V. bednalli)* at Aru but not elsewhere in Indonesian waters. We found two species of *Amoria (A. jamrachi* and an unusual color form of *A. praetexta)* at Aru. One of these species, *A. praetexta,* was found also in the Tanimbar and Kai Islands. As far as we know this is the first record of the genus beyond Australian waters. The Southeast Asian species *Aulicina vespertilio* was common at most islands we visited including Aru. The presence of this volute on the Australasian shelf was something of a surprise, but the explanation may be simply that it is a common intertidal animal widely used for food in the region and may easily be transported alive by man. Distribution of the genus *Melo* in the Moluccas-Australasian region is particularly perplexing. The common species in the northern and central Moluccas is *M. aethiopicus.* One of the northern Australian species is *M. amphora* and we took typical specimens at Aru. But the *Melo* we found at the intermediate islands of Kai and Tanimbar have characteristics of both species, suggesting a close relationship between them.

Several other families that have direct development or very brief pelagic larval stages showed similar distribution patterns to the Volutidae. Some noteworthy examples taken by the expedition at Aru are *Tudicula spinosa, T. inermis* (Vasidae), *Ancillista cingulata* (Olividae), and *Syrinx aruanus* (Galeodidae), all of which are usually regarded as characteristically Australian species.

It is concluded that the shelf fauna around Aru is primarily Australian in character. The faunas of Kai and Tanimbar are primarily Southeast Asian with a few Australian elements. No typically Australian species were found by the expedition in the central and northern Moluccas.

It is our expectation that the final report on the collections will provide a detailed analysis along these lines and that the data will constitute a substantial contribution to knowledge of the molluscan fauna of the central Indo-West Pacific Region and its evolutionary history.

REFERENCES

REHDER, HARALD A.
  1971. Malacological expedition to the tropical South Pacific. Nat. Geogr. Soc. Res. Rpts., 1965 Projects, pp. 213-218.
  1974. Marine biological research in southeastern Polynesia. Nat. Geogr. Soc. Res. Rpts., 1967 Projects, pp. 243-254, illus.
REHDER, HARALD A., and WILSON, BARRY R.
  1975. New species of marine mollusks from Pitcairn Island and the Marquesas. Smithsonian Contr. Zool., no. 203, 16 pp., illus.
ROSEWATER, JOSEPH
  1972. The family Littorinidae in the Indo-Pacific, pt. 2: The subfamilies Tectariinae and Echininae. Indo-Pacific Mollusca, vol. 2, no. 12, pp. 507-534, illus.
  1973. Ibid., vol. 3, no. 4, pp. 63-70.
WALLACE, ALFRED RUSSEL
  1886. The Malay Archipelago ..., 653 pp., illus. London. (Several editions of this work were published, beginning in 1869.)
WILSON, BARRY R.
  1971. Preliminary report on the results of the Mariel King Memorial Moluccas Expedition 1970. Hawaiian Shell News, vol. 19, no. 10, pp. 3-4, 6; vol. 19, no. 11, pp. 4-5, illus.

BARRY R. WILSON

The Role of the Austrian Forest Reserves in the "Green Plan" of Austria

Principal Investigator: Else A. Schmidt, Illinois State University, Normal, Illinois.

Grant No. 747:   For a study of the Austrian Forest Reserves.

The preservation of the Austrian forests is a matter of national and international importance today as it was in the past. Profits and benefits derived from timbered alpine slopes should not be measured by the amount of money derived from lumber alone, though the income from forest products is very important for the forest proprietors of this alpine country. Forests serve a number of purposes within the framework of the national economy, and their conservational and recreational values are better understood and appreciated in our age than at any time in the past. Intensified industrialization, urbanization, and large-scale farming increased the desire in the people of industrial nations of Europe to preserve the natural landscapes of the continent. The above-mentioned objectives — the commercial, recreational, and conservational values of the alpine forests — are also of concern to the geographer. The present investigation was based on official statistics, interviews, observation, and silvicultural, biogeographical, and historical bibliographies.

The present account is a condensation of a fuller report, including an extensive bibliography, a copy of which is on file in the National Geographic Society Library, Washington, D. C.

Forest production on a worldwide scope (1962) is briefly appraised in the introduction. The writer subsequently focuses on comparative forest statistics of the three most forested countries of Europe (outside the USSR), which are Finland, Sweden, and Austria. The structure of their GNP and the share of the forest industries are compared within the framework of the national economies of these countries.

Structural changes in agricultural and agrarian policies were introduced into Austria by the application of modern technology — the motorization of farming and forestry, transmission of electric power to every village and farm, and road building, including logging roads. These changes are representative of the new capital composition of the farm enterprises affecting the decline in the number of holdings, land consolidation, changes in lines of production, and close adjustment to particular qualities of the land. At the end of the 1960's Austria was able to supply 87 percent of its home food requirements.

The financing of the Green Revolution was aided by income derived from forest products. Since the end of World War II, 800 million dollars were transferred from forests to agriculture. The farm forest, which averages 5.6 hectares if related to the 250,000 farms with woodland out of a total of 402,000 Austrian farm units, proved to be the green savings account of the Austrian farmer. The increasing inputs of capital into agriculture enabled the peasant to make his farm more productive. Thus he was able to carry out the necessary structural changes, including land acquisition and consolidation, drainage or irrigation, and the rehabilitation or construction of new farm buildings within the short period of 20 years.

The motorization of agriculture brought about significant changes in the labor force of the agricultural economy. In 1951, 23 percent of the total population of nearly 7 million was engaged in agriculture. By 1965, the percentage had declined to 13 percent. Hired labor also declined from 21 to 12 percent. Family labor still supplies the overwhelming part of the labor needs. By and large, Austria has experienced the same transformation that affected the rural population of Germany, namely, the growth of the group of worker-peasants, and the exodus from the countryside to the city. The rural folk who stay in agriculture have to face further rationalization and increase in the disparity of income, i.e., the inequality of income between farmers and comparative industrial labor, which is the problem of all industrial nations. Nevertheless the prominence of agriculture as an important busines in Austria is visible in the well-groomed landscape and in the attractive rural life style. Forty-seven percent of the land area is devoted to agriculture and livestock raising, 39 percent is covered by forests, and 14 percent is unproductive, including settlements.

Income derived from woodlands was one means of updating the farm enterprise. Other sources of revenue to provide more capital for more efficient management and production were low-interest loans from the European Recovery Program (ERP), which is still used as a rotating fund. Tax concessions and, after 1961, disbursements from the Green Plan are provided with the intention of raising family incomes, strengthening the family farms, and improving management of farm forests, community forests, and large forest enterprises. The assistance extended through this postwar credit system aided rural renewal; it helped to rescue the fundamental values of the alpine society and to secure the rural economy and the rural way of life, which constitutes a very important goal of government policies.

Forest ownership categories are to a large extent the outcome of geographical factors and the feudal economic structure of centuries ago. The categories listed in terms of economic efficiency and importance comprised the following percentages of the total forest lands of Austria in 1968: Federal forests, 15.1 percent; private forests over 50 hectares (including 5.8 percent institutional forests), 33.6 percent; communal forests, 11.8 percent; and private forests under 50 hectares, 39.5 percent.

The cost-revenue balance of a great number of small-size farm forests and communal forests is slightly positive because costs for management are negligible and the principal source of income is derived from agriculture. Forest estates larger than 200 hectares under silvicultural management and fully mechanized yield a profit but are not invulnerable to market price developments. North European and East Bloc countries with low production costs and large-scale exports keep lumber prices under pressure. Disastrous for any category of forest owners in Central Europe was the stockpiling of poor quality lumber on European markets after the 1967 catastrophic storm. The five largest forest estates, comprising one-fifth of the total forest area of Austria and ranging in size from 13,000 to 27,000 hectares, belong to the old aristocratic Austrian families: the Counts of Hoyos, Hubert Salvator von Habsburg-Lothringen, Prince Liechtenstein, Mayr-Melnhof, and Prince Esterhazy.

The two silvicultural systems employed in Austrian forestry and in the remainder of Central and Northern Europe are the age-class forest and the selection forest. Austrian forests are arranged in graduated age classes or even-aged allotments, which are to be cut and replanted periodically according to a rotation plan. Small-size forests are operated as selection forests. The normal increment is taken as the allowable sustained cut in both cases, the age class and the selection forest. Harvesting in an age-class forest is done by cutting all timber (clear-cut) on the allotted strip. Strip allotments are marked on large-scale forest maps depicting all age classes of the tree population. The maps are subject to revision at 10-year intervals. The management department then schedules the working procedures for the forthcoming decade. Harvesting in a selection forest is restricted to selected single mature trees taken from the total forest area. The trees to be cut are marked by the local district ranger. Felling regulations are well observed by the Austrian forest proprietors and the farmers who own small woodland patches.

With regard to the size of an allowable cut, the legislation of the Department of Agriculture and Forestry follows a very conservative policy. Cutting regulations in brief are: (1) In regions with low relief the large clear-cut (50 meters wide and 2 hectares in area) is not dependent on official permit. (2) Clear-cutting at alpine elevations (also 50 meters wide) becomes subject to permission if the area involved is larger than half a hectare. (3) Some provinces with varied terrain are subject to tripartite regulations, and the clear-cuts on rough terrain require government authorization.

The three types of Austrian forest are: (1) The High forest in which merchantable timber (almost exclusively coniferous) is allowed to grow to full size. The full growing period takes about 120 years. Seventy-four percent of the total forest land is covered by High forest. (2) The Coppice forest is a deciduous forest under a 5-25 year rotation, forming a negligible part of the total forest area. (3) The Middle forest, also called coppice-with-standards, is a selection forest and most characteristic of the farm woodland. The Middle forest occupies the remainder of the total forest area of Austria.

The development and transformation and decline of the Austro-Hungarian feudal estates are a much-neglected chapter in the agricultural geography of Europe. The writer of this study treats the land reform of 1848 as a special topic, since knowledge of the rural history is essential to the understanding of the role of forestry and agriculture. The spatial pattern of the rural landscape of Austria is today the same as it was in 1848. Forests still cover the areas that were woodland at the time of the forest legislation in 1853, and mountain meadows occupy essentially the same locations today. The blend of old and new cultural features against the scenic landscape makes Austria, after Switzerland, the most preferred holiday-land of industrial Europe and international tourism.

The land reform of 1848 initiated the redistribution of farmland in the estates of the nobility. The peasant received the land on which he lived and had worked as a freehold. The size of the new peasant holdings ranged from "dwarf" properties (less than 2 hectares) to medium-sized holdings (5-20 hectares) and large holdings (more than 20 hectares). Estates above 100 hectares included 33 percent of the entire territory. The agrarian reform was completed before the beginning of the 20th century. Few luxurious, big, landed estates survived World War II.

The funding of the land reform (317 million gold florins) and the technical aspects of the project which affected the lives of about 70 percent of the 4.5 million people who lived in the alpine provinces of the monarchy, was completed in 6 years. The necessary capital was derived from taxes imposed on the liberated peasantry. These taxes were formerly paid by the peasants to the feudal lords, who in turn had functioned as administrators of their district and financiers of the national defense.

An important and characteristic Austrian legislation, which benefits especially the mountain farmer, concerns the use of forests and pastures either owned communally or belonging to a large-landed proprietor or to the federal government, is referred to as forest servitude and pastures servitude. For example, *all* peasants of Salzburg had vested rights in the forests of the archbishop — cutting timber, collecting firewood and litter, and using alpine pastures — until the ecclesiastical state collapsed in 1802. The sovereign of Salzburg as well as the one of Tyrol needed enormous quantities of fuel for the evaporation of brine in the salt mines of the two states. One has to consider that the fires under the evaporation pans had burned without interruption for 600 years (1275-1875). But the farmers insisted on their rights. The farmers of Tyrol fought legally for 300 years for the title to forest land, and two-thirds of the Tyrolian forest area was finally transferred from public property to the communes of Tyrol by imperial decree of 1866.

The peasant seldom used the forest on a sustained-yield basis. Forest and mining ordinances were issued at an early date (16th century) to protect the vegetation cover against misuse. Overcutting and overgrazing of woodland lead to forest destruction. Forests on sloping land surfaces (60 percent of the surface of Austria is mountainous) protect the soil against erosion, landslides, "Muren" (rock flows in torrent valleys), formation of debris, wind erosion, desiccation, drenching, avalanches, frost, and wind. They also keep the ground-water supply evenly charged and exert a regulating effect on water flow in streams and river valleys. The need for forest and land resource conservation was well recognized by the monarch and his advisers in 1852. By decision of the legislators (Imperial Forest Law for Cis-Leithania, 1835, and decree of 1853) large tracts of forest land remained undivided in private ownership.

Regulations concerning the liquidation of forest servitudes, issued in the decree of 1853, specified the compensation for servitudes in the form of parcels of agricultural or forest lands. The liquidation by compensation in money is still going on today. For example, 10,000 participants of forest and pasture emoluments as listed in 1966 received redemption in money and 13,000 participants agreed to new regulations affecting 144,000 hectares of forest land and pasture.

In the chapter on the vegetation of Austria, the physical, climatic, and biological factors determining the supply of forest resources are brought together. The ecological principles governing the various species of the vegetation formation classes are explained. This chapter covers the issues of major concern and interest to foresters, geographers, conservationists, and biologists alike.

The greater part of the woodlands of the Eastern Alps belongs to the vegetation provinces and subprovinces of the European-Siberian-North American vegetation region. Species such as spruce and larch migrated into the alpine area after the Pleistocene period. Immigrants from East Europe are species of the steppe flora; and re-migrants from southeastern and southern Europe are thermophile oaks, chestnut, and other representatives of the Illyrian (Mediterranean) flora. The altitudinal zones of the Eastern Alps span a great climatic range which compares well to a latitudinal spread of forest belts from south-central France to Lappland.

The vegetation stages in the Eastern Alps are outlined as follows:

(1) Oak-hornbeam woodlands occupy the warm zone of the relatively dry plain and hill region in eastern Austria (Weinviertel, Lower Austria; Burgenland; and eastern Styria).

(2) The beech region in Central Europe and in the outer zone of the Alps encompasses the cool zone of the humid sub-mountain stage above the oak tier. It dovetails at its upper and lower boundaries with the adjacent vegetation. Spruce forests may extend like tongues through narrow valleys into the beech region or cover locations such as frostholes at intermediate elevations.

(3) Between the beech *(Fagus)* and spruce *(Picea)* levels lies a transition zone occupied by beech, spruce, pine, and fir. However, forest management is responsible for the displacement of much of the beech in this zone by economically more favored needleleaf species.

(4) The humid mountain stage, which is dominated by needleleaf species in the cold zone, extends upward to the timberline. The characteristic tree of this cold woodland zone is the spruce. In the Outer Alps other species such as fir, beech, and mountain maple are scattered throughout the spruce forest and ascend almost as far as the timberline. The somewhat drier Inner Alps are the undisputed realm of the *Picetum,* composed of straight-trunked, conical-shaped and short-branched, somber-looking spruce trees; they may form uniform stands. *Pinus silvestris* is the dry facies of the mountain stage.

(5) The belt of "Krummholz" that extends along the boundary of the needleleaf forest thrives under subarctic climatic conditions. The stunted growth of any woody plant, termed "Krummholz," is characteristic of the subalpine stage. The dominant tree of the adret (sunny slope) on subalpine and dry limestone sites is the mountain pine. The larch occupies the ubac (shady slope) as well as the adret. A thicket of green alder shrub, dwarf juniper, dwarf willow mixed with rowanberry, and alpine rhododendron is well established on fresh soils of the ubac subalpine and on wet sites.

(6) The alpine elevations below the bare rocks and the perpetual snow of the peaks of Central Europe are treeless because of the length of winter drought, but there is a great variety of alpine sedges, rock flora, and species of alpine tundra. The climate is referred to as alpine stage.

Characteristic trees, dominant plants, and rather unusual floristic elements are discussed in great detail and pinpointed at their sites. Their significance for the current society is amply explained.

The closing chapter contains a selection of utilitarian reasons that led to forest conservation, restoration of wildlife, and protection of the environment. It is emphasized that the environment of Austria is protected in the interest of the public. However, long-range planning, as, for instance, in forestry, always includes a sacrifice of the present generation for the future generation. The Austrian people were forced by an environment of scarcity to a sustained way of land use and an effective control of nature conservation.

The investigation closes with a choice selection of nature reserves and protected landscapes, including the Rothwald in the Northeastern Limestone Alps, Lower Austria, which represents the largest remnant (300 hectares) of the Central European primeval forest. The study is also supplemented by tables, figures, maps, pictures, and a bibliography of important recent publications on the subject.

REFERENCE

SCHMIDT, ELSE A.
    1976. Forestry—the Austrian context.   Amer. Forests, vol. 82, no. 7 (July), pp. 24-27, 59-61.

ELSE A. SCHMIDT

A Study of Desert Snails: Problems of Heat, Desiccation, and Starvation

Principal Investigator: Knut Schmidt-Nielsen, Duke University, Durham, North Carolina.

Grant No. 782: In support of a study of the Near East desert snail *Sphincterochila boissieri* in relation to its major problems of survival.

The survival of animals in hot, dry deserts poses some intriguing problems. Desert vertebrates, notably mammals and birds, have been extensively studied, but little attention has been paid to xerophilous invertebrate animals. A case in point is the existence of snails in hot deserts, especially since snails usually are considered associated with humid habitats.

One desert snail, *Sphincterochila boissieri,* occurs commonly in the deserts of the Near East. Live specimens of this snail, withdrawn in the shell and dormant, can be found on the desert surface in midsummer, fully exposed to sun and heat. The temperature of the surface itself may exceed 70° C., and more than a year may pass between rains. The snails remain dormant in their shells during the summer and emerge and feed only after rains, which usually occur irregularly during the winter months.

The severity of the desert habitat poses three seemingly insurmountable problems for these snails, (a) thermal death, (b) desiccation, and (c) death from starvation.

These problems were studied in the Central Negev Desert by a research team located at the Midrasha Sde Bokher near Avdat during the summer 1969. The participants were Dr. Knut Schmidt-Nielsen, professor of physiology in the Department of Zoology, Duke University; Dr. C. Richard Taylor, then a research associate at Duke University and now Agassiz professor of biology at Harvard University; and Dr. Amiram Shkolnik, professor of zoology, Tel-Aviv University, Israel. In the area under study the mean annual rainfall is less than 100 millimeters. The rains are concentrated in the winter months, from November to March, and during this period the snails are active, feed, and reproduce. During the remainder of the year they are found inactive, with the shell closed by an epiphragm. The animals presumably remain dormant throughout the dry part of the year.

Further laboratory studies were carried out at Duke University.

Temperature Tolerance

The lethal temperature of snails was determined by observing survival of individuals exposed to constant temperatures of 50, 55, and 60° C. for various periods of times. Snails heated to 60° C. invariably died within one-half hour. Snails heated to 55° C. survived for one-half hour, some died after 1 hour of exposure, more than one-half of the exposed individuals died within 2 hours, and 8 hours' exposure to 55° C. gave no survivors.

In contrast, exposure to 50° C. gave 100 percent survival, even for exposures up to 8 hours. Longer exposures were not tested in connection with this study, because the maximum heat of the desert day usually lasts for only a few hours during the early afternoon.

It can be concluded that temperatures near 55° C. are lethal to dormant *Sphincterochila* if the exposure lasts for a few hours.

Measurements of the temperature of snails under field conditions were carried out with copper-constantan thermocouples made from 0.025-millimeter wire. During the most severe conditions, with snails fully exposed to the desert sun on hot summer days, records showed that the highest temperature reached within that part of the shell where the living animal was located in no case exceeded a maximum of 50.3° C., and usually it was far lower. In other words, snails located on the desert surface, although placed in the sun on soil where the surface temperature reached over 65° C., did not attain lethal temperatures.

The main features that protect the animals from reaching the lethal temperatures are: (a) the high reflectivity of the shell to solar radiation, which is between 90 and 95 percent over the entire solar spectrum; (b) the shell is in contact with the substratum only at a few points, leaving an air cushion under the snail, thus reducing heat transfer by conduction, and (c), most importantly, the snail is withdrawn to the upper, smaller whorls of the shell, while the largest whorl, located in contact with the ground, is filled with air. Thus, inside the snail shell there is a substantial insulating air cushion that impedes heat flow into that part of the shell where the living animal is located. Nevertheless, heat does flow from the substratum into the snail, but since the air temperature remains lower than the snail's (the maximum air temperature we measured was 43° C.), heat will be conducted from the snail into the cooler air.

Water Loss

The water loss of snails was determined by weighing on an accurate analytical balance with a precision of 0.05 milligram. The recorded weight loss could include carbon loss in the form of CO_2, but since in that event actual water loss would be less than the weight loss, it was considered that weight loss could be used as a valid approximation of the maximum water loss.

Snails used for the study of water loss were placed on the natural desert surface, fully exposed to the sun during the day. They were weighed daily before sunrise and again in the evening. These snails showed a daily pattern of a weight gain at night and a loss during the day. The magnitude of the nightly gain was a few milligrams, and the loss during the day was of a similar magnitude, although always slightly greater than the preceding gain. Interestingly, dead shells similarly exposed showed approximately the same weight gain, which was again lost during the day; dead shells, however, lost exactly the amount gained during the preceding night. Live snails on the other hand, declined in weight from day to day, giving an average daily weight loss of 1.7 milligrams per day.

It was concluded from these experiments, as well as from a number of related observations, that the nightly weight gain was due to adsorption of water on the outside of the shell. The day-to-day weight loss of live snails, however, was considered to be true water loss. If snails were left undisturbed for several weeks, instead of being weighed twice daily, the rate of such weight loss decreased to a minimum of about 0.5 milligram per day.

Since an average full-sized snail contains about 1,400 milligrams of water, an estimate of a possible survival time can be derived from the observed weight loss. If it is assumed that a snail can tolerate the loss of one-half of its water, a probable survival time of 4 years can be calculated. However, since the water loss during the cooler parts of the year probably is lower, we can conclude that water loss is not a major limiting factor in the survival of the snails, even during prolonged periods of drought lasting for several years.

Energy Reserves

The energy needs of dormant snails were measured as the oxygen consumption of individual snails at various constant temperatures.

The oxygen consumption of dormant snails was variable and fluctuated with distinct periodicity. The oxygen consumption was, in periods, below a measurable magnitude, i.e., less than one μ 1 oxygen per day per snail; on the other hand, it might increase to as much as 30 or 40 μ 1 oxygen per hour.

The influence of temperature on oxygen consumption was as could be expected for a poikilotherm animal, with a Q_{10} of 2.44 in experiments that averaged determinations for 50 individual dormant snails. This finding is of importance, because it indicates that the snails have no mechanism for depressing the metabolic rate at high temperature, a mechanism that hypothetically could serve to prolong the period that nutrient reserves would last. On the other hand, the average metabolic rate is so low that the nutrient reserves in the snail, at the measured rates of oxygen consumption, are likely to last for several years. If a snail metabolizes at an average rate of 5 μ 1 oxygen/hr, we estimate that a snail should have a half-life of 48 months, or 4 years. If starvation periods extend over several seasons, which could happen in case of long droughts, it is possible that the metabolic rate and the use of nutrient reserves would decline further, thus extending the survival time beyond this estimate.

Summary

The survival of snails in hot, dry deserts was studied in *Sphincterochila boissieri,* a pulmonate snail common in desert areas in the Near East. These snails, which are found in a dormant state on the barren soil surface, fully exposed to the sun during summer, encounter three major physiological problems, high temperature, lack of water, and lack of opportunity to feed.

The lethal temperature of *Sphincterochila* was found to be between 50° and 55° C., depending on time of exposure. The temperature within the animals, exposed on the desert surface in summer, does not reach the lethal level, although the adjacent soil surface far exceeds this temperature.

The rate of water loss from dormant snails, exposed on the desert surface in summer, is about 0.5 milligram per day per snail. If a snail can tolerate the loss of one-half of its total water content (1.4 grams water in a 4-gram specimen), it can be estimated that a snail may survive 4 years of drought without reaching critical levels of water loss.

The oxygen consumption of dormant snails varies with temperature, but is so low that the nutrient reserves of the body tissues can be expected to last for several years. The relative importance of water and energy reserves in the tolerance to prolonged drought periods has not been established.

In conclusion, accurate measurements of lethal temperature, rates of water loss, and energy metabolism indicate that dormant desert snails can survive several years of unfavorable conditions.

REFERENCES

SCHMIDT-NIELSEN, KNUT; TAYLOR, C. RICHARD; and SHKOLNIK, AMIRAM
  1971. Desert snails: Problems of heat, water, and food. Journ. Exp. Biol.,
       vol. 55, pp. 385-398.
  1972. Desert snails: Problems of survival. Pp. 1-13 *in* "Comparative Phys-
       iology of Desert Animals," G. M. O. Maloiy, ed., 413 pp., illus. (Sym-
       posia of the Zoological Society of London, no. 21). Academic Press,
       London.

KNUT SCHMIDT-NIELSEN

Tracking a Nursing California Gray Whale

Principal Investigator: John E. Schultz, La Jolla, California.

Grant No. 757: For testing equipment and techniques for tracking a California gray whale.

In the fall of 1968 plans were made for an effort to track a lactating California gray whale *(Eschrichtius gibbosus)* and nursing calf from the mating and calving grounds on the Baja California peninsula. Previous expeditions by this research group had established the feasibility of attaching tracking instruments in a precise way to a free-swimming whale.

The intentions were: 1, to develop further the tracking instrument attachment technique; and 2, to track a specific animal as far as possible, in order to learn the routes followed during the presumed northward migration.

Arrangements were made to accompany U. S. Fish and Wildlife personnel on a ship chartered annually by them for whale tagging. The plan was to supplement their random technique with information gained from following a specific animal. The National Geographic Society provided a grant to cover the cost of tracking instruments and equipment and of logistic support for the expedition crew. Departure was planned to coincide with the end of the calving season, when the maximum number of animals would be ready to leave the lagoons. Shortly before the scheduled departure date the ship-sharing agreement with the Fish and Wildlife Survey was canceled. Another smaller fishing vessel, the *RV Hugo,* captained by William Kellermaan, was chartered for the expedition.

The *Hugo* sailed south from San Diego early in March 1969. All operations were conducted in Ojo de Liebre Bay (Scammon's Lagoon), located about 400 miles south of San Diego. Ojo de Liebre is the largest of the northern, seaward-side lagoons of Baja California, and is where the greatest number of gray whales congregate annually during their round trip from the summer feeding grounds north of the Bering Strait.

A shore camp was established in a central location on the north shore of the lagoon under the direction of David Pain of San Diego. Supplies were brought in by truck and by airplane to a strip near camp. A 10-gallon-per-day

539

solar still was constructed by Horace McCracken of the Sunwater Co. in order to meet the needs of the 15-person crew.

The tracking-instrument package to be attached to the whales consisted of:

1. A one-watt radio transmitter. Broadcasting with a carrier frequency of 27.195 megacycles (between the channels designated 19 and 20 of the citizen's band in the United States), the carrier is modulated with a 900 cps signal at intervals of about 1/2 second. The transmitter operates only when the whale is on the surface, and so the signal consists of a series of "beeps" lasting about 1 to 4 seconds, occurring when the whale comes up to breathe at intervals ranging from 1/2 to 5 minutes. The signals can be received at distances from about 5 to 25 kilometers. The manufacturer is Carlson Electronics, of San Diego.

2. A flashing light and colored streamers. Designed to provide night and daytime visibility, each tracking-instrument package was attached to a sterilized dart implanted near the first dorsal protuberance of a whale within 6 to 12 inches of the highest point of the whale's body (only whales with young calves alongside were tagged). The instrument package dart, smeared with antibiotic ointment before each use, was designed to pivot and withdraw after a period. Catgut was used to hold the dart in a turned position after implantation as with a standard "toggle-harpoon" dart. The whale's body fluids were expected to dissolve the catgut in about two weeks, releasing the dart and instrument package, so that the tagged animal would not be burdened after the experiment was terminated.

Proper dart placement is of crucial importance to the success of this tracking technique. The dart must be placed within a very small target area of the whale's body — as high as possible near the dorsal "bumps" — since during normal sounding the bumps are the last portion of the body to remain above water. In addition, a carelessly placed dart could easily puncture a lung or other vital organ. In order to strike such a small target on a fast-swimming whale it was necessary to implant from very close range.

3. A sonar transmitter. The sonar "pinger" operates continually and broadcasts an acoustic signal at 37 kilohertz for approximately 20-30 milliseconds, followed by an "off" time of approximately 500 milliseconds (the manufacturer is Burnett Electronics Laboratories). The sonar pinger signal, which sounds much like the ticking of a clock, can be received at distances up to 2 kilometers or more with suitable instruments, and sensitive naval vessel sonar equipment, operated in the passive mode, may be able to receive the signals at even greater range. The battery-pack capacity of both the

radio and sonar transmitters were designed to permit operation to continue through at least April 10, 1969.

It had been discovered during previous expeditions that a small, high-performance sailing catamaran (we used P-Cats manufactured by the Pacific Catamaran Co. of Costa Mesa) was an effective harpooning platform.

Trying to approach the whales slowly and quietly from behind was discarded early during previous work, since the animals were always aware of even the quietest, most drifting approach of the sailboat. An effective method was found to make a high-speed approach at about a 45° angle to a whale's expected course. Many attempts were necessary for the timing to be correct, but on occasion the catamaran would be just off the whale's head as it surfaced to blow. A resolute, immediate turn as if to ram the animal would often result in the boat arriving within 2 or 3 feet of the proper dart-placement area as the whale tried to sound quickly.

This procedure occasionally provided a 1/2- to 1-second interval in the right position for the harpooner to insert the dart. The procedure was hard on boats as, while surprised by the sudden course change and attempting to dive quickly in order to avoid the catamaran, the whales sometimes became confused and either rammed the boat or struck it with their flukes. On three occasions a whale apparently deliberately attacked the "whalecat," twice causing major damage but no personal injuries. (Captain Scammon mentions in some detail the hazards of pursuing "devil-fish," especially when with young.)

Another less vigorous method, with which we had some success, was to pursue the whales patiently at very slow speed with the *Hugo*. Maneuvering in the shoal lagoon water was quite difficult and tedious; however, at least one dart was solidly placed by harpooning from the bows of the *Hugo*. Note that use of a large vessel in this way was never previously successful in the open ocean.

We also used a small high-speed power boat, pursuing the animals by the Norwegian "prayer-jag" method. This consists of circling at high speed, attempting to prevent the whales from having time to blow adequately, thus tiring them out. After the animals begin to "pant" — or blow frequently — it is easier to approach to implant the dart. Skill in estimating where an animal is likely to come up to blow can be developed. This method is probably best for tagging a free-swimming whale in the open ocean. However, it has the disadvantage of putting great stress on the animals; and after the dart is attached, it takes some time (several hours) for the whale to resume normal swimming speed.

While in Scammon's Lagoon for a period of about three weeks, we inserted a dart about 20 times. In most cases the dart came out quickly. On three occasions the dart remained in place for significant periods.

After successful attachment of the tracking instrument package there was often considerable difficulty in following the animal. The shoal water and torturous passages of the lagoon made it difficult to maneuver the *Hugo* to follow the tagged whale.

We lost contact with the first animal several hours after implant. The instrument package was later recovered by a local fisherman about 20 miles away on the beach outside of the lagoon.

The second implant of some duration ended with the dart coming loose in several hours.

The expedition was extended considerably past the planned duration because of the large number of "near misses" and almost successful implants. Funds for chartering the *Hugo* ran quite low, as did the food and fuel. The fatigue of the crew and attrition to equipment were extreme.

The final implant of the expedition was the longest-lived (although we had previously tracked another animal for 13 hours at sea during the year before.)

On March 20 at about 3:00 p.m., local time, a good implant was made by expedition photographer Mike Hoover. During the first hour of tracking the tagged whale surfaced an average of once every 50 seconds. The signal was lost for about an hour. It resumed at dark but the *Hugo* was unable to follow because of the shoal water and darkness. The whale surfaced less frequently as the night continued—from about once per minute at dusk to once every 2 minutes by 1:00 a.m. the following morning. The signal direction finders indicated that the whale had gone out to sea with her calf. The *Hugo* left the lagoon at first light but was unable to pick up the signals again.

Two separate, conflicting reports were later received concerning the tagged whale. The first was from the U. S. Navy, which received a sonar pinger signal south of the lagoon. One day later the Mexican Navy received a radio signal that seemed to match the tracking transmitter about 90 miles north.

Conclusions and Recommendations

The hand-held direction finder could not be operated quickly enough to get a reliable bearing on a surfacing whale's position, especially when the animal was at some distance. An automatic direction finder has been developed for use with dolphins, which would considerably expedite this type of tracking.

The research question remains: What is the northward migration route of the nursing gray whales? It is probably of considerable significance to determine this, since there is reason to suspect poaching activities by whalers who have discovered the migration route of the animals during their return trip.

As in any expeditionary effort, machine-shop facilities and multiple redundancy in equipment are necessary in order to be able to continue to operate effectively under trying situations.

The tracking tape recordings are available for analysis, as well as transcription of the number of times the tracked animal surfaced.

JOHN E. SCHULTZ

Archeological Investigations in the Grand Canyon

Principal Investigator: Douglas W. Schwartz, School of American Research, Santa Fe, New Mexico.

Grant Nos. 755, 857, 949.   In support of a joint archeological project at Grand Canyon, Arizona.

Between 1967 and 1970, the School of American Research, with support from the National Geographic Society, the National Science Foundation, and the National Park Service, conducted the first major archeological program within Grand Canyon National Park. The four objectives of this project were:

(1) To conduct extensive archeological excavations in selected areas throughout the Grand Canyon and its various environmental zones.

(2) To determine the sequence of culture history and the details of man's use of the canyon and how this sequence relates to the general prehistory of Grand Canyon.

(3) To determine the relation of the prehistoric settlements in Grand Canyon to the various contrasting environments of Grand Canyon.

(4) To use the Grand Canyon as a laboratory to study the postmigration culture and to study what effects a migration to a new area, in this case, a major new environment, has on the culture of the people moving.

Background and History

Before the four-year project reported on here began, I had done extensive archeological work throughout the Grand Canyon region, specifically in parts of the Havasupai area, Shinumo Canyon, Nankoweap Canyon, Cremation Canyon, and Clear Creek, and made extensive surveys along the river between Nankoweap and Unkar Delta. A summary of this work laid a foundation for the major project described here (Schwartz, 1966).

In the first phase of the project, conducted during the summers of 1967 and 1968 with support by the National Science Foundation, 25 crew members and 5 tons of equipment were transported from the south rim of the

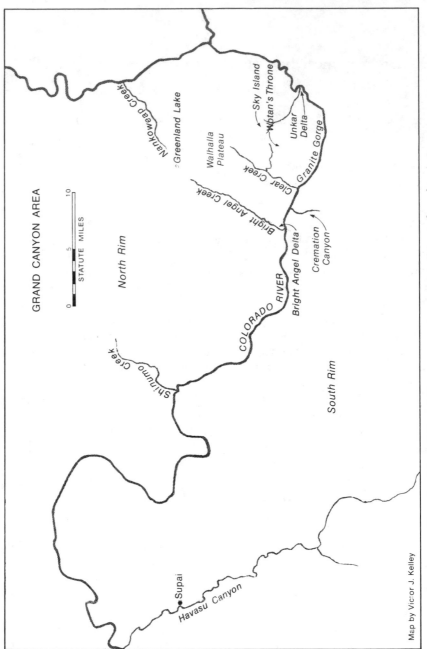

FIG. 1.   Map of Grand Canyon area showing localities referred to in text.

Grand Canyon to Unkar Delta, a 150-acre area of land just above the level of the Colorado River within Grand Canyon. During both of these summer periods, extensive survey, excavation, and ecological research were conducted in this area, as well as surveys up Unkar Creek toward the North Rim. In the following two summers, 1969 and 1970, work on the North Rim included survey, excavation, ecological work, and a continued attempt to determine trail passages between the North Rim and the inner canyon. In addition, rock pillars containing evidence of archeological material were surveyed and one was extensively excavated. The National Geographic Society supported this later phase of the project on the North Rim, while the National Park Service supported the excavation of a small site at the mouth of Bright Angel Creek in the Granite Gorge in Grand Canyon.

Research Design

From the beginning, the project was conceived as an attempt to determine the full range of archeological material in the inner canyon and on the North Rim. Survey work, previously referred to, had determined that the South Rim material had a different culture history; thus it was not included in this project. During the first phase of the work, more than 50 sites on Unkar Delta were located by survey, including pueblos, granaries, agricultural terraces, hunting lookout sites, and firepit areas. During the second two years on the North Rim, 73 sites were located by survey. In both cases, the survey work was closely coordinated with the ecological work, in an attempt to determine the relationship of archeological sites of various time periods to the ecological zones, which range from the spruce-fir zone of the North Rim through the Lower Sonoran zone of the inner canyon. In total, during the four years of the project, 51 sites were wholly or partially excavated. With the results of the survey as a guide, sites were excavated that represented each of the major time periods in each of the major ecological zones.

Concomitant with the survey and excavation the ecological work included detailed description of each local biotic community from the riparian zone of the Colorado River to the spruce-fir forest of the North Rim. In addition, in an attempt to determine something of the problems encountered by the prehistoric farmers, experimental gardens were grown both in the inner canyon and on the North Rim. Analysis of prehistoric flora, fauna, and pollen from the excavated sites supplemented the ecological work. From all this material, a detailed description of the nature of the environment and its changes during the major occupation could be constructed.

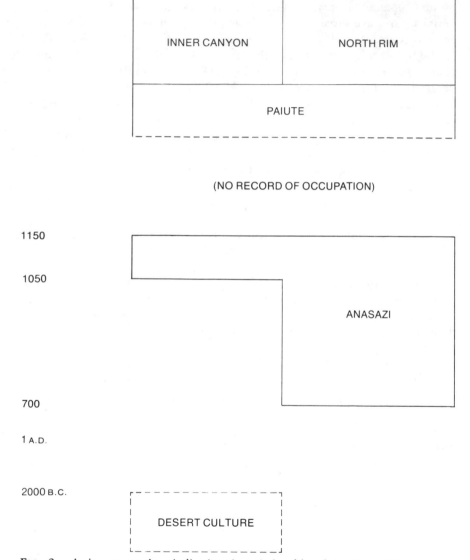

FIG. 2.   A time-space chart indicating the relationship of the North Rim material
to that found in the inner canyon.

Results

The results of the work can be divided into two major categories, historical and theoretical. Both are summarized below.

Historical. Sometime near 2000 B.C., small bands of hunters occasionally traveled from the rim to the bottom of the Grand Canyon and, after collecting willow branches, took them to caves high in the canyon walls. There, following an age-old ritual, they precisely fashioned twigs from the branches into small figurines, symbolically representing animals they were about to pursue in coming hunts. Some figurines were pierced with small effigy spears, and all of them, after being carefully placed in shallow basins hollowed out in the dust of the cave floor, were covered with piles of rock. Following this ritual, the hunters left the caves, believing that they would have success in the hunt. There is no evidence about their other activities; only the hunters' occasional visits to the caves provide insights into their culture. These hunters, perhaps the first people to use the Grand Canyon, began a long and interestingly varied record of man's association with the canyon.

Two millennia passed before man again occupied the Grand Canyon area. About A.D. 1, another hunting and gathering people occupied areas of the North and perhaps the South Rim. Apparently they stalked, hunted, and butchered game on both rims; certainly they did on the North Rim around the wooded edges of ponds and meadows. Most of their subsistence activities apparently took place elsewhere, perhaps in the warmer areas such as Houserock Valley. No evidence that this second group of hunters used the inner canyon has been found.

A 250-year period of increasingly sedentary Pueblo occupation began around A.D. 900 when a few habitations were first built on the North Rim, at the edge of the canyon. Near these one-room sites, the early Anasazi people began practicing a rudimentary agriculture and adapting their crops to the nearly 8,000-foot elevation. However, they were still largely dependent upon hunting and gathering, and the house sites were little more than base camps for seasonal gathering trips. At the same time, they attempted twice to settle the inner canyon; both attempts appear to be of short duration, perhaps because the technology the Indians had developed on the rims was insufficient to conquer the much more difficult environment of the canyon bottom.

By A.D. 1050, they had adapted to the ponderosa-pine forest and the population of the North Rim increased significantly. Habitation sites grew

FIG. 3.   Aerial view from North Rim to inner canyon with archeological camp in
foreground and Unkar Delta at top of photo.

FIG. 4. Work in progress on the Walhalla ruin on the North Rim.

much larger and storage rooms appeared, indicating that dependence upon or success with agriculture had increased and that the sites were no longer merely base camps for seasonal gathering trips. Throughout the pine forest up to the 8,200-foot line, the Anasazi farmers distributed themselves evenly over the landscape in approximately 26-acre territories, farming on agricultural terraces built mainly on the edges of the gently sloping valleys. Beyond the 8,200-foot line, where the fir forest begins, it was impossible to practice agriculture, but the Indians nevertheless hunted and gathered around the ponds and meadows in the higher elevations as their ancestors had done hundreds of years earlier. They probably also descended into the Grand Canyon to hunt mountain sheep and perhaps deer. Fairly active trade relationships with the heartland of the Anasazi culture to the east are reflected in design styles of pottery, forms of arrow points, and tool types.

The most significant event occurring during this period of population climax, however, was perhaps sparked by a change from winter-dominant to summer-dominant rainfall. For the first time, large numbers of people moved into the canyon itself. This is reflected at Unkar Delta where four large and complex sites represent settlements of multifamily units. As on the North Rim, these Unkar sites appear to reflect economically self-sufficient communities, dependent upon agriculture. Extensive terrace systems indicate the ability of the inhabitants to adapt to this desert environment only 10 miles from the North Rim forests but nearly 6,000 feet lower in elevation.

Around A.D. 1100, the population of the North Rim began to level off and perhaps decrease, while significant changes were occurring both on the rim and in the canyon. The North Rim settlements increased slightly in size, sometimes by addition to existing structures, but these sites were now farther apart than in the early period. Perhaps earlier agricultural practices had made some areas unfit for production, or perhaps the environment was already beginning to change again. Although some sites, especially Sky Island, a rock pillar standing apart from the rim, have specialized functions, indicating that earlier economic autonomy had decreased, the way of life was essentially a continuation of the previous pattern.

The Unkar Delta settlement, on the other hand, was characterized in the later period by a complete reversal of the earlier settlement. The habitation-storage-ceremonial room complexes were abandoned, and much smaller, more numerous 2-room structures were built in unproductive areas, so that maximal use of land suitable for agriculture was possible. The number of storage rooms and bins increased; the significance of this is yet undetermined. The architectural styles on the delta at this time varied

FIG. 5. Work in progress on the Walhalla ruin on the North Rim.

dramatically from site to site. Despite their proximity, the sites may have been inhabited by autonomous social units. By now the Indians had learned to utilize the inner canyon completely. The best areas for agriculture were saved for farming; the worst were used for habitation. Although life was hard, the inhabitants of the delta had adapted completely.

Then by about A.D. 1150 everything changed. The experiment in Grand Canyon living began to end, almost simultaneously both on the rim and in the inner canyon. The cause was probably in part the return to a winter rainfall pattern that began near the middle of the Pueblo III Period, but this hypothesis cannot yet be thoroughly tested. Gradually the inhabitants of the canyon retreated east; their descendants may have come to rest in the land of the Hopi. Hopi legends that tell of their ancestors emerging from an opening in the bottom of the Grand Canyon may be a symbolic reflection, a folk memory, of this early attempt to survive in the Grand Canyon.

Theoretical. Although the final analysis and publication will take several years to complete, there is some indication that the use of the Grand Canyon material as a case study for examining the postmigration culture will provide important insights for general anthropological theory. The ethnographic literature suggests that each migrating community undergoes three phases of change: pioneering, consolidation, and stabilization. A summary of this sequence gives some indication of the direction that this research is taking.

1. *Pioneering Phase.* For the initial one to four years following a migration, a community is likely to be directing its effort toward physical survival; the first shelters are built, fields are prepared, and the first crops are planted. During the pioneering phase, the total group is likely to be characterized by stronger solidarity and greater ethnocentricity than was the case in the premigration situation. On the other hand, some families or groups may develop disagreements with the main group, some to the point of abandoning the new settlement.

2. *Consolidation Phase.* Generally, after the first or second good harvest, more permanent shelters are constructed and the first community structures are added. Also, at this time, the development and crystallization of formal and informal social institutions and associations are likely to occur. Factions are also likely to arise during the consolidation phase; in some cases, these will split from the new community as a group or they may simply continue to exist within the new community.

3. *Stabilization Phase.* Eventually, depending on the degree of change from the original settlement, the effects of migration pass, and the community settles down to develop along lines not directly related to the move.

From this base, plus cross-cultural information on a wide range of topics concerning the postmigration community, the Grand Canyon material will be examined.

Continuing Analysis

While the field work for this project and all the major laboratory analyses have been completed, the development of descriptive monographs and synthesis is still under way. Three descriptive monographs are planned: one each on the Bright Angel site, the Unkar Delta settlement, and the North Rim project. A fourth volume will synthesize the total Grand Canyon prehistoric culture sequence and relate this to the larger developments in the Southwest.

REFERENCES

SCHWARTZ, DOUGLAS W.
    1958. Split-twig figurines in the Grand Canyon. Amer. Antiq., vol. 23, no. 3, pp. 264-273. (With Arthur L. Lange and Raymond DeSaussure.)
    1966. A historical analysis and synthesis of Grand Canyon archaeology. Amer. Antiq., vol. 31, no. 4, pp. 469-484.
    1969. Grand Canyon prehistory. Four Corners Geological Society: Geology and Natural History of the Grand Canyon Region, pp. 35-40.
    1970. The postmigration culture: A base for archeological inference. Pp. 175-193 *in* "Reconstructing Prehistoric Pueblo Societies," William A. Longacre, ed. School of American Research, University of New Mexico Press, Albuquerque.

DOUGLAS W. SCHWARTZ

Use of "Starlight Scope" in Studies of Animal Behavior

Principal Investigator: Reay H. N. Smithers, National Museums of Rhodesia, Causeway, Rhodesia.

Grant No. 815:   To assist in providing an instrument (Starlight Scope) for studying the behavior of nocturnal animals in Botswana.

The Starlight Scope is a night-vision image-intensifier device developed by the U. S. Army. The purpose of the present grant was to underwrite the cost of shipment of one of these instruments from South Africa to me particularly in aid of my long-term studies of nocturnal mammals of Botswana. It arrived here on October 21, 1971.

I was anxious to use the instrument in the observations, particularly of certain small mammals at breeding sites, but unfortunately we were not able to locate active breeding holes of the black-backed jackal *(Canis mesomelas),* side-striped jackal *(C. adustus),* or the bat-eared fox *(Otocyon megalotis),* which were the three species in which I was particularly interested.

One hole (obviously not a breeding hole) of *C. mesomelas* was kept under observation for several nights but, except for the emergence of the single individual occupying the hole and its later return on a number of occasions, nothing of particular behavioral interest was recorded. These observations showed that the instrument is ideal if active breeding holes of the species can be found. However, the movements of the rusty-spotted genet *(Genetta tigrina),* feeding scrub hares *(Lepus saxatilis),* and the common duiker *(Sylvicapra grimmia)* were observed for limited periods. Unfortunately, we missed the peak of breeding, and it was obvious by the end of the year that we would have to wait until the following season.

In order to make the maximum use of the Starlight Scope, therefore, it was turned over to our keeper of zoology at the Umtali Museum, H. D. Jackson, who is working, as a long-term project, on the Caprimulgiformes, more especially their behavior. As these are nocturnal birds, observations of behavior are extremely difficult without the use of an instrument of this type. Mr. Jackson reports as follows:

"Aside from one fortuitous view of a hare, I used the Starlight Scope exclusively on nightjars, particularly on the pennant-wing *(Macrodipteryx vexillarius)* and the fiery-necked *(Caprimulgus pectoralis)*. This proved to be an ideal instrument for my purpose, and I learned more about certain aspects of caprimulgid ethology in two months with the Starlight Scope than I had in several years of trial and error with less satisfactory methods of observation. Further use of the instrument would enormously benefit my research on the Caprimulgiformes by reducing the time required to resolve the life history of each species and so permitting me to cover more species in the time available.

"The observations on *M. vexillarius* were particularly valuable. I was able to watch the complete courtship dance for several evenings and accumulated sufficient data to enable publication of a description of this fascinating performance. Part of the display involves low-level flights, and I found that with some practice I could follow the bird in flight quite easily with the Starlight Scope. This species displays in rather open habitat so that maximum use is made of the light available, but in the case of *C. pectoralis* I found that at times the Starlight Scope was ineffective on account of the shady situations in which this species nests. Nevertheless, extremely useful observations were made during the incubation period at one nest; unfortunately, this is the least active period during the breeding cycle, and the eggs did not hatch before I had to return the Starlight Scope. Supplementary observations during the nestling period were made with the use of a light fitted with a red filter, and it was noticeable how this light affected the behavior of the birds; this is where the real value of the instrument lies — the subject is completely unaware of the observer, provided that a reasonable distance is maintained.

"The actual performance of the instrument requires little comment; it is simple to operate even though the focusing is somewhat slow. It provides excellent visibility in open situations on clear nights, with or without a moon; even in miombo woodland of medium cover it provides good visibility on clear nights, particularly if there is a moon. Cloudy conditions are the most difficult and in overcast it is virtually ineffective."

REAY H. N. SMITHERS

Functional Cranial Anatomy of the Subfossil Malagasy Lemurs

Principal Investigator: Ian Tattersall, American Museum of Natural History, New York, New York.

Grant No. 818: For research on the subfossil Malagasy lemurs.

The island of Madagascar, the world's fourth largest, is justly renowned for its unique flora and fauna. Isolated from the African Continent for perhaps 75 million years, and untrodden by the foot of man until at most 1,500 years ago, for millions of years Madagascar provided an undisturbed refuge for the lemurs, its primate inhabitants. These animals, derived from a number of invading prosimian stocks that crossed from Africa at a time when the island was much closer to the mainland than it is today, and before the higher primates appeared on the evolutionary scene, flourished and diversified in the almost total absence of competition and predation by other animals.

Since the arrival of man on the island, however, several genera of the Malagasy primates have become extinct. Between 1893, when the subfossil remains of the first of these were described, and the present, a substantial literature has accumulated on them, but many misconceptions about them still survive. Moreover, prior to the work reported here, very little effort had been directed toward the understanding of their functional cranial anatomy, and no critical overview had been undertaken of the relationships of the Malagasy primate fauna as a whole. The following brief notes summarize my efforts to date to fill these lacunae.

Age and Relationships of the Subfossils

The sites from which the extinct lemurs are known are distributed widely over the central, western, and southern areas of Madagascar. A single site is known from the northwest. Although the subfossil lemurs are generally referred to as being "Pleistocene" in age, radiocarbon dates in fact reveal that they are much more recent than this; credible dates range from 2,850 to 1,035 years B.P. Figure 1 shows the location of the sites, together with available dates.

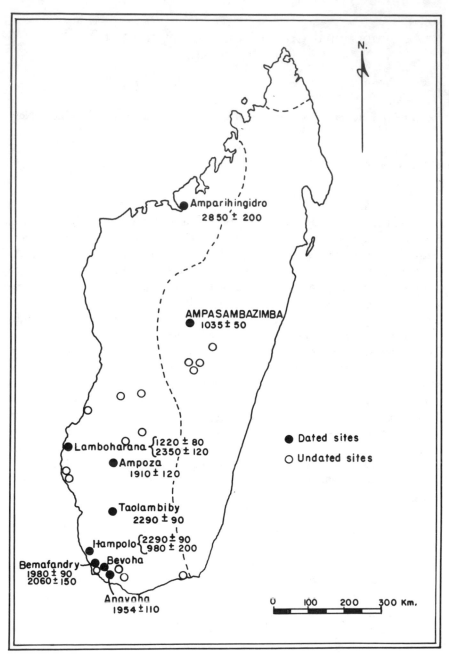

FIG. 1.   Sites, with dating where available, from which subfossil lemurs have been
recovered. Dates from Mahé (1965), Mahé and Sourdat (1972), and Tattersall
(1973c). The dotted line indicates the western limit of the damp eastern flora.

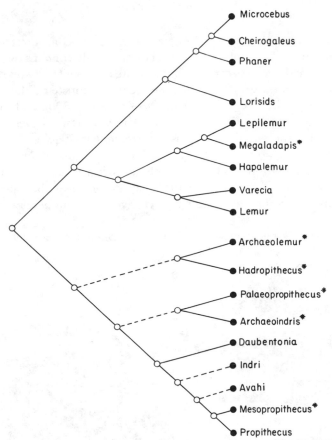

FIG. 2. Provisional theory of relationships of the Malagasy lemurs. Branching points have no temporal or morphological significance. Extinct forms are denoted by asterisks.

The relationships of the extinct to the living forms are reasonably clear. Most of the extinct lemur fauna is derived from a common stock with the living indriines and *Daubentonia,* while *Megaladapis* is closely related to *Lepilemur.* A tentative theory of relationships of the entire lemur fauna is given in figure 2; extinct genera are denoted by asterisks. Following are brief discussions of the crania of the three subfamilies (Archaeolemurinae, Palaeopropithecinae, and Megaladapinae), represented solely by extinct forms.

Archaeolemurinae

Most of the research briefly summarized here was concentrated on the archaeolemurines (Tattersall, 1973a, b). The subfamily contains two genera, *Hadropithecus* and *Archaeolemur,* the latter being represented by two species, *A. majori* and *A. edwardsi.* Although even recent authors (e.g., Mahé, 1972), following the earlier suggestions of Major (e.g., 1896) and Standing (e.g., 1908), continue to discover a "monkeylike" *Gestalt* in these animals, they have in fact, despite their increase in size, remained quite close in their cranial anatomy (fig. 3) to a primitive condition closely approximated by the living indriine *Propithecus.* There is nothing, for instance, in the external morphology of their brains, or in the bony evidence of their peripheral cranial sensory organs, to suggest any change from the general indriine condition.

The most striking adaptations of the archaeolemurines are seen in their

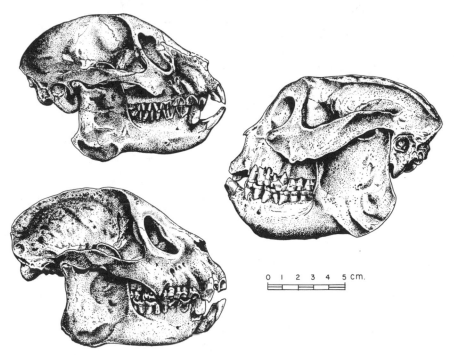

0 1 2 3 4 5 cm.

FIG. 3.   Archaeolemurine crania in lateral view. Top left: *Archaeolemur majori;* right: *Hadropithecus stenognathus;* bottom left: *Archaeolemur edwardsi.*

dentitions. The incisors of *Archaeolemur* are enlarged, and the lowers are far less procumbent than are those of the indriines. The premolar rows retain three teeth (only two are present in the indriines and palaeopropithecines), which are modified to form a continuous longitudinal shearing blade. The molars are squarish, and classically bilophodont, the lowers being virtual mirror-images of the uppers; they receive substantially less wear than do the premolars.

In *Hadropithecus* the incisors, canine and caniniform, are greatly reduced, the posterior premolars are molariform, and the molars themselves are high-crowned and bear a complex pattern of enamel folds on their occlusal surfaces.

The contrasts in molar morphology between *Archaeolemur* and *Hadropithecus* correspond closely to those noted by Jolly (1970) between the baboons *Papio* and *Theropithecus,* respectively. *Papio* exists on a more generalized, frugivorous diet than does *Theropithecus,* which feeds on small, tough, gritty particles gathered on the ground and conveyed directly to the molars with the fingers, eliminating any role of the anterior teeth in food preparation. A similar diet to that of *Theropithecus* would satisfactorily explain the anterior dental reduction and molar complication seen in *Hadropithecus.*

Related to the reduction of the anterior teeth in *Hadropithecus* is the extreme brevity of the animal's face, unique among nonhominid primates. A model of the operation of the masticatory musculature was developed to explain the relationship of this feature to the form of the braincase, which is likewise foreshortened relative to that of *Archaeolemur.* Briefly, the model holds that the more anterior the point at which biting takes place, the more effort is required of the posterior (horizontally-directed) portion of the temporalis muscle; as the bite-point moves posteriorly, the anterior (vertical) fibers of temporalis come to dominate the production of occlusal forces. The system is further explained by Tattersall (1973a, 1974) and Roberts and Tattersall (1974). The posterior concentration of mastication in *Hadropithecus* would thus require the predominance of the anterior part of temporalis, with the observed result that the braincase is abbreviated anteroposteriorly (fig. 3).

An extension of this proclivity for powerful chewing is found in the fusion of the mandibular symphysis in the archaeolemurines. Such fusion, not found in the living forms, would permit the employment of the contralateral muscles, particularly temporalis, in producing lateral motion at the ipsilateral molars.

Palaeopropithecinae

This subfamily is represented by the two large-sized genera *Palaeopro-pithecus* and *Archaeoindris* (fig. 4). These are most strikingly distinguished from the indriines and archaeolemurines by the loss of the inflated auditory bulla and the development of a tubular bony external auditory meatus. I have suggested that, in view of the occurrence of a similar conformation in the remotely related *Megaladapis,* this condition may be size-related in large, small-brained lemurs (Tattersall, 1973b). It may well be that in such forms a tympanic cavity large enough to avoid excessive damping of the tympanic membrane can be accommodated within the lateral cranial base,

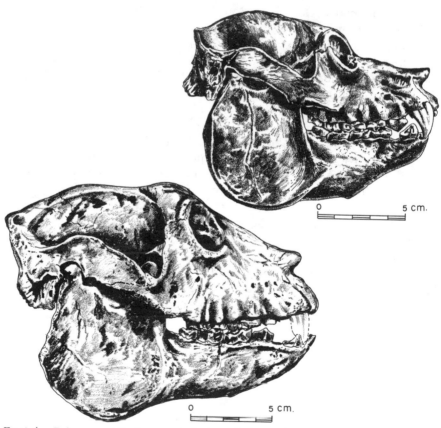

FIG. 4.   Palaeopropithecine crania in lateral view. Above: *Palaeopropithecus ingens* (= *P. maximus*); below: *Archaeoindris fontoynonti.*

eliminating the need for a salient bulla enclosing a voluminous hypotympanic sinus.

Although cranially the paleopropithecines are less similar to the indriines than are the archaeolemurines, *Palaeopropithecus* is reminiscent in its cranial proportions of *Indri,* differing from the latter primarily in the relatively small size of its brain and orbits. In the morphology of its dentition (except the incisors), this genus is quite close to *Propithecus.*

The cranial proportions of *Propithecus* and *Archaeoindris* are mutually reminiscent, largely owing to the abbreviation of the facial skeleton, and hence also the neurocranium, in both. In absolute terms, however, the cranium of *Archaeoindris* is substantially deeper than that of *Propithecus;* this may well have been due to the need to resolve far greater occlusal forces. The plausibility of this suggestion gains from the fact that the mandibular symphysis is fused in the palaeopropithecines.

Megaladapinae

This subfamily contains the single genus *Megaladapis,* with three species (fig. 5), which are, in order of increasing size, *M. madagascariensis, M. grandidieri,* and *M. edwardsi.* The cranium of the last of these frequently measures over 300 millimeters in length. Superficially quite unlike all other lemurs, *Megaladapis* is nonetheless very close to *Lepilemur* in cladistic terms, and, indeed, its strange allure can quite simply be explained in functional terms.

The enormous elongation of the face of *Megaladapis* forms part of an adaptive feeding complex, which also includes the retroflexion of the face on the cranial base, the backward orientation of the foramen magnum, and the vertically positioned occipital condyles. This functional complex is also seen in *Phascolarctos,* the koala bear, which is in its locomotion, as *Megaladapis* was (Walker, 1967), a modified vertical clinger and leaper. The koala feeds, and *Megaladapis* presumably fed (like its close relative *Lepilemur),* by pulling leaves by hand toward its mouth and cropping them with its anterior teeth *(Megaladapis* in fact lacked permanent incisors; these appear to have been replaced by a horny pad, as in some ruminants). The functional complex previously noted in effect turns the entire head into a long extension of the neck, thus maximizing the radius within which the animal can feed from a single clinging position. This would undoubtedly have been highly advantageous for a bulky and relatively unagile form such as *Megaladapis,* which may have been largely confined to the major vertical trunks of the trees in which it fed.

The cranial proportions of *Megaladapis* underline dramatically the workings of the model of masticatory mechanics referred to earlier. One of the most remarkable features of the cranium of *Megaladapis* is the possession of huge frontal sinuses, which extend far back into the braincase, separating the tiny brain from the peripheral sensory systems of the face and resulting, for instance, in the development of extremely long olfactory

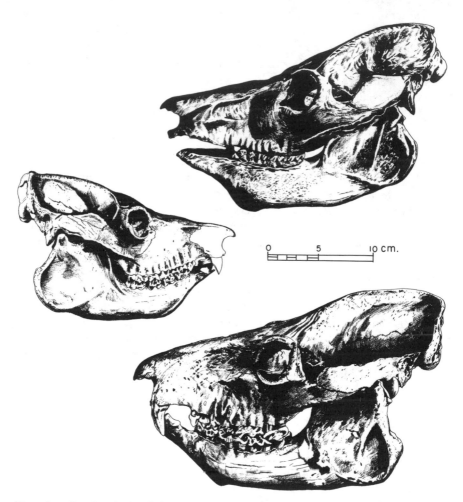

FIG. 5.   Crania of *Megaladapis* in lateral view. Top right: *M. grandidieri;* left: *M. madagascariensis;* bottom right: *M. edwardsi.*

tracts. This is evidently related to the great elongation of the face, which carried the point of ingestive and masticatory activity far anteriorly. The geometry of the masticatory system demands under these conditions the possession of a large, horizontally directed posterior temporalis muscle. The tiny brain, however, would not by itself provide sufficient exocranial attachment area for the muscle, and, if situated directly behind the face, would not be positioned to support posterior temporalis fibers of the requisite orientation. The sinuses therefore exist to fill the gap between the necessary functional positions of the facial skeleton and the braincase proper.

Extinction of the Subfossil Lemurs

As Walker (1967) has pointed out, all the vanished lemur genera were large and almost certainly diurnal. They are, in fact, precisely those forms that would have proved most vulnerable to the direct predation of man, once he had arrived on the island. There is absolutely no plausible evidence to suggest the extinction of these lemurs from causes other than man. But we do not merely have cause to regret that these fascinating animals have escaped us by so short a period of time. For the same processes that led to the extinction of the subfossils are threatening their surviving counterparts today. Destruction of the forests in which they live, not least by overseas commercial interests, is steadily diminishing the already vastly reduced habitat of the lemurs. If realistic conservation measures, backed by an international effort, are not taken in the very near future, the living lemurs, too, will soon be represented only by their bones.

REFERENCES

JOLLY, CLIFFORD J.
    1970. The seed-eaters: A new model of hominid differentiation based on a baboon analogy. Man, new ser., vol. 5, pp. 5-26.
MAHÉ, JOEL
    1965. Les subfossiles malgaches, 11 pp. Imprimerie National, Tananarive.
    1972. The Malagasy subfossils. Pp. 339-366 *in* "Biogeography and Ecology of Madagascar," R. Battistini and G. Richard-Vindard, eds. W. Junk, The Hague.
MAHÉ, JOEL, and SOURDAT, M.
    1972. Sur l'extinction des vertébrés subfossiles et l'aridification du climat dans le sud-ouest de Madagascar. Mém. Soc. Géol. France, vol. 17, no. 14, pp. 295-309.
MAJOR, C. I. FORSYTH
    1896. Preliminary notice on fossil monkeys from Madagascar. Geol. Mag., decade 4, vol. 3, pp. 433-436.

ROBERTS, DAVID, and TATTERSALL, IAN
    1974. Skull form and the mechanics of mandibular elevation in mammals.
        Amer. Mus. Novitates, no. 2536, 9 pp.
STANDING, HERBERT
    1908. On recently discovered subfossil primates from Madagascar. Trans.
        Zool. Soc. London, vol. 18, pp. 69-112.
TATTERSALL, IAN
    1971. Revision of the subfossil Indriinae. Folia Primat., vol. 16, pp. 257-269.
    1972. The functional significance of airorhynchy in *Megaladapis*. Folia Primat.,
        vol. 18, pp. 20-26.
    1973a. Cranial anatomy of Archaeolemurinae. Anthrop. Pap. Amer. Mus.
        Nat. Hist., vol. 52, pt. 1, pp. 1-110.
    1973b. Subfossil lemuroids and the "adaptive radiation" of the Malagasy
        lemurs. Trans. New York Acad. Sci., vol. 35, pp. 314-324.
    1973c. A note on the age of the subfossil site of Ampasambazimba, Miarina-
        rivo Province, Madagascar Republic. Amer. Mus. Novitates, no.
        2520, 6 pp.
    1974. Facial structure and mandibular mechanics in *Archaeolemur*. Pp. 563-577
        in "Prosimian Biology," R. D. Martin, G. A. Doyle, and A. C. Walker,
        eds., 983 pp., illus. Gerald Duckworth & Co., London.
    1975. Notes on the cranial anatomy of the subfossil Malagasy lemurs. Pp. 111-
        124 *in* "Lemur Biology," Ian Tattersall and Robert W. Sussman, eds.,
        365 pp., illus. Plenum Press, New York.
TATTERSALL, IAN, and SCHWARTZ, JEFFREY H.
    1974. Craniodental morphology and the systematics of the Malagasy lemurs
        (Primates, Prosimii). Anthrop. Pap. Amer. Mus. Nat. Hist., vol. 52,
        pt. 3, pp. 139-192.
WALKER, A. C.
    1967. Patterns of extinction among the subfossil Madagascan lemuroids. Pp.
        425-432 *in* "Pleistocene Extinction," P. S. Martin and H. E. Wright, eds.
        Yale University Press, New Haven.

IAN TATTERSALL

Natural History of the Railroad Worm

Principal Investigator: Darwin L. Tiemann, China Lake, California.

Grant No. 772:   In support of a research on the life history and biochemistry of the railroad worm *(Phrixothrix)*.

The beetle genus *Phrixothrix* in the family Phengodidae contains over 15 species in South and Central America. The larvae and adult larviform females of this genus are unique in possessing red lanterns in the head, as well as yellow-green lanterns on the thorax and abdomen. The present study was concentrated on the natural history of one of the species of this bioluminescent organism.

The city of São José dos Campos, São Paulo, Brazil, was chosen for a research area because there I had found two railroad-worm larvae in October and November 1960 and adult males in January 1963. Since the length of the insect's life cycle was not known, four months — August to November 1969 — were chosen for the field work with the option of remaining through January 1970 if mature females were obtained.

The rationale used for the research was the one developed in the study of a related species, the western-banded glowworm, in California (Tiemann, 1967) and the work of H. L. Parker reported by E. Newton Harvey (1952).

Two work areas were developed; one on the campus of the Centro Técnico de Aeronáutica, the second in a newer real-estate development called Jardim Esplanada on the edge of the city. I am certain that many work areas could have been developed in and around the city, but since the initial two were productive there was little incentive to spend time developing others.

Approximately 100 cement blocks, fabricated for the purpose, were placed with plastic dishes beneath in one of my two work areas. It was expected that these pitfall traps would contain the larvae that fell in during the night. It did not work out this way, however, because the nature of the soil was such that the larvae would find the interface between the dish and the soil and go beneath the dish. The cement blocks did, however, provide shelter for the larvae at morning twilight. When this was learned, approximately 150 tiles, the type used in house building, were placed in the second work area.

During August and September few larvae were found and those were relatively small and were collected under the blocks and tiles. Spot checking at night with the safari light during this period did not yield a single specimen.

I was aided fairly regularly by this time by a young Brazilian boy, Isaac Cassemiro de Souza, and on weekends during the school year by a schoolboy, José Eugenio Lemes dos Santos.

Things began to happen in October as spring advanced and the rains increased. We placed 120 additional tiles in the second work area and began 2-4 hours of searching with the safari light 7 days a week except in heavy rain. These nightly forays became the high points of the days. In addition to the object of our search, we observed much of the activity of the night such as lines of termites (3 species) carrying bits of plant material into their nests. The railroad worms we tracked would not attempt to cross these lines but would turn aside. The parasol ants also worked day and night, stopping only for extremes in temperature and sudden rainfalls when they would drop their burdens and quickly retreat into their underground sanctuary.

Two kinds of trap-door spiders occurred in the work areas; one had a thick heavy door and the other, a smaller one, a fragile door, which it would throw completely open when it went forth to hunt. These were watched in case they would turn out to be predators on the railroad worms. Other spiders, large and small toads, and various snakes were also seen during our nightly search. We did not, however, observe any predation on the railroad worms in the field. In captivity when the quarters were close they would kill and sometimes eat one another.

In all, 280 specimens were collected. Some of these died for various reasons; a few escaped but 90 were sent to the United States for studies on their bioluminescence. The females that matured in Brazil were all mated in Brazil with males collected at night at lights. The flights of the males usually took place from midnight until about 3:30 a.m., with just a few earlier in the evening.

The females laid about 40 eggs each, some stained with a red secretion, which was secreted by larvae as well as adults. Other, unstained eggs were a light amber.

Over one-half of the larvae were collected in one 5-week period beginning in mid-November. Then there was a rapid fall off, with no larvae collected after December 26. The first adult males were collected on January 1 but probably were active sooner.

Initially the captive railroad worms were fed millipeds, but as their numbers increased all other insect larvae collected were offered, and they ate larvae of Lepidoptera, Scarabaeidae, Elateridae, etc. When food was scarce I tried feeding the railroad worms on fresh beef, which they ate. The beef, however, did not prove to be a good item of diet because it would spoil too soon and use up the oxygen in the container. Finally a source of meal-worms was found at the Museum of Zoology in São Paulo, and these then were used exclusively for food for the larval railroad worms. The adults did not feed. The adult female, however, would use her mandibles for defense.

The species under study at São José dos Campos turned out to be undescribed. It and a second undescribed related species have subsequently been described by Walter Wittmer of Basel, Switzerland, as *Phrixothrix tiemanni* Wittmer and *Brasilocerus impressicollis* Wittmer. The holotypes for these are now in the Museum of Zoology, São Paulo, Brazil.

REFERENCES

HARVEY, EDMUND NEWTON
    1952. Bioluminescence. 649 pp., illus.   Academic Press, New York. (Pp. 452-460.)
TIEMANN, DARWIN L.
    1967. Observations on the natural history of the western banded glowworm *Zarhipis integripennis* (LeConte) (Coleoptera: Phenogodidae).   Proc. California Acad. Sci., ser. 4, vol. 35, no. 12, pp. 235-264.
    1970. Nature's toy train, the railroad worm.   Nat. Geogr. Mag., vol. 138, no. 1, pp. 56-67, illus.
WITTMER, WALTER
    1970. 30.Beitrag zur Kenntnis der neotropischen Malacodermata.   Mitt. ent. Ges. Basel, new ser., vol. 20, no. 3, pp. 55-59.

DARWIN L. TIEMANN

Archeological Investigations at El Castillico, near El Sabinar, Murcia, Spain

Principal Investigator: Michael J. Walker, University of Sydney, New South Wales, Australia.

Grant No. 779:   To conduct archeological excavations at the hilltop fortress site of El Castillico in southeastern Spain.

The El Castillico site is situated on a limestone promontory between two canyons at about 1,200 meters above sea level and is defined by the coordinates N. 38° 10′ 52″, E. 1° 30′ 00″. It lies roughly halfway between the two hamlets of Arroyo Tercero and Calar de la Santa and about 4 kilometers southwest of the village of El Sabinar, término de Moratalla, Murcia. The site is only a few kilometers from where the asphalted main road from Archivel (Murcia) passes through the Sierra de Taibilla into the province of Albacete to descend the deep valley of the Río Taibilla (fig. 1). The canyon on the north side of the site, the Cañaíca del Calar, contains a number of well-known rock paintings of both the Levantine and the schematic types. A spring, the Fuente del Sabuco, provides clear water here throughout the year. On the tongue of land between the two canyons and below the cliffs on which the prehistoric site stands are some ruined constructions known to the local inhabitants as the Corral de Los Villaricos, although others refer to the prehistoric site on the top of the promontory by this name also. The site will here be called by the name El Castillico by which it is also known. The name is appropriate, as it refers to a massive stone wall of unfaced cyclopean masonry which in places is 4½ meters in height and of similar width. The wall seals off the tip of the promontory from the flat land that stretches away to the hamlet of Calar de la Santa. Elsewhere, the tip of the promontory is guarded by vertical cliffs of limestone some 30 meters in height, falling away to a steeply inclined limestone talus slope.

I noticed the site in December 1968 while walking in the area with the purpose of viewing the rock paintings on the land of Sr. D. Sebastián Chanes of El Sabinar. The site itself lies on the land of Sr. D. Pedro Alvárez Martínez of Puebla de Don Fadrique (Almería). The existence of a site in the

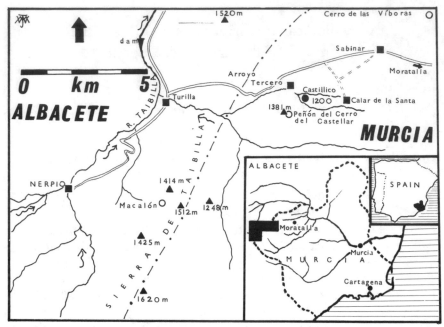

FIG. 1.   Map showing location of Castillico site.

neighborhood of El Sabinar had been mentioned to me by Sr. D. Emeterio Cuadrado Díaz; he had visited it 30 years ago in connection with his work as directing engineer of the Taibilla waterworks project. However, the site does not entirely correspond to the one called "Castillico, near Nerpio, northeast Murcia ... a large rocky hill accessible on only one side" at which he found sherds of hand-made pottery, quartzite pebbles, pieces of flint (one of which had a serrated edge), Argaric material, and a polished stone ax.[1] However, other information conveyed verbally by Sr. Cuadrado to me in December 1968 suggested the existence of a prehistoric settlement site near the one noted by me. It is possible that there are other settlement sites nearby to be discovered.

Kind permission was given to excavate the site by the then Comisario Nacional de Excavaciones Arqueológicas, Dr. Martín Almagro, whose

---

[1] Appendix by E. Cuadrado Díaz to article by J. Sánchez Jiménez "Excavaciones y Trabajos Arqueológicos en la Provincia de Albacete." Informes y Memorias No. 15, 1947, pp. 123-127, by E. Cuadrado, "Yacimientos Arqueológicos Albacetenses de la Cuenca del Río Taibilla."

assistance and advice were invaluable in bringing the project to its successful realization. Our gratitude also goes to the Delegado Provincial de Excavaciones, Sr. D. J. M. Aragoneses, with whom the material finds have been lodged at the Museo Provincial, Murcia. I also wish to thank my photographer P. Morrissey and my draftsman and surveyor Alan Douglas.

The Survey

It was necessary to survey the area in order to relate the irregular stony alignments or features that were conspicuous within the enclosure formed by the massive defensive wall and the promontory. A grid was laid out from a base line that was the common side of two major triangles within which triangulation of some of the major features was carried out. There was very close agreement between the determinations made by triangulation and those made by measurements along the lines of the grid.

The Excavation

In order to determine the number and sequence of building phases of the defensive wall, two cuttings were laid down, trenches T 1 and T 2 (fig. 2). Trench 1, measuring 10 by 30 feet, passed across the maximum spread of rubble on the outer side of the wall where it was believed that a wall-tower or bastion might lie concealed, of which one angle appeared to be visible above the very large heap of stones. Trench 2, measuring 18 by 10½ feet, passed across the entire width of the defensive wall at a point where it stood less than 1½ meters in height. It was hoped from this to ascertain the material culture associated with its erection. Trench T 2 yielded only nine sherds of coarse pottery, of which seven came from the west side of the wall and only two from the wall footings themselves. Trench T 1 gave no ceramic finds whatever. However, a fragment of a polished stone ax was found in the loose rubble within the foundations of the wall-tower, and a minute amount of carbonized material was found below the outer face thereof close on the limestone bedrock. The carbonized material was associated with fossilized arthropod spores and may have been intrusive at some time in antiquity.

Trenches T 1 and T 2 (figs. 3, 4) were more informative about the mode of construction of the defensive wall and of the wall-tower. The wall stands today to an irregular height, but rather curiously it shows also an irregular width, which must undoubtedly have affected the height of the wall from place to place. Thus at T 2 the wall was no more than 3½ meters wide. Large

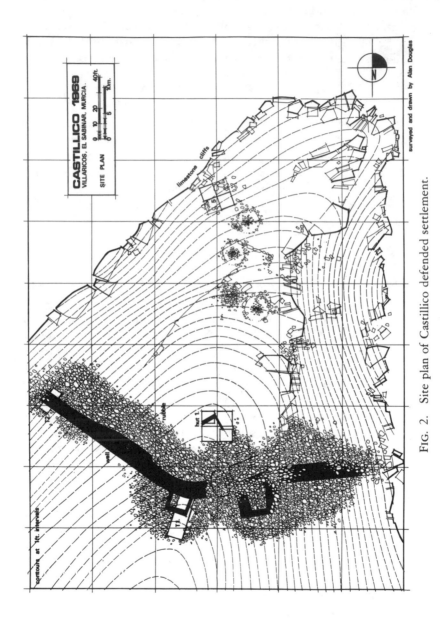

FIG. 2.   Site plan of Castillico defended settlement.

cyclopean limestone boulders were arranged to form a rough wall face at each side of the wall, but were not treated with chiseling. The two rows of stones rarely touched internally, nor was there any attempt by the builders at an interlocking form of construction. Large and small rubble and loose earth filled the space between the two rows of stones. The internal aspect of the boulders was rough and jagged, and small stones and earth were used to maintain the stability of the large and irregular boulders one on top of another. Only occasionally were tie-stones placed transversely in order to bond the whole structure. The lowest course of boulders was laid on bare limestone bedrock, which appeared therefore to have been cleared of vegetation prior to construction.

The wall-tower revealed by Trench T 1 (fig. 5) was of a similarly primitive construction, built on the limestone bedrock in a lean-to fashion against the main wall with which the stones of the wall-tower did not bond. Its external dimensions were 4½ by 4½ meters. The almost complete absence of soil made a stratigraphical comparison between the structures impossible. The only discoveries that might more firmly date the building of the wall-tower and the main wall, respectively, are the carbonized material from the footings of the former and the pottery from the latter.[2] Otherwise structural details alone must form the basis for an interpretation. The lean-to wall-tower may have been an intentional part of the original defensive plan, the mode of erection being due to the lack of building expertise by the builders. This hypothesis might be further supported by the presence in the base of the main wall behind the wall-tower of a low doorway 1 meter wide by 1½ meters high. However, on further consideration of the wall-tower it is doubtful if the doorway could have ever been used, since the size of the large boulders that form the outer wall of the tower at its base leaves little room within it for any kind of stairway or ladder that might have been needed to ascend to the top, if we assume that it was originally of a similar height to the main wall. Moreover, the jagged and irregular internal aspects of the boulders would have required many large boulders to pack and to support the upper part of the tower, and the rubble encountered by the excavators might well have had that function. Such a rubble fill would have blocked the doorway in the manner encountered by the excavators. It is, of course, possible that the doorway was placed in the wall with a view to providing access to a subsequently erected wall-tower, but that the mode of

---

[2] It subsequently developed that the carbonized material was insufficient for radiocarbon dating.

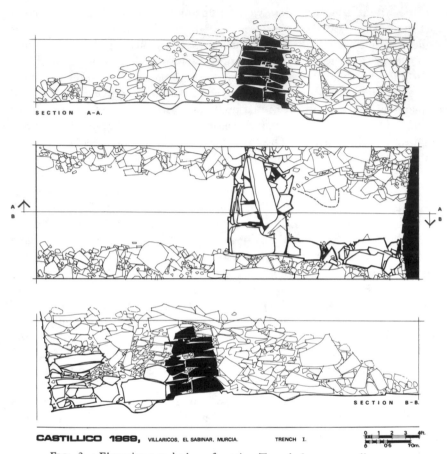

SECTION A-A.

SECTION B-B.

CASTILLICO 1969, VILLARICOS, EL SABINAR, MURCIA.   TRENCH I.

FIG. 3.   Elevations and plan of cutting Trench 1 across wall tower.

erection and limited skill of the builders resulted in the doorway being found impractical. A third possibility is that the tower was built somewhat later than the wall and placed strategically to overcome a weakness in the defenses caused by the doorway. In favor of this view is the interpretation of the fragment of polished stone ax as a vestige of an earlier occupation, perhaps responsible for the main wall, that was thrown in among the rubble used to supply the foundations of the later wall-tower. The ground plan suggests a second possible tower, which, if placed in front of another doorway, would perhaps render this last interpretation unlikely. This tower has not

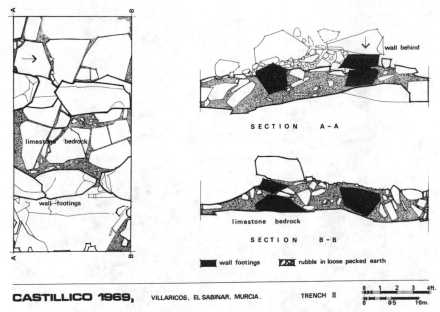

SECTION   A – A

SECTION   B – B

limestone   bedrock

wall behind

limestone   bedrock

wall footings

wall footings   rubble in loose packed earth

CASTILLICO 1969, VILLARICOS, EL SABINAR, MURCIA .   TRENCH II

0 1 2 3 4ft.
0   0·5   1·0m.

FIG. 4.   Elevations and plan of cutting Trench 2 across defensive wall.

been excavated. In any case, additional and wider entrances to the enclosure must have been necessary for the passage of animals and bulky materials. Perhaps such an entrance lay between the two wall-towers.

The excavation of T 1 was a laborious and slow undertaking on account of the large boulders that had to be removed. Consequently, the number of constructions within the settlement that could be excavated was less than had been hoped for. Stony features had been numbered from 1 to 5 on the ground plan. Numbers 1 and 5 were excavated. Thirty-foot-sided squares were excavated in staggered quadrants. Stony feature 5 soon transpired to be a natural geological feature of the limestone, and only two opposing quadrants were excavated. Loose soil from this feature yielded 28 sherds of nondescript coarse wares. This shallow soil continued uniformly to bedrock.

Stony feature 1, subsequently named Hut 1 (figs. 6, 7) was more interesting. Two walls of a rectangular construction were exposed. The walls seem to have been constructed on a flimsy stone base associated with daub. The structure had been destroyed by firing, and a layer of burnt daub that had presumably fallen inward during the accident was encountered some 5

FIG. 5.   Defensive wall of Castillico. (Photograph, P. Morrissey.)

centimeters thick. During excavation the daub layer was termed layer 2, and the layers of loose earth with rubble above and below it were termed layers 1 and 3. This soon proved unsatisfactory as the daub layers did not extend continuously across the hut. Moreover, fragments of one vessel found in layer 2 were later found to unite with similar fragments from layer 3 (fig. 9, no. 157a). Layers 1-3, therefore, have been recognized as belonging to a single phase, phase 2, of the occupation area represented at stony feature 1.

The stone foundations of the hut were laid over the hard-packed earth and daub of layer 4 that passed continuously below it. No construction is known associated with this layer. Layer 5 contained a few sherds in a somewhat lighter soil, but it is believed that these are contemporary with those of layer 4 and that both layers represent Phase 1 of the occupation.

Further excavations had been planned, but a series of freak thunderstorms caused much destruction of the cuttings and work was abandoned after complete excavation of the cuttings described above.

A number of artifacts were discovered on the surface of the enclosure. They included large fragments of the everted rim of what was probably a carinated Argaric-type of bowl, and a number of millstones of the saddle-quern type. A local inhabitant found a curious bronze piece some years ago while walking near the wall (fig. 8,C). These materials have been lodged with the Museo Provincial, Murcia.

Samples of some of the sherds were taken for petrological examination.

The Finds

Stone. Unlike most southeastern Spanish late Bronze Age settlement sites, the site did not yield flint or quartzite stone tools. One fragment of a polished stone ax was found in the rubble fill within the foundations of the wall-tower. The cross section of the implement measures 38 by 26 millimeters. The small segment, broken at either end, is but 27 millimeters wide. It appears to be of a granodioritic rock.

Pottery. In all, 227 sherds were found, a selection of which, bearing inventory numbers, is illustrated in figure 9. For fuller illustrations, see Walker, 1971.

(1) Sherds 1-9. Trench T 2 provided two sherds from within the wall footings, of which one was a rim sherd of a straight-walled hand-made pot. From without the wall there were seven sherds, of which six, like the foregoing, were of buff or yellowish body in which particles of mineral filler were seen. One sherd was of harder and lighter ware of pink color glistening on both surfaces with mica particles. It bore the stump of a handle and had been smoothed on the outside, and either smoothed or wheel-turned marks were seen on the inner surface. This sherd was less worn than the others.

(2) Sherds 10-37. Stony feature 5 yielded 28 sherds of coarse hand-made pottery, mostly of buff-color, sometimes smoothed and frequently showing flecks of mineral filler. One sherd was of smoothed gray burnished ware. Another was part of a red strap handle and adjoining part of the body. As in the cases of the sherds from T 2, all were too small for the forms to be extrapolated.

(3) Sherds 38-40. Three gray rim sherds probably of a late Argaric carinated vessel.

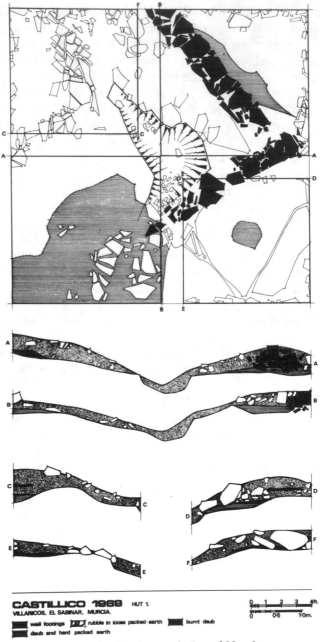

CASTILLICO 1969 HUT 1.
VILLARICOS, EL SABINAR, MURCIA.

wall footings   rubble in loose packed-earth   burnt daub
daub and hard packed earth

FIG. 6.   Sections and plan of Hut 1.

(4) Sherds 41-205. Occupation Phase 2 of stony feature 1, corresponding to Hut 1. Thirty-six of the 164 sherds (22 percent) were wheel-turned. These were the only wheel-thrown wares found at the site. Moreover, five of these were painted in concentric bands between 3 and 10 millimeters wide, either brown or cream or black on pink. One sherd was painted both inside and outside. Two sherds were of brown burnished ware. Twenty-one rims were among the sherds, and among these were straight-sided or slightly incurving sherds; others were everted rims, occasionally with a small carination. Most of the sherds from this occupation phase were hand-made wares on buff- or cream-colored body with mineral filler, often quite large particles. Some sherds were black and others of a smoothed gray ware. Some were of a hard pink body with little filler. Nos. 69-76 were of a hard red ware, very similar. Nos. 109-125 were of a creamy thick ware with large crystals of mineral filler, perhaps belonging to no more than two vessels. These seem to have been simple troncoconic bowls. Nos. 156-164 were of a hard gray ware and represent the base of the vessel, and some sherds of the walls.

(5) Sherds 206-227. Occupation Phase 1 yielded 21 sherds of hand-made ware, including three simple rim sherds. These are mainly of a buff- or yellow-colored body with mineral filler, some rough and others smoothed, and some of a soapy texture. All were very worn. One sherd seemed to be of chaff-tempered ware. These sherds resembled those from T 2.

The percentages of rim sherds from trench 2, and the two occupation phases of stony feature 1, are between 11 and 14 percent. No rim sherds were found at Stony Feature 5.

Seven sherds from T 2, 11 from Stony Feature 5, 7 from the second occupation phase, and 5 from the first were sampled for subsequent petrological studies. Many surface samples found from the talus slope below the cliffs were taken for similar studies and corresponded to the wares from occupation Phase 2.

Metal. An iron chain 130 millimeters long was found in occupation Phase 2 near the foundations of Hut 1. It consists of four pairs of spectacle-type loops 22 millimeters in diameter. The iron is cast in circular cross section 5 millimeters thick. The piece is so much corroded that two interlocking loops are obliterated.

A local inhabitant found a bronze piece when walking near the defensive wall several years ago. The piece consists of half of a bronze buckle or clasp measuring 28 by 26 millimeters with a simple tongue of bronze behind and a motif in the form of a human head in front. The hair and beard of the face are highly stylized in waves, and a long curling moustache joins

FIG. 7.   View of defensive wall from within wall tower to show blocked doorway.

with two outsize ears. The piece would seem to be Celtic and may be a later object casually dropped on the site in Celtiberian times.

All the above pieces have been deposited in the Museo Provincial in Murcia, as have also a number of stone querns of the saddle-quern variety found at different places on the surface of the settlement.

Discussion

Occupation Phase 2 with its wheel-turned wares and painted bands of ceramic decoration belongs to the earliest stage of the Iberian culture of the early Iron Age. This phase corresponds to the assemblage found by García Guinea and San Miguel Ruiz (see 1960 and 1962 refs.) at the settlement site of El Macalón some 15 kilometers to the southwest near Nerpio in Albacete province. Here they found lying stratified below typical Iberian layers similar pottery painted in wide bands in layers 8 and 9 to that which we have recorded from occupation Phase 2 at El Castillico. Likewise, Pellicer and Schüle (1962) have noted this kind of painted pottery at Cerro del Real near Galera in Granada province. At this site it was from their layer 4, below more typically Iberian strata, but it was preceded by layers with wheel-thrown wares, including burnished examples, but lacking painted decoration. As at El Macalón, the excavators found Graeco-Punic type wares in the same layers as the broad band painted pottery. Burnished sherds occurred in the same layers, too, at all the sites, including El Castillico. On the other hand, the red varnish wares for which Cuadrado has argued a 6th century B.C. attribution, appear to be later in the stratigraphical sequence where they occur. At all the sites there are a number of rim sherds of curving everted rims splaying outward from a carination. These seem to be typical of the later Argaric culture, perhaps reinforced by late Urnfield forms, although to say this is not to say very much since everted rim and carinated forms are common throughout the Peninsula during the late Bronze Age. Perhaps more significant of the Urnfield influence is the tendency toward more and more flat-based troncoconic vessels, contrasting with the round-based conical or subhemispherical bowls of the earlier Argaric. It is curious that the everted rim and carinated sherds both at El Macalón and at El Castillico were found in circumstances that prevented any stratigraphic relationship being deduced vis-à-vis the early Iberian phase. This phase, called by García Guinea "pseudo-Iberian," may have to be placed about the 7th century B.C., on account of the subsequent Iberian layers that seem to belong to the following century or thereabouts, and one may remark upon the characteristic metalwork from El Macalón in this connection, namely, the fibula with rhomboidal arc and the pedunculated arrow points. At El Castillico the only metal object located in the stratigraphical succession was the iron chain. Often it is held that iron chains belong quite late in the Iberian culture. This is not necessarily to be assumed, however. Double loops cast in bronze resembling a spectacle frame were found in the famous

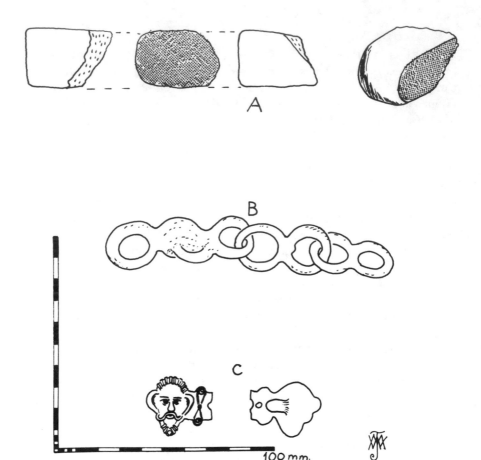

FIG. 8.   A, fragment of polished stone ax head. B, iron chain found beside Hut 1.
C, bronze clasp found on surface by local inhabitant.

hoard at the estuary of the Río Odiel (Huelva) to which an 8th-century
attribution is given. These are not unlike the links of the Castillico chain,
which, it may be noted, is utterly different from the single links of the chains
associated with the bird ornament of clear Halstatt derivation from El
Bovalar (Castellón) from which site there is tall-footed fibula (see Esteve
Gálvez, 1966). (However, it is perhaps worth remarking that Schüle has
cautioned against deriving all peninsular tall-footed fibulae from Halstatt D
prototypes north of the Alps; see Schüle, 1962.)

Although there does not seem to me to be any prima-facie evidence for Halstatt influences in the early Iberian phase with broad band painted pottery, apart from rather unspecific features such as burnished and painted wares, troncoconic forms, and everted rims on carinated vessels, it is interesting to note that in the Albacete Museum there is a fine group of unpublished but quite typical bioconical urns covered with inverted bowls, and that there were sherds of chip-carved ware at the late bronze age settlement at Cabezo Redondo near Villena (Alicante) that are now displayed in the Museo Soler in the Palacio Municipal, Villena, and that must be compared with excised pottery from the Ebro Valley. It is instructive to return to Bosch Gimpera (1940) and to reflect upon his argument for an early Celtic penetration of the Peninsula. That there were indeed people inhabiting the Meseta in the 9th and 8th centuries B.C. is clear from the distribution map of the early fibulae of the "Cypriot," "Sicilian" (c.p. Pantalica II), "Huelva," and "ad occhio" types published by Cuadrado (see Cuadrado Díaz, 1963). Indeed, the "Sicilian" type may have to be dated as early as the 10th century B.C.. The problem is then one of who the purchasers of such exotic ornaments were. If they were not Celts, it is hard to see who they might have been.

It seems as if the northern Urnfield culture from Catalonia and the subsequent Halstatt C incursions exerted their influence as far as the very boundary of what had formerly been the Argaric Cultural heartland, the provinces of Murcia, Almería, eastern Granada, and southern Alicante. The larger and earlier Argaric townships such as La Bastida, near Totana (Murcia), and El Agar itself, near Antas (Almería), seem to have had no defenses other than those provided by nature in the eroded valley slopes above which they were perched. Later, and more especially toward the north, the settlements became both smaller and more strongly defended, often situated in inaccessible positions. It is beyond the scope of this paper to list the many "Bronze II" defended settlement sites of Alicante and Valencia, many of which it must be granted seem to have been of limited and of wholly Bronze Age occupation. Nevertheless it is noteworthy that some of the strongest defended settlements lie most peripherally; thus El Acequíon (see Martínez Santa Olalla, 1951), a strange lake settlement with remains of walls, and also the sub-rectangular defended site at Cañaverosa, near Moratalla (Murcia) (see Cuadrado Díaz, 1943). El Castillico differs from these by its rectangular wall-towers that jut outward from the defenses. The crude cyclopean mode of building recalls the earlier defensive walls of the "Bronze II" defended settlements of Alicante and Valencia, rather than later Iberian constructions.

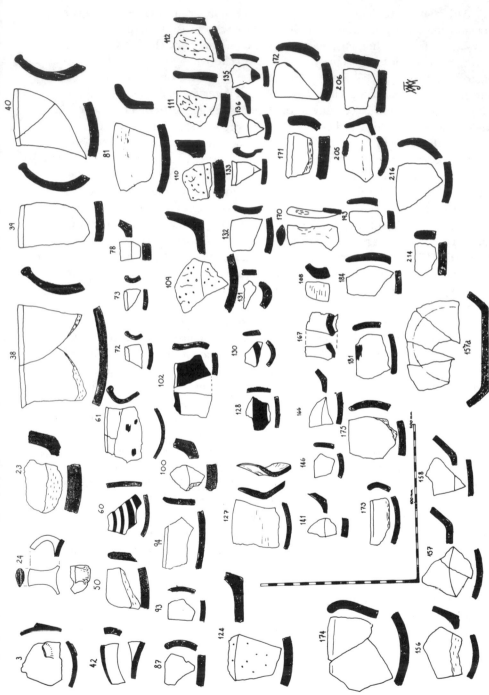

FIG. 9.   Selected pottery from the excavation: decorated rim, basal potsherds, handles, etc.

Wall-towers may well have been a constructional device borrowed from the Carthaginian traders who were well established by the 8th century on the Andalusian and southeastern coast and who may have stimulated the adoption of the potter's wheel and an iron technology. Rather rapidly, under the conflicting pressures of both Celtic and Carthaginian influences, the impoverished and nondescript late Bronze Age settlements of the montane zone between the two spheres of influence underwent a revival, perhaps the first effects of the Iberian culture that had developed out of the late Argaric of the southeast and Andalusia under foreign influence, and which was eventually to spread northward as far as Catalonia absorbing much of the Celtic legacy. Perhaps it is not fanciful to speculate that the appearance and spread of the Iberian Culture represented the direct efforts of Graeco-Punic traders to expand their overseas markets and to protect them from destruction as well as to exploit the rich gold, silver, copper, tin, and iron ore of the Peni-Baetic metamorphic rocks. More excavations need to be performed at defended settlement sites in the borderland, especially those that may offer a greater depth and sequence of stratigraphy than El Castillico and those that appear to present complex defenses in order that some of the speculations raised here may be tested.

REFERENCES

BOSCH GIMPERA, P.
   1940. Two Celtic waves in Spain. Proc. Brit. Acad., vol. 26, pp. 25-48.
CUADRADO DÍAZ, E.
   1943. El poblado argárico de Cañaverosa. Saitibi Noticiario de Historia, Arte, y Arqueología de Levante, nos. 9-10, pp. 5-15.
   1963. Procedentes y protitipos de la fíbula anular hispánica, map 1. Trabajos de Prehistoria del Seminario de Instituto Español de Prehistoria del Consejo Superior de Investigaciones Científicas, no. 7, pp. 1-61.
ESTEVE GÁLVEZ, F.
   1966. La necropólis ibérica de El Bovalar (Benicarló, Castellón de la Plana). Archivo de Prehistoria Levantina, vol. 11, pp. 125-148.
GARCÍA GUINEA, M. A., and SAN MIGUEL RUIZ, J. A.
   1960. Excavaciones y estratigrafías en el poblado ibérico de El Macalón, Nerpio (Albacete). Revista de Archivas, Bibliotecas, y Museos, vol. 68, pp. 709 ff.
   1962. Poblado ibérica de El Macalón (Albacete). Excavaciones Arqueológicas en España, vol. 25, pp. 1-43.
MARTÍNEZ SANTA OLALLA, J.
   1951. El "crannog" de la laguna de Acequión en la provincia de Albacete. Anales del Seminario de Historia y Arqueología de Albacete, vol. 1, pp. 1-12.

PELLICER, M., and SCHÜLE, W.
  1962. El Cerro del Real, Galera (Grenada).   Excavaciones Arqueológicas en
        España, vol. 12, pp. 3-15.
SCHÜLE, W.
  1962. Dos elementos llamados halstátticos en el hierro de la Meseta.   VII
        Congreso Nacional de Arqueología, Barcelona, 1960, pp. 227-232.
WALKER, MICHAEL J.
  1971. Excavaciones en El Castillico, Corral de los Villaricos, El Pabinar, término
        de Moratalla, Murcia, 1969.   Noticiario Arqueológico Hispánico, vol.
        13-14 (1969-1970), pp. 139-162.
  1976. Neolithic and Chalcolithic pottery of SE. Spain.   Australian Studies in
        Archaeology, vol. 2, pp. _____.

Postscriptum

Since submitting the above for publication in 1970, a radiocarbon estimation has been performed by Dr. R. L. Otlet of the Atomic Energy Research Establishment (Harwell, England) on animal bones from Hut 1. The sample comprised 265 grams of bone and yielded 78.1 cm^3 CO_2, giving the date S178-III of 1500 ± 100 B.P. or A.D. 450 (delta-C-13 $= -21.4 \pm 1$). This is a reliable date for the specimen according to Dr. Otlet. However, it disagrees with the archeological assessment of Hut 1, and it may be surmised that the bones represent admixture of later material by vertical downward movement, perhaps due to treadage, in the thin layer of soil at the site.

Initial examination of the sherds by thin-sectioning and X-ray emission spectrometry has commenced. The petrological inspection of ceramic filler has demonstrated use of a fine, 0.25 millimeter in diameter, quartz filler in some 30 sherds. The following data are available for semiquantitative composition of the clay body of 3 sherds submitted to X-ray emission spectrometry:

Parts per million

Ba	Zr	Sr	Rb	Pb	Zn	Ni	Fe_2O_3
600	250	450	100	< 100	50	150	4
400	200	250	100	< 100	50	< 50	3
350	200	350	200	< 100	100	450	10

Although further investigations are needed, these findings deserve a word of comment. About 2 kilometers from El Castillico there lies a Bronze Age hilltop settlement at Peñón del Cerro del Castellar. The clay body of a sherd sampled from that site gave a Ba concentration of 1,950 p.p.m. but was otherwise similar. Some 10 kilometers away, at another Bronze Age site known as Cerro de las Víboras, 9 sherds have so far been submitted for X-ray emission spectrometry, all of which resemble those from El Castillico. However, whereas the sherds from El Castillico and from Peñón del Cerro del Castellar (14 sherds sectioned from the latter site) demonstrate quartz filler, a sherd sectioned from Cerro de las Víboras suggests that crushed limestone was used at that site, by contrast. Quartz is not commonly used as ceramic filler in southeast Spain; rather, crushed limestone is common in the limestone region of Valencia, Alicante, and around the Segura headwaters in Albacete and Murcia (Walker, 1976). Toward the coast, in Murcia and Alicante, the lamproitic intrusions around Jumilla were exploited for the local "jumillitic" phlogopite in the lower Vinalopó and lower Segura Valley systems. In southern Murcia and Almería, however, the more common local mica-schists were used by potters. Whereas the foregoing observations relate to the Neolithic and Bronze Ages, during the subsequent iron age finely crushed quartz particles characterize the Iberian culture pottery in all the regions mentioned. Variations in clay elements are common as between all sites and periods, and local manufacture of wares employing local clay sources seems to have been the rule.

MICHAEL J. WALKER

Determinants of Coexistence in a Colonial Raptor

Principal Investigator: Hartmut Walter, University of California, Los Angeles, California.[1]

Grant No. 781:   In support of a study of territory and aggression in Eleonora's falcon.

A falcon leaves its aerie, makes a kill, and returns to its breeding cliff with the prey in its talons. This is not unusual; however, in the case of Eleonora's falcon (*Falco eleonorae* Gené, 1839), the kill is made in a piratelike fashion by attacking migrant birds over the open sea, and the breeding cliff may harbor a colony of well over a hundred falcon pairs.

This report deals with the territorial aspects of social behavior in Eleonora's falcon. It attempts to answer two questions: What mechanisms have evolved to enable this aggressive raptor to coexist with others of its kind in densely populated breeding colonies; and, do different ecological settings affect the social interaction of colony members?

The adaptive significance of social organization has been studied in many animals, particularly birds (Crook, 1965). Emphasis has been placed on the functions of nest dispersion, territory, and aggressive or agonistic behavior in breeding populations of birds (Hinde, 1956; Tinbergen, 1957; Brown, 1964, 1969; Brown and Orians, 1970). Many colonial sea birds have been extensively studied, but only recently have investigators begun to determine experimentally some of the factors or components of the system that relates the individual bird to its physical and biotic surroundings and especially to its conspecific neighbors (Patterson, 1965; Bongiorno, 1970; Simmons, 1970; Manuval, 1974). A parallel study of a colonial bird of prey

[1] Sincere thanks go to my wife, Geraldine, and my brother, Ernst-Christian, who were alert and patient field assistants. H. Deetjen (Bonn) and the Department of Water and Forests (Rabat) assisted with their diplomatic and technical expertise. In addition to the support of the National Geographic Society of the field study in Morocco, the Deutsche Forschungsgemeinschaft provided financial aid during the initial evaluation of this research at the Zoologisches Forschungsinstitut und Museum Alexander Koenig in Bonn.

— almost a contradiction in terms — could be of value to social biology for comparative reasons.

Few investigators have studied the behavior and social interaction of raptors under natural conditions; what little we know concerns for the most part nongregarious species like the peregrine falcon (Cade, 1960; Monneret, 1974). Direct and indirect impacts of human activity have decreased the former density of many birds of prey and as a result some species have become scarce while others have abandoned their gregarious or colonial traits (e.g., osprey). This makes it more difficult to study their social organization.

Eleonora's falcon (fig. 1) appears to be an almost perfect choice for a study of this kind. It is a handsome bird, smaller than a peregrine, and occurs in two color phases. Most falcons can be individually identified in the field from their morphological features. About a dozen large breeding colonies with more than 100 pairs each are known, as well as some 50 of smaller size. All of them are situated on small rocky offshore islets or on the cliffs of large islands and of the continental shore ranging from the Canary Islands and Morocco in the west to the Greek Islands and Cyprus in the east.

Because Eleonora's falcon has the latest regular breeding season of any bird north of the Sahara, it is able to exploit the large biomass of migrating birds. Its chicks are fed with migrants captured while crossing the Mediterranean or a small part of the Atlantic on their way to the seasonal winter quarters in Africa. The interesting predator-prey relationships, particularly the hunting behavior and the synchronization of the reproductive season with the Palearctic-African bird migration in late summer and fall, have already received some attention (Krueper, 1864; Vaughan, 1961; Walter, 1968). At the end of October and in November, the falcon population disappears from the Mediterranean region, migrating to the southern Indian Ocean areas of Madagascar and Mauritius where it remains for several months. The species returns to the Mediterranean in April and May but usually does not reoccupy its breeding habitats until the end of June and July. From November to July its food consists almost exclusively of flying arthropods.

Eleonora's falcon is either solitary or gregarious during the nonbreeding season and always gregarious or colonial at the breeding sites. The latter belong to type 2 and 3 of Crook's (1965) classification, i.e., "open ground nests protected by features of siting from approach by predators (e.g., on islands, etc.)" and "cliffs, ledges or clefts providing increased inaccessibility to predators." As in most colonial species, no individual feeding territories exist in Eleonora's falcon.

FIG. 1. Pair of Eleonora's falcons *(Falco eleonorae)* in breeding territory. The male (left) belongs to the dark color phase, the female to the light one. (Photo by D. Ristow.)

Study Areas and Methods

Field observations were collected primarily in two of the largest presently known colonies of Eleonora's falcon in the southern Aegean Sea (here called "Crete colony") and off the Moroccan coast ("Morocco colony"). Other, smaller colonies will be referred to as the "Sardinia colony" and "Maghreb colony." The main study, supported by a research grant of the National Geographic Society, was conducted in the summer of 1969 (July 11 to August 22) in the Morocco colony. The other colonies provided relevant data during the 1965 (Crete), 1966 (Crete, Morocco, Maghreb), and 1974 (Sardinia) breeding seasons.

In 1969 I attempted to carry on a comprehensive behavioral analysis of the breeding population. However, a promising start was soon followed by a tragic boat accident in which one human life was lost and several others endangered. As if that were not enough, nearly the entire falcon colony lost its eggs on August 1 when two young European egg robbers interrupted the falcons' breeding cycle in a drastic fashion.[2] From then on the social behav-

---

[2] The falcons did not abandon their breeding sites after the egg-robbing incident. They adjusted in different ways, thereby providing some unusual insight into their behavioral mechanisms.

FIG. 2.   The "submarine" cliff from the south; from here the left section of the eastern side of the cliff is clearly visible. The author's observation point was on top of the cliff on the right. Right (opposite page): Top of cliff. The left half of this rock constituted the territory of pair no. 1.

ior of a relatively small falcon population breeding on a tiny cliff was monitored. This cliff, resembling the command tower of a submarine emerging
out of the foaming surf, is about 12 meters high, 20 long, and 12 wide at
high tide. Its walls are more or less oblique and vertical. The terrain is not
only rugged but also is strewn with many small craters, potholes, clefts,
needles, ridges, and small caves (fig. 2).

Two observers monitored the activities of a small study population on
the "submarine" from a rocky peninsula of an adjacent larger island. In
between were 35 meters of foaming waters. Observations were noted, sometimes tape-recorded, and often secured by checking with the second observer by means of walkie-talkies. The falcons did not appear to be influenced by human activity at this place as long as sudden movements and arm
waving were avoided. All observations of the "submarine" study population
took place in July and August.

Dispersion and Selection of Nesting Sites

The density per unit area of a breeding population of Eleonora's falcon
appears to vary in a predictable manner depending on: (a) the macro- and
microstructure of the physical landscape (terrain, relief, substrate); (b) the
number and density of available nest sites; (c) the size of the falcon population; (d) the behavior of the breeding population; and (e) the effect of factors
limiting population growth and survival (e.g., human predation and disturbance). A nearly inaccessible island with a rugged and dissected surface is
likely to harbor more falcon pairs per unit of area than an island of relatively
even surface terrain and easy access to predators. We may also postulate
(analogous to the findings of students of gull behavior) that a high fledgling
rate and a low predation rate are likely to increase the local population
density since falcons can be expected to return to those places where they
were born or have successfully completed a breeding cycle. Being a gregarious species, Eleonora's falcon may be attracted also to already densely
populated areas; such a factor has been detected by Patterson (1965) in the
highly gregarious black-headed gull *(Larus ridibundus)*.

Dispersion, Crete Colony: The total population of about 150 pairs was
distributed over the entire island (fig. 3). The distance between neighboring
nests varied from 6.4 to about 50 meters and averaged 20-30 meters. The
"upper slope" contained 11 pairs; it had the highest breeding density of the
whole colony; 210 square meters per pair. Similar dispersion patterns were
found to prevail over several seasons.

FIG. 3.   Typical terrain in breeding habitat of the Crete colony. The "upper slope" area can be seen in the background.

Dispersion, Morocco Colony: The total population of about 175 pairs was concentrated on three small rocky islets. The distance between nests was less than 2 meters in several cases and rarely exceeded 15 meters (average 4-10 meters, depending on the particular cliff). The spatial concentration was astonishing; counting vertical, oblique, and horizontal rock surface alike, the main clusters of nest sites achieved a density value of 140 square meters (south-facing walls of the "atoll" islet), 69 square meters (isle "Smea"), and only 43 square meters per pair on the "submarine" where 23 pairs were located (1966 season). In 1969 this latter number had dropped to 18 pairs.

Dispersion, Maghreb Colony: Along a 5-kilometer-long series of "falaises," 30 nest sites were found. Distances between them varied from 15 to 70 (average about 30) meters. The density of the most populous bay (16 pairs) reached a value of about 1,000 square meters per falcon pair.

Dispersion, Sardinia Colony: A cluster of five nest sites, at least 120 meters from the nearest nest of another cluster, had distances between nests of 4 to 12 (average 7) meters. The density cannot be estimated since there was much unoccupied rock surface surrounding this cluster.

As regards the nest site — better called a nest scrape — Eleonora's falcon generally selects one that will provide shelter from strong winds and surf spray and will protect it from ground predators, either because of its inaccessibility (ledges or vertical cliffs) or its cryptic quality (under boulders or shrubs or in holes and caves). Typical nest site locations are illustrated in figure 4 (A-E).

Nest Sites, Crete Colony: Most nest sites in the "upper slope" section were located under boulders; the remainder were found under shrubs (types A and B). In other parts of the colony, ledges and caves were occasionally used (type C). Most falcons had a rather restricted view of their

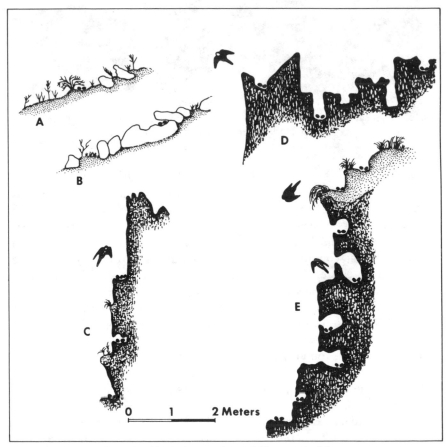

FIG. 4.   Typical nest sites of Eleonora's falcon.

surroundings from their nest scrape. The "upper slope" falcons were able to command a view of only part, at best, of the downhill section. There were definitely more nest sites available than there were falcons.

Nest Sites, Morocco Colony: On the "submarine" rock (fig. 2) four blocks project from the base rock of the cliff, separated by deep fissures. Most nest sites lay at the edges and outside of these blocks, on the more oblique and vertical surfaces. All nests were located in holes (type D) in such a way that their contents were hidden except from directly above (fig.5). A falcon lying or standing in its nest scrape was unable to see anything but a patch of blue sky and perhaps some rock projection above. The other parts of the Morocco colony had predominantly type C and E nest sites on the more-or-less vertical cliffs. There was an abundance of additional and nonused nest sites in all parts of the colony.

Nest Sites, Maghreb and Sardinia Colonies: Nest scrapes were located in holes, caves, protected corners, and open ledges (type C). Few nest sites were available, as many cliffs were sheer and without surface texture.

Discussion: The differing degree of dispersion observed, particularly within the same colony, deserves some comment. The falcon population living in the most complex and dissected terrain (the "submarine") had the highest density and smallest average distance between neighbors, while those settling in simpler and more even terrain had a low density and large distances between neighbors. This fact cannot simply be explained by the scarcity or abundance of nest sites. In both Crete and the Morocco colony there were countless potential nest sites available between the occupied ones. Also this dispersion cannot be explained by territoriality, since each territory is initially small and expands after the nest site has been selected.

If we consider four of the initially mentioned dispersion factors equal (a, c, d, and e) — this is reasonable, in view of the more densely settled areas of the two large colonies — then we find that terrain complexity is inversely related to nest-spacing. Indeed, we might ask what mechanism Eleonora's falcon possesses that guides in spacing nest sites.

The cryptic nature of most nest sites appears to provide a clue to the nature of this mechanism. The fact that most falcons can see little or nothing from their nest scrape also means that they themselves cannot be seen. Indeed all nests are positioned so that no visual control can be exerted from one nest site entrance over any other. This suggests that the selection of the nest site is related to a "security factor" that has its roots in a visual perception of the environment. A falcon may feel comfortable only where it enjoys a certain degree of privacy from its nest site. A complex terrain with

FIG. 5.   Egg of Eleonora's falcon in nest scrape on "submarine" cliff. Some feather
remains of captured migrant birds are visible.

many visual obstacles increases this privacy and reduces the importance of
spacing out nest sites (fig. 6). We may postulate the existence of a visual
prerequisite for a suitable nest site in Eleonora's falcon. The visual information received from an actual rocky substrate would be considered (perhaps influenced by interaction with already settled neighbors) and translated
into distance required for this particular terrain. Such a visual mechanism
would result in nest spacing related to terrain complexity and would well
explain the dispersion patterns of Eleonora's falcon.

The existence of the perception or image of a species' structural and
spatial environment has recently been pointed out in several species of
songbirds by Berndt and Winkel (1974), who have termed it the "Ökosche-
ma" (ecoscheme). Bongiorno (1970) has shown that laughing gulls (*Larus
atriculla*) select their nest site more in response to substrate and landscape
structure than to distance and other factors existing in their colonies. Beebe
(1960) noted in an unusually dense cluster of the noncolonial peregrine
falcon that no nest site was visible from any other one. Finally Kiester,

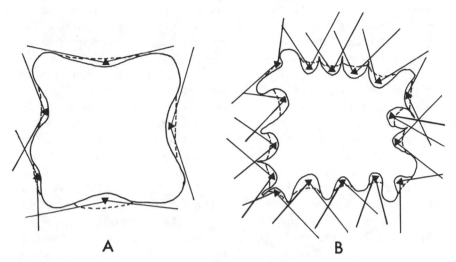

FIG. 6. Terrain structure and breeding dispersion: Two model ground plans of
breeding cliffs with horizontal ledges and projections show:A, simple surface
structure allows wide view from nest site and is correlated with large spacing-out
and low density of breeding pairs; B, highly complex surface structure limits view
from nest site to a narrow sector and is correlated with small distance between
nest sites and high breeding density.

Gorman, and Arroyo (1975) have experimentally shown that several species
of *Anolis* lizards select differently structured habitats by "visually surveying
a surrounding area and then moving to the appropriate structural niche."
These examples indicate that the perception of the physical environment
may be an important ecological factor in determining dispersion patterns in
different groups of animals.

Size and Role of the Territory

Most pairs and some nonbreeding adult falcons were found to possess a
well-defined territory during the breeding season. Initially consisting only
of a perch and one or two potential nest scrapes it was often extended
throughout the breeding season to cover between 1 and more than 200
square meters on the ground and 1 to 10 meters of air space above the
ground. The territory is an *exclusive area* to an individual or a pair with

respect to rivals. Its shape and size can be determined by recording the ways in which, and where, a falcon makes use of it and/or defends it. The populations studied showed characteristic differences with respect to the size and role of the territory.

Crete Colony: The "upper slope" study population possessed rounded territories with a radius of 5 to 20 meters around the nest site. The size varied considerably (60 to 200 square meters). The boundaries were relatively fixed in the latter part of the breeding season. Some no-man's land (undefended and unused areas) lay in between territories (fig. 7). All activities except flying, hunting, and bathing (in sand) took place in the territory. Thus it served as the area in which the falcon rested, courted, copulated, raised its young, prepared prey, took a sunbath, preened, and kept a careful watch on its neighbors and the general cliff environment. In addition, the territory was a virtual sanctuary for the young. The latter often left the nest scrape when they were barely three weeks old and hiked around, exploring the neighborhood and looking for shaded spots during the hot midday periods. The fledglings were never bothered by other falcons as long as they were located in their parents' territory. Whenever the young attempted to soar clumsily in the updraft of the hill they would try to land again in their own territory; failing this would result in their being stooped upon by other adults until they managed to somehow reach again their own ground. I took a number of banded fledglings and set them free about 100 meters from and out of sight of their birthplaces. A few hours later all had returned to their original location. This attests not only to the excellent memory and visual perception of the young birds but also to the importance of being within one's territory in this colony of raptors.

Morocco Colony, Submarine Population: Of the submarine population of 18 pairs (1969) only 7 could be studied regarding their utilization of territorial space. These were located on the east-facing side of the cliff, the center of which consisted of a projection with sheer walls. To the left of it lived 4 pairs (nos. 1, 2, 7, 8) and to the right, 3 pairs (nos. 9, 10, 12). Both groups were visually but not acoustically isolated from each other and formed distinct "neighborhoods." Social interactions occurred frequently within but rarely between these two neighborhoods. For some time a single male falcon occupied a small perch and potential nest scrape below the territory of pair no. 8. This male interacted chiefly with pair no. 12 of the right neighborhood.

Compared to the Crete colony, the territories were small indeed. By August 1, four weeks after the beginning of the reproductive season, the falcons hardly used more than 1 to 3 square meters each (see fig. 8). Gradually the territories expanded (especially into those areas which had been

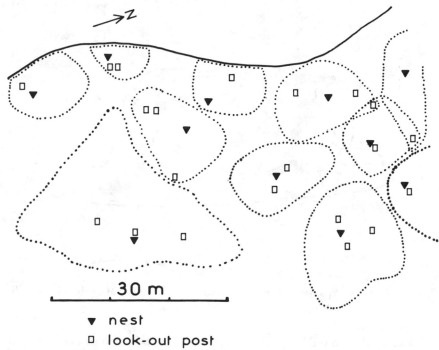

FIG. 7. Territories in "upper slope" zone of Crete colony. The solid line represents the edge of a vertical cliff.

occupied by gulls) until the maximum size was attained. The territories, averaging 10 square meters and very irregular in shape, left few unclaimed areas in the neighborhoods and so constituted a stable network within which most falcon activities were carried out. Despite smaller territories these activities remained substantially the same as in the Crete colony.

Each territory contained a number of key places (see fig. 9): the *nest site,* one or more *lookout posts* from which the surroundings were monitored and from where a falcon could instantly take off, *feeding and food-storage areas,* and *sunbathing sites.* In order to move from one of these "central places" to another a falcon flew or hiked over the terrain. Surprisingly often, it did the latter. Surveillance and rest periods were frequently interrupted by preening, sunbathing, a brief and circular territorial flight in front of the cliff, searching for unfinished prey items stored away in some cleft or hole, and feeding activities. Figure 10 shows how four pairs (nos. 1, 2, 7, 8) spent their time during 3,300 minutes of observation between 9 and 17 hours.

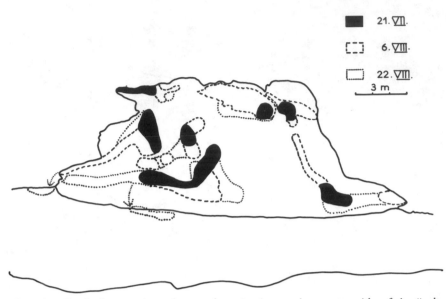

FIG. 8.   Gradual expansion of ground territories on the eastern side of the "submarine" cliff in July (VII) and August (VIII).

I divided each territory arbitrarily into a number of segments, each of
which was separated from the others by some terrain feature such as ridges
and crevices. From August 10 to 22, the mobility of the study population of
14 falcons was recorded minute by minute during the observation hours.
The results are illustrated in figures 11 and 12. Figure 11 shows that six out
of seven females spent over 50 percent (often 75 percent) of the observed
time within the territorial segment containing the nest scrape. The males, on
the other hand, spent only 25-75 percent, respectively, in that particular segment. They were found much more often in the adjoining and outlying parts
of their territory.

The mobility diagrams in figure 12 give an even better indication of a
falcon's use of its territory. They bring out the main "pathways" to and from
the "central" places within the territory as well as the much greater spatial
mobility of the male falcons. An in-depth analysis of individual differences
will be provided elsewhere (Walter, in press).

Morocco Colony, Other Parts: A number of pairs were breeding in completely inaccessible pigeonholes in vertical cliffs of the "atoll" islet. These
pairs did not possess much if any territory. All activities on the ground were

confined to the sometimes "atrium"-like entry to the hidden nest scrape. These falcons could not hike over or on the cliff surface in any way. They paid more attention and defended immediate air space in front of their nest entrance. Their young were unable to move about the rock. The few pairs that were breeding on open ledges (fig. 13), visible from far away, occupied elongated (up to 6 meters long) territories along and above or below their ledge. One male falcon occupied several square meters of dissected cliff surface some 15 meters away and across an open archway from its nest hole on the other side.

Maghreb and Sardinia Colonies: Since both colonies are situated on a rather large and mostly sheer cliff, territories appeared to be defined less in terms of private rock surfaces than as exclusive rights of access to the nest site and unlimited flight maneuverability in the updraft in front of the cliff.

Discussion: The territory of Eleonora's falcon can be understood as an essential and efficient mechanism or vehicle of individual survival and reproductive success within the context of the breeding colony. The dispersion of nest sites alone does not provide for a safe and efficient way of life. As long as anyone, particularly other Eleonora's falcons, can walk or fly right up to the nest site and perch next to it, a falcon, its mate, and its brood face constant danger. If the nest site is, however, surrounded by a well-defined and exclusive territorial space that must be left alone by others in order to avoid an agonistic interaction (see below) it becomes a safe haven. The territory appears to reduce significantly the threat of intraspecific interference and predation in this colonial species. Hole- and cave-breeding Eleonora's falcons do not require such a space when their nest sites are inaccessible except from the air.

It is impossible to judge whether the falcons prefer to settle in areas where a need for territories exists. The fact is that where such territories have been established and maintained on oblique and horizontal surfaces they are used for additional purposes — sunbathing, the storage and hiding of prey items (a very elaborate process in the Crete colony), and as a "playground" for the young falcons.

Falcons keep their territory under frequent visual control; it can be surveyed in its entirety from a lookout post. This apparent need for constant monitoring is probably responsible for the strangely shaped territories of the "submarine" populations. More circular or regular shapes of similar size would have included visual barriers like pinnacles and ridges, which would have made it impossible to have a visual command of the whole territory. This leads me to suggest that size and shape are related not only to the

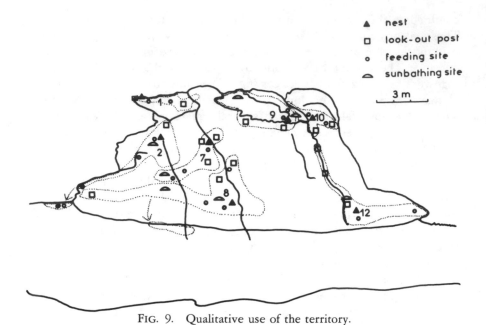

FIG. 9.   Qualitative use of the territory.

general dispersion pattern of a population (if distances between nests are short, territories must be small) but also to the visual complexity of the terrain. Rounded and larger territories can be expected on a terrain that contains few features obstructing the falcon's view (model A in fig. 14), tiny and irregularly shaped ones in locations where terrain complexity allows for only small fields of a falcon's vision (model B, fig. 14).

The territorial organization has been described for some noncolonial raptors. Cade (1960) explains those of peregrine falcons as a series of circles around nest sites with only the innermost circle being always defended, while outer circles include rarely defended hunting grounds within the home range. Cavé (1968) showed for the European kestrel *(Falco tinnunculus)* that individual feeding areas and breeding territories can be separate entities.

It would be worthwhile to study other gregarious raptors in terms of their dispersion and territorial systems. Eleonora's falcon resembles many colonial sea birds (Patterson, 1965; Bongiorno, 1970; Simmons, 1970; Manuval, 1974) except that shape and size of its territory show a wider range; in addition, prey storage and hiding have become important attributes not found in most (any?) of the other species.

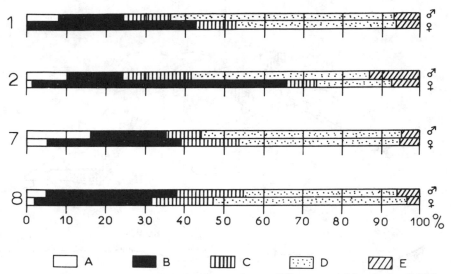

FIG. 10. Time percentage spent by four pairs on different activities during 3,300 minutes of observation time (100%) between 9 and 17 h. A, absent from the cliff, B, incubating clutch or empty nest scrape, C, preening, D, resting outside the nest or watching, E, other activities (feeding, hiking, sunbathing).

Agonistic Behavior

If we compare the territory to a "vehicle" essential to a falcon's reproductive success, then agonistic behavior provides the "fuel" or energy necessary to run it or make it work. The establishment, expansion, and the daily maintenance of a territory would be impossible without effective behavioral patterns related to threat and appeasement, to offensive and defensive actions. In other words, the rights of "privacy" and "exclusive" territorial space have to be gained and confirmed. As in other species, certain agonistic behaviors serve also an important function in sexual relationships. We shall concentrate here on territory-related phenomena.

Intraspecific Interactions: Constant fighting would be to the disadvantage of this heavily armed but colonial species. It would inflict heavy losses and create permanent disturbance factors within the breeding population. Instead, a number of acoustic and visual signals are employed to communicate elements of agonistic behavior to other falcons. Such signals often prevent the outbreak of serious conflicts involving physical fighting. They worked so well that to a casual observer the observed colonies appeared to

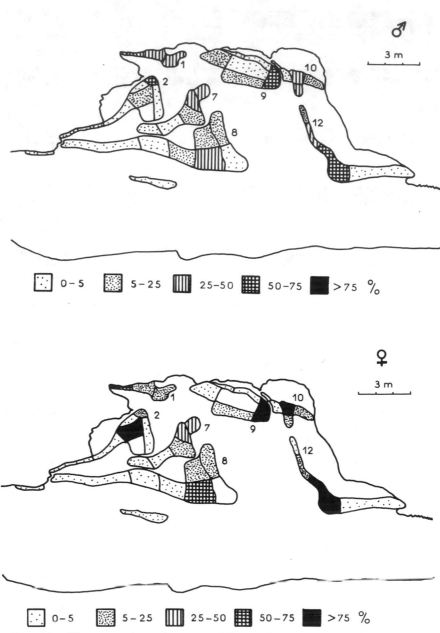

FIG. 11.   Time spent by male (top) and female falcons in territorial segments.

consist of remarkably (and perhaps disappointingly) peaceful falcon populations. Acute conflict situations filled less than 2 percent of the 3,780 minutes of observation time of the 1969 "submarine" study population. The falcons used a number of vocalizations (e.g., "territorial call") and body postures to ward off a physical confrontation (e.g., "fanned tail high over back" advertises occupancy of "exclusive area"; "head down, hunchback, and horizontal tail" posture serves as a mild threat and intimidation attempt; "rapid forward bowing" is the most often used submission and appeasement signal).

When such signals did not suffice, a falcon defended its territory through an aerial attack. This occurred at once if a falcon other than its mate dared to set foot on the territory. Such an attack consisted of one or a series of swift nose dives followed by the aerial pursuit of the intruder or aggressor. In rare and serious instances both falcons grappled with each other's feet and hit each other's breast while falling downward; such fierce fighting, accompanied by sharp and intense vocalizations, continued even on the ground. However, they do not appear to cause severe injuries. Occasionally neighbor falcons will come to the aid of a falcon that fights off an intruder.

In the Morocco colony, careful monitoring of the "submarine" study population yielded data on 82 territorial conflicts between colony members at the aerial attack level and above. Their origin and outcome were related to the dominance that specific falcons had established over their neighbors. Fourteen of these involved the single male no. 14 that unsuccessfully tried to challenge the "rights" of male no. 12 to mate and territory. Falcons occupying the best-lookout posts (protected but with a side and commanding view) as well as comparatively large territories were found to be dominant, i.e., were rarely attacked or intimidated by a neighbor. Whether dominance creates the site or the site creates dominance could not be determined.

Agonistic behavior related to disputes over food items was rare on the "submarine" (10 records), where males returning from the sea with prey reached their nest site in a direct and swift flight pattern that allowed little if any time to intercept them. Of course, once they had alighted within their territory, no falcon would bother them. Disputes over food were quite common, however, on the nearby "atoll" where more than 50 pairs were present within a circular cliff 40 meters in diameter. Falcons carrying prey in their talons were spotted simultaneously by dozens of perched falcons. Before the former had a chance to alight within their "exclusive" cliff area, the latter had launched a hot pursuit attempting to seize their prey item. This occurred several times per hour. Some falcons lost their food item, some actually fell into the water fighting for it.

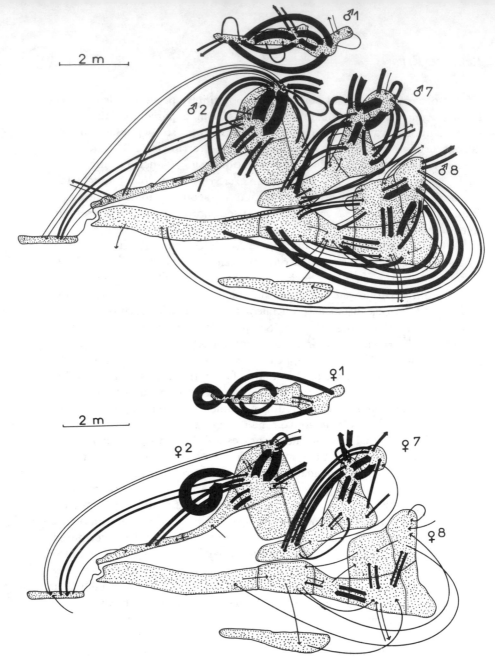

FIG. 12. Mobility diagrams of 7 pairs during 5 days (August 10, 13, 15, 19, and 22) from 9-17 h. Each movement was recorded that resulted in take-off, arrival, and transfer to another segment. The thinnest lines represent one flight or hike only while the thickest ones represent more than 30 such moves. Almost circular arrows leading back to the take-off segment indicate take-offs for brief circular flights. Lines do not necessarily correspond to the falcons' actual routes.

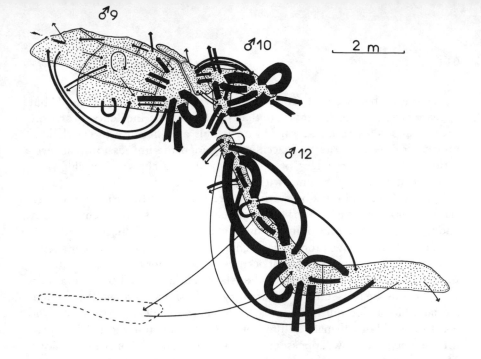

♂9   ♂10   2 m

♂12

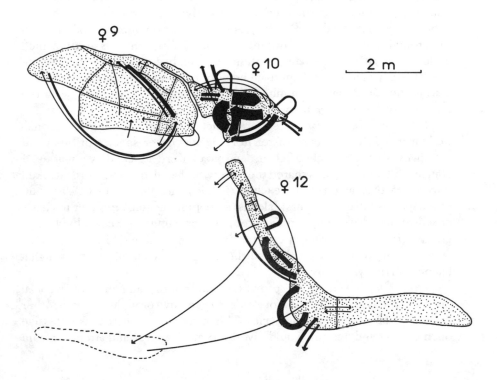

♀9   ♀10   2 m

♀12

Agonistic behavior related to territory was observed on the "atoll" but appeared to be less prevalent there than on the "submarine." However, only occasional studies could be carried on in this area because of restrictions imposed on us after the boat accident. I gained the impression that territories on the upper ledges of this circular but rather vertical cliff were occupied more often than not with dominant falcons.

In the Crete colony, observations were made mostly during the young-raising phase. Agonistic behaviors related to disputes over items of prey and the harassing actions of intruding immature (nonbreeding) falcons were frequent; conflicts over territorial rights involving neighboring pairs were rare. One rather dramatic incident occurred on October 8, 1965, at 7:30 a.m. Male 52 had caught a bird above the island. Hard pressed by several pursuing falcons, he missed his own territory when shooting down from a high altitude. He landed not far from nest 24 where female 24 was present (he was her neighbor). Female 24 did not attack the sudden guest in her territory; she began to bow (appeasement sign) and beg for the prey in his talons. Male 52 hesitated to deliver it to her, but finally she succeeded in tearing it out of his bill. He began to bow in an apparent attempt to regain his prey, but she hid it under a bush, then began to drive the intruder out of the territory. Since male 52 did not move, female 24 attacked him several times on the ground, pounding her claws into his chest. The fight was accompanied by loud and pitched cries and continuous wing beats. After about 10 minutes of heavy fighting a falcon from neighboring pair 13 swooped down and assisted female 24 with a number of aerial attacks to drive male 52 in the direction of his own territory.

Interspecific Interactions: Eleonora's falcon will employ vigorous agonistic behavior in the defense of territory against other species of birds and mammals. Kestrels, eagles, herons, and goats were attacked as a matter of course. Gulls and pigeons shared the cliffs with the falcons and were attacked only when they alighted in "exclusive" falcon neighborhoods. When another species intruded several falcons (sometimes dozens) took off to chase, nosedive and drive the intruder from the proximity of the colony. This group defense was extremely effective in preventing larger birds from flying over the colony. It also accelerated the movement of feral goats through a falcon's territory.

Discussion: In spite of the prowess of this raptor, the nature of its social interaction was generally not more or less aggressive or violent than in other gregarious and solitary bird species. This had to be expected, as excessive open conflict and fighting would divert too much energy and attention from

FIG. 13. Breeding pair in its territory consisting of a ledge and small cove of the rather inaccessible "atoll" walls.

the other priorities of the breeding season. Acoustic signals and body postures employed to communicate and defuse conditions of tension and conflict do not differ much from those of other, solitary falcons (Cade, 1960; Monneret, 1974; Glutz von Blotzheim, Bauer, and Bezzel, 1971). This behavioral system functioned well, providing an orderly and protective instrument for the colonies as a whole as well as for each breeding pair.

The not infrequent "intra-neighborhood" conflicts on the "submarine" were probably a combined result of extreme or near-maximum breeding density on nonvertical surfaces and of the generally heightened social interaction of those pairs (about 50 percent) that had lost their entire clutch and failed to replace it. Under these circumstances the presence of a single male falcon added a stress factor further complicating coexistence on this tiny cliff. However, residents nearly always completely avoided neighboring territories even in the absence of their owners.

Visual stimuli appeared once again as decisive factors in triggering territorial behavior. The close location (about one meter apart) of two lookout posts of different males (nos. 10 and 12, see fig. 9) created constant tension and a higher mobility of these pairs. Had one of them found a perch at the same distance but hidden from view of the other male, no tension would have occurred. Many such data on the personal relationships between different individuals of the "submarine" study population lead me to believe that a doubling of the breeding population and the addition of another single male would have created so many additional "hot spots" and their

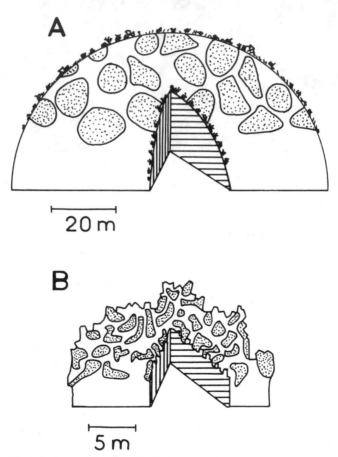

FIG. 14. Model of two islands with different surface texture. A, Large island with relatively smooth terrain; territories of Eleonora's falcon are large and of rounded shape. B, Small island with rugged and dissected terrain; territories are small and of irregular shape.

accompanied agonistic behaviors that normal breeding activities might have been adversely affected.

The high frequency of disputes over items of prey was typical in most colony segments. The prey resources of this species consist of a passing stream fluctuating from week to week and sometimes from hour to hour depending on geographic and climatological factors. Falcons are keen to keep food provisions and may accumulate piles of killed migrant birds in their territory. These provisions are an important protein resource in times of reduced hunting success. The careful hiding of prey in the Crete colony may be related to the more open terrain, a generally scarcer food supply, and the existence of commensal lizards and rats on the breeding island. The deposition of considerable quantities of captured protein in the falcon's ground territory adds an important defense factor to the territorial behavior of Eleonora's falcon that is absent in gulls and other colonial sea birds but common in social predators like lions. The high frequency rate of the disputes over items of prey was correlated with high breeding density and good visibility of prey-carrying falcons; it put the inhabitants of the "atoll" at a disadvantage since they stood a good chance of being pursued and "tackled" by other cliff residents on return from hunting. Low density and poor visibility of incoming falcons, on the other hand, favored the undetected and dispute-free landing of prey in a territory.

Conclusions

This study of the social organization of Eleonora's falcon in different ecological settings attempted to investigate the interesting combination of a bird being both a raptor and a colonial. This species seems to have evolved several adaptive mechanisms that enable it to coexist with other colony members and still preserve its character as a raptor.

The dispersion of nest sites is related to terrain complexity and appears to be the result of an innate or acquired image of a privacy distance and area needed around a falcon's nest site. This might also be considered the critical distance at which a falcon will tolerate another falcon and nest site. Important in this distance is the "landscape" factor, the structural complexity of which determines or codetermines the actual distance between nest sites. If other ecological factors are constant, different physical terrains will result in different breeding densities.

The size and shape of what is essentially a microterritory in comparison to other raptors also vary with terrain complexity. Some pairs do not possess a territory at all. They breed in caves and pigeonholes that are inaccessible and offer great privacy; i.e., neighbors have little opportunity to participate visually in a falcon's activities during the reproductive season. Thus they are secure both from an inter- and intraspecific viewpoint. Others have small and irregularly shaped territories whose utilization and defense indicate this species' need of visual control. As illustrated in figure 14, this "landscape" factor in complex terrain will result in predominantly small territories of a very irregular shape while in simpler, more evenly surfaced terrain, effective visual control over larger areas will result in relatively regular-shaped territories.

The reported observations on agonistic behavior also indicate why dispersion and territorial systems of different colonies are beneficial to individual falcons. Although Eleonora's falcon has a much higher distance-tolerance to other members of its species than other raptors, its raptorial nature has not in any way been suppressed. Individual survival, the possession of a mate, its young, and stored food resources might be in danger if falcons could monitor one another's activities. Visual privacy appears to be a solution to the problem of how to combine the advantage of a colonial existence with a rather aggressive nature. (Even so, disputes over food items and territorial boundaries do occur.)

The flexible nature of the dispersion mechanism allows falcons to breed in higher densities where more complex terrains generally have also supplied larger numbers of suitable nest sites. Since the latter are scarce in many parts of the Mediterranean this might also be seen as an adaptation to maximize breeding wherever possible.

Do different ecological settings affect social interaction in this colonial raptor? The answer must be yes and no and has already been given. The basic and numerous behavior patterns related to agonistic interaction were the same in the principal study sites regardless of their rather different structure and topography. Characteristic differences were observed in the frequency and strength of many social interactions; they were very particular even to small clusters of nest sites ("neighborhoods") and were determined by a multifactor system including slope direction, the nature of the local predator-prey system, the nearest neighbor-distance (see above), the dominance level of individual falcons, etc.

In conclusion, the three functionally related mechanisms of dispersion, territory, and agonistic behavior are determinants of a specific optimal density for each type of terrain that is the site of a falcon colony. Optimal means here the spacing-out and visual isolation of pairs large enough to result in the smallest rate of predation and disturbance, and small enough to maximize the beneficial effects of group defense and other interactions among colony members. The degree to which colony members approximate the optimal density value in practice should, at least in the long term, exert an influence on the success of coexistence in Eleonora's falcon.

REFERENCES

BEEBE, FRANK L.
    1960. The marine peregrines of the Northwest Pacific Coast. Condor, vol. 62, pp. 145-189.
BERNDT, RUDOLPH, and WINKEL, WOLFGANG
    1974. Ökoschema, Rivalität und Dismigration als öko-ethologische Dispersionsfaktoren. Journ. für Orn., vol. 115, pp. 398-417.
BONGIORNO, S. F.
    1970. Nest-site selection by adult laughing gulls *(Larus atriculla)*. Anim. Behav., vol. 18, pp. 434-444.
BROWN, JERRAM L.
    1964. The evolution of diversity in avian territorial systems. Wilson Bull., vol. 76, pp. 160-169.
    1969. Territorial behavior and population regulation in birds. Wilson Bull., vol. 81, pp. 293-329.
BROWN, JERRAM L., and ORIANS, GORDON H.
    1970. Spacing patterns in mobile animals. Ann. Rev. Ecol. Syst., vol. 1, pp. 239-262.
CADE, THOMAS J.
    1960. Ecology of the peregrine and gyrfalcon populations in Alaska. Univ. California Publ. Zool., vol. 63, no. 3, pp. 151-290.
CAVÉ, A. J.
    1968. The breeding of the kestrel, *Falco tinnunculus* L., in the reclaimed area Oostelijk Flevoland. Netherlands Journ. Zool., vol. 18, pp. 313-407.
CROOK, JOHN HURRELL
    1965. The adaptive significance of avian social organization. Symp. Zool. Soc. London, vol. 14, pp. 181-218.
GLUTZ VON BLOTZHEIM, U. N.; BAUER, K. M.; and BEZZEL, E.
    1971. Handbuch der Vögel Mitteleuropas, vol. 4 (Falconiformes). Akademische Verlagsgemeinschaft, Frankfurt am Main.
HINDE, ROBERT A.
    1956. The biological significance of territories in birds. Ibis, vol. 98, pp. 340-369.
KIESTER, A. R.; GORMAN, G. C.; and ARROYO, D. C.
    1975. Habitat selection behavior of three species of *Anolis* lizards. Ecology, vol. 56, pp. 220-225
KRUEPER, THEODOR
    1864. Beitrag zur Naturgeschichte des Eleonorenfalken, *Falco eleonarae* Gené. Journ. für Orn., vol. 12, pp. 1-2.

MANUVAL, DAVID A.
    1974. Effects of territoriality on breeding in a population of Cassin's auklet.
        Ecology, vol. 55, pp. 1399-1406.
MONNERET, R. J.
    1974. Repertoire comportemental du faucon pelerin *Falco peregrinus:* Hypo-
        thèse explicative des manifestations adversives.   Alauda, vol. 42, pp.
        407-428.
PATTERSON, I. J.
    1965. Timing and spacing of broods in the black-headed gull, *(Larus ridibundus).*
        Ibis, vol. 107, pp. 433-459.
SIMMONS, KENNETH E. L.
    1970. Ecological determinants of breeding adaptations and social behaviour in
        two fish-eating birds.   Pp. 37-77 *in* "Social Behaviour in Birds and
        Mammals: Essays on the Social Ethology of Animals and Man," J. H.
        Crook, ed. Academic Press, London and New York.
TINBERGEN, NIKO
    1957. The functions of territory.   Bird Study, vol. 4, pp. 14-27.
VAUGHAN, RICHARD
    1961. *Falco eleonarae.*   Ibis, vol. 103a, pp. 114-128.
WALTER, HARTMUT
    1968. Zur Abhängigkeit des Eleonorenfalken *(Falco eleonorae)* vom mediter-
        ranen Vogelzug.   Journ. für Orn., vol. 109, pp. 323-365.
    1970. Zum Baderverhalten von *Falco eleonorae.*   Journ. für Orn., vol. 111, pp.
        242-243.
    1971. Juli-Zugbelege aus Marokko in Rupfungen von *Falco eleonorae.*   Die
        Vogelwarte, vol. 26, p. 142.
    _____. The Eleonora's falcon: A study of adaptation to prey and habitat.   Uni-
        versity of Chicago Press, Chicago. (In press.)

                                                                        HARTMUT WALTER

Submarine Polarized Light and the Behavior
of Aquatic Animals

Principal Investigator: Talbot H. Waterman, Yale University, New Haven, Connecticut.

Grant No. 788:   In support of a study of the effects of submarine polarized light on the behavior of aquatic animals.

The research done under this grant proved to have a decisive effect on our ongoing research program dealing with polarized light and aquatic animals, as well as on our related work on visual function and eye fine structure supported by a continuing grant from the National Institutes of Health. The program planned for the Society grant was addressed to the still-unsolved problem of the use to which marine and other aquatic animals capable of perceiving it may put the natural polarized light in their environment.

We know from our previous work, as well as from that of others, that rhabdom-bearing eyes seem quite generally able to detect the *e*-vector direction of linearly polarized light. Consequently we expected to use small crustaceans or squids in the field experiments. We were seeking to get positive evidence that submarine or sky polarization affected the oriented behavior of such animals. Although many aquatic forms were known to be *e*-vector sensitive, no information was available on the possible significance of the natural polarization under water. Palau in the western Caroline Islands was selected as the site for the experiments because of its rich inshore fauna and the ready availability of calm clear water. Also adequate facilities and cooperation were offered to us there. SCUBA was to be used for conducting the experiments under water.

By chance we became interested in the behavior of a common Palauan fish and subsequently devoted almost all our efforts to studying its orientation in polarized light. On inspection, the behavior of this fish, the half-beak *Zenarchopterus*, seemed extraordinarily suitable for the kind of study we had planned for the invertebrates mentioned above. In a relatively small experimental vessel juvenile specimens showed an appropriate (and rather rare) combination of visual alertness and quiet patterns of motor activity. In addition, although consistent quantitative data have been difficult to obtain, this fish appeared to show oriented responses to linearly polarized light. Consequently our research focus was shifted forthwith from the intended invertebrates to *Zenarchopterus*.

The fortunate coincidence of this animal's behavior with our general interest has had an important influence on the subsequent course of our research. Despite some suggestive earlier evidence to the contrary, it had been widely believed that vertebrates (except man) are unable to discriminate the plane of vibration in linearly polarized light. Our work in Palau suggested that this notion might be incorrect, a hypothesis later supported by our subsequent work on fishes as well as by the results of others on amphibians and birds.

The field results in Palau comprised underwater experiments in which the azimuth orientation of juvenile halfbeaks confined in a closed lucite experimental vessel was recorded photographically at appropriate intervals (usually 5 or 10 seconds). Records were made with natural illumination alone and with imposed additional linear polarization.

Data analysis, completed mainly back at Yale, showed two main results. First, under natural illumination *Zenarchopterus* showed significant spontaneous azimuth preference relative to the sun's bearing. There were multiple peaks in this distribution but the mean vector was significant. Second, when a Polaroid filter was placed over the vessel the mean vector of the circular distribution of the fishes' swimming direction usually changed from that showed without the polarizer. However, when the e-vector was oriented at 90° to the sun's bearing the mean vector was not significantly different from that without polarizer.

Two conclusions seemed justified by these results. First, the halfbeaks behaved as if they could perceive the e-vector of imposed linear polarization. Second, the fact that no different response was obtained when the imposed e-vector coincided with that in the sky overhead may suggest that sky polarization (observed from under water) is part of the fish's azimuth indicating "compass." These results were published in *Nature* (Waterman and Forward, 1970).

Laboratory experiments were continued in New Haven on a variety of fish species, particularly *Dermogenys,* a fresh-water relative of *Zenarchopterus* available through commercial fish dealers. These confirmed that halfbeaks do orient spontaneously to e-vector directions not only in the field but also in the laboratory. Continuing work later yielded evidence that the fishes' response to polarized light must involve e-vector perception rather than a mere discrimination of an extraocular intensity pattern. Hence there must be an intraocular mechanism sensitive to the direction of the plane of vibration.

These experiments, however, did not yield statistically decisive results quickly. Various protocols and techniques of running the tests were tried in a largely unsuccessful effort to improve matters. Hence a large number of replications were needed for a given test to reach significant levels. Consequently a second period of field work in Palau intervened during the summer of 1970 before decisive laboratory results were completed. Since these were in part supported by a subsequent Society grant for the second period of field work, a more detailed account will be more appropriate for the report on that later grant.

REFERENCES

WATERMAN, TALBOT H.
  1976. Information channeling in the crayfish retina.   Nat. Geogr. Soc. Res. Rpts., 1968 Projects, pp. 467-472.
WATERMAN, TALBOT H., and FORWARD, RICHARD B., JR.
  1970. Field evidence for polarized light sensitivity in the fish *Zenarchopterus*. Nature, vol. 228, pp. 85-87, illus.

TALBOT H. WATERMAN

Studies of Neotropical Mammals

Principal Investigator: Ralph M. Wetzel, University of Connecticut, Storrs, Connecticut.

Grant No. 794:   In support of a study of the distribution, zoogeography, and systematics of Neotropical mammals.

These studies have been concerned with the identity, zoogeography, age and sex composition, and habitat selection of 51 species of mammals (as presently listed by Cabrera, *Catalogo de los Mamíferos de America del Sur,* vol. 1, 1958; vol. 2, 1961) occurring in South and Central America to Mexico. They include the sloths, armadillos, and anteaters (order Edentata); the jaguar, puma, ocelot, and margays (family Felidae); fox and doglike species (Canidae); weasel, tayra, grison, skunk, and otters (Mustelidae); crab-eating raccoon, coati, kinkajou, olingo, and mountain coati (Procyonidae); spectacled bear (Ursidae); and, of the hoofed animals (Ungulata), four species of deer, two species of peccary or javelina, and the tapir.

As the focal point of the study has been the mammals collected by the Smithsonian Venezuelan Project, the species were selected that included Venezuela or its adjacent borders in their ranges. This project, directed by Dr. Charles O. Handley, Jr., of the National Museum of Natural History, and with many collaborators in the United States and South America, collected over 40,000 specimens of mammals, with their ectoparasites, from the extremely varied habitats of Venezuela. This collection bridges an important gap in the basic data needed to understand the wide-ranging species or related species groups that occur from the southern temperate or northern tropics of North America to middle or southern South America. These considerations, in turn, are expected to add to the growing body of knowledge of the interrelationships of biota of the two continents.

The grant from the National Geographic Society (as well as support from the Smithsonian Venezuelan Project, the University of Connecticut Research Foundation, and the American Philosophical Society) enabled me to remain in residence at the Smithsonian Institution and to travel to most of the other significant collections of mammals from South and Central America. I visited 36 museums in South America, Europe, and the

United States and studied most of the types of the species involved, still extant, and all other pertinent materials.

The verification of the geographical sources of the specimens examined has been accomplished through the use of published reports of varied expeditions, records in the museums concerned, and postal guides, maps, and gazetteers at the Smithsonian Institution, the Map Division of the Library of Congress, and the University of Connecticut. As a result of this time-consuming search, maps have been prepared that will be new contributions to our knowledge of the distribution of the different species. Examination of the scattered literature on the taxonomy and distribution of the species, including references cited by Linnaeus *(Systema Naturae,* 10th ed. 1758) is nearly completed. Subsamples of the data have been established, and statistical treatment has progressed through approximately half of the species of the order Edentata.

A common denominator to the approach to the different studies has been the detailed treatment of the Venezuelan segment of the range of each species. As many of the species are poorly understood, this has required a complete study and a revisional approach to many of the species or species complexes. In other cases the status of the Venezuelan portion of the species could be approached with greater confidence; hence the coverage could be more restricted. In these latter cases the different Venezuelan samples were compared only with samples from adjacent areas. These uniformly included Trinidad, Guyana, Surinam, French Guiana, Brazil north of the Amazon River, Ecuador, Colombia, and Panama.

Certain manuscripts are in progress. Publication plans for the ensuing years will be for both revisional and geographically oriented papers.

REFERENCES

WETZEL, RALPH M.
   1975. The species of *Tamandua* Gray (Edentata, Myrmecophagidae). Proc. Biol. Soc. Washington, vol. 88, pp. 95-112.
   197_. A review of the Recent species of *Bradypus* L. and *Choloepus* Illiger (Edentata). Paper given at the First International Theriological Congress June 6-12, 1974, Moscow. Theriology, vol. 3.
WETZEL, RALPH M., and KOCK, DIETER
   1973. The identity of *Bradypus variegatus* Schinz (Mammalia, Edentata). Proc. Biol. Soc. Washington, vol. 86, pp. 25-34.

RALPH M. WETZEL

Personality Change in Cultural Adaptation

Principal Investigator: Glyn Williams, University College of North Wales, Bangor, Wales.

Grant No. 793:   In support of a study of the social behavior of Welsh populations in Wales and Patagonia in relation to personality changes as affected by environment.

Theory

The basic purposes of this study were: (1) to investigate the impact of variation in antecedents of child rearing resulting from the adaptive response of members of a single culture in contrasting ecological settings upon socialization practices, and (2) to discern whether this variation in socialization produces corresponding changes in the adult personality to the extent that personality can be employed as an index of cultural change.

It is maintained that in adapting to a physical environment man modifies his agricultural practices and molds himself into the existing ecological setting. His economic frame of reference is often dictated by his previous experience and the potential of adapting this experience within the limitations imposed by the physical environment and by external forces. Thus as the external situation varies so also does man's individual behavior vary in his attempt to come to terms with the modifications imposed by the need to adapt to the new situation. Man attempts to develop methods of exploiting the physical environment in the manner he perceives as most fruitful, and consequently his rationality will often produce institutional change related to environmental change. This manner of environmental exploitation in effect influences all other aspects of culture, although, of course, these other aspects can themselves have a profound bearing upon the mode of environmental exploitation. The interest of this study lies in an attempt to investigate the adaptive process in what might be regarded as a natural laboratory in which economic change is viewed as an antecedent variable of social and cultural change.

The research design links aspects of the physical environment, settlement pattern, social structure, agricultural economy, and socialization in an

627

integrated attempt to establish the impact of several variables upon personality formation. The theories employed are not totally new but are derived from earlier research. Much of the theoretical framework applies the ideas of learning theorists, social psychologists, and anthropologists to an underlying comparative approach within the same culture. The conceptual system is to a great extent derived from the "Six Cultures Study in Child Rearing" (Whiting et al., 1966) and the "Culture and Ecology Project" (Goldschmidt, 1965). It is represented in a simplified form in the chart below.

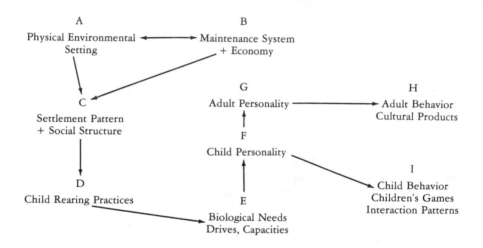

The research setting is a Welsh culture in Wales and Patagonia. As a result of political aggression and economic deprivation, about 3,000 members of the Welsh culture emigrated to Patagonia between 1865 and 1914 (Williams, 1975, 1976). They became the first nonindigenous group successfully to pioneer this portion of Argentina, the adaptive framework therefore being by necessity innovative in nature. In so doing they settled two quite distinct ecological settings, the Lower Chubut Valley on the arid eastern seaboard and Cwm Hyfryd [1] in the transitional semi-arid-moist east Andean

---

[1] This is the Welsh name meaning "pleasant valley," which is usually substituted for the official name of Colonia de 16 de Octobre.

foothills. In the former location the settlement was based upon irrigation farming, whereas in the Andean settlement the adaptation involved micro-environmental exploitation by the use of transhumant pastoralism, although with modifications from the traditional transhumance of Wales.

Method

The National Geographic Society funding was applied to the initial part of the project, involving 9 months of field work in Wales during 1969-70. The village of Ysbyty Ifan and the two parishes that constitute its hinterland were chosen as the research setting. This village was felt to be typical of the numerous transhumance communities in Wales. Its population of approximately 250 included only six non-Welsh speakers. Furthermore, this number was almost the minimum composition of a Primary Social Unit that would include 24 families with children between the ages of 3 and 13 years as a basis for the socialization study. It was felt also that this village was similar enough, with reference to homogeneity, to the two communities that would constitute the Primary Social Units in Patagonia. For example, it focused upon a small village that functioned as a central place. One of the most important institutions within the community is the nonconformist chapel, which in Patagonia is nondenominational in nature, thus necessitating for comparative purposes a study community in Wales with only a single denominational representation. In Ysbyty Ifan both the chapel and the small primary school drew upon a hinterland that conformed to the limits of the two parishes. Finally, since it was felt that the existence of a semifeudal estate system with its strong centralized authority would have repercussions in terms of socialization practices (Fromm and Maccoby, 1970), and this being one of the main antecedent variables, it was necessary to choose a village such as Ysbyty Ifan that was part of such an estate.

The first stage of the data-collecting work consisted of detailed household surveys that served also as introductory visits. This process was followed by the collection of in-depth genealogical data, which served as the basis for establishing intracommunity kinship networks. While this stage of the work was being undertaken all the voluntary associations in the village were attended and careful detail was noted, not only about social interaction but also about leadership and membership. The next stage involved the gathering of data about the economic structure of the households, particular emphasis being placed upon socialization into the labor force and agricultural mutual-aid practices, which served as the basis of a social network.

The economic data pertained to land-use practices, production costs, and output. An attempt was made also to determine the impact of secondary employment and market trends upon the household economy. Finally, data were collected about expenditure trends.

Once this phase of the work was completed, a picture of social and economic variation within the community was established, this serving as the basis of compiling a stratified population sample, which in turn would serve as the basis for the socialization and projective data gathering. Such sampling was based upon the need to obtain a representative homogeneous group of people within each of the three communities in order to minimize the differences in practices *within* each place. The families for the socialization study were selected partly on the basis of their potential for child-rearing observations. There had to be a wide cross section in the ages between 3 and 13 years of the child membership, as well as a balance in the sex and age differences. In all, 24 children drawn from different families were selected for study. The children were stratified by sex, age, and dispersed-nucleated settlement residence. Both parents of all the children were interviewed, and the mothers were asked to keep a careful diary of child behavior.

The observational aspect of child study involved 24 five-minute observations for each child spread over time and setting so as to be representative of each child's typical day. The emphasis was on various major theoretical responses ranging from self-reliance to aggression, together with a calculation of the amount of time usually spent by each child in each setting in order to ascertain the frequency of occurrence of different situations.

Rather than attempting to employ a projective device as a basis for assessing child personality, it was felt that a systematic recording and observation of children's games would be more fruitful. Thus a variety of children's games were observed in various natural settings, these being carefully coded with reference to actors and their behavior.

In the assessment of personality attributes the foremost question involved the extent to which ecological, social, and economic changes reshape the basic cultural response patterns in values, attitudes, and personality characteristics. Thus both the individual and the model personality had to be considered. After several weeks in the community it was possible to filter out individual deviations and idiosyncratic behavior from those that were culturally patterned, as a basis for deciding upon the sample from which "in depth" information was to be elicited as well as upon what traits were to be emphasized as significant in the daily round of life and in relation to the analytic categories to which such traits referred. This initial period had also been employed to collect such expressive information as ministers' sermons, folk tales, folk poetry and sayings, jokes, games, and dream protocols.

However, the main feature of the work involving adult personality was to quantify various psychological traits by the use of projective techniques, the results serving as the basis for discerning the model and variant characteristics maintained by people in different psychological situations. The projective tests selected were a Sociometric Test, the Sentence Completion Test, the Thematic Apperception Test, and a sampling of life histories. The Sentence Completion Test of 62 items was constructed with a view to investigating the psychological areas that corresponded to the "systems" of behavior investigated in the study of child rearing. The Sociometric Test was employed as a means of ascertaining the relationship between the ideal or preferred personality and the model personality. In addition, a modified version of the Kluckholn "Variation in Value Orientation" test (Kluckholn and Strodtbeck, 1961) was employed in order to determine inter- and intra-generational variation in values.

The sample selected for the projective test consisted of 100 individuals, the initial criterion for selection being a desire for representativeness involving both sexes and "young" and "mature" categories as defined within the community. By the time this phase of the study was reached it was felt that a recognition of the dominant personality types from the observation of overt behavior had been sufficiently achieved to insure us that the sample was representative. However, two further considerations arose: First, the need to include the community members who occurred as "stars" or "isolates" in the Sociometric Test and, second, the need to include the parents of the children included in the socialization study so that the relationship between agent behavior and agent personality in child-rearing patterns could be ascertained. Finally the life histories of eight individuals held to be representative of "young" and "mature" males and females in the community were recorded.

Findings

The original transhumance pattern of upland Wales was based primarily upon cattle herding, but by the end of the 18th century the emphasis had shifted to sheep rearing. Similarly, the traditional settlement pattern involving an upland summer residence (hafod) and a lowland winter residence (hendref) had disappeared from the landscape by the beginning of the last century. The village of Ysbyty Ifan has a long history as part of one feudal estate or another, most of Wales having been subdivided and donated by the English Crown to the loyal gentry following one of England's early ventures into colonial conquest. The social and, often, physical distance between landlord and peasant was expanded by the presence of the intermediary land agent who more often than not was of a non-Welsh cultural background. Thus while Welsh village-based communities such as Ysbyty Ifan were economically tied to the manor, both socially and culturally they remained distinct.

It was within this framework that the village of Ysbyty Ifan became the focus of a settlement pattern of dispersed farms controlled by an economy based upon transhumant sheep herding on open upland community grazing lands. By today the reduction in agricultural labor needs and local services has resulted in a change in the demographic composition of the village, where many tenants live who have retired from the farms to make room for their children. This pattern, and the endogamous marriage tendency, mean that most of the tenant farmers have relatives resident in the village.

In addition to these kinship-based centrifugal associations, internal cohesion is fostered by the economic system, with essential reciprocal networks working to facilitate animal husbandry on unenclosed land. In summer while the animals are in the uplands the almost random distribution of sheep walks means that such networks cut across the community. However, with the animals spending the winters in the lowlands, the agriculturally based reciprocity networks become localized. Almost as if to compensate for this localization a variety of voluntary associations focus upon the village during the winter months, thereby serving to bring the entire community into frequent face-to-face contact (Williams, in press).

These economic and social conditions serve as important antecedents of child rearing. The chief agents of socialization, especially on the dispersed farms, are the parents, with relatives and neighbors assuming a secondary role. Relatives in the village assume an increasing importance after the child begins to attend the village school, usually serving as custodians as well as supplements to parental discipline. The few farm families who do not have such relatives in the village usually enter into a form of fictive kinship relationship with someone in the village. The demanding nature of work on a family farm means that older siblings are drafted as agents at an early age.

The demands of the farms call both males and females into the work force, the latter being primarily responsible for dairying and farmyard chores. While the mother is working, the child is often left alone for long periods of time, and from about the age of 3 the child accompanies the mother, giving minor assistance with her work. By the time they are about 8 years of age the children can be relied upon for a variety of tasks, and thereafter the sex-identification variation becomes marked. Clearly there is implied a strong emphasis upon physical independence, this also being a major feature of the ideal model they are taught to emulate. Yet, a low emphasis is placed upon self initiative, and it appears that the strong international authority of the estate system has promoted a strong respect for authority, this being one of the main facets of early child training. Thus independence is tempered by this respect for authority. Discipline is mainly the responsibility of the mother. The father supports this authority, remaining distant and stern, his main contact with children often being related to discipline.

The isolation of the individual farms limits the child's opportunity to relate to other community members. Prior to attending the village primary school at the age of 5 the only contact children have with the community is in the formal setting of the weekly Sunday school, where a strong emphasis is placed upon conformity. As a result the early child personality tends to be lacking in sociability. However, after the age of 5 entry into the school environment and contact with relatives in the village insure a rapid change. It is also at this stage that the mothers become more permissive in their treatment of the child. Generally it is felt that children become more aggressive after this age, and indeed they are trained to counter aggression by being aggressive themselves.

Achievement-orientated training appears to be tempered by a tendency to limit self-expression by stressing conformity. Children are constantly told not to try to be different and not "to show themselves off." Such behavior is expressed as "childish behavior." As a result, innovative creativity appears to be stifled.

The changes emanating from the child's entry into the elementary school also obtain when he enters the comprehensive school, which is situated in a market town some 11 miles outside the community. This change is preceded by considerable anxiety concerning the need for fluency in the English language, for in the elementary school Welsh is the main language used. Children attend the comprehensive school from the age of 11 after which they come into contact with peers and situations of a wider diversity. This experience can have varying repercussions tending to make them either more cosmopolitan or to promote an emphasis upon the local environment. This transition is marked by a greater degree of independence from the family.

The most conspicuous theme discernible in the behavior of the residents of Ysbyty Ifan involved a belief that for the community to function cohesively interpersonal social anxiety must be reduced to a minimum. The behavior associated with this theme was involved. It was to be found in the expression of egalitarianism, which tended to overcome the feeling of anxiety associated with the uneven distribution of limited resources. Thus although there existed distinct socio-economic differences within the community the allocation of social credit was often undertaken in a manner that contradicted this difference. It was apparent also in face-to-face relationships, the actors continuously employing what was termed by one of the residents as "conversational courtesy," which involved an elaborate degree of role flexibility. This was achieved by not committing oneself to any ideological stance for fear that in conversation it might lead to a conflict that would embarrass both members of the dyad. As a result, situations were encountered in which everyone appeared to be in complete agreement even though in another situation the opposite beliefs were subscribed to by some of the actors. In this manner individual stances are continuously shifting in an attempt to lend conformity and harmony to the social scene. Yet such a situation can also tend to promote suspicion and mistrust, since in many instances the actors are not sure of their opposite's position. Thus harmony and potential conflict exist side by side, with members of the community continuously striving to create harmony but inadvertently creating a potentially divisive situation. By and large competition is not well developed.

Within the above framework there arises the problem of tension management. Since the children are socialized to be independent and, to a certain extent, aggressive in their actions, it is obvious that goal satisfaction must involve the channeling of aggressive tendencies. This involves the use of such diverse entities as animals, the family, and the "outside world" as items against which aggression is directed. The family is held to be private domain, separate from the community and within which behavior tends to be relatively open. The father tends to be highly authoritarian and emotionally isolated from the children. In contrast the mother becomes the nurturant figure, the relationship between her and the children involving a high degree of dependency, which serves to alleviate much of the anxiety emanating from the wider society. Within the family the love-hate relationship becomes particularly evident, stemming as it does from a belief that harmony can be achieved only by reaching a balance between good and evil, i.e., love must be tempered by emotional distance. Thus the family becomes the focus of both positive and negative emotional expression.

The relationship to the "outside world" is one in which caution is of the utmost importance, the wider society being kept at arm's length. In many concepts a feeling of social discomfort is experienced when relating to the outside; the anxiety emanating from such a situation is overcome either by retreating to the source of self-identity or by identifying with identity objects such as other community members. This latter strategy is particularly apparent among the youth of the community who venture to the more cosmopolitan urban centers for entertainment, which often is regarded as deviance within their own community. Invariably this takes the form of group activity, which serves to sanction the behavior while also relieving the anxiety of individual deviance.

While the above observations are to a great extent impressionistic in nature, the analysis thus far completed supports the implied trends. Complete analysis of the data will be undertaken when the second phase of the project is completed and a comparative base has been established for the further refinement of the analytic procedure.

REFERENCES

FROMM, ERIC H., and MACCOBY, MICHAEL
    1970. Social character in a Mexican village, 303 pp.   Prentice-Hall, Englewood
        Cliffs, New Jersey.
GOLDSCHMIDT, WALTER
    1965. Theory and strategy in the study of cultural adaptability.   Amer. Anth-
        rop., vol. 67, pp. 402-408
KLUCKHOLN, FLORENCE LOCKWOOD, and STRODTBECK, FRED L.
    1961. Variations in value orientations, 449 pp.   Row, Peterson & Co., Evans-
        ton, Illinois, and Elmsford, New York.
WHITING, JOHN W. M., et al.
    1966. Field guide for a study of socialization, 176 pp.   John Wiley & Sons,
        New York.
WILLIAMS, GLYN
    1975. The desert and the dream: A study of Welsh colonization in Chubut
        1865-1915, 130 pp.   University of Wales Press, Cardiff.
    1976. La emigración galesa en la Patagonia 1869-1915.   Jahrb. Gesch. von
        Staat, Wirtsch. und Ges. Latinamericas, vol. 13, pp. 239-293.
    _____. Social ranking in a Welsh community.   In "Social and Cultural Change in
        Contemporary Wales," Glyn Williams, ed. Routledge & Keegan Paul,
        London. (In press.)

GLYN WILLIAMS

The National Geographic Society — South Dakota School of Mines and Technology Expedition into the Poleslide Member of the Big Badlands of South Dakota, 1969: A Program of Conservation Collecting

Principal Investigator: Robert W. Wilson, South Dakota School of Mines and Technology, Rapid City, South Dakota.

Grant No. 759:   For continuation of conservation collecting of rocks, minerals, and fossils in the South Dakota Badlands.

In recent years amateur "rock hounds" and commercial collectors have visited the Big Badlands of South Dakota in increasing numbers to obtain specimens of fossil vertebrates. For this reason a considerable number disappear each year into private hands, and many are mutilated in order to obtain their dentitions, or are otherwise improperly collected. With the opening up of new areas to the public and with the increased use of 4-wheel-drive vehicles, localities once reasonably safe from nonscientific collecting are being stripped of their fossil treasure. Consequently, the Museum of Geology, South Dakota School of Mines and Technology, proposed to the National Geographic Society to supply "conservation" collecting in two areas, one around the base of Sheep Mountain Table and the other in the Palmer Creek drainage. Both projects were to center on the Poleslide member (upper Oligocene) of the Brule Formation. The Poleslide was selected because knowledge of its fauna was still incomplete and because we felt that both areas would experience, increasingly, the pressure of amateur and commercial collecting. An additional factor was that collecting in these areas, and at this stratigraphic interval, would build our collections at points where we had real research interests. We hoped not only to remove many of the more obvious specimens of medium to large fossil mammals but also to increase our holdings of small mammals such as insectivores, lagomorphs, and rodents. By doing so we would combine conservation with some long-time and still active research interests aimed at increasing knowledge of the Poleslide fauna and at applying faunal information to the problem of late

Oligocene environment in western South Dakota and adjacent northwestern Nebraska. Ideas concerning environment have ranged from regarding the areas as then semitropical with at least moderate rainfall to truly arid.

Consequently, a field party worked from June 26 through August 19, 1969. It consisted of Dr. George Callison, then of the South Dakota School of Mines and Technology but now of the California State University at Long Beach; Dr. Philip R. Bjork, formerly of the University of Wisconsin at Stevens Point, now director of its Museum of Geology; and Michael T. Greenwald, a graduate student at the School of Mines. Dr. Callison acted as field leader. The party spent June 26 through July 3 at Sheep Mountain Table, the remainder of the field time in the Palmer Creek area.

Museum of Geology Work in the Poleslide

The South Dakota School of Mines and Technology first worked in the Poleslide in 1928 and 1929, mostly in the Palmer Creek drainage. In 1940, a joint expedition of the National Geographic Society and the School of Mines thoroughly prospected the channel sandstones of the Palmer Creek drainage (Connolly and Bump, 1947; Wilson, 1975). After the 1969 expedition herein reported, Dr. Bjork led parties into the Poleslide in 1970, 1971, and 1972. The last two years' work was partially financed by a grant from the National Science Foundation to the University of Wisconsin at Stevens Point and concerned the Cedar Pass area near headquarters for Badlands National Monument in the eastern part of the Monument. All specimens so obtained have been deposited at the Museum of Geology. This post-1969 work is mentioned because intensive study of the 1969 collections has been postponed awaiting conclusion of all field work in the Poleslide. This accounts for lack of published studies except for interim notes (see *References*). Dr. Bjork is currently studying Poleslide moles, hedgehogs, and heteromyid rodents. Dr. John G. Lundberg, of Duke University, and Dr. Ted Cavender, of Ohio State University, both formerly of the University of Michigan, have worked on the fish remains, and Dr. George Callison is interested in the herpetological aspects of the fauna.

Facies in the Poleslide

The Poleslide member of the Brule, as has long been recognized, consists of two rather distinct lithologic facies. Sandstone lenses represent deposits laid down by streams emanating from the Black Hills and carry stream

and stream border dwellers as fossils. These fossils may be distinctly different from those in the fine-grained deposits, the so-called clays, interbedded
with the sandstone, and may be typified by animals living on more open
plains between streams. The former deposits have been called the Protoceras channels and the latter the Leptauchenia clays, after two of the more
characteristic fossils of these facies.

1969 Collections: Sheep Mountain Table

Our records show the following specimens from the channel phase of
the Poleslide of Sheep Mountain Table:

Amia sp. A vertebral centrum is the only Oligocene record from South Dakota of the
bowfin.
Scaphiopus (Spea) sp. One specimen is an excellent skull with nearly complete postcranial
skeleton. This is the earliest record of *Spea* in North America.

Among mammals, the following skulls, jaws, or postcranial skeletons
are to be recorded:

	Specimens		Specimens
Palaeolagus	1	Peccary	1
Castorids	8	*Leptomeryx*	1
Canid	1	*Protoceras*	1
Carnivores, undet.	2	*Leptauchenia*	3
Equids	2	Oreodonts, undet.	10

It is difficult at this locality, with its steep exposure, to keep clay and
channel facies separate in collecting. Most of the specimens were in clay
interbedded with small sandstone stringers. Although several of the specimens (beavers, fish, *Protoceras*) suggest stream and stream border, the presence of *Leptauchenia* indicates that some of the sediments were deposited
in a more open plains environment.

1969 Collections: Palmer Creek Area

More time was spent and more fossils were collected at the second locality in the vicinity of Palmer Creek than at Sheep Mountain Table. Here
also it was easier to determine the environment of occurrence of individual
fossils than at Sheep Mountain. Major specimens from the Leptauchenia
facies of the Palmer Creek area are as follows:

	Specimens		Specimens
Proterix	2	Carnivores, undet.	2
Talpid	1	Equids	5
Lagomorphs	15	Rhinoceroses	23
Eomyid(?)	1	Peccaries	10
Eumys	9	Leptomeryx	10
Hyaenodon	1	Leptauchenia	27
Canids	11	Oreodonts, undet.	36
Felids	5		

In addition, a vertebra of a boid snake, *Calamagras,* is the first record of a snake in the Poleslide. A skull from the channel facies of a channel catfish, *Ictalurus (Ictalurus)* sp., is the oldest ictalurid that can be related positively to living forms.

A statistical collection also was made for a later environmental study. This collection, obtained from a small restricted area, includes every scrap of visible fossil material. It is hoped that this collection will give some idea of relative abundance of fossils in the Leptauchenia clay, and hence some idea of abundance in the living population.

One highly fossiliferous anthill on Poleslide outcrops was collected in the Palmer Creek area. This hill seems to be without contamination from material of other ages than late Oligocene, although of mixed facies. A preliminary identification of fossils indicates the presence of the following vertebrates:

Lizards	*Adjidaumo*
Peratherium	*Proheteromys*
Geolabis	*Prosciurus*
Sinclairella	Aplodontid
Erinaceid	Castorid
Domnina	*Eutypomys*
Proscalops	*Eumys*
Palaeolagus	*Scottimus*
Sciurid	

Proscalops, Adjidaumo, prosciurines, and *Proheteromys* are most abundant, suggesting an environmental change from the middle Oligocene Scenic member, from which similar micromammalian assemblages are known. Several of the anthill genera seem to be new to the Poleslide, and one, *Sinclairella,* if correctly identified, is a new and latest record for the genus, and for the family Apatemyidae to which it belongs, anywhere in North America.

Comparison of the two Palmer Creek facies (including the 1940 collections) reveals some major differences, as would be expected. Tapirs, *Subhyracodon,* leptochoerids, anthracotheres, entelodonts, and *Protoceras* are either restricted to, or decidedly more common in, the channel facies. *Palaeolagus, Hyracodon,* and *Leptomeryx* are more common in the clays; *Leptauchenia* is restricted to them. The collections indicate that *Perchoerus* specimens are more common in the clays, but all the reasonably good skulls and jaws come from channel deposits. *Agnotocastor* is much more common in the channels also, but beavers at other localities in the upper Oligocene are common in the clays, perhaps anticipating a wider variety of habitats for them in the early Miocene than simply stream and stream border.

In 1971 and 1972, under a National Science Foundation grant to the University of Wisconsin at Stevens Point, prospecting for small mammals of the Leptauchenia clays at Cedar Pass on the eastern edge of the Monument produced the following list:

	Specimens		Specimens
Palaeolagus	767	*Proterix*	15
Proheteromys	240	Cricetids	13
Leptomeryx	139	*Adjidaumo*	9
Agnotocastor	42	*Geolabis*	5
Prosciurus	39	Aplodontids	4
Peratherium	35	Soricids	4
Proscalops	33	Erinaceids	3
Hesperocyon	23	Zapodids	3

It is to be noted that the Leptauchenia clays at Cedar Pass have a much more abundant microfauna than those in the Palmer Creek drainage, presumably largely owing to more persistent and easier collecting. A census of the collections made at the former locality, as given above, shows *Palaeolagus* to be the most common small mammal, followed by *Proheteromys*. Any of those in the first ten or so must have been abundant, even if figures are distorted by such factors as selective predation.

Climate

Climatic conclusions based on the micromammalia should await thorough study of all material. Nevertheless, it does seem that a truly arid climate was not present. On the other hand, the seemingly increasing numbers of heteromyids over their presence lower in the section suggests Miocene rather than Oligocene frequency of occurrence, and possibly somewhat less precipitation. Presence of *Scaphiopus (Spea)* seems to indicate semiarid grassland or open woodland scrub. The disappearance of *Ischyromys* and the decline of typical cricetids need further study before significance can be attached to these changes in faunal structure.

REFERENCES

BJORK, PHILIP R.

    1971. Comments on small mammals from the late Oligocene of South Dakota. Paper presented at annual meeting of the Society of Vertebrate Paleontology, Washington, D. C. Program, p. 9.

    1973. *Proterix,* an Oligocene hedgehog.   Paper presented at annual meeting of the Society of Vertebrate Paleontology, Dallas, Texas. Program, p. 13.

    1975. Observations on *Proscalops tertius* (Mammalia: Insectivora) of the Upper Oligocene of South Dakota.   Journ. Paleont., vol. 49, no. 5, pp. 808-813, illus.

CONNOLLY, JOSEPH P., and BUMP, JAMES D.

    1947. Big game hunting in the land of long ago.   Nat. Geogr. Mag., vol. 91, no. 5, pp. 589-605, illus.

LUNDBERG, JOHN G.

    1970. The evolutionary history of North American catfishes, family Ictaluridae. Ph.D. thesis, University of Michigan.

WILSON, ROBERT W.

    1969-70. Environment of Upper Brule deposition in the Big Badlands of South Dakota.   *In* "Annual Report of Research, South Dakota School of Mines and Technology," C. F. Lutz, ed., p. 37.

    1975. The National Geographic Society—South Dakota School of Mines and Technology Expedition into the Big Badlands of South Dakota, 1940. Nat. Geogr. Soc. Res. Rpts., 1890-1954 Projects, pp. 79-85.

ROBERT W. WILSON

APPENDIX

List of Grants for Research and Exploration made by the National Geographic Society, 1974

No. 1286: Dr. George J. Simeon, Macquarie University, North Ryde, New South Wales, Australia, for a study of native diseases and cures among islanders of the Torres Straits south of New Guinea.

No. 1287: Dr. Charles C. Porter, Fordham University, Bronx, New York, in support of studies of the systematics and zoogeography of Neotropical ichneumon-flies.

No. 1288: Dr. Susan E. Reichert, University of Tennessee, Knoxville, Tennessee, for continuation of her study of the ontogeny and diversification of feeding behavior of the desert funnel web spider.

No. 1289: Dr. John M. Legler, University of Utah, Salt Lake City, Utah, for continuation of his research on Australian fresh-water chelid turtles.

No. 1290: Dr. Geerat J. Vermeij, University of Maryland, College Park, Maryland, in aid of a study of crab predation and shell architecture in high intertidal snails.

No. 1291: Dr. James R. Carpenter, Kent State University, Kent, Ohio, for excavation of an early Bronze Age settlement in Cyprus.

No. 1292: Dr. Erik H. Erikson, Jr., Juniata College, Huntingdon, Pennsylvania, in further support of grantee's studies of the petrology and geochemistry of the Mount Stuart Batholith, Cascade Mountains, Washington.

No. 1293: Mrs. Judith Ann Rudnai, University of Nairobi, Kenya, for a study of the ecology of lions in the Kitengela Conservation Area adjoining Nairobi National Park.

Nos. 1294, 1309: Dr. Farish A. Jenkins, Jr., and Dr. A. W. Crompton, Museum of Comparative Zoology, Harvard University, Cambridge, Massachusetts, to collect and study rare Early Cretaceous mammals at a site in south-central Montana.

No. 1295: Dr. Peter Dodson, Peabody Museum of Natural History, Yale University, New Haven, Connecticut, for a study of the ecology of the Morrison dinosaur fauna of Western United States.

No. 1296: Dr. S. Jeffrey K. Wilkerson, Florida State Museum, Gainesville, Florida, in aid of his study of culture ecology of the Mexican

Gulf Coast from the earliest cultures to the development of Mesoamerican civilization.

Nos. 1297, 1336, 1382: John G. Newton, Duke University Marine Laboratory, Beaufort, North Carolina, in support of the search for the wreck of the ironclad *Monitor,* in cooperation with the U. S. Navy and Dr. Harold E. Edgerton.

No. 1298: Dr. Mary D. Leakey, National Centre for Prehistory and Palaeontology, Nairobi, Kenya, in further support of the archeological program at Olduvai Gorge, Tanzania.

Nos. 1299, 1320, and 1369: Richard E. Leakey, National Museums of Kenya, Nairobi, Kenya, in further support of the archeological and geological project at Lake Turkana, Kenya.

No. 1300: Dr. William V. Davidson, Arkansas State University, State University, Arkansas, in continued support of a study of the cultural geography of the Black Caribs of Central America.

No. 1301: Dr. Charles F. Martin, Texas Memorial Museum, University of Austin, Texas, for a study of reproduction, range expansion, and status of Texas cave swallows.

No. 1302: Dr. Ray T. Matheny, Brigham Young University, Provo, Utah, for a study of prehistoric house mounds and canal systems of Edzna, Campeche, Mexico.

No. 1303: Mrs. Deborah Gewertz, East-West Center Population Institute, Honolulu, Hawaii, for an investigation of the integrative potentials of dispersed networks of trade, migration, and marriage in New Guinea.

No. 1304: Dr. William E. Duellman, University of Kansas, Lawrence, Kansas, in support of a study of Andean biogeography, with special reference to the distribution of amphibians and reptiles.

No. 1305: Dr. Ian Tattersall, American Museum of Natural History, New York City, for a study of the ecology, behavior, and distribution of the lemur *Varecia variegatus* in Madagascar.

No. 1306: Dr. Marvin J. Allison, Medical College of Virginia, Richmond, Virginia, in continued support of a study of Precolumbian American disease.

No. 1307: Dr. Talbot H. Waterman, Yale University, New Haven, Connecticut, in continuation of studies of the vision and the orientation of marine animals.

No. 1308: Dr. Arthur G. Miller, Yale University, New Haven, Connecticut, in further support of an archeological study of the mural painting of Tulum and Tancah, Quintana Roo, Mexico.

No. 1310: Dr. Lionel A. Stange, Universidad de Tucumán, Argentina, for field studies of the insect order Neuroptera in South America.

No. 1311: Dr. Raymond D. Clarke, Sarah Lawrence College, Bronxville, New York, in aid of a study of niche overlap and species diversity of coral-reef fishes.

No. 1312: Dr. Kenelm W. Philip, University of Alaska, Fairbanks, Alaska, in support of a survey of Alaskan Lepidoptera.

No. 1313: Dr. Dennis F. Whigham, Rider College, Trenton, New Jersey, for a study of structure and function of a fresh-water tidal marsh ecosystem (Trenton marshes).

No. 1314: Dr. Charles W. McNett, Jr., American University, Washington, D. C., in support of the initial season of the Upper Delaware Valley Early Man Project.

No. 1315: Dr. Marie-Helene Sachet, Smithsonian Institution, Washington, D. C., to collect materials for a flora of the Marquesas Islands.

Nos. 1316, 1412: Dr. M. Philip Kahl, Naples, Florida, in further support of grantee's world-wide study of flamingos.

No. 1317: Dr. George F. Bass, American Institute of Nautical Archeology, College Station, Texas, in support of a project to excavate the remains of an Iron Age shipwreck off Turkey.

No. 1318: Dr. Craig C. Black, Texas Tech University, Lubbock, Texas, in aid of a continuing study of the geology, archeology, and paleo-ecology of the Lubbock Lake site.

No. 1319: Dr. John S. Hall, Lowell Observatory, Flagstaff, Arizona, to develop highly accurate measurements for sensitive assessment of air quality.

No. 1321: Dr. Clifford Ray Johnson, University of California, Berkeley, California, to study head-body temperature control and behavioral thermoregulation in the American alligator.

No. 1322: Dr. Elwyn L. Simons, Peabody Museum, Yale University, New Haven, Connecticut, for an exploration of fossil ancestors of man in the Kathmandu Valley and in the Siwalik deposits of the Himalayan foothills, Nepal.

No. 1323: Hugh A. Freeman, Hillcrest High School, Dallas, Texas, in support of a distributional study of the Hesperiidae (Lepidoptera) of Mexico.

Nos. 1324, 1376: Dr. Peter S. Rodman, University of California, Davis, California, for a population survey of nonhuman primates in East Borneo.

No. 1325: Dr. Eugenie Clark, University of Maryland, College Park,

Maryland, for a study of sleeping sharks in Mexican caves.

No. 1326: Mrs. Julie C. Webb, University of California, Los Angeles, California, in support of a study of the ecology of the lowland gorilla in West Africa.

No. 1327: Dr. John Sloan Dickey, Jr., Massachusetts Institute of Technology, Cambridge, Massachusetts, for a study of volcanic ejecta on Nunivak Island.

No. 1328: Dr. Kalman A. Muller, Tucson, Arizona, in aid of a research-film elicitation project on the island of Tanna, New Hebrides.

No. 1329: Larry G. Marshall, University of California, Berkeley, California, for a study of South American continental geomorphology and marsupial evolution.

No. 1330: Dr. Douglas H. Ubelaker, Smithsonian Institution, Washington, D. C., in aid of a study of prehistoric demography of coastal Ecuador.

No. 1331: Dr. Bruce J. Bourque, Maine State Museum, Augusta, Maine, for archeological research at the Turner Farm site, North Haven, Maine.

No. 1332: Dr. Robert W. Wilson, South Dakota School of Mines and Technology, Rapid City, South Dakota, for continuation of grantee's research on Late Cretaceous mammals of South Dakota.

Nos. 1334, 1343: Dr. Dennis J. Stanford, Smithsonian Institution, Washington, D. C., for continued support of archeological investigations of the Jones-Miller bison-kill site, eastern Colorado.

No. 1337: Dr. Daniel J. Stanley, Smithsonian Institution, Washington, D. C., for a study of Recent Nile Cone history based on sediment-core analysis.

No. 1338: Dr. John P. Marwitt, University of Akron, Akron, Ohio, for continued support of construction of an archeological chronology for the Ariari River region, Colombia.

No. 1339: Dr. Michael H. Jameson, University of Pennsylvania, Philadelphia, Pennsylvania, in further support of the study of the submerged sanctuary of Apollo at Halieis, Greece.

No. 1340: Dr. Jeffrey P. Brain, Peabody Museum, Harvard University, Cambridge, Massachusetts, in aid of archeological studies focusing on the protohistoric and early historic contact period in the lower Mississippi Valley.

Nos. 1341, 1397: Dr. George E. Stuart, National Geographic Society, Washington, D. C., for participation in the Coba Archeological

Mapping Project of the Mexican Government, Quintana Roo, Mexico.

No. 1342: Dr. Michael E. Moseley, Peabody Museum, Harvard University, Cambridge, Massachusetts, and Dr. Carol J. Mackey, California State University, Northridge, California, in continued support of the Chan Chan—Moche Valley Project—a study of the prehistoric urban-rural relationships on the north Peruvian coast.

No. 1344: Dr. Jay M. Pasachoff, Williams College, Williamstown, Massachusetts, for an investigation of interstellar deuterium and its relation to cosmology.

No. 1345: Dr. Frederick J. Brenner, Grove City College, Grove City, Pennsylvania, in further support of grantee's program to study the behavior of vertebrate populations on strip-mine lands.

No. 1346: Dr. David L. Pearson, University of Washington, Seattle, Washington, for a comparative study of bird-community structure in Old World and New World tropical lowland forests.

No. 1347: Dr. Charles J. Vitaliano, Indiana University, Bloomington, Indiana, for an attempt to determine the precise dating of the Bronze Age eruption of Santorini Volcano, Aegean Sea.

No. 1348: Dr. Francis H. Brown, University of Utah, Salt Lake City, Utah, and Dr. F. Clark Howell, University of California, Berkeley, California, for recovery of hominid skeletal remains from Upper Pliocene localities in Ethiopia.

No. 1349: Galen B. Rathbun, University of Nairobi, Nairobi, Kenya, in support of a study of the social behavior and ecology of the shrew *Elephantulus rufescens*.

No. 1350: Dr. Wolfgang M. Schleidt, University of Maryland, College Park, Maryland, for a study of calling behavior patterns of *Coturnix* quails.

Nos. 1351, 1393: Mrs. Biruté M. F. Galdikas-Brindamour, University of California, Los Angeles, California, in aid of a long-term study of the behavior and ecology of the wild orangutan of Tanjung Puting, Indonesia.

No. 1352: Dr. Yosihiko H. Sinoto, Bernice P. Bishop Museum, Honolulu, Hawaii, for excavation of an Archaic habitation site on Huahine, Society Islands.

Nos. 1353, 1381: Dr. Kenan T. Erim, New York University, New York City, in continued support of archeological excavations at Aphrodisias, Turkey.

No. 1354: Dr. Merrill P. Spencer, Institute of Environmental Medicine and Physiology, Seattle, Washington, for a study of the cervico-spinal rete mirabile of Cetacea.

No. 1355: Dr. Bradford Washburn, Museum of Science, Boston, Massachusetts, in continued support of the project "mapping of the Grand Canyon of the Colorado."

No. 1356: Dr. John W. Terborgh, Princeton University, Princeton, New Jersey, in support of a project to study the foraging ecology and population density of Neotropical primates in Manu National Park in southeastern Peru.

No. 1357: Dr. Jared M. Diamond, University of California Medical Center, Los Angeles, California, for a study of survival of bird populations stranded on land-bridge islands.

No. 1358: Mrs. Carol A. Hill, University of New Mexico, Albuquerque, New Mexico, for a study of saltpeter conversion and the origin of cave nitrates.

No. 1359: Dr. Alexander R. McBirney, University of Oregon, Eugene, Oregon, in support of geological studies of the Skaergaard region, east Greenland.

No. 1360: Dr. Maynard M. Miller, Michigan State University, East Lansing, Michigan, for a regimen investigation of a prototype glacier system, Atlin Park, British Columbia.

No. 1361: Dr. Theodore Downs, Natural History Museum of Los Angeles, California, in support of a vertebrate paleontologic reconnaissance of Baja California.

No. 1362: Humberto Alvarez, Cornell Laboratory of Ornithology, Ithaca, New York, for a study of the social organization and ecology of the green jay in Colombia.

No. 1363: Dr. E. Earl Willard, University of Montana, Missoula, Montana, in aid of an ecological study of the Nez Perce Creek bighorn-sheep herd.

No. 1364: Dr. Ned K. Johnson, University of California, Berkeley, California, for a study of the systematics of sibling species of birds in northwestern South America.

No. 1365: Dr. Robert W. Mitchell, Texas Tech University, Lubbock, Texas, in support of a survey of the cave fauna of the Yucatán Peninsula.

No. 1366: Dr. Roger S. Payne, New York Zoological Society, New York City, for a study of the behavior of the dusky dolphin (*Lagenor-rhynchus obscurus*).

No. 1367: Dr. Charles A. Woods, University of Vermont, Burlington, Vermont, to study the life history and evolution of the Haitian hutia (*Plagiodonta aedium*).

No. 1368: Dr. Bryan Patterson, Museum of Comparative Zoology, Harvard University, Cambridge, Massachusetts, in support of field investigations of the vertebrate paleontology of Tropical South America.

No. 1370: Dr. William A. Longacre, University of Arizona, Tucson, Arizona, in support of a long-term project to reconstruct the prehistoric habitat by mammalian microfaunal analysis of the Grasshopper Pueblo in east-central Arizona.

No. 1371: Dr. C. Vance Haynes, University of Arizona, Tucson, Arizona, in aid of a cooperative archeological survey in the Libyan Desert of Egypt.

No. 1372: Dr. Austin E. Lamberts, Grand Rapids, Michigan, for a study of coral reefs and coral-reef destruction in American Samoa.

No. 1373: Dr. Donna J. Howell, Princeton University, Princeton, New Jersey, to study the effects of pollinating bats on plant communities, in Costa Rica and Arizona.

No. 1374: Dr. William R. Stanley, University of South Carolina, Columbia, South Carolina, for a field study of relic ports on the West African Grain Coast.

No. 1375: Dr. Richard H. Kesel, Louisiana State University, Baton Rouge, Louisiana, to investigate Quaternary river terraces on the Reventazon and General Valleys, Costa Rica.

No. 1377: Dr. Edwin O. Willis, Manaus, Amazonas, Brazil, for a study of ant-following birds of northeastern Brazil.

No. 1378: Dr. Walter E. Vokes, Tulane University, New Orleans, Louisiana, to complete a study by the late Dr. E. Wyllys Andrews IV of the shallow-water marine molluscan fauna of the Yucatán Peninsula, Mexico.

No. 1379: Dr. Donald R. Johnson, University of Idaho, Moscow, Idaho, for a radio-tracking study of Idaho's last mountain-caribou herd.

No. 1380: Augusto Ruschi, National Museum of Rio de Janeiro University, Rio de Janeiro, Brazil, in support of grantee's continuing studies of the ecology and geographical distribution of hummingbirds in South America, Central America, and Mexico.

No. 1384: Dr. William R. Coe, University of Pennsylvania, Philadelphia, Pennsylvania, in aid of archeological investigations of the ruins and setting of Quirigua, Guatemala.

No. 1385: Dr. James N. Douglas, University of Texas, Austin, Texas, in continued support of the project "Mapping the Radio Sky."

No. 1386: Dr. Eldon E. Ball, Australian National University, Canberra City, Australia, for a study of the biogeography of New Guinea lakes and biological colonization of a recently formed volcanic island.

No. 1387: Dr. George G. Spooner, University of Idaho, Moscow, Idaho, for ecological and physiological investigations of alpine cushion plants.

No. 1388: Dr. James L. Reveal, University of Maryland, College Park, Maryland, for biosystematic and evolutionary studies of the sage genus *Salvia,* subgenus *Calosphace.*

No. 1389: Dr. Robert G. Douglas, University of Southern California, Los Angeles, California, in aid of his studies of deep-sea Foraminifera in the Pacific Ocean.

No. 1390: Dr. Timothy E. Gregory, Ohio State University, Columbus, Ohio, for an analysis of the society, economy, and culture of Greece in the Later Roman Empire, developed from archeological, epigraphic, and numismatic studies.

No. 1391: Dr. Thomas K. Wood, Wilmington College, Wilmington, Ohio, for field studies in Florida of the brooding and aggregating behavior of the membracid treehopper *Umbonia crassicornis.*

No. 1392: Mr. and Mrs. Mark J. Owens, Maun, Botswana, for a behavioral study of cheetahs, with special reference to population dynamics and reproductive biology.

No. 1394: Dr. G. M. Ole Maloiy, University of Nairobi, Kenya, in aid of a study of ionic and osmotic regulation in East African fishes: The lungfish and *Tilapia grahami.*

No. 1395: Dr. William J. Sladen, Johns Hopkins University, Baltimore, Maryland, to study migrations of the whistling swan between Alaska and its wintering grounds.

No. 1396: Dr. Nicholas C. David, University of Ibadan, Nigeria, for an archeological investigation of Central African megaliths.

No. 1398: Dr. Thomas W. Noonan, State University of New York, Brockport, New York, in aid of a study at the Hale Observatories of the sizes of distant clusters of galaxies.

No. 1399: Dr. Deane M. Peterson, State University of New York, Stony Brook, New York, for studies of peculiar early-type stars.

No. 1400: Dr. Alwyn H. Gentry, Missouri Botanical Garden, St. Louis, Missouri, in support of a biological exploration of Cerro Tacarcuna, Panama-Colombia border.

No. 1401: Dr. Robert S. O. Harding, University of Pennsylvania, Philadelphia, Pennsylvania, for a study of the ecology and behavior of olive baboons in Gilgil, Kenya.

No. 1402: Dr. Maurice J. Hornocker, University of Idaho, Moscow, Idaho, for an ecological study of the wolverine in northwestern Montana.

No. 1403: Dr. John Huizinga, State University of Utrecht, The Netherlands, for an anthropological study of early African migrants, particularly the Bani-Niger people and their culture.

No. 1404: Dr. Nancy M. Farriss, University of Pennsylvania, Philadelphia, Pennsylvania, to recover and study underwater evidence for seaborne contact between the Maya of the eastern Yucatán coast and the highland cultures of Mesoamerica.

No. 1405: Drs. A. M. J. Gehrels and Krzysztof Serkowski, University of Arizona Lunar and Planetary Laboratory, Tucson, Arizona, in aid of a project to develop a method for a search for other planetary systems in the universe.

No. 1406: Dr. Masashi Yamaguchi, University of Guam, Agana, Guam, for a study of larval development and geographical distribution of coral-reef asteroids.

No. 1407: Dr. John H. Mercer, Ohio State University, Columbus, Ohio, in support of a study of glacial and floral changes in southern Argentina since 14,000 years ago.

No. 1408: Dr. Amos M. Nur, Stanford University, Stanford, California, for a geophysical field study of joint and fracture patterns, in Israel and Iceland.

No. 1409: Dr. Storrs L. Olson, Smithsonian Institution, Washington, D. C., for comparative studies of fossil and present-day birds on Trindade Island, South Atlantic Ocean.

No. 1410: Dr. Thomas B. Thorson, University of Nebraska, Lincoln, Nebraska, to study the evolution of fresh-water adaptation in stingrays.

No. 1411: Mrs. Julia Marian Wentworth-Shepard, Cornell University Laboratory of Ornithology, Ithaca, New York, to study behavioral differences among male ruffs (*Philomachus pugnax*).

No. 1413: Dr. F. Clark Howell, University of California, Berkeley, California, in support of publication of results of conference on stratigraphy, paleoccology, and evolution in the Lake Turkana Basin, Kenya.

No. 1414: Dr. William N. Fenton, State University of New York, Albany, New York, for a field study of differential acculturation of the Maori of New Zealand.

No. 1415: Peabody Museum of Archaeology and Ethnology, Harvard University, Cambridge, Massachusetts, for a supplemental grant in aid of publication of the Chan Chan maps.

No. 1416: Miss Maria Reiche, Servicio Aerofotográfico Nacional Lima, Peru, for a project to map the Nazca (Peru) ground lines.

No. 1417: Dr. Richard Despard Estes, Academy of Natural Sciences, Philadelphia, Pennyslvania, in continuation of grantee's East African antelope studies.

No. 1418: Dr. Robert F. Martin, University of Texas Memorial Museum, Austin, Texas, for a study of the reproduction, range expansion, and status of the Texas cave swallow.

No. 1419: Dr. Stephen T. Emlen, Cornell University, Ithaca, New York, for studies of cooperative breeding among East African bee-eaters.

No. 1420: Dr. Dian J. Fossey, Ruhengeri, Rwanda, in continuation of her study of the behavior and ecology of the mountain gorilla, central Africa.

No. 1421: Dr. Harold E. Edgerton, Massachusetts Institute of Technology, Cambridge, Massachusetts, for building improved camera equipment for underwater archeology, geology, and marine biology.

Index

653